GENERAL CHEMISTRY

P.W. SELWOOD

Professor of Chemistry, Northwestern University

GENERAL
CHEMISTRY

REVISED EDITION

New York: **HENRY HOLT AND COMPANY**

July, 1954

PREFACE TO NEW EDITION

The . . . mind is not a vessel to be filled but a fire to be kindled.—Plutarch

This book, like the first edition on which it is based, was written for the student whose major interest may, or may not, lie in chemistry. With the whole field of chemistry from which to choose, I have selected those topics which appealed to me most for effective presentation, and I have not hesitated to use whatever devices were available in an effort to arouse and maintain student interest. One of these devices is the use of a narrative style.

Our flattering experience at Northwestern has been that students are often thus attracted to a life of professional chemistry, even though their earlier interests may have lain elsewhere. Most classes in elementary college chemistry have a majority of students who are not potential chemists, or who are undecided about a career. It is to that majority that this book is principally addressed. One hopes that, even if the student goes no farther in chemistry, he will continue to read, enjoy, and profit by some acquaintance with the subject for the rest of his life.

The use of a narrative style imposes a difficulty on the student. He is likely to remember that Robert Boyle was the seventh son of the Earl of Cork, at the expense of knowing the meaning of a chemical equation. The student has no way of distinguishing between important text material and material which is put in to lend general interest and point to the discussion. This difficulty has been combated in the following way: at the end of each chapter there will be found a set of exercises. These are meant to be not merely representative, but all inclusive. The students are told that their quizzes and examinations will be based directly on the current set of exercises, and that an ability to answer all these exercises correctly will be considered (if you will pardon the expression) par for the course. The exercises have been rigidly limited to important matters. I do not mean that the examination questions and problems should repeat word for word and number for number those in the exercises, but rather that all significant ideas are represented in these exercises, and that mastery of the exercises means effective mastery of the course.

In this Second Edition, the number and kind of exercises have been greatly expanded. I have profited by opportunities to try this material with students at other institutions. The exercises have been revised so as to minimize, so far as may be possible in a subject like chemistry, the burden on the memory. At the same time, much effort has been expended in adding exercises of that intrusive quality which tends to throw light on obscure problems and which emphasizes comprehension rather than memory.

Another major difference in this edition is the weaving into several chapters of more advanced material on physical chemistry. For instance, oxidation-reduction, chemical equilibria, pH, and particularly ionic equilibria, are treated much more extensively; the last named being the subject of an entire new chapter. These changes have called for extensive revision of several chapters, especially that on Electrochemistry, which has been modified to add material on single electrode potentials. Some descriptive inorganic and organic material has been removed or simplified so that the overall length of the book is not greater than before. The net result has been to make the book somewhat more rigorous than the First Edition. Every industrial chemical process mentioned in the text has been checked against the most authoritative sources available. The astonishing progress of chemistry has called for revisions and changes of emphasis in almost every chapter.

Specific development of the text in this as in the previous edition, has followed, in general, the modern atomistic school, rather than the historical. This is not to say that the historical approach has been ignored. There is frequent inclusion of historical matter and, in fact, the book opens with a more or less historical treatment of Dalton's Atomic Theory. But the chronological development of chemistry as a science has been avoided. Biographical material has been kept out of the main part of the text but has been incorporated in connection with a selected group of portraits.

The inclusion of a large portion of organic chemistry material, as well as some biochemical, has posed a special problem. The mere recital of imposing structural formulas is certainly not education. An attempt to overcome this difficulty is made by presenting a few theories of organic chemistry and a few fundamental reactions in some detail. An effort has been made to leave the text in as readable a manner as is consistent with the subject matter, and to weave into the exercises some important organic reactions. For instance, a Cannizaro reaction is illustrated once or twice and then followed by a problem of synthesis based on the reaction. In this way, a serious student can find out how organic synthesis proceeds, while the average student need not be forced out of the main stream of the narrative, which is presented in the text itself.

We have found it most satisfactory to have three lectures a week throughout the school year. In the early part of the course, we have two quiz meetings per week, but this drops to one meeting later as the students gain confidence with their mathematical problems. There are three hours of laboratory work per week throughout the year. The experiments are chosen from the laboratory manual which I have written to accompany the text. Part of the first lecture period each week is devoted to an explanation of the current laboratory assignment, although this too may be relaxed as the students gain confidence in the laboratory.

Our experience has also been that it does not make very much difference in a course of this type, whether the student has had high school chemistry or not. But for reasons of educational psychology, it is expedient to place those with high school chemistry in a separate section from the rest, whenever this is possible.

It is a pleasant duty to acknowledge the aid received from Mr. John O'Rourke, who prepared all the drawings.

P. W. S.

Northwestern University
Evanston, Illinois
February 1954

ACKNOWLEDGMENTS

The author wishes to express his thanks to the following organizations, which provided illustrative material as indicated.

Figure 11-3. Standard Oil Co. (N. J.). Photo by Corsini.

Figures 13-2, 13-3, 13-4. Texas Gulf Sulphur Company. Photo by Elwood M. Payne.

Figure 14-6. Hooker Electrochemical Co. Photo by Byron Morgan.

Figure 15-4. E. I. du Pont de Nemours and Company.

Figure 17-4. Corning Glass Works.

Figure 19-2. Aluminum Company of America.

Figures 21-3, 21-4, 21-5. United States Steel Corporation.

Figure 22-1. The Consolidated Mining and Smelting Company of Canada, Ltd.

Figure 22-2. Anaconda Copper Mining Company.

Figure 26-4. Koppers Company.

Figure 27-5. Gulf Oil Corporation.

Figure 28-2. E. I. du Pont de Nemours and Company.

Figures 31-2, 31-3. Eli Lilly and Company.

Figures 32-1, 32-2. United States Rubber Company.

Figure 32-3. E. I. du Pont de Nemours and Company.

In this book there are many references to substances which are used, or may be used, as drugs. It should be understood that this is not a medical book, and that under no circumstances should any of the information be so considered.

CONTENTS

GENERAL CHEMISTRY

CHAPTER
1
ATOMS

. . . the universe is a concourse of atoms . . . —Marcus Aurelius

The science of **chemistry** treats of matter and its transformations. Matter is often simply defined as anything that has weight and occupies space. Transformations of matter are familiar to everyone. The rusting of iron, burning of wood or coal or gasoline, digestion of food, drying of paints, explosions, manufacture of perfumes, plastics, and fertilizers, life itself—all involve the transformations of matter, and as such are part of chemical science.

1. ATOMISM *

Atomism is the philosophical doctrine that matter is made of small, indivisible particles, or **atoms.**† Long ago it was thought that if an object, say a piece of iron, were cut in two, then into four, then into eight, and so on— in theory at least, an infinite number of times—the tiny ultimate specks remaining would still be iron, and nothing but iron. This view of the *continuous,* rather than the *atomistic,* quality of matter was held by the Aristotelian or Peripatetic School in ancient Greece.

No one knows the origin of atomism. The notion of imperishable atoms is found in writings from India and from Greece, but whether these beliefs traveled from one country to the other or whether they grew up independently is not known. Even the early Greek records are fragmentary. We are indebted to Plato and to Aristotle for descriptions of these theories, although these two celebrated philosophers did not believe in the truth of atomism.

The first clearly defined atomic theory is that of Leucippus, the teacher of Democritus. Leucippus left no written records, but Democritus, who lived from approximately 460 to 370 B.C., recorded his teacher's views, which were that matter is indestructible and consists of very minute but not infinitely

---

* J. C. Gregory, *A Short History of Atomism* (London: Black, 1931). Books and other publications to which reference is made in footnotes usually contain more advanced treatments of topics mentioned in the text. The reader will be amply rewarded by study of these references.

† The word "atom" is derived from the Greek *atomos,* meaning "indivisible."

divisible particles, or *atoms*. According to Leucippus the atoms differ in size, shape, position, and perhaps in weight. They exist in empty space and are endowed with eternal movement. The combinations and separations of atoms account for all the varied phenomena of nature.

Aristotle rejected this theory because he could not conceive the existence of a completely empty space in which the atoms might be free to move. He found it impossible to imagine the existence of something which is itself nonexistent.

The atomic theory of Leucippus and Democritus was briefly revived by Epicurus (342-270 B.C.) and expounded by the poet Lucretius, after which it slept in the minds of men for nearly two thousand years until it was resurrected by the French philosopher, Pierre Gassendi, about the year 1647. By 1666, the atomic theory had been welcomed back into philosophy, and Robert Boyle, in his celebrated book of that period, *The Sceptical Chymist,* states:

It seems not absurd to conceive that the first Production of mixt Bodies, the Universal Matter whereof they among other Parts of the Universe consisted, was actually divided in little Particles of several sizes and shapes variously moved.

In the minds of Sir Isaac Newton and of later scientists there remain few doubts about the "little Particles" of which, with Leucippus, we now believe all matter is made.

The atomism of ancient Greece bears little resemblance to the modern atomic theory. Superficially there are points of similarity between what Leucippus taught and what we now believe. But his theory was purely a product of the mind, a result of contemplative philosophy rather than of experimental science. Science and human knowledge progress by observation, by inductive thinking or generalization from observation, and, most important, by experimental testing of conclusions. The Greek philosophers looked to their own intellects for fundamental truth. The scientific method is, on the other hand, to ask of and receive from *nature* every extension of knowledge. Robert Boyle, who died in 1697, was among the first of all men to understand the virtues of the scientific method. But it was not until the beginning of the nineteenth century that the method was applied by John Dalton with brilliant success to found the modern atomic theory.

2. DALTON'S ATOMIC THEORY

As early as the middle of the seventeenth century it was clearly shown by Robert Boyle that some kinds of matter are readily broken up or decomposed into simpler forms, but that other kinds of matter resist decomposition by whatever means it is attempted. Substances which could not be broken up into simpler forms were called by Boyle "chemical elements." Some of these chemical elements, such as hydrogen, oxygen, carbon, iron, and copper, are very familiar to us nowadays. By the beginning of the nineteenth century it was understood that certain of these elements could combine with each other to form new substances. For instance, hydrogen and oxygen unite to form water. It was also understood that in such combinations of chemical elements two clearly defined rules were always obeyed.

The first of these rules is illustrated by the fact that water always contains 11 per cent by weight of hydrogen and 89 per cent of oxygen, and that no matter where or how the water is obtained, these percentages always hold. We might state the rule, or law, as follows: **When two or more elements combine they always do so in a fixed, or definite, proportion by weight.** This is known as the **Law of Definite Proportions.**

The second rule arises from the fact that sometimes elements combine with each other in more than one proportion by weight. This, at first glance, seems to be a contradiction of the Law of Definite Proportions, but actually it is an extension rather than a contradiction. Carbon, for instance, unites with oxygen to form the deadly poisonous gas carbon monoxide. Carbon also unites with oxygen to form carbon dioxide, a harmless substance which is found in the exhaled breath. We find that, say, 3 parts by weight of carbon unite with 4 parts by weight of oxygen to form carbon monoxide. We also find that 3 parts of carbon unite with 8 parts of oxygen to form carbon dioxide. Notice that there is just twice as much oxygen per weight of carbon in carbon dioxide as in carbon monoxide. The rule illustrated here may be stated as follows: **If an element unites with another element in more than one proportion by weight, the weights of one element which unite with a fixed weight of the other bear a simple ratio to each other.** This is known as the **Law of Multiple Proportions.** The "simple ratio" in the case illustrated is 4 parts of oxygen to 8 parts of oxygen, or, more simply, 1 to 2.

In the year 1803 the English schoolmaster, John Dalton, proposed a theoretical explanation for these two experimentally established laws. Taking the union of carbon with oxygen as an example, Dalton suggested that these chemical elements consisted of very minute atoms, and that all the atoms of carbon were of the same weight, and that all the atoms of oxygen were of the same weight, but that the weight of the carbon atoms was different from the weight of the oxygen atoms. He also supposed that the weight of the carbon atom was $\frac{3}{4}$ the weight of the oxygen atom, that is, that the weights of the atoms of carbon and oxygen stood in the ratio 3 to 4.

In Dalton's time the proportions in which elements combine were known much less accurately than they are now. The numbers he obtained for the relative weights of the atoms of carbon and oxygen were 5.4 to 7, but this does not invalidate his conclusions in the least.

Dalton further proposed that the atoms of carbon and oxygen could combine with each other in more than one way. Either one atom of carbon could combine with one of oxygen, or one of carbon with two of oxygen. Using Dalton's own symbols, long since outmoded, we may write ○● for carbon

Fig. 1-1. John Dalton

John Dalton was born in England in 1766. His family was poor, and his formal education stopped when he was eleven years old. He became a school teacher. He was color-blind, his appearance and manners were awkward, he spoke with difficulty in public. As an experimenter he was clumsy and slow; he had few, if any, outward marks of genius.

Dalton's atomic theory was presented in a series of publications which began in 1808. It ranks among the greatest of all monuments to human intelligence. No scientific discovery in history has had a more profound effect on the development of knowledge.

Dalton died in 1844. His stature as one of the greatest scientists of all time continues to grow. (*Bettmann Archive*)

monoxide, and ○●○ for carbon dioxide, where ○ stands for an atom of oxygen, and ● for an atom of carbon.

Now it is clear why carbon monoxide always contains 3 parts by weight of carbon to 4 of oxygen. For every atom of carbon there is one of oxygen, and the ratio of the weights of these atoms is 3 to 4. It is clear also why carbon dioxide contains exactly twice as much oxygen per weight of carbon. In carbon dioxide, for every atom of carbon there are two atoms of oxygen. For every carbon atom in carbon dioxide there are twice as many oxygen atoms, and so twice the weight of oxygen, as may be found in carbon monoxide. Many other examples of combination between the chemical elements Dalton explained by similar arguments. This theory, first presented in 1803, was published in full in Dalton's *A New System of Chemical Philosophy* (1808-1810).

It then became evident that Dalton had been anticipated by several years by another English scientist, William Higgins, who, in 1789, had published a book containing, among other material, practically all the essential features of the atomic theory. Higgins's work had attracted no attention at the time it was published, and even to the present day, scientists have only rather lame explanations as to why Higgins was ignored while Dalton was hailed as one of the Founders of Modern Chemistry. About the only reason we have for this curious, and to some extent unjust, state of affairs is that "time was not ripe" for the atomic theory until the beginning of the nineteenth century.

The simplicity and elegance of Dalton's theory appealed to everyone, as did the precision with which it explained those basic experimental facts of chemistry, the Laws of Definite Proportions and of Multiple Proportions.

Do not think, however, that Dalton's original statement of the theory has survived unmodified to the present day. It has undergone expansion, clarification, and modification until Dalton himself might scarcely recognize it. Particularly is this true of the notion that atoms are indivisible, that all the atoms of a given element are the same weight, and that the ratio of weights in which atoms combine give the relative weights of the atoms themselves. But in spite of these shortcomings the germ of the truth was there. Scientists are now as convinced of the reality of atoms as they are that the earth is round. Dalton's atomic theory is the cornerstone of modern chemistry and it marks the inception of a new era in physical science. It has had a profound influence on scientific thought and, indeed, on the history of the world.

3. MODERN ATOMISTICS *

In its modern form the atomic theory may be stated as follows:

All matter is made of minute particles. These atoms are so small that no one has ever seen them, nor is there much likelihood that anyone ever will. In a single grain of sand there are about 1,000,000,000,000,000,000 atoms.

There are different kinds of atoms. Each different kind of atom is called a chemical element. How these kinds of atoms differ from one another will be clear from the following pages. Altogether there are about ninety-eight different kinds of atoms. Many of these chemical elements, as has already been pointed out, are familiar to us. Silver, chlorine, radium, helium, and sulfur are examples of chemical elements. But things like air, brass, water, and wood are made up of different kinds of atoms combined or mixed together.

All the atoms of one kind are of the same or nearly the same weight. Hydrogen is an extreme case. Its heaviest atom weighs three times as much as its lightest atom.

Most of the atoms are able to combine with each other, either in pairs or

* H. S. Taylor and S. Glasstone, *A Treatise on Physical Chemistry,* Vol. I (New York: Van Nostrand, 1942).

in more complicated structures. These combinations follow very definite rules such as the Law of Definite Proportions and other natural laws. Such combinations make up all the vast, varied kinds of matter with which the world is filled.

The atoms, far from being indivisible, have all been broken into simpler particles. Some atoms do this spontaneously; others disintegrate when placed in special instruments, such as the cyclotron, or nuclear reactor.

4. THE MASS SPECTROGRAPH

The masses or weights of the different kinds of atoms are of great interest to the chemist. If the weights are known for the atoms of hydrogen and of

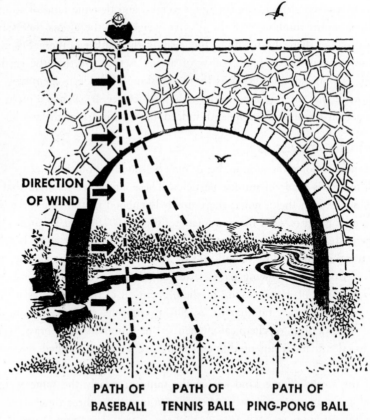

DIRECTION
OF WIND

PATH OF   PATH OF   PATH OF
BASEBALL   TENNIS BALL   PING-PONG BALL

Fig. 1-2. This figure and the next show the principle upon which the mass spectrograph operates. Fig. 1-2 shows how atoms could be weighed by the analogy of weighing balls by dropping them from a height in a strong wind. The relative weights of three balls could be roughly found by comparing the position where each ball lands on the ground.

oxygen, it may be calculated what weight of hydrogen, or of oxygen, will be obtained by decomposing a ton of water with electricity. Weights of the atoms allow the chemist to compute the nitrogen necessary to make a pound of fertilizer, or of sulfur to make a grain of sulfanilamide, or of carbon to make a kilogram of synthetic rubber.

Atoms are incredibly light. One atom, or for that matter many millions of atoms, will have no effect whatever on the most delicate set of scales that might be devised. The ink with which this page is printed probably contains at least 1,000,000,000,000,000 atoms. It would be far easier to count the national debt, dollar by dollar, than it would be to count the atoms in a single grain of sand. If every man, woman, and child in the United States started counting as fast as possible, it would take them about forty thousand

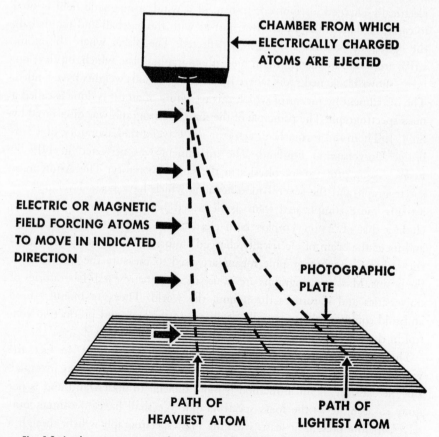

Fig. 1-3. In the mass spectrograph atoms are electrically charged and then ejected into an electric or magnetic field. The field serves the same purpose as the wind in Fig. 1-2, namely to deflect the atoms a varying distance, depending on the weight of the individual atoms.

years to count all the atoms in a drop of water. No ordinary weighing machine will do for weighing atoms.

Suppose you stand on a bridge on a day when the wind is blowing. You drop a baseball straight down. The ball will land a short distance to one side because the wind will carry it. Now if you drop a tennis ball it will be carried farther because it is lighter. A ping-pong ball might be carried to the end of the bridge. If you did not know the relative weights of the three balls, you might be able to make a rough estimate of these by measuring how far each ball had been carried by the wind before it hit the ground. The lighter the ball, the farther will it be carried.

The same principle is used in weighing atoms. No one stands dropping atoms into space. An electric field ejects the atoms into a chamber from which all the air has been pumped. At the same time the atoms become electrically charged, or ionized. Instead of a wind, a magnetic field is used to carry, or deflect, the atoms. But, just as with the baseball and tennis ball, the lighter the atom the more it is deflected. The places where the atoms strike are found by having them hit a photographic plate which, on development, shows blackened spots where the atoms of various weights have landed. The instrument by means of which this weighing of atoms is done is called a **mass spectrograph.** The principle of the mass spectrograph was discovered by Sir J. J. Thomson, formerly director of the Cavendish Laboratory of Cambridge University in England. The instrument was perfected in 1919 by F. W. Aston, professor of physics in the same laboratory. The Aston mass spectrograph and the several modifications which have been developed are actually more complicated than as described here. Some instruments, including that of Aston, employ both electric and magnetic fields to deflect and focus the beam of electrically charged atoms. In some instruments, electric rather than photographic means are used to measure the deflection of the beams. Mass spectrographs are in use in scientific research laboratories of universities and industries throughout the world. They are manufactured and sold commercially, especially as an aid to research and production control in the petroleum industry.

There are other methods for finding the weights of atoms. In fact, the weights were well known long before the mass spectrograph was invented. But the classical chemical method is more difficult to understand and is not quite so accurate as the mass spectrograph. We shall have to content ourselves, for the present at least, with the mass spectrograph which, though a rather formidable piece of electrical machinery, nevertheless operates on a principle understandable by all.

5. ATOMIC WEIGHTS

These methods for finding weights of atoms may be used to find the actual weights in ounces of the various atoms. More frequently they give only the relative weights, not the true weights. The mass spectrograph, for instance, will readily indicate that an atom of sulfur weighs twice as much as an atom of oxygen, or that an atom of hydrogen weighs about one-twelfth as much as an atom of carbon. Obtaining the true weights is a much more difficult operation. It so happens that for most practical purposes the relative weights of the atoms are of as much use as the absolute weights. This is true because we cannot deal with individual atoms; they are too small. We are interested in large aggregates of atoms, sufficient in number so that we can examine them, measure and weigh them, and compare them with atoms of different elements.

If our major interest lies in the relative rather than the absolute weights of atoms, then it is necessary to have a standard of weights. It is no use saying that one atom is twice as heavy as another unless it is specified what atom is twice as heavy as what other atom. The hydrogen atom is the lightest and simplest of all atoms. A man called Prout once suggested that hydrogen would make a good standard and that it should be said to have the weight of 1 unit, or simply, an **atomic weight** of 1. All other atoms would then be compared with that of hydrogen. An element the atoms of which weighed 200 times as much as that of hydrogen would be said to have an atomic weight of 200. This suggestion of Prout's, by no means a bad idea, was abandoned because too many of the elements turned out to have atomic weights that involved cumbersome fractions, and certain other difficulties arose in practice. Instead, oxygen is chosen as the standard of atomic weights and it is given the value 16. Hydrogen, on this basis, has an atomic weight of 1.008. Iron has an atomic weight of 55.85. This means that the atoms of iron weigh 55.85/16 as much as the atoms of oxygen. The use of oxygen as the standard of atomic weights has become universal and has met with few, if any, major difficulties. The chemical elements arranged in alphabetical order, and their atomic weights, are given on the inside front cover of this book.

6. ISOTOPES

It was once believed that all the atoms of a given element had exactly the same weight. But the first studies made with the mass spectrograph showed this to be not true. Taking chlorine as an example, it was found that there are two kinds of chlorine atoms, some with an atomic weight of 35 and others 37.

This condition is found in nearly all the chemical elements. Atoms of the same element but having different weights are called **isotopes.** Thus sulfur has four isotopes of weights 32, 33, 34, and 36. Tin has ten isotopes of weights 112, 114, 115, 116, 117, 118, 119, 120, 122, and 124. A few elements have only one natural isotope. Examples of these are fluorine (19), phosphorus (31), and manganese (55). Sometimes atoms of different elements have the same atomic weights. An example is ruthenium which has an isotope of atomic weight 104, as does palladium. Such atoms are called **isobars.**

The isotopes of the various elements are always found mixed in nature. Chlorine, for instance, is never found having an atomic weight other than 35.457. This value is an average produced by the mixture of isotopes having weights of 35 and 37. It is clear that there must be more of isotope 35 than of 37 because the average value obtained is much nearer 35.

Because, when we find the elements in the earth or the air, the isotopes of each element are almost always mixed in the same proportions, we can continue to use and have confidence in the table of atomic weights. But it must be remembered that for most elements the atomic weights are just average numbers accidentally reached by the mixing of different isotopes. In a very few cases, notably hydrogen, oxygen, and lead, there are measurable differences in the concentrations of the isotopes found in different places. For instance, the atomic weight of oxygen obtained by decomposing water is slightly different from that of oxygen obtained from air. This is a little embarrassing because oxygen is supposed to be our standard of atomic weights. But the differences found are so exceedingly small that they have not yet given rise to any practical difficulties.

Although the isotopes of the elements have slightly different weights they all behave chemically in almost exactly the same way. That is, the chlorine isotope of mass 35 behaves no differently from the isotope of mass 37. They unite with the same elements and at practically the same rates to give compounds which to all intents and purposes are identical except for the slight difference in mass. For some isotopes, notably those of the lighter elements, there are small differences, especially in the rates at which they combine with other elements. The outstanding example of this effect is shown by hydrogen whose three isotopes of masses 1, 2, and 3, vary in weight, at least on a percentage basis, very greatly from each other.

For many years efforts were made to separate the isotopes of the various elements. Considerable success has been achieved in this direction and the pure separated isotopes of hydrogen and some other elements are now available on a commercial basis. But this success has been possible only since about 1934, and for most elements it is still difficult and extremely expensive to obtain the pure separated isotopes.

7. CHEMICAL SYMBOLS

It will be remembered that Dalton used symbols such as ○ and ● to represent the atoms of oxygen and carbon respectively. Even earlier, the alchemists, the forefathers of modern chemical science, used symbols such as ♀ for copper, ☽ for silver, and ⚛ for sulfur.

Chemists now almost universally use a system of abbreviations based on the names of the elements. These **symbols** such as Al for aluminum, O for

Fig. 1-4. The Alchemist

The early history of chemistry includes a long period during which the principal efforts of experimenters were directed to the practice of alchemy, or the changing of inexpensive metals, such as lead, into gold. The reproduction above is of a painting by Cornelius Pietersz Bega (ca. 1660), supposed to represent an alchemist in his laboratory.

Needless to say, the alchemists were unsuccessful in their attempts to obtain gold in this way, although they not infrequently claimed success. Their efforts led to a gradual accumulation of knowledge which contributed to the slow decline of alchemy and the rise of modern chemistry in the seventeenth century. (*Fisher Collection of Alchemical and Historical Portraits*) oxygen, and H for hydrogen are, for the most part, easily recognizable as derived from the first letter or the first two letters of the name of the element. Symbols for most known chemical elements are given in the Table on the inside front cover. In some cases the symbol is derived from the Latin or latinized name of the element rather than from the English name. Sb for antimony is from the latinized name *stibium*. Au for gold is from the Latin *aurum;* Fe (iron), from *ferrum;* Pb (lead), from *plumbum;* Hg (mercury), *hydrargyrum,* i.e., silver water; K (potassium), *kalium;* Ag (silver), *argentum;* Na (sodium), *natrium;* Sn (tin), *stannum.* The symbol W for tungsten is derived from *wolfram,* an early name for tungsten.

8. THE METRIC SYSTEM

Scientists use the metric system in measurements of weight, length, and volume. The standard of weight in this system is the **kilogram,** which is about 2.2 pounds avoirdupois. One one-thousandth part of the kilogram is called a **gram.** A table showing the relationship between English and metric systems will be found in the appendix.

It may be noted that a piece of matter does not necessarily weigh exactly the same on different parts of the earth's surface. The weight of an object is a measure of the mutual gravitational attraction between it and the earth. On the moon a man would weigh only a few pounds and, if he could live there, would find that he could jump many yards with little effort. An object in interstellar space, far from any planet or star, would have practically no weight. The mass of an object, on the other hand, does not change with the position of the object. That is to say, the mass of an object is a measure of the actual quantity of matter present, while the weight is a measure of its mutual gravitational attraction to another object. This difference, however, does not greatly concern us and we shall for the present use the terms **weight** and **mass** interchangeably.

The unit of length in the metric system is the **meter.** A meter is 39.371 inches or slightly longer than a yard. One one-hundredth part of a meter is called a **centimeter.** One tenth of a centimeter is a **millimeter.** Slightly more than two and a half centimeters equal one inch.

The volume of a cube one centimeter on a side is called a **cubic centimeter.** The **liter,** which is the unit of volume in the metric system, was originally intended to be exactly equal to one thousand cubic centimeters. But a slight error was made and the liter is actually larger than one thousand cubic centimeters by about half a drop. This difference is so small that it need not concern us. The liter is a little bigger than a quart. Chemists use most frequently the gram (g.), the centimeter (cm.), and the cubic centimeter (cc.) or milliliter (ml.). The milliliter, one one-thousandth of a liter, is almost identical in size with the cubic centimeter. It may be convenient to remember that a dime is approximately 1 mm. thick and weighs about 2.5 g.

EXERCISES *

A. *Define or explain the following:*

atomic weight	isotope
atomism	kilogram (kg.)
centimeter (cm.)	liter (l.)
chemical symbol	mass spectrograph
chemistry	meter (m.)
cubic centimeter (cc.)	milliliter (ml.)
gram (g.)	millimeter (mm.)

B. *State or explain the following:*
1. Dalton's atomic theory (this consists of several parts)
2. Law of definite proportions
3. Law of multiple proportions
4. How did the "atomism" of ancient Greece differ from Dalton's atomic theory?
5. How does Dalton's theory explain the Laws of Definite Proportions and of Multiple Proportions?
6. How is the mass spectograph used to weigh atoms?
7. What is meant by the *relative* weights of atoms?
8. Why are relative rather than absolute weights of atoms used?
9. What is the standard of atomic weights?
10. If isotopes are always found mixed in the same proportion, how do we know that they exist?

C. 1. If an element has 15.0 per cent of its atoms with an atomic weight of 21.0, and 85.0 per cent with a weight of 23.0, what is the average atomic weight of the element?
2. Chlorine consists of two isotopes of weight 35 and 37. What percentage of each is present? For the average atomic weight consult the Table on the inside front cover.
3. Two elements X and Y combine in two different ways to form two different substances. The first substance contains 29.4 per cent of X, the second substance contains 45.5 per cent of X, the balance being Y in each case. Show whether these substances properly illustrate the Law of Multiple Proportions.
4. Dalton developed his atomic theory by consideration, in part, of the Law of Multiple Proportions. This law may be illustrated by the fact that three

* Most of the exercises in this book are divided into three classes. Classes A and B, as shown above, are designed to test the student's acquaintance with basic definitions, facts, and statements of principles. Class C tests in part the ability to reason on the basis of memorized facts and principles. The exercises should be used as a basis for study. Ability to answer all questions at the end of each chapter will show an excellent grasp of the subject.

parts by weight of carbon unite with four parts of oxygen to form carbon monoxide, represented by Dalton as ◯ ● ; and that three parts of carbon unite with eight parts of oxygen to form carbon dioxide, represented by Dalton as ◯ ● ◯. Dalton was not aware that there is another substance consisting of three parts of carbon with six parts of oxygen. Show what, if anything, Dalton could have done with this new information.

ATOMIC STRUCTURE

Atoms are not simple. Rather, like the solar system, they are exceedingly complex. High on the list of modern scientific miracles is the fact that we know so much about things which are so small. More is known about atomic structure than, a few hundred years ago, was known about the Western Hemisphere. We turn to the science of physics for a glimpse at the architecture of the infinitesimal.

9. ELECTRONS

Air is not a very good conductor of electricity. But if the air is partly pumped out of a glass vessel, the remaining air will conduct the electric current quite well. This is easily proved by using a tube fitted with a wire, or metal strip,

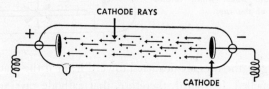

Fig. 2-1. Cathode-ray tube.

through each end. If a source of high voltage, such as a spark coil, is attached to the metal electrodes, no current will flow at first. But then, if the air is partly pumped out of the tube, bluish streamers begin to appear and soon fill the tube from end to end. These streamers are called cathode rays because they seem to come from the cathode or negative electrode. If the cathode rays strike the sides of the glass tube, the glass emits a yellowish-green glow.

The cathode rays have several peculiar properties. If a strip of metal is placed inside the tube, where the rays can strike it, a shadow appears behind the metal strip, and a shadowy image of the strip is found where the rays strike the glass sides of the tube. The rays cannot penetrate through metal; in fact, they are very easily stopped by almost any kind of matter, sometimes even by a thin sheet of paper. On the other hand, the rays can be shown to have considerable force, because if a little metal paddle wheel is mounted inside the tube it will spin around when the rays strike it. The speed with which the rays travel has been measured and may be as high as 100,000 miles per second. This is far greater than the speed of a bullet, which seldom is

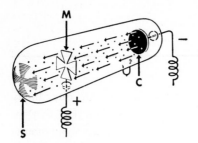

Fig. 2-2. Cathode-ray tube having a metal ob-struction (M) in the path of the rays. The obstruc-tion casts a shadow (S) because the rays cannot penetrate it.

much more than $\frac{1}{2}$ mile per second. It is more like the velocity of light, which is 186,000 miles per second.

If an electrically charged wire or plate is held near the outside of the cathode-ray tube, the rays are deflected, or bent, to one side. If the plate is

Fig. 2-3. Cathode-ray tube containing a small, light, paddle wheel which rotates under the impact of the rays.

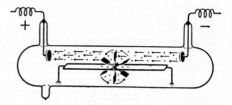

positively charged, the rays are attracted toward it; or if the plate is negative, the rays are repelled. It is clear, therefore, that cathode rays are themselves electrically charged, and that the charge is negative. Opposite electric charges attract each other.

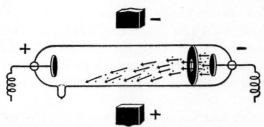

Fig. 2-4. Cathode rays may be deflected by an electric or a magnetic field. The rays are thus shown to carry a negative charge.

The heavier an object, the less readily is it deflected from its path by an electric or magnetic field. Careful measurements by Sir J. J. Thomson have shown that the cathode rays have an extremely high electric charge compared with their mass. The electric charge and the mass have both been accurately measured. The mass of an individual cathode-ray particle works out to be only 1/1837.6 of the mass of a hydrogen atom. The atoms themselves are incredibly small and light. The individual cathode ray particles are much smaller and nearly 2000 times lighter. They are the stuff of which electricity is made. These tiny, subatomic, fundamental particles of electricity are called **electrons.**

10. RADIOACTIVITY

Uranium is a chemical element found in northern Canada, in Colorado, Africa, Bohemia, and elsewhere. In 1896 a French chemist, Henri Becquerel, placed a piece of material containing uranium near a photographic plate.

Fig. 2-5. Gold-leaf electroscope. The metal rod R is insulated (at I) from the metal case C. If R is electrically charged, the gold-leaf G will stand away from R until the electric charge is removed.

The plate was covered with black paper. Becquerel was therefore greatly surprised when he found the plate had been fogged as if it had accidentally been exposed to light. He discovered that some kind of emanation was coming from the uranium, and that it had the power to penetrate through paper and thin sheets of metal. The emanation or rays from uranium also have the ability to discharge an electroscope. An **electroscope** consists essentially of a metal rod to which is attached a delicate strip of gold leaf. The electroscope may be electrically charged by holding near it a piece of hard rubber which has just previously been rubbed with cat's fur. When the electroscope is charged, the gold leaf stands away from the metal rod as far as possible and may continue to do so for many hours until the electric charge leaks away. But if a piece of uranium is brought near the charged electroscope, the gold leaf will fall within a few seconds.

An explanation for these strange effects was sought by a French scientist, Pierre Curie, and his Polish assistant, Marie Sklodowska, who later became his wife and his partner in one of the most spectacular achievements in the history of science.

Fig. 2-6. Spinthariscope. Rays from the speck of radium strike the zinc sulfide layer, which then emits scintillations. The scintillations may be observed through the lens.

The phenomenon discovered by Becquerel is called **radioactivity.** Pierre and Marie Curie soon found that pure uranium is less radioactive than pitchblende, a mineral which contains uranium. They correctly assumed that pitchblende contains something else, more active than uranium. Through endless difficulties and laborious procedures they discovered, first polonium, so named after Mme. Curie's native land, and then they discovered radium, the key to modern atomistics.

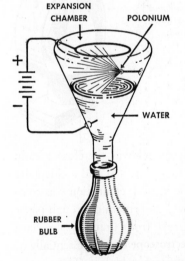

Fig. 2-7. Wilson Cloud Chamber.

Radioactive elements, of which radium is one, are constantly exploding, or disintegrating. The rate of disintegration of some of these radioactive elements, such as uranium, is exceedingly slow—sometimes over periods of billions of years; others such as radium C' disintegrate in a fraction of a second. These elements constantly emit rays of various types. The rays not only affect photographic plates and discharge electroscopes; they produce a variety of other effects, such as severely burning the flesh of anyone coming too near a powerful preparation. The rays from radium are used for luminous dials on watches and aircraft instruments, and to cure certain types of cancer. But the chief importance of radium has been that it opened a new world of subatomic phenomena to scientific research.

Effects from the rays of radium are easily made visible. If a piece of paper is coated with zinc sulfide, and then held near a minute speck of radium or other radioactive substance, the zinc sulfide screen seems to glow. Examination of this glow under a magnifying glass shows myriads of tiny scintillations, like stars twinkling in the sky.

These scintillations are caused by the particles shot out by disintegrating atoms. The particles strike the zinc sulfide which in turn emits a flash of light wherever it is struck. A device called a **spinthariscope** can be used for examining these scintillations and for actually counting the number of particles shot out by a given quantity of radium.

The paths taken by the rays from radium are normally invisible. They may, however, be made visible by a device called a **Wilson Cloud Chamber.** If moist air is compressed, then suddenly decompressed, there is a tendency for a fog or mist to form in the air. The fog seems reluctant to form unless there are nuclei such as dust particles present on which the little water droplets can collect. Ordinarily in dust-free air the fog does not form. The particles shot out by radioactive atoms create disturbances in the air through which they pass. These disturbances serve as centers for the formation of water droplets. The paths of the rays are then made visible by thin little streamers of fog, fog tracks which reveal the direction and distance traversed by the invisible radiations from disintegrating atoms, like vapor trails left by airplanes high in the substratosphere.

Fig. 2-8. Fog tracks obtained with the Wilson Cloud Chamber.

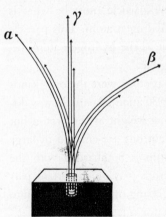

Fig. 2-9. Deflection of alpha (α), beta (β), and gamma (γ) rays in a magnetic field. This shows that alpha and beta rays are electrically charged but of opposite sign. The gamma rays carry no charge.

By their behavior in an electric or a magnetic field, the rays from radioactive substances are shown to be of three types, and their nature is made clear. The three types are called alpha (α), beta (β), and gamma (γ) rays. **Alpha rays** are bent in such a direction in a magnetic field as to indicate that they are positively charged. The mass is four times that of the hydrogen atom and the charge is twice that of the electron but opposite in sign; that is, the charge is positive instead of negative. Alpha rays are atoms of helium which have acquired a double positive charge. They are ejected from radioactive atoms with velocities about 10 per cent of that of light. **Beta rays** are bent in a magnetic field in a direction opposite to alpha rays. They are negatively charged. They turn out to be electrons, traveling with velocities up to 90 per cent of that of light. **Gamma rays** are quite different. They are not deflected in an electric or a magnetic field. They have no weight. They have the properties of waves rather than of particles. They are similar to light and travel with the velocity of light, although they have enormously more energy than does visible light.

11. PROTONS AND NEUTRONS

The fact that electrons are given off by radioactive atoms suggests that electrons are one of the building blocks, or fundamental structural units, of matter. But electrons are negative. Atoms are generally electrically neutral. Atoms must therefore contain something with a positive charge to neutralize the electrons. At first glance it might be thought that the alpha particles, with their positive charges, would serve to neutralize the electrons. Perhaps they do, but there is a difficulty in that the atom of hydrogen with an atomic weight of 1 is too light to contain even a single alpha particle with a weight of 4. It is thought that the fundamental positive particle must be what is left after an electron has been removed from a hydrogen atom. This particle is called a **proton.** It has almost the same weight as the hydrogen atom, because the weight of the electron is all but negligible.

At one time it was thought that electrons and protons were the only kinds of fundamental subatomic particles. But about 1930 another particle was discovered. This particle has approximately the same weight as the proton but has no electric charge. It is called a **neutron.** Neutrons are emitted in large numbers when a light element such as beryllium is bombarded with the alpha particles from radium or polonium. Neutrons play an important part in the chemistry of atomic transmutations, or changing one element into another. But their detailed discussion must wait for a later chapter.

TABLE 1

FUNDAMENTAL PARTICLES

Name	Charge	Mass
Electron...........	−	$\frac{1}{1837}$ (of H atom)
Proton...........	+	1
Neutron...........	0	1

So far as can be seen at present, all matter is made up of these three building blocks, the electron, the proton, and the neutron. Other particles have been discovered, but they need not concern us for the present.

12. THE RUTHERFORD-BOHR ATOM

Two facts about atoms stand out. The first is that atoms are very heavy in comparison with electrons. And the second is that atoms seem to be mostly empty space. The Wilson Cloud Chamber is filled with air and the particles shot out by radioactive atoms go through this air. But only extremely rarely does a fog track indicate by an abrupt change of direction that an atomic collision has occurred. The alpha and beta rays are like comets that dart through space but scarcely ever strike the sun or a planet. We can only conclude that an atom must be something like the solar system, mostly empty space, but having concentrations of matter situated at comparatively vast distances from each other, as is the earth from the sun.

Substantially all the mass of an atom must be associated with the positive charge which goes to neutralize the electrons. But this mass and positive charge must be concentrated into an extremely small particle. No one knows what an atom looks like. But scientists often find it convenient to establish a "working hypothesis" in their efforts to understand nature. A hypothesis is simply a well-reasoned guess as to what the situation may actually be. In the present case such a hypothesis of atomic structure has been proposed by Lord Rutherford of England, and by Niels Bohr of Denmark. Their hypothesis may not be correct and it has already suffered much modification from the form in which it was originally stated in the period 1905-13. But few scientific hypotheses or theories have been so extraordinarily useful as has the Rutherford-Bohr concept of the atom. It has stimulated endless research and has paved the way for countless new discoveries.

It is assumed that the atom is made up of a central core, called the **nucleus,** and that this nucleus is surrounded by one or more electrons. In the neutral atom the number of electrons is, of course, equal to the positive charge of the nucleus. The structure of the nucleus has not been understood until fairly recently. It is now believed that the nucleus consists of protons and neutrons, although in the hydrogen atom of mass one there is only one proton and no neutron. Our hypotheses concerning nuclear structure will doubtless, however, suffer considerable modification in coming years.

At relatively tremendous distances from the nucleus are situated the electrons. These contribute little to the weight of the atom, but they balance or neutralize the positive charge on the nucleus, and they determine the behavior of each atom toward other atoms. The nucleus and all the electrons together take up only a very little space. The "emptiness" of matter is appalling. "The atom is as porous as the solar system. If we eliminated all the unfilled space in a man's body and collected his protons and electrons into one mass, the man would be reduced to a speck just visible with a magnifying glass." *

Fig. 2-10. Niels Bohr

Bohr was born in Denmark in 1885. His theory of atomic structure, which was presented in 1913, laid a broad foundation for the great atomic progress of recent years.

Second only in importance to his celebrated theory are the facts that it was in Bohr's laboratory that the implications of nuclear fission were first predicted, and that he obtained an understanding of nuclear stability which contributed greatly to the spectacular development of atomic energy. (For portrait of Rutherford see p. 456.) (Acme Photo)

The number of electrons in each atom is generally considered to be known with complete accuracy. Thus we say the atom of chlorine has 17 electrons, the atom of gold has 79. The energy that would be necessary to remove each electron from its atom is also known with a very fair degree of accuracy. At one time it was thought that the electrons moved in orbits like the earth around the sun. Perhaps there is still some truth in this idea. But electrons are strange, shadowy conceptions. For instance, it seems impossible to say, at one and the same time, that an electron is at a certain point in space and that it is moving with a certain velocity. Electrons do, of course, have mass and electric charge but they act as though they consisted merely of a cloud of negative electricity, perhaps more concentrated in one spot, less in another. In some respects they act more like waves than like forms of matter.

* A. S. Eddington, *The Nature of the Physical World* (New York: Macmillan, 1928; and the Cambridge University Press).

13. ELEMENTS, ATOMIC NUMBERS, AND MASS NUMBERS DEFINED

A chemical element is a substance in which all the atoms have the same positive charge on the nucleus. The nuclear charge is fixed by the number of protons; we might therefore define an element as a substance in which all the atoms have the same number of protons.

The nuclear charge of an atom is called its atomic number. All the atoms of a chemical element have the same atomic number. If the atom as a whole is electrically neutral, then the atomic number is numerically equal to the number of electrons in the atom. Many atoms gain or lose a few electrons when they enter into chemical combination; it is only the neutral atom which has the same number of electrons as protons. Notice that our definition of a chemical element says nothing about the weights of the atoms. The different isotopes of an element may have different weights, and may even undergo radioactive disintegration by entirely different mechanisms. But if the charges on the nuclei of two atoms are the same, then they are to be considered as atoms of the same chemical element.

Mass numbers are the sum of the weights of protons and neutrons in the nucleus. If an atom of chlorine has 17 protons and 18 neutrons in its nucleus, then the mass number of the atom is 35. Another isotope of chlorine has 17 protons and 20 neutrons; its mass number is 37. In this definition of mass number it has been assumed that the weights of protons and neutrons have been stated relative to the weight of the oxygen atom which is our standard, with the arbitrarily assigned weight of 16. The relation between mass numbers and atomic weights is as follows: If an element has only one isotope, then the atomic weight is equal to the mass number; * if an element is found to have several isotopes, then the atomic weight is the average of the several mass numbers, each being weighted in accordance with the amount present. For instance, in the case of chlorine as given above, the atomic weight is about 35.5. This means that of the two isotopes with mass numbers 35 and 37, the first must be present in ordinary chlorine to the extent of about 75 per cent, and the 37-isotope only 25 per cent.

Now that atomic number has been defined as the nuclear charge of an atom, we shall proceed to show how atomic numbers are experimentally determined. This was first done by Rutherford, who measured the scattering of alpha particles brought about by very thin layers of heavy atoms such as might be found in gold foil. This method gave a clear indication of the nuclear charge for a few elements, but the results were not very accurate. It remained for a young scientist at the Cavendish Laboratory in Cambridge

* A very slight deviation from this rule will be ignored until a later chapter.

University, H. G. J. Moseley, to devise a supremely accurate and ingenious X-ray method for determining these fundamental natural constants.

It will be recalled that cathode rays, or streams of electrons, may be produced by passing an electric current through a partially evacuated tube to which suitable electrodes are attached. The electron beam may readily be focused to strike a small spot if the cathode, or negative electrode, is given a concave shape. In 1895 a German physicist, W. C. Roentgen, discovered that in such circumstances powerful rays emanate from the spot where the electron beam strikes. These rays have the ability to pass through glass and other solid matter. Their most spectacular property is the penetration of human tissue, whereby the bones and other physiological structures are, with the aid of a fluorescent screen, made visible. Roentgen named the rays X rays. They have, as everyone knows, been of inestimable aid to the medical profession in rendering visible foreign bodies imbedded in the flesh, lungs, or other organs; in diagnosing diseases such as tuberculosis; and in the diagnosis and treatment of cancer. The uses of X rays in scientific research have been no less important.

X rays, it turns out, have a remarkable resemblance to the gamma rays emitted by radioactive substances. They have no mass or electric charge but are waves

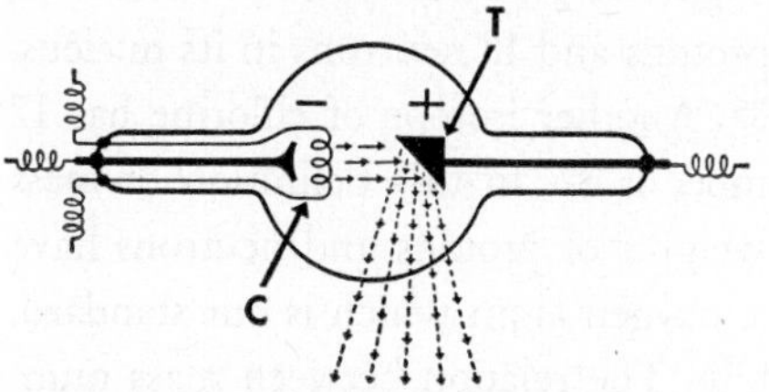

Fig. 2-11. X-ray tube. Cathode rays (electrons) from the hot wire C strike the target T, from which X rays are then emitted.

similar to radio waves or light waves, but differing in being of very much shorter wave length. Waves of these kinds constitute what is known as radiant energy. Radio waves, heat or infrared waves, visible light, ultraviolet, X rays, and gamma rays differ in the length of the waves. This array of different wave lengths of radiant energy is called the electromagnetic spectrum. Radio waves are often several kilometers long, the waves of visible light less than $\frac{1}{1000}$ of a millimeter, X rays about 5000 times still smaller than visible light.

When light is passed through a prism, a rainbow of colors (a spectrum) is produced. The same effect is obtained if the light is passed through a sheet of glass on which a large number of parallel scratches have been made. Such a piece of glass is called a diffraction grating. X rays have such a short wave length that it would be very difficult to rule a diffraction grating suitable for producing an X-ray spectrum. But it happens that the atoms in crystals, such as rock salt, are lined up in orderly rows and that these rows of atoms serve the same purpose as do the scratches on a glass diffraction grating. A crystal interposed in a beam of X rays serves to break the beam up into a spectrum. We are not dealing with visible light, therefore no rainbow of colors is produced. But what amounts to the same thing, the different wave lengths of the X rays present in the beam, are separated by the crystal and may be recorded on a photographic plate. Identification of the actual wave lengths of the X rays is then not much more difficult than is recognition of the various colors of the rainbow.

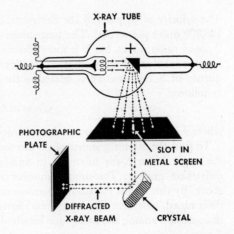

Fig. 2-12. Diffraction of X rays. The rays from the tube are first narrowed by a slot in a metal screen, then allowed to strike a crystal. The crystal diffracts the X rays, and the exact angle through which the X rays are diffracted is found by having the rays strike, and thus mark, a photographic plate. From this diffraction angle and other data it is possible to calculate the wave length of the X rays.

X-RAY TUBE

PHOTOGRAPHIC PLATE

SLOT IN METAL SCREEN

DIFFRACTED X-RAY BEAM

CRYSTAL

What Moseley discovered in 1914 is that different chemical elements used as the target for electrons in the X-ray tube produce different wave lengths of X rays as determined by the aid of the crystal diffraction grating. Furthermore, there is a simple and important relationship between the wave length of X rays produced and the atomic number of the element used as target.

Radio stations operate, as is well known, on certain frequencies assigned by a central authority, in the United States the Federal Communications Commission. The frequency of a radio wave is the number of vibrations per second. Standard radio stations generally use frequencies in the neighborhood of 500,000 to 1,000,000. The frequency is related to the wave length by the expression

$$velocity = frequency \times wave\ length.$$

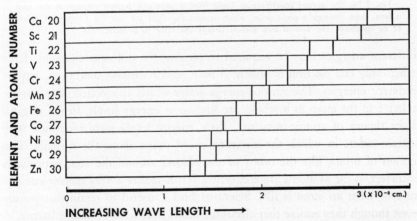

ELEMENT AND ATOMIC NUMBER

Ca 20
Sc 21
Ti 22
V 23
Cr 24
Mn 25
Fe 26
Co 27
Ni 28
Cu 29
Zn 30

0   1   2   3 (x 10⁻⁸ cm.)

INCREASING WAVE LENGTH ⟶

Fig. 2-13. Moseley relationship. This figure is diagrammatic only. It shows how if different elements are made the target in an X-ray tube, the wave length (and hence the frequency) of the rays depends on the atomic number of the element. The vertical lines are meant to represent the relative positions where the photographic plate would be blackened if the several elements indicated were placed, one at a time, as the target in the X-ray tube of Fig. 2-12. It will be noted that each element gives more than one line.

The velocity of all parts of the electromagnetic spectrum is that of light, namely 186,000 miles per second. The frequencies of X rays are very much greater than those of radio waves, but it is more convenient to state Moseley's law in terms of frequencies than of wave lengths. Moseley found that the square root of the frequency of X rays emitted is related to the atomic number of the target element as follows:

$$\sqrt{\nu} = a(Z - b)$$

where ν is the frequency, a and b are constants, and Z is the atomic number.

To find the atomic number of an element, we have only to make the element the target in an X-ray tube and to analyze the X rays emitted with a crystal diffraction grating. The atomic number is then calculated from the equation above. By this means the atomic numbers of practically all the elements have been determined, new elements have been identified, and order has been brought out of confusion among the nearly one hundred elements of which the world is made.

14. ENERGY LEVELS

The energy necessary to remove an electron from an atom is known with considerable accuracy. When more than one electron is present in an atom,

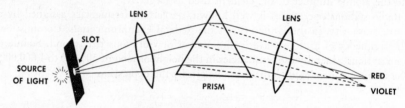

Fig. 2-14. The optical spectroscope. Light from a source is passed through a slot and a lens, then through a glass prism which breaks the light up into the component colors of its spectrum. The second lens merely brings the light to a focus.

different energies may be required to remove the different electrons. Even when only one electron is present it may, under varying conditions, require different energies. The various energy states which an electron may possess, relative to the atom as a whole, are known as **energy levels.** In the original Bohr theory of atomic structure, these energy levels were identified with certain orbits in which the electrons could move about the nucleus. This notion of orbits, like the orbits of the planets around the sun, is probably incorrect so far as atoms are concerned, but it makes a very convenient picture of what an atom is like. Scientists find it useful to retain this picture even though they realize that electronic orbits may have no real existence. A peculiar feature of an atom is that the electrons are permitted to have only certain definite energy levels and that intermediate levels are not tolerated. According to rules which appear to control the atoms, an electron may move from one energy level to another but it may not stop between levels. The situation is like an elevator in a modern building. The elevator is controlled by automatic devices which cause it to stop only at the various floors, but not

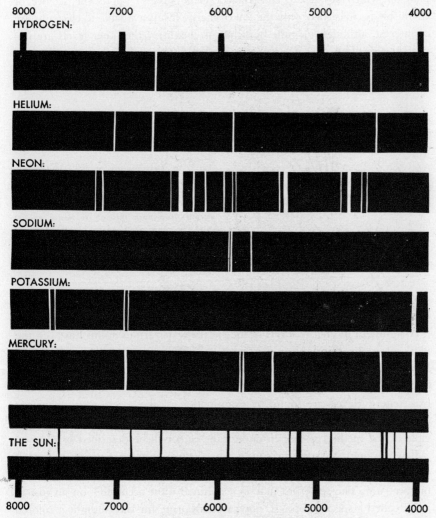

Fig. 2-15. The spectra of several different elements and of the sun. For most elements the spectrum consists of bright lines of various wave lengths on a dark background. Only the brightest lines are shown in the above diagram. The numbers indicate wave lengths and are given in Ångström (Å) units. The spectrum of the sun consists of a bright background interspersed with dark lines. The significance of these dark lines will be discussed later in the text on p. 140.

between floors. By putting energy into the motors which operate the elevator, the car may be raised to various levels. When the elevator comes down, energy is released and could, if it were so desired, be used. Why electrons

have certain discrete energy levels and not others is not completely understood, but this seems in some way to be an important part of the architectural
plan on which atoms are constructed. Generally, so far as the science of
chemistry is concerned, only the lower energy levels available to electrons are
of interest, although in some branches of chemistry the other levels are important also. This is as if, on entering a building, we found we could trans-
act most of our business on the ground floor. The lowest energy level is often
called the ground state.

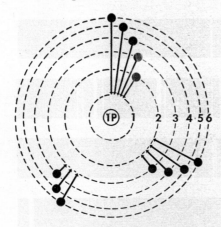

Fig. 2-16. Electrons are normally in the lowest, or ground, state of energy in an atom.
The electrons may be raised to higher energy
levels by heat or by electric fields. As the
electrons drop back through successive energy
levels, the atom emits energy in the form of
light. This light constitutes the spectrum of the
element as observed with a spectroscope.

Assignment of energy levels to the electrons in various atoms has been the
work of many minds. For this achievement we are indebted to Bohr in
Denmark, Sommerfeld in Germany, Lewis and Langmuir in the United
States, Bury, Main-Smith, and Stoner in England, and to many others. The
exact energy levels are found by examination of the spectroscopic behavior
of the elements. The method is complicated and mathematical, but the principle of the method is easy to understand and will be described briefly.

If white light, as from the sun, is passed through a glass prism, the result
is, as already mentioned, that the light is broken up into a rainbow of colors,
or spectrum. The spectrum may be examined most accurately on an instrument called a spectroscope. If, now, we substitute for the sunlight a colored
flame, such as might be observed from fireworks displays, the spectrum takes
on an entirely different appearance. Instead of a continuous rainbow we see
only a few sharp colored lines. The lines are different for each chemical element which may be present in the colored flame. Some elements produce only
a few lines, others many thousands of lines. The various elements may readily be identified by the position of their characteristic lines in the spectrum.
This is the basis of the art of spectrochemical analysis. Many new elements
have been discovered in this way.

The spectrum of hydrogen may be excited by passing an electric discharge through a tube in which hydrogen is contained under low pressure. The spectrum so obtained is simple and consists mainly of lines in the red, blue, violet, and ultraviolet. It is believed that these several spectrum lines are produced by electrons falling from a higher energy level to a lower level. The precise color, or wave length, of the spectrum line depends upon what energy level the electron originally was in, and to what energy level it fell. In other words, the difference in energy between the initial and final state of the electron determines the wave length of light emitted by the atom. A careful examination of the various wave lengths of light emitted by the hydrogen atom makes it possible to assign energy levels to all the states in which a hydrogen atom might be found under various conditions of excitation. This has also been done for nearly all the other chemical elements. It is therefore possible to tabulate the various energy levels for all the elements in their ground states and to assign the numbers of electrons normally found in each of these levels. This is done in Table 2.

The hydrogen atom has a nuclear charge of +1 which is balanced by a single electron. A convenient representation of these facts is given by the diagram

This is not intended to be a picture of a hydrogen atom. It is rather, in a sense, a symbol for hydrogen. It carries the information that the charge on the nucleus of hydrogen is +1, and that a single electron occupies a definite

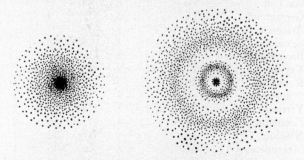

Fig. 2-17. The wave-mechanical concept of an atom is represented by these figures for hydrogen and argon. The electron, or electrons, are represented as a cloud of varying density around the nucleus. (After L. Pauling, General Chemistry, W. S. Freeman and Company, 1947. By permission of L. Pauling)

TABLE 2

ARRANGEMENT OF ELECTRONS IN THE ATOMS

Atomic Number	Element	Symbol	Number of Electrons in Each Energy Level						
			1	2	3	4	5	6	7
1	Hydrogen	H	1						
2	Helium	He	2						
3	Lithium	Li	2	1					
4	Beryllium	Be	2	2					
5	Boron	B	2	3					
6	Carbon	C	2	4					
7	Nitrogen	N	2	5					
8	Oxygen	O	2	6					
9	Fluorine	F	2	7					
10	Neon	Ne	2	8					
11	Sodium	Na	2	8	1				
12	Magnesium	Mg	2	8	2				
13	Aluminum	Al	2	8	3				
14	Silicon	Si	2	8	4				
15	Phosphorus	P	2	8	5				
16	Sulfur	S	2	8	6				
17	Chlorine	Cl	2	8	7				
18	Argon	A	2	8	8				
19	Potassium	K	2	8	8	1			
20	Calcium	Ca	2	8	8	2			
21	Scandium	Sc	2	8	9	2			
22	Titanium	Ti	2	8	10	2			
23	Vanadium	V	2	8	11	2			
24	Chromium	Cr	2	8	13	1			
25	Manganese	Mn	2	8	13	2			
26	Iron	Fe	2	8	14	2			
27	Cobalt	Co	2	8	15	2			
28	Nickel	Ni	2	8	16	2			
29	Copper	Cu	2	8	18	1			
30	Zinc	Zn	2	8	18	2			
31	Gallium	Ga	2	8	18	3			
32	Germanium	Ge	2	8	18	4			
33	Arsenic	As	2	8	18	5			
34	Selenium	Se	2	8	18	6			
35	Bromine	Br	2	8	18	7			
36	Krypton	K	2	8	18	8			
37	Rubidium	Rb	2	8	18	8	1		
38	Strontium	Sr	2	8	18	8	2		
39	Yttrium	Y	2	8	18	9	2		
40	Zirconium	Zr	2	8	18	10	2		
41	Niobium	Nb	2	8	18	12	1		
42	Molybdenum	Mo	2	8	18	13	1		
43	Technetium	Tc	2	8	18	14	1 *		
44	Ruthenium	Ru	2	8	18	15	1		
45	Rhodium	Rh	2	8	18	16	1		
46	Palladium	Pd	2	8	18	18			
47	Silver	Ag	2	8	18	18	1		
48	Cadmium	Cd	2	8	18	18	2		

TABLE 2 (*Continued*)

ARRANGEMENT OF ELECTRONS IN THE ATOMS

Atomic Number	Element	Symbol	Number of Electrons in Each Energy Level						
			1	2	3	4	5	6	7
49	Indium	In	2	8	18	18	3		
50	Tin	Sn	2	8	18	18	4		
51	Antimony	Sb	2	8	18	18	5		
52	Tellurium	Te	2	8	18	18	6		
53	Iodine	I	2	8	18	18	7		
54	Xenon	Xe	2	8	18	18	8		
55	Cesium	Cs.	2	8	18	18	8	1	
56	Barium	Ba	2	8	18	18	8	2	
57	Lanthanum	La	2	8	18	18	9	2	
58	Cerium	Ce	2	8	18	20	8	2	
59	Praseodymium	Pr	2	8	18	21	8	2	
60	Neodymium	Nd	2	8	18	22	8	2	
61	Promethium	Pm	2	8	18	23	8	2 *	
62	Samarium	Sm	2	8	18	24	8	2	
63	Europium	Eu	2	8	18	25	8	2	
64	Gadolinium	Gd	2	8	18	25	9	2	
65	Terbium	Tb	2	8	18	26	9	2	
66	Dysprosium	Dy	2	8	18	28	8	2	
67	Holmium	Ho	2	8	18	29	8	2	
68	Erbium	Er	2	8	18	30	8	2	
69	Thulium	Tu	2	8	18	31	8	2	
70	Ytterbium	Yb	2	8	18	32	8	2	
71	Lutetium	Lu	2	8	18	32	9	2	
72	Hafnium	Hf	2	8	18	32	10	2	
73	Tantalum	Ta	2	8	18	32	11	2	
74	Tungsten	W	2	8	18	32	12	2	
75	Rhenium	Re	2	8	18	32	13	2	
76	Osmium	Os	2	8	18	32	14	2	
77	Iridium	Ir	2	8	18	32	17	(?)	
78	Platinum	Pt	2	8	18	32	17	1(?)	
79	Gold	Au	2	8	18	32	18	1	
80	Mercury	Hg	2	8	18	32	18	2	
81	Thallium	Tl	2	8	18	32	18	3	
82	Lead	Pb	2	8	18	32	18	4	
83	Bismuth	Bi	2	8	18	32	18	5	
84	Polonium	Po	2	8	18	32	18	6	
85	Astatine	At	2	8	18	32	18	7 *	
86	Radon	Rn	2	8	18	32	18	8	
87	Francium	Fr	2	8	18	32	18	8	1 *
88	Radium	Ra	2	8	18	32	18	8	2
89	Actinium	Ac	2	8	18	32	18	9	2
90	Thorium	Th	2	8	18	32	20	8	2(?)
91	Protactinium	Pa	2	8	18	32	21	8	2(?)
92	Uranium	U	2	8	18	32	22	8	2(?)

Electron distribution in elements 90 to 98, including Np, Pu, Am, Cm, Bk, and Cf are uncertain at time of publication.

* Probable.

energy level in the atom. What a hydrogen atom actually looks like is not known and may never be known. The most advanced "wave-mechanical" theory of atomic structure suggests that atoms may somewhat resemble the diagrams in Fig. 2-17. But so far as chemical problems are concerned, the representation given above is of more general utility, although perhaps less accurate.

The atom of helium has a nuclear charge of two, balanced by two electrons in the same energy level. These facts may be represented thus:

There is no justification, other than convenience, for putting one electron on each side of the atom. The wave-mechanical model of the helium atom shows simply a spherical cloud of negative electricity for the two electrons together. But, always keeping in mind that our diagrams are meant to be symbols rather than pictures, we shall attempt the representation of a few more atoms.

In lithium, with atomic number 3, two electrons are in the first energy level, and the third is in the second energy level.

In these representations, nothing is shown about the nucleus other than its electric charge. If it were desired to indicate the number of neutrons in a particular isotope of lithium, this might readily be done.

Lithium isotope of atomic weight 6. The nucleus contains 3 protons and 3 neutrons.

Lithium isotope of atomic weight 7. The nucleus contains 3 protons and 4 neutrons.

The next seven elements in order of increasing atomic number are shown below.

beryllium

boron

carbon

nitrogen

oxygen

fluorine

neon

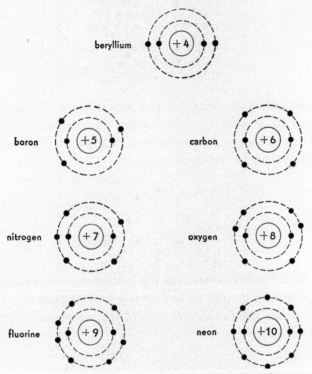

Eight electrons is the maximum number the second energy level can hold. In the next element, sodium, the extra electron goes into the third energy level.

sodium

magnesium

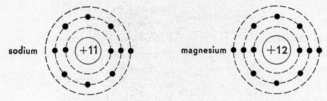

With these few examples, and the aid of Table 2, it should be possible for the reader to construct a diagram for any element. For instance, let us take the element bromine. The atomic number of this element is 35. The nuclear charge is 35; therefore there must be 35 electrons in the neutral atom. Reference to Table 2 will show that these electrons are arranged in groups of 2, 8, 18, 7. The diagram is then

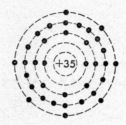

In most cases, only those electrons which appear in the outermost ring (in our diagram) are of importance to chemistry. These are the electrons which determine how an atom will behave toward its neighbors. For most purposes we might abbreviate the bromine diagram to

Perhaps it should also be pointed out that refinements of spectroscopy show each energy level to be split up into several sublevels and that sometimes these sublevels are still further split. But of this complication we need for the present say no more.

EXERCISES

A. *Define or explain the following:*

alpha ray	neutron
atomic number	nucleus
atomic weight	proton
beta ray	radioactivity
cathode ray	radium
chemical element	Rutherford-Bohr atom
electron	spectroscope
electroscope	spectrum
energy level	uranium
gamma ray	Wilson cloud chamber
mass number	X-ray tube

B. *State or explain the following:*

1. Moseley's law, or discovery
2. How cathode rays are produced
3. How we know that radioactive substances emit rays
4. How the types of rays are distinguished
5. Why a proton weighs almost as much as a hydrogen atom

6. Why it is believed that an atom is mostly empty space
7. Why it is believed that the nucleus of an atom must be comparatively heavy
8. Of what the nucleus of an atom is believed to consist
9. Why we say that the number of electrons in an atom is equal to the positive charge of the nucleus
10. What X rays are. How they are produced
11. How X rays can be used to find the atomic numbers of the elements
12. What, in outline, is the method for assigning energy levels to electrons in atoms
13. Represent the electron arrangement in the elements of atomic number 1 to 12, without reference to the text

C. 1. By reference to Table 2 represent electron arrangement in phosphorus, calcium, krypton, iodine, and uranium.
   2. What is the probable constitution of the nucleus of the oxygen atom which has a mass number of 16; of the oxygen atom with mass number of 18; of the uranium atom with mass number 238?

CHAPTER 3 ATOMIC COMBINATIONS

Atoms unite with other atoms. Sometimes the union is so weak and transient that no effective combination may be said to have taken place. At other times the union is so strong that very powerful forces are necessary to tear the atoms apart again. By the union of atoms there are formed the chemical compounds. Air, water, rocks, trees, animals, all are formed by atomic combination. Sometimes the combinations are comparatively simple, as for instance the union of two atoms of hydrogen. Sometimes the combinations are of such extraordinary complexity, as in the proteins of animal tissue, that we are still far from understanding how these substances are made.

The combining power of an atom is called **valence.** At one time the term "valence" had a much more restricted meaning. But the word has gradually lost its original significance until now chemists use it to mean any manifestation of a more or less stable attraction between one atom or group of atoms and another. There are several different ways in which atoms may combine. To the two major kinds of valence our attention will be first directed.

15. ELECTRON SHARING

If two hydrogen atoms approach each other they may unite. These hydrogen atoms behave as though each had a hook which could be used to catch and hold other atoms.

We say that each hydrogen atom has a valence of one; and we believe that the particles so formed constitute the substance known to us as hydrogen gas. Of course, atoms do not have hooks; the forces acting within and around atoms are predominantly electrical.

How these forces act is complicated, and was not understood until the development of a new branch of mathematical physics, called **quantum mechanics,** in 1926. We cannot present the complicated mathematics of quantum mechanics here, but we can indicate in a general, over-simplified way why the two hydrogen atoms are attracted to each other. The nuclei of these atoms, both being positive, exert a mutual repulsion. The electrons, both being negative, do likewise. But both electrons are attracted toward both nuclei, because opposite electric charges tend to move together. There are therefore two major forces acting between two atoms of hydrogen, one a repulsion, the other an attraction. The interaction of these opposing forces leads to the result that at a certain small distance between the hydrogen atoms there is a region of stability, or more accurately, of minimum potential energy. When two hydrogen atoms have thus combined, they remain combined at or near the same distance from each other, unless quite powerful energies, such as are found in an electric arc, are used to force them apart.

The union of two hydrogen atoms is conveniently represented as a sharing of electrons.

The process of electron sharing is called **covalence.** Recalling the diagrams of atoms given in the previous chapter, it must be emphasized that these repre-

Fig. 3-1. This drawing shows the probable distribution of electrons, averaged over a period of time, in a particle formed by the union of two hydrogen atoms. Such representations are doubtless much nearer the truth than the formal diagram previously given above, but the more accurate drawing is obviously much less convenient to use. (After L. Pauling, *General Chemistry*, W. H. Freeman and Company, 1947. By permission of L. Pauling)

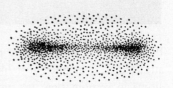

sentations are to be considered as symbols rather than as true pictures of atomic combinations. If we could see two hydrogen atoms combined (which we cannot do), we would presumably see nothing but an elongated blur.

The element carbon has a valence of 4. An atom of carbon can unite with four atoms of hydrogen to form methane.* The atom of carbon has

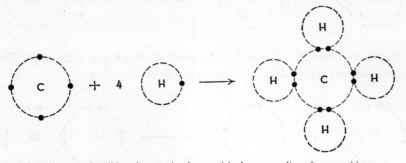

* Methane is a combustible substance in the municipal gas supplies of many cities.

four electrons in its highest normal energy level. These four electrons are shared with the four electrons in four hydrogen atoms to form four covalent bonds.

This belief that electrons are paired off in covalent bond formation receives support in many ways. One of the most convincing ways was first demonstrated by Professor Gilbert N. Lewis at the University of California, about

Fig. 3-2. Gilbert Newton Lewis

Lewis was born in Massachusetts in 1875. He studied at Nebraska, Harvard, Leipzig, and Gottingen. He taught at Harvard, at Massachusetts Institute of Technology, and at the University of California. Most of his active life was spent at Berkeley.

The work of Lewis on molecular structure forms the basis for all modern developments in this field. He was no less active in the field of chemical thermodynamics. A substantial fraction of all outstanding American and foreign physical chemists had the privilege of studying with him.

Lewis died in his laboratory in 1946. He was engaged in making important discoveries to the very end of his life. (*Photo by Johann Hagemeyer*)

1923. Electrons act like little magnets. For instance, atoms of hydrogen are attracted to a magnet, just like a compass needle. But with two hydrogen atoms in combination, no such attraction exists. This substance is actually slightly repelled by a magnet, presumably because all the electrons are paired off, as if compass needles were tied together with north pole to south pole, and vice versa.

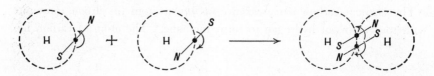

Atoms of chlorine unite with each other in much the same way. The highest normal energy level of chlorine has seven electrons.

These are shared in such a way that each of two chlorine atoms has effectively a completed level containing eight electrons. Similarly, carbon tetrachloride (used in fire extinguishers) is formed by electron sharing between one carbon atom and four chlorine atoms.

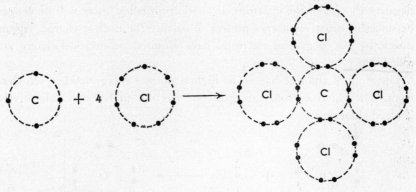

Water is formed by covalent bond formation between one oxygen atom and two hydrogen atoms.

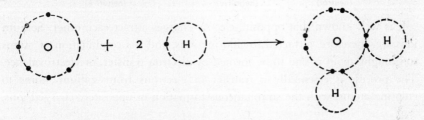

16. ELECTRON TRANSFER

It happens not infrequently that electrons, instead of being shared between atoms, are completely transferred from one atom to another. This will be illustrated by the formation of ordinary table salt, sodium chloride, from its elements, sodium and chlorine.

The atom of sodium has a single electron in its highest normal energy level. Not a very large amount of energy is necessary to remove this electron completely.

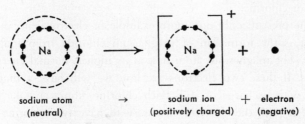

sodium atom   →   sodium ion   +   electron
(neutral)   (positively charged)   (negative)

The particle left after the removal, or addition, of one or more electrons from a neutral atom is, of course, electrically charged. If an electron has been lost, the particle acquires a positive charge. This is true because in the neutral atom, the positive charge on the nucleus just balances the combined negative charges of the electrons. If an electron is lost there will no longer be sufficient negative charges present to balance the nuclear charge. Atoms which, by loss or gain of electrons, have acquired an electrical charge are called **ions.**

The atom of chlorine has, in its highest normal energy level, seven electrons. The chlorine atom can gain one electron to become a negatively charged chlorine ion.

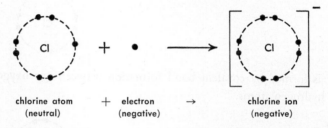

chlorine atom   +   electron   →   chlorine ion
(neutral)   (negative)   (negative)

It is well known that opposite electric charges attract each other. Sodium ions are, therefore, attracted to chlorine ions, and the combination of atoms so brought about is said to be formed by **electron transfer,** or **electrovalence.** The process is essentially a transfer of electrons from sodium atoms to chlorine atoms, with the simultaneous formation of oppositely charged ions.

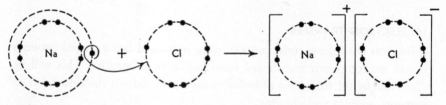

The charge acquired by atoms during the gain or loss of electrons is generally indicated by a + or − sign at the upper right-hand corner of the symbol for the atom. Thus Na^+ is the symbol for the ion of sodium, Cl^- for the ion of chlorine.

For the present, only one more example of electrovalence will be given, and that is the formation of magnesium chloride from magnesium and chlorine. The magnesium atom has, in its highest normal energy level, two electrons. If these two electrons are lost, we will have a magnesium ion, Mg^{++}, with a charge of +2. Each chlorine atom can take up only one electron. It will, therefore, be necessary to have two chlorine atoms, each acquiring a −1 charge, to take up both electrons from one magnesium atom, and to balance the double positive charge acquired by the magnesium.

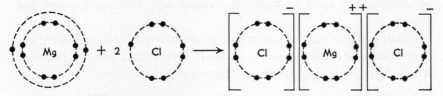

The various examples given above are extreme cases of electrovalence and of covalence. The great majority of substances are neither completely electrovalent nor completely covalent. In other words, most substances are borderline cases, tending perhaps more to one side or to the other. Even a substance such as sodium chloride shows a slight tendency toward covalent character, and on the other hand, carbon tetrachloride shows slight electrovalent characteristics. Electrovalent substances may often be distinguished from covalent substances by the fact that when melted they conduct the electric current. Covalent substances do not conduct electricity.

The behavior of a borderline substance will be illustrated with a single example, hydrogen chloride.

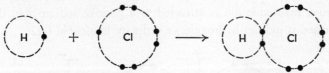

This substance, prepared from hydrogen and chlorine, does not conduct electricity. It is, therefore, to be considered as essentially covalent. Nevertheless, this substance has considerable tendency to form ions. If hydrogen chloride is put between electrically charged plates, the particles tend to turn so that the hydrogen, the positive end of the particle, is directed toward the negative plate. Furthermore, if hydrogen chloride is placed in water, the mixture immediately becomes a very good conductor of electricity. Neither of these effects is observed with a more strictly covalent, nonpolar substance like carbon tetrachloride.

In many chemical substances the atoms are combined both by covalence and by electrovalence. Such substances contain what are called **complex ions.** Complex ions are ions containing two or more atoms. The valence bonds within the com-

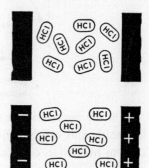

Fig. 3-3. *Upper,* random orientation of hydrogen chloride particles before application of electric charge to plates. *Lower,* directed orientation of hydrogen chloride particles after application of charge to plates. A substance showing this effect is said to be "polar."

plex ion are generally covalent or partially so, but the forces that attract one ion to another of opposite charge are electrovalent. These substances will be illustrated by three examples of complex ions, two negative and one positive.

Water, it will be recalled, consists of groups of atoms, each containing one oxygen atom and two hydrogen atoms. If from such a group a proton is removed, the remaining particle will have a negative charge.

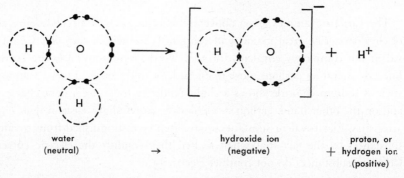

water   →   hydroxide ion   proton, or
(neutral)   (negative)   + hydrogen ion
                                                  (positive)

This particle is called a **hydroxide ion.** The hydrogen atom remaining may be thought of as being attached to the oxygen by a covalent bond. If now this negative hydroxide ion is attracted to a positive sodium ion, the substance formed is sodium hydroxide, or ordinary household lye.

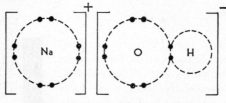

positive sodium ion attracted to negative
hydroxide ion to form sodium hydroxide

Or if the positive ion is calcium, which has a double positive charge, two hydroxide ions will be required for every calcium. The substance formed is calcium hydroxide, or quicklime.

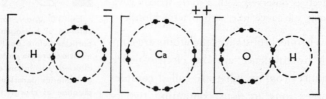

doubly charged positive calcium ion attracted to two
negative hydroxide ions to form calcium hydroxide

Another example of complex ion formation is the union of a sulfur atom with four oxygen atoms plus two electrons to form the sulfate ion. The oxygen atoms are combined with the sulfur by covalence.

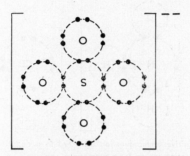

doubly negative charged sulfate ion

The sulfate ion, carrying a double negative charge, may be attracted to two sodium ions, each with a positive charge of one, to form sodium sulfate. Or the sulfate ion may be attracted to one calcium ion, with a positive charge of two, to form calcium sulfate.

A simple example of positive complex ion formation is found in the covalent union of one nitrogen atom to four hydrogen atoms, less one electron, to form the ammonium ion.

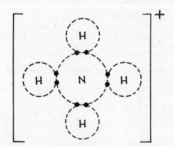

ammonium ion with charge of positive one

This, in turn, can unite with a negative ion such as that of chlorine to form the substance ammonium chloride.

With a few exceptions, all the chemical elements enter into electrovalent bonds, and, with a few exceptions, all enter into covalent bonds. What kind of valence bond to expect in definite cases lies, for the moment, beyond us. More will have to be said about this topic later; but valence has long been an obscure branch of chemistry. Only since about 1920 has definite progress been made in understanding the reasons why one atom is able to combine with another, and many problems still remain unsolved. The types of *ions* formed by the more familiar chemical elements are shown in Table 3.

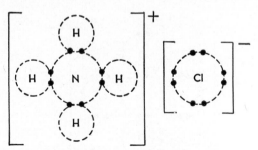

positive ammonium ion attracted to a negative
chlorine ion to form ammonium chloride

17. COMPOUNDS, MIXTURES

The combination of atoms of different elements produces substances known as chemical compounds. It makes no difference whether the combination is by covalence or by electrovalence. Carbon tetrachloride is a chemical compound, as are sodium chloride and hydrogen chloride. There are only ninety-odd chemical elements, but the combinations of these elements yield compounds numbering in the hundreds of thousands.

It will be recalled that the formation of chemical compounds is described by the Law of Definite Proportions, which is stated: "When two or more elements combine they always do so in a fixed, or definite, proportion by weight." We shall find it somewhat more convenient to use this as a definition of a pure chemical compound rather than as the statement of a law of nature. Thus we shall define a **chemical compound** as a substance which always contains the same elements in a fixed, or definite, proportion by weight. Sodium chloride will be considered to be a chemical compound because every pure sample of sodium chloride contains by weight 39.4 per cent of sodium and 60.6 per cent of chlorine. Water will be considered to be a chemical compound because every pure sample of water contains 2.016 parts by weight of hydrogen to 16.000 parts of oxygen.

The existence of isotopes, with their several atomic weights, raises some difficulties with this definition of a chemical compound. For instance, a sample of pure water prepared from hydrogen and the heaviest known isotope of oxygen would contain 2.016 parts by weight of hydrogen to 18 parts of oxygen. We shall choose, however, to ignore this difficulty until a later chapter.

Most of the substances with which we are familiar in everyday life do not meet our definition of a pure chemical compound. Water, as found in lakes and oceans, may contain more or less salt, the air may contain more or less moisture, our breakfast coffee does not contain a fixed, or definite, proportion of sugar, but may be sweetened to taste. Such substances are called **mixtures.** Mixtures may be composed of elements, or of compounds, or of both. *But the fact which distinguishes a mixture from a chemical compound is that in the latter the elements are always combined in a definite proportion by weight.*

Mixtures are often characterized by a lack of homogeneity. Examined under a microscope, mixtures often exhibit several different kinds of substances which may be separated mechanically. A mixture of sand and sugar could be separated by laboriously picking out the separate grains, or more readily, by the operation of dissolving the sugar in water and pouring it off. The sand would not dissolve in the water and would be left behind in the pouring operation. Salt water could be separated by letting it evaporate in the sun. The salt would be left behind. But pure compounds are, on the other hand, homogeneous. They appear to be the same throughout. A pure compound cannot be separated into its components without disrupting the atomic combinations and so destroying the compound. Water cannot be separated into its constituent elements, hydrogen and oxygen, without decomposing the water.

Still another way in which a chemical compound differs from a mixture is found in the study of its properties. It is common experience that iron differs from copper in being harder, being a different color, being attracted to a magnet, and in other ways. These characteristics by which we, perhaps subconsciously, identify one substance from another are called **properties.** The freezing point of water, its lack of color, its transparency, the fact that it boils at 212° F., the fact that under the influence of an electric current it decomposes into hydrogen and oxygen—these are properties of water. We commonly speak of lead as being much "heavier" than water. We mean that a lump of lead of a certain size weighs much more than the same volume of water. More precisely we should say lead has a higher density than water. **Density** may be expressed as the weight in grams per cubic centimeter of a substance. Water has a density of 1 g. per cc., lead a density of about 11 g. per cc.

Problem: A rectangular block of silver is 2.0 cm. wide, 10 cm. long, and 1.5 cm. thick; the block weighs 315 g. What is the density of silver?

Solution: The volume of the block is $(2.0 \times 10 \times 1.5)$ cc. = 30 cc. This volume of silver weighs 315 g. Therefore 1 cc. of silver would weigh $\frac{1}{30} \times 315$ g. = 10.5 g. The density of silver is 10.5 g. per cc.

Like freezing point, boiling point, and so forth, density is a characteristic property of a pure substance. A pure chemical compound is characterized not only by the fact that it always contains the same elements in a definite proportion by weight, but also by the fact that it has a characteristic set of properties which serve to distinguish it from other compounds. But mixtures, on the other hand, have no characteristic sets of properties. Our breakfast coffee, being a mixture, may contain much sugar and have the property of being very sweet, or it may contain little sugar and be scarcely sweet at all.

It should be pointed out that not all properties are characteristic of pure substances. A sample of water may weigh 100 grams. This is a property of that particular sample of water but not necessarily of other samples of water. But the property pure water has of freezing at 32° F. is a property of all pure samples of water. Properties such as freezing point, boiling point, density and so forth which are characteristic of *all* pure samples of a substance are called **specific properties.** Other properties such as size, weight, and temperature, may be called accidental properties.

If atoms combine to form groups of atoms, or if such groups are changed or disrupted, we say that a **chemical change** has taken place. Thus the union of hydrogen and oxygen to form water is a chemical change. Whenever chemical change takes place, there is an abrupt change of specific properties. Water differs in its specific properties and in almost every respect from the two elements of which it is formed. But if a sample of water is warmed slightly, a change in accidental properties may have taken place, but no major change in specific properties. Changes of temperature, shape, degree of magnetization, and the like, which do not involve the making or breaking of bonds between atoms—that is, the formation or destruction of chemical substances—are called **physical changes.** For instance, the breaking of a lump of coal is a physical change, the burning of that lump of coal in the furnace is a chemical change.

18. FORMULAS

Just as we have symbols for the chemical elements, so we find it convenient to have **formulas** for groups of atoms in combination. The formula NaCl can be used to represent the ultimate pair of atoms, or ions, which may be thought of as comprising the substance sodium chloride. The formula not only indicates that sodium chloride is made of sodium and chlorine, but that there is one atom of sodium for each atom of chlorine.

The formula for water is H_2O. This implies, by use of the subscript 2 after the symbol for hydrogen, that there are in this substance two atoms of hydrogen for each atom of oxygen.

TABLE 3

Ions of the More Familiar Chemical Elements

Name	Ion	Name	Ion
Acetate	$C_2H_3O_2^-$	Hydroxide	OH^-
Aluminum	Al^{+++}	Hypochlorite	ClO^-
Ammonium	NH_4^+	Iodate	IO_3^-
Antimony	Sb^{+++}	Iodide	I^-
Barium	Ba^{++}	Lead (plumbous)	Pb^{++}
Bicarbonate	HCO_3^-	Magnesium	Mg^{++}
Bismuth	Bi^{+++}	Manganous	Mn^{++}
Bromide	Br^-	Mercurous	Hg_2^{++}
Cadmium	Cd^{++}	Mercuric	Hg^{++}
Calcium	Ca^{++}	Nickel	Ni^{++}
Carbonate	$CO_3^=$	Nitrate	NO_3^-
Chlorate	ClO_3^-	Nitrite	NO_2^-
Chloride	Cl^-	Oxalate	$C_2O_4^=$
Chlorite	ClO_2^-	Oxide	$O^=$
Chromate	$CrO_4^=$	Perchlorate	ClO_4^-
Chromic	Cr^{+++}	Permanganate	MnO_4^-
Cobaltous	Co^{++}	Phosphate (ortho)	$PO_4^{\equiv}$
Cupric	Cu^{++}	Potassium	K^+
Cupric ammonia	$Cu(NH_3)_4^{++}$	Silicate (ortho)	$SiO_4^{\equiv}$
Cuprous	Cu^+	Silver	Ag^+
Cyanide	CN^-	Sodium	Na^+
Dichromate	$Cr_2O_7^=$	Strontium	Sr^{++}
Ferric (iron)	Fe^{+++}	Sulfate	$SO_4^=$
Ferricyanide	$Fe(CN)_6^{\equiv}$	Sulfide	$S^=$
Ferrocyanide	$Fe(CN)_6^{\equiv}$	Sulfite	$SO_3^=$
Ferrous (iron)	Fe^{++}	Thiosulfate	$S_2O_3^=$
Fluoride	F^-	Tin (stannous)	Sn^{++}
Formate	HCO_2^-	Zinc	Zn^{++}

Formulas for all the other substances discussed in the previous sections are hydrogen, H_2; * methane, CH_4; chlorine, Cl_2; * carbon tetrachloride, CCl_4; magnesium chloride, $MgCl_2$; hydrogen chloride, HCl; sodium hydroxide, $NaOH$; calcium hydroxide, $Ca(OH)_2$; sodium sulfate, Na_2SO_4; and ammonium chloride, NH_4Cl. It will be noticed that calcium hydroxide is written $Ca(OH)_2$, rather than CaO_2H_2. The first, correct, way implies that two hydroxide ions unite with one calcium. The second, incorrect, way suggests that one calcium atom is combined with two oxygen atoms and two

* The union of two atoms of an element to form a single particle does not imply that the element becomes a chemical compound. Many of the atoms of elements combine in this way; in fact, this seems to be their normal state of existence. The question of how it is known that the formula for hydrogen is H_2 rather than H, and that chlorine is Cl_2 rather than Cl, will be discussed later. Other examples of this phenomenon are O_2, N_2, O_3, and S_8.

hydrogen atoms. The subscript 2 outside brackets means that the whole group of atoms inside the bracket is to be taken twice. The formula for aluminum sulfate, $Al_2(SO_4)_3$, shows that there are three sulfate ions for every two aluminum ions in this compound.

Table 3 shows most of the ions of the more important elements. With the aid of this table it should be possible to write the formula for almost any compound formed essentially by electrovalence. Unfortunately we have no such convenient table for covalent compounds. The method for using the table is simple: it is only necessary to remember that the formula as a whole must be electrically balanced. That is, there must be just as many negative charges as positive. Let us write the formula for magnesium phosphate. The magnesium ion, Mg^{++}, has a charge $+2$. The phosphate ion, $PO_4^{\equiv}$, has a charge -3. It will, therefore, be necessary to take three magnesium ions with total charges of $3 \times 2 = 6$, to balance two phosphates of total charge $2 \times -3 = -6$. The formula for magnesium phosphate is $Mg_3(PO_4)_2$. In writing formulas it is customary to put the positive ion first.

Just as there are atomic weights for the chemical elements, there are **formula weights** for the compounds. The formula weights are found by adding together the atomic weights of all the atoms present in the formula. Thus the formula weight for sodium chloride, $NaCl$, is $22.997 + 35.457 = 58.454$. The formula weight for water, H_2O, is $(2 \times 1.0080) + 16.0000 = 18.0160$. The formula weight for magnesium phosphate, $Mg_3(PO_4)_2$, is $(3 \times 24.32) + \{[30.98 + (4 \times 16.0000)] \times 2\}$, or $(3 \times 24.32) + (2 \times 30.98) + (8 \times 16.0000) = 262.92$.

19. CHEMICAL EQUATIONS

Iron combines with sulfur to form iron sulfide, the formula for which is FeS. The atomic weights of iron and sulfur being 55.85 and 32.07 respectively, it follows that when an atom of iron unites with an atom of sulfur, 55.85 parts by weight of iron unite with 32.07 parts by weight of sulfur. But this statement is of little more than academic interest because it is impossible to handle individual atoms, and quite difficult to obtain their weights. Chemists find it expedient to avoid this difficulty. Take n atoms of iron, and the "weight" of these atoms will be $n \times 55.85$. For each atom of iron one atom of sulfur is required. Therefore, n atoms of iron require n atoms of sulfur and the "weight" of this sulfur will be $n \times 32.07$. Now let n be large enough so that the actual weight of the iron is 55.85 grams. The weight of sulfur required will then be 32.07 grams. These quantities of iron and of sulfur are easy to handle, yet they maintain the weight relationships existing between actual atoms of two elements. The formula weight of a substance, whether element or compound, expressed as grams is called a **mole** of that substance.* The mole of any substance is easily obtained provided the formula is known: for instance, 1 mole of helium, He, is 4.003 grams; of water, H_2O, is 18.016 grams; of sodium chloride, NaCl, is 58.454 grams; of glycerine, $H_8C_3O_3$, is 92.0948 grams.

The statement that iron combines with sulfur to form iron sulfide may be written

$$iron + sulfur \rightarrow iron\ sulfide$$

or, with the use of symbols and formulas

$$Fe + S \rightarrow FeS$$

This is known as a **chemical equation.** It carries the information not only that iron combines with sulfur to form iron sulfide, but that 1 mole of iron (55.85 grams) combines with 1 mole of sulfur (32.07 grams) to form 1 mole of iron sulfide (87.92 grams). A chemical equation has both a qualitative and quantitative significance. It tells what substances combine to form what product, and it tells what weight of each is involved in the transformation.

When methane burns in air, the products are carbon dioxide and water. In words

$$methane + oxygen \rightarrow carbon\ dioxide + water$$

or, using formulas,

$$CH_4 + O_2 \rightarrow CO_2 + H_2O$$

As this equation stands it is incomplete; in fact, it cannot properly be considered to be an equation in the strict sense because there are 4 atoms of hydrogen on the left of the arrow and only 2 on the right. Also, there are 2 atoms of oxygen on the left and 3 on the right. Furthermore, the total weight of moles on the left of the arrow is

$$(16.042 + 32.000) = 48.042\ grams$$

while the weight on the right of the arrow is

$$(44.010 + 18.016) = 62.026\ grams$$

What actually happens when methane burns in air is that 1 mole of methane combines with 2 moles of oxygen to form 1 mole of carbon dioxide and 2 moles of water. These facts are represented

$$CH_4 + 2O_2 \rightarrow CO_2 + 2H_2O$$

* The number n, referred to above, is very large and is of theoretical interest only. It is estimated to be about 600,000,000,000,000,000,000,000, or 6×10^{23}.

Now the same numbers of atoms of each kind is found on each side of the arrow, and the weight of moles on the left exactly equals the weight on the right, namely 80.042 grams. This operation, just described, is called **balancing** the equation. One more example should serve to make the method clear.

When steam is passed over hot iron, the products are magnetic oxide of iron and hydrogen:

$$\text{word equation: steam} + \text{iron} \rightarrow \text{iron oxide} + \text{hydrogen}$$

$$\text{skeleton equation: } H_2O + Fe \rightarrow Fe_3O_4 + H_2$$

$$\text{balanced equation: } 4H_2O + 3Fe \rightarrow Fe_3O_4 + 4H_2$$

This represents the facts that 4 moles of steam react with 3 moles of iron to form 1 mole of iron oxide and 4 moles of hydrogen. (Fe_3O_4 may be thought of as being formed from FeO plus Fe_2O_3.)

It will be noticed that 4 moles of water are written $4H_2O$ rather than $(H_2O)_4$, or H_8O_4. The first method carries the information that the ultimate particle of water is H_2O, but that these particles are not necessarily combined with each other. The formulas $(H_2O)_4$ and H_8O_4 would imply that 8 hydrogen atoms were in some way combined with 4 oxygen atoms. We know that this is not the case.

Without his equations the chemist would be lost. The equations give, in concise form, a record of experimental observations concerning the nature and quantities of substances undergoing the transformations that make up the science of chemistry. Every equation is the statement of experimentally determined facts. It is quite possible to write down imaginary substances reacting in what appears superficially to be a logical, balanced equation. But unless the equation is subject to experimental verification it is false, and has no meaning.

Useful as chemical equations are, it should be pointed out that they have their limitations. An equation tells nothing of the speed with which substances react, nor does it ordinarily give the conditions under which the chemical changes take place.

20. CONSERVATION OF MASS

The emphasis placed on the operation of balancing chemical equations implies that **in any chemical reaction the initial weight of the reacting substances is exactly equal to the final weight of the products.** This statement is known as the **Law of Conservation of Mass.** Like all natural laws, this law has been formulated after the most exhaustive experimental testing. Natural laws are not the result of action by a legislative body or a political ruler. They are careful statements of what is believed to be the true course of natural phenomena. It not infrequently happens that natural laws turn out to be wrong, or at least subject to modification. This is true of the Law of Conservation of Mass. But this is not because of any whimsy or caprice on the part of Nature. Rather it is because the Law has not been stated quite accurately. Statements of natural laws are convenient approximations to the truth, to be used until something more precise can be formulated.

The Law of Conservation of Mass was first stated by a Russian scientist, Lomonossov, in 1756. Independently, it was restated by the great French chemist, Lavoisier, in 1774. Both these men heated tin with air in a closed container. They found that there was no change in weight, even though the tin united with the oxygen of the air to form a white powder, stannic oxide. Over a period of years from 1893 to 1908, a German chemist, H. Landolt, subjected this law to the most searching tests. Taking various reactions, such as the union of iodic acid with hydrogen iodide,

$$HIO_3 + 5HI \rightarrow 3I_2 + 3H_2O$$

Landolt found no deviation from the law within a possible error of 1 part in 10,000,000.

Einstein's celebrated Theory of Relativity predicts that whenever energy is given off, or absorbed, a change of mass will occur. As practically all chemical changes involve energy changes, it follows that for every chemical change there will be a mass change, so that the Law of Conservation of Mass will not be exactly true. For all ordinary chemical changes this mass change is too small to be measured, even with the refinements used by Landolt. But for certain atomic transmutations, in which one element is converted into another, the energies are so great that the masses of the atoms are measurably affected. In this sense, therefore, the Law of Conservation of Mass is subject to modification.

EXERCISES

A. *Define or explain the following:*

ammonium ion	mass
chemical change	mixture
chemical compound	mole
covalence	natural law
density	physical change
electrovalence	"polar" substance
formula	property (as applied to chemical substances)
formula weight	sulfate ion
hydroxide ion	valence
ion	

B. *State or explain the following:*
1. Law of Conservation of Mass
2. By what means do atoms combine?
3. What difference exists between electrovalent and covalent substances?
4. Why does the existence of isotopes complicate our definition of a chemical compound?
5. Show by appropriate electron diagrams how the following substances or ions are formed:

a. H_2
b. H^+
c. CH_4
d. Cl_2
e. CCl_4
f. H_2O
g. Na^+
h. NaCl

i. $MgCl_2$
j. HCl
k. OH^-
l. $Ca(OH)_2$
m. $SO_4^=$
n. NH_4^+
o. NH_4Cl

C. 1. Classify, with explanations, the following as compounds or mixtures: milk, air, soil, salt, water, wood, sugar.
2. Calculate the density of an element if a rectangular block 8.0 cm. long, 2.0 cm. wide, and 1.4 cm. thick weighs 43 g.
3. Calculate the length of a cylindrical rod of osmium 6.2 cm. in diameter, and weighing 215 g. The densities of the elements will be found in the Appendix.
4. Fill in the following table with appropriate formulas for the compounds formed between the negative ions at the left and the positive ions at the top.

	Aluminum	Calcium	Sodium
Chloride			
Hydroxide			
Nitrate			
Phosphate			
Oxide			
Sulfate			

5. By reference to Table 3 write formulas for each of the following: aluminum chlorate, ammonium acetate, ammonium hydroxide, antimony ni-

trate, barium carbonate, barium perchlorate, bismuth ferrocyanide, cadmium sulfide, calcium bicarbonate, calcium fluoride, chromic hydroxide, cobaltous hydroxide, cupric hydroxide, cupric ammonia hydroxide, ferric nitrate, ferrous carbonate, lead chloride, lead sulfide, magnesium oxide, manganous oxide, mercuric chloride, nickel oxide, silver sulfate, silver chloride, sodium silicate, sodium iodide, sodium fluoride, sodium cyanide, sodium carbonate, strontium sulfate, tin (stannous) chloride, zinc chloride.

6. By reference to Table 3 name each of the following: $AlFe(CN)_6$, NH_4Br, NH_4NO_3, Sb_2O_3, $BaCl_2$, BaO, $Bi(NO_3)_3$, $CdCl_2$, $CaCO_3$, $Ca(ClO)_2$, $CaSO_3$, Cr_2O_3, $Co(NO_3)_2$, CuO, $Cu(NO_3)_2$, $Fe(ClO_4)_3$, $Fe(OH)_2$, $PbCrO_4$, $Mg_2Fe(CN)_6$, $Mn(ClO_3)_2$, MnS, $NiCl_2$, $NiSO_4$, Ag_2O, $Na_2S_2O_3$, $NaClO_4$, $NaIO_3$, $Na_4Fe(CN)_6$, Na_2CrO_4, $NaBr$, SrO, ZnO.

7. Balance the following equations:
   a. $Fe_2O_3 + Al \rightarrow Fe + Al_2O_3$
   b. $Na_2SO_3 + HCl \rightarrow NaCl + SO_2 + H_2O$
   c. $CO + H_2 \rightarrow CH_4 + H_2O$
   d. $Mg_3N_2 + H_2O \rightarrow Mg(OH)_2 + NH_3$
   e. $Pb + PbO_2 + H_2SO_4 \rightarrow PbSO_4 + H_2O$

8. $$Zn + H_2SO_4 \rightarrow H_2 + ZnSO_4$$
   a. State in words the qualitative (substances only) meaning of the above equation.
   b. State the meaning of the equation in terms of moles of substances.
   c. State the meaning of the equation in terms of grams of substances.

9. Repeat question 8 for each of the first two equations in question 7, after they have been balanced.

10. Show by appropriate electron diagrams how the following substances are formed: $CaCl_2$, $Mg(OH)_2$, $(NH_4)_2SO_4$.

CHEMICAL ARITHMETIC

4

Some sciences, like botany and geology, are, for the most part, descriptive sciences. They consist of great accumulations of facts and principles, logically arranged by the labors of many careful investigators. But mathematics plays a minor role in these sciences. Other sciences, like physics and astronomy, are exact sciences. The facts and principles of these sciences may be, and must be, stated with mathematical precision and conciseness. Chemistry lies between these extremes. Chemistry, in its various branches, is both descriptive and exact, and here, for many chemists, lies its fascination. As time goes on, chemistry becomes more and more an exact science, with consequently more and more emphasis on the mathematical description of chemical phenomena. No student of elementary chemistry can hope to gain an understanding or appreciation of the subject unless he gains first some mental proficiency in a few simple arithmetical methods. Anyone who tells a student that he can succeed in chemistry without a good basis in mathematics is doing that student a disservice.

A few simple operations in chemical arithmetic are presented in this chapter. They are concerned chiefly with the composition of a chemical compound and the formula of that compound.

21. FORMULA FROM COMPOSITION

Water consists of approximately 1 part by weight of hydrogen for every 8 parts by weight of oxygen. That is, in 9 grams of water there are approximately 1 gram of hydrogen and 8 grams of oxygen. Similarly, in 25 grams of calcium sulfide there are 13.9 grams of calcium and 11.1 grams of sulfur. Our first problem is, with the above information and the atomic weights of calcium and sulfur, to find the formula for calcium sulfide.

Let us start by reviewing briefly the concept of the *mole*. We have seen how chemical compounds have formulas, and how the *formula weight* of a compound may be obtained by adding the atomic weights of all atoms in the formula. Thus, the formula weight for H_2O is $(2 \times 1) + 16 = 18$. A very useful quantity in chemistry is the *formula weight expressed as grams*. This quantity is called a *mole*. A mole of water is then simply 18 grams of water.

There is one additional term which we shall introduce. It would be quite correct to refer to a mole of H (1 g.) or a mole of O (16 g.), but the custom, when referring to the atoms of elements, is to use the term **gram-atom.** Thus we shall refer to a mole of water (18 g.), but to a gram-atom of H (1 g.) and to a gram-atom of O (16 g.).

To find the formula for calcium sulfide, it is necessary to find the ratio of gram-atoms of Ca to gram-atoms of S in the compound. The atomic weight of calcium is 40.1; * hence 40.1 g. of Ca would be 1 gram-atom of Ca. Then 13.9 g. of Ca would be 13.9 g./40.1 g. = 0.347 gram-atoms of Ca.

For the sulfur the number of gram-atoms of S is given by 11.1 g./32.1 g. = 0.347 gram-atoms, where 32.1 is the atomic weight of sulfur. Notice that 0.347 gram-atoms of Ca are combined with 0.347 gram-atoms of S. Therefore 1 gram-atom of calcium could be combined with 1 gram-atom of sulfur, and the formula of calcium sulfide is CaS.

The arithmetical operations shown above may conveniently be summarized in a table, as follows:

Symbol	Parts by Weight	Atomic Weight	Gram-Atoms
Ca........	13.9	40.1	13.9/40.1 = 0.347 gram-atoms of Ca
S.........	11.1	32.1	11.1/32.1 = 0.347 gram-atoms of S

The ratio 0.347 to 0.347 is equal to the ratio 1 to 1; hence the formula is CaS.

Now we shall find the formula for a slightly more complicated compound, sodium carbonate (washing soda). A 10-gram sample of sodium carbonate contains 4.34 grams of sodium, 1.13 grams of carbon, and 4.52 grams of oxygen. Proceeding as before:

Symbol	Parts by Weight	Atomic Weight	Gram-Atoms
Na........	4.34	23.0	4.34/23.0 = 0.189
C..........	1.13	12.0	1.13/12.0 = 0.094
O..........	4.52	16.0	4.52/16.0 = 0.283

The ratio of numbers is 0.189 Na to 0.094 C to 0.283 O. It is not clear from these numbers what the ratios would be in whole numbers, but these whole numbers are readily found by dividing each of the numbers by the *smallest* one of the three: that is, by 0.094. Then

$$0.189/0.094 = 2 \text{ gram-atoms of Na}$$

$$0.094/0.094 = 1 \text{ gram-atom of C}$$

$$0.283/0.094 = 3 \text{ gram-atoms of O}$$

* We shall, for ease in making calculations, generally round off atomic weights to the first decimal place.

The formula of sodium carbonate is therefore Na_2CO_3. Notice that 0.283 divided by 0.094 is not exactly 3, but is nearer 3.01. But 3.01 is so near to 3 that we conclude the small discrepancy is due to experimental error. No experiment, no matter how carefully performed, can yield perfect numerical results. In such problems as these, *small* deviations from whole numbers are often encountered.

One more example of formula finding will be given. This is for the compound ferric (iron) oxide. This substance contains 70.1 per cent iron, and 30.0 per cent oxygen. Expression of the composition in percentage means, simply, that 100 parts by weight of ferric oxide contain 70.1 parts of iron and 30.0 parts of oxygen. The very slight deviation of the total from 100 per cent is not unusual in experimentally measured compositions.

Symbol	*Parts by Weight*	*Atomic Weight*	*Gram-Atoms*
Fe..........	70.1	55.8	$70.1/55.8 = 1.26$
O..........	30.0	16.0	$30.0/16.0 = 1.88$

Dividing, as usual, by the smaller one of the two quantities we have $1.26/1.26 = 1$ gram-atom of Fe, and $1.88/1.26 = 1.49$ gram-atom of O. It still is not clear what the formula should be in whole-number subscripts until we multiply both quantities by 2, then 2 gram-atoms of Fe are combined with 3 gram-atoms of O. The formula is Fe_2O_3. Notice that the ratio of gram-atoms of iron to oxygen is not changed in these final operations which lead to whole numbers. The ratio 1.26 to 1.88 is the same as 1 to 1.49, and these are both the same (within experimental error) as 2 to 3.

22. COMPOSITION FROM FORMULA

If the formula of a chemical compound is known, then the parts by weight of each element present are easily found. This type of calculation is simpler than the reverse type, which has just been described in the preceding section.

The formula for carbon dioxide is CO_2. The composition may be expressed as follows: 1 formula weight of carbon dioxide—that is, $(1 \times 12.0) + (2 \times 16.0) = 44.0$ parts by weight—contains 12.0 parts by weight of carbon and $2 \times 16.0 = 32.0$ parts by weight of oxygen. The fraction of the total weight which is carbon is $12.0/44.0$. Expressed as a decimal, $12.0/44.0 = 0.273$. Or, expressed as percentage by moving the decimal point two places to the right, $12.0/44.0 = 0.273 = 27.3$ per cent. That is, carbon dioxide contains 27.3 per cent by weight of carbon. Similarly, carbon dioxide contains $2 \times 16.0/44.0 = 0.727 = 72.7$ per cent of oxygen. These statements may be summarized as follows:

COMPOSITION OF CARBON DIOXIDE, CO₂

	Vulgar Fraction	*Decimal*	*Percentage*
Parts by weight of carbon...	$12.0/44.0$	$= 0.273 =$	27.3
Parts by weight of oxygen..	$2 \times 16.0/44.0 =$	$0.727 =$	72.7

$$100.0$$

A slightly more complicated case is calcium phosphate, $Ca_3(PO_4)_2$. We shall find the percentage composition of this substance. First, find the formula weight. This is

$$3Ca = 3 \times 40.1 = 120.3$$
$$2P\ \ = 2 \times 31.0 = \ \ 62.0$$
$$8O\ \ = 8 \times 16.0 = 128.0$$

$$310.3$$

The composition for each element is then given as follows:

Parts by weight of calcium $120.3/310.3 = 0.387 = $ 38.7%
Parts by weight of phosphorus $62.0/310.3 = 0.200 = $ 20.0%
Parts by weight of oxygen $128.0/310.3 = 0.413 = $ 41.3%

$$100.0\%$$

Next, suppose we wish to find the weight of carbon in 85 grams of carbon dioxide. Proceed as follows: the formula is CO_2; therefore 44.0 grams of carbon dioxide contain 12.0 grams of carbon. Then 1 gram of carbon dioxide contains $(1/44.0) \times 12.0$ grams of carbon, and 85 grams of carbon dioxide contain $85 \times (1/44.0) \times 12.0 = 23.2$ grams of carbon.

One more example of this type will be given. What weight of sulfur is present in 25 grams of sulfuric acid, the formula for which is H_2SO_4?

The formula weight for sulfuric acid is $(2 \times 1.0) + 32.1 + (4 \times 16.0) = 98.1$. Then 98.1 grams of sulfuric acid contain 32.1 grams of sulfur. Therefore, 1 gram of sulfuric acid contains $(1/98.1) \times 32.1$ grams of sulfur, and 25 grams of acid contain $25 \times (1/98.1) \times 32.1$ g. $= 8.2$ g. of sulfur.

23. CALCULATIONS FROM EQUATIONS

One of the most important types of chemical calculations is "stoichiometry," or finding the relative weights of substances taking part in a chemical change. Take the manufacture of iron from iron ore, which may be represented by the equation

$$2Fe_2O_3 + 3C \rightarrow 4Fe + 3CO_2$$
ferric oxide + carbon → iron + carbon dioxide

Our problem is to find the weight of carbon necessary to react with a given weight of iron oxide.

Problem: What weight of carbon is necessary to react with 100 g. of ferric oxide, according to the above equation?

Solution: The first necessity is to see that the equation is accurate and balanced. Then proceed as follows: recall that the equation may be interpreted: 2 moles of ferric oxide plus 3 gram-atoms (or moles) of carbon yield 4 gram-atoms (or moles) of iron plus 3 moles of carbon dioxide. The formula weight of ferric oxide is $(2 \times 55.8) + (3 \times 16.0) = 159.6$. Therefore 159.6 g. is 1 mole, then 1 g. is 1/159.6 moles, and 100 g. are 100/159.6 moles. The equation states that 2 moles of ferric oxide require 3 gram-atoms of carbon. Therefore 1 mole of ferric oxide requires $\frac{3}{2}$ gram-atoms of carbon. Then 100/159.6 moles of ferric oxide will require $100/159.6 \times \frac{3}{2}$ gram-atoms of carbon. Now 1 gram-atom of carbon is 12.0 g., therefore $100/159.6 \times \frac{3}{2}$ gram-atoms of carbon would be $100/159.6 \times \frac{3}{2} \times 12.0$ g. $= 11.3$ g. of carbon.

Another example will be given:

Problem: What weight of potassium chlorate is needed to obtain 250 g. of oxygen according to the following equation?

$$2KClO_3 \rightarrow 2KCl + 3O_2$$

Solution: 250 g. of O_2 is 250/32.0 moles of O_2, this will require $250/32.0 \times \frac{2}{3}$ * moles of $KClO_3$, and this is equivalent to $250/32.0 \times \frac{2}{3} \times 122.6$ † = 640 g. of $KClO_3$.

After experience is gained, the whole solution of the problem may be stated in one line. For instance:

Problem: What weight of hydrogen chloride, HCl, is required for the production of 100 g. of chlorine gas, Cl_2, according to the following equation?

$$4HCl + MnO_2 \rightarrow MnCl_2 + Cl_2 + 2H_2O$$

Solution: The weight of hydrogen chloride needed is $100/71.0 \times 4 \times 36.5 = 205$ g. of HCl.

24. CONVERSION OF UNITS

Scientists, in general, use the C.G.S. (Centimeter, Gram, Second), or Metric, System of Units. Engineers, and others, often use the English System. It will be

---

* Because 3 moles of O_2 are obtained from 2 moles of $KClO_3$, according to the equation.
† 122.6 is the formula weight of $KClO_3$; hence 1 mole of $KClO_3$ weighs 122.6 g.

worth while therefore to show how chemical calculations may be made in the English System almost as easily as in the Metric System.

Problem: How many pounds of sulfuric acid, H_2SO_4, are needed to neutralize 500 lbs. of sodium hydroxide, NaOH, according to the following equation?

$$H_2SO_4 + 2NaOH \rightarrow Na_2SO_4 + 2H_2O$$

Solution: We have, up to this point, defined a mole as a formula weight expressed as grams. It would be quite in order to use "pound-moles" or "ton-moles" instead of "gram-moles." Using pound-moles, 500 lbs. of sodium hydroxide would then be 500/40.0 pound-moles. This would require:

$$500/40.0 \times \tfrac{1}{2} \text{ pound-moles of } H_2SO_4$$

or

$$500/40.0 \times \tfrac{1}{2} \times 98.0 \text{ pounds of sulfuric acid} = 613 \text{ lbs.}$$

One more problem will be sufficient to illustrate the use of other than metric units.

Problem: What weight of chlorine is necessary to liberate all the bromine in 100 tons of sodium bromide?

Solution: The equation is

$$2NaBr + Cl_2 \rightarrow Br_2 + 2NaCl$$

and the weight of chlorine necessary is

$$100/102.9 \times \tfrac{1}{2} \times 71.0 \text{ tons} = 34.5 \text{ tons of chlorine}$$

EXERCISES

A. *Define or explain the following:*

gram-atom   pound-mole

C. 1. How many grams are there in one mole of each of the following?

   a. H_3PO_4 (phosphoric acid)
   b. $CHCl_3$ (chloroform)
   c. $MgSO_4$ (magnesium sulfate)
   d. $Al_2(SO_4)_3$ (aluminum sulfate)
   e. C_7H_{16} (heptane)

  2. How many moles are there in the following?

   a. 100 g. of Cl_2
   b. 35 g. of H_2SO_4
   c. 1000 g. of SO_2
   d. 500 g. of KNO_3
   e. 125 g. of $K_4Fe(CN)_6$

3. How many grams are there in the following?
    a. 1.85 moles of HCl
    b. 0.63 moles of Br_2
    c. 0.00159 moles of UF_6
    d. 1000 moles of H_2
    e. 3.3 moles of O_3 (ozone)

4. Find the formulas of the compounds with the following composition:
    a. 2.00 g. silver, 0.662 g. chlorine
    b. 5.00 g. of the compound contains 2.82 g. of phosphorus, the balance being oxygen
    c. sodium, 36.5%; sulfur, 25.4%; oxygen, 38.1%
    d. sodium, 22.9%; boron, 21.5%; oxygen, 55.7%
    e. potassium, 26.58%; chromium, 35.40%; oxygen, 38.02%

5. Express in percentages for each element the composition of the substances indicated:
    a. NH_4Cl (ammonium chloride)
    b. $Na_2S_2O_3$ (sodium thiosulfate)
    c. $Pb(CH_3CO_2)_2$ (lead acetate)

6. $Na_2SO_3 + 2HCl \rightarrow 2NaCl + H_2O + SO_2$. How many grams of SO_2 are available through the use of 2.7 moles of HCl?

7. $3Cu + 8HNO_3 \rightarrow 3Cu(NO_3)_2 + 2NO + 4H_2O$. What weight of NO (nitric oxide) may be obtained by the use of 100 g. of copper?

8. $2KMnO_4 + 16HCl \rightarrow 5Cl_2 + 2KCl + 2MnCl_2 + 8H_2O$. How many moles of chlorine, Cl_2, are obtainable by the use of 0.15 moles of $KMnO_4$ (potassium permanganate)?

9. How many moles of chlorine can be obtained by the action of excess HCl on 0.50 moles of MnO_2? The equation is: $4HCl + MnO_2 \rightarrow Cl_2 + MnCl_2 + 2H_2O$.

10. What weight of potassium chlorate, $KClO_3$, can be made from 225 g. of potassium hydroxide, KOH? The equation is: $6KOH + 3Cl_2 \rightarrow KClO_3 + 5KCl + 3H_2O$.

11. What weight of aluminum must be used per kilogram of iron oxide, Fe_3O_4, in the reaction $8Al + 3Fe_3O_4 \rightarrow 4Al_2O_3 + 9Fe$.

12. When barium peroxide is treated with dilute hydrochloric acid, hydrogen peroxide is formed. $BaO_2 + 2HCl \rightarrow H_2O_2 + BaCl_2$. How much BaO_2 is required to make 500 g. of a 3 per cent, by weight, solution of H_2O_2?

13. What weight of Fe_2O_3 would be obtained by burning 1.5 kg. of iron pyrites, FeS_2? The equation is: $4FeS_2 + 11O_2 \rightarrow 2Fe_2O_3 + 8SO_2$.

14. What weight of sulfur is precipitated when 10 g. of sodium thiosulfate is treated with hydrochloric acid according to the equation $Na_2S_2O_3 + 2HCl \rightarrow 2NaCl + SO_2 + S + H_2O$.

15. What fraction of the total oxygen in MnO_2 is evolved as O_2 according to the equation: $3MnO_2 \rightarrow Mn_3O_4 + O_2$?

STATES OF MATTER
5

God give me strength to face a fact though it slay me—Thomas Huxley

Matter exists in three states: solid, liquid, and gas. The earth is a solid, water is a liquid, air is a gas.* It is well known that water may exist not only as a liquid, but also as a solid, or as gas. In the form of ice, water is a solid. At higher temperatures, it is a liquid. And at still higher temperatures it is converted into a gas, commonly called water vapor or steam.

The outstanding characteristic of solids is that they possess both *volume* and *shape*. A piece of iron, for instance, has a definite volume which may be expressed in cubic centimeters. A piece of iron also has a definite shape, whatever it may happen to be, and this shape is not easily changed. The iron retains its original shape unless heated or hammered strongly. Liquids, however, while having definite *volumes,* do not have definite shapes. A sample of water, for instance, may have a definite volume, say 1 liter. But the water will instantly assume the shape of any container in which it may be put. The water may be said to lack a definite shape of its own. Gases, by contrast with both solids and liquids, have neither volume nor shape. A gas, such as air, will completely and uniformly fill any vessel in which it may be contained. The volume and shape of a gas are the volume and shape of its container. The gas will not only penetrate to all parts of the vessel, but equal weights of gas will be found in equal portions of the volume.

25. PROPERTIES OF GASES

Gases have three properties of special importance. These are diffusibility, compressibility, and thermal expansion. By **diffusibility** is meant the ability of a gas to permeate any space in which it may be put. If a gas is placed in an otherwise empty container, the gas almost instantly diffuses throughout the container, filling it completely. Or, if the container already is filled with air or some other gas, diffusion of an added gas, although much slower, nevertheless reaches the same final stage of completely and uniformly filling

---

* The ancients classed earth, water, and air, together with fire, as the elements of which all matter was composed.

the container. The gas is said to **diffuse** through the space or through another gas. When a bottle of perfume is opened in a room, the perfume may soon be detected in all parts of the room. We say that the perfume, as a gas, has diffused throughout the room.

The rate at which a gas diffuses depends upon the density of the gas, according to **Graham's Law.** This law is stated as follows: **the rate of diffusion of two gases is inversely proportional to the square roots of the densities of the gases.** That is, the less dense the gas, the more rapidly does it diffuse, or, stated mathematically,

$$\frac{r_1}{r_2} = \sqrt{\frac{d_2}{d_1}}$$

where r_1 and r_2 are the rates of diffusion of two gases, and d_1 and d_2 are their respective densities. Hydrogen, having the lowest density of any gas,

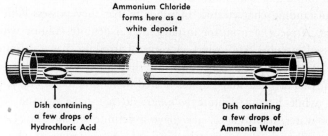

Ammonium Chloride
forms here as a
white deposit

Dish containing
a few drops of
Hydrochloric Acid

Dish containing
a few drops of
Ammonia Water

Fig. 5-1. Ammonia (NH_3) is less dense than hydrogen chloride (HCl). If ammonia is put in one end of a long glass tube and hydrogen chloride in the other end, the two gases will diffuse along the tube toward each other. The ammonia diffuses more rapidly; hence the meeting place, indicated by the formation of white ammonium chloride, is nearer one end of the tube than the other.

will diffuse at a much higher rate than chlorine, the density of which is over thirty times as great. The density of hydrogen is 0.089 grams per liter, and the density of chlorine, at the same temperature and pressure, is 3.17 grams per liter; then the respective rates of diffusion are as $\sqrt{3.17}$ is to $\sqrt{0.089}$, that is, approximately as 6 to 1. The rate of diffusion of hydrogen is about six times that of chlorine.

By **compressibility** is meant the property of a gas to change its volume when the pressure is changed. Everyday experience shows that when pressure is applied, a large amount of air may be compressed into a small space, such as an automobile tire. But when the pressure is reduced, as by opening the valve, the air rapidly expands out into the atmosphere. If a gas is placed in a cylinder under a certain pressure, the gas will, of course, occupy a definite volume. If now the cylinder is made larger by moving out a piston, then the gas will expand until it fills the new volume just as uniformly, though not as densely, as it did the old. The gas may be thought of as having a sort of elastic quality, its volume responding rapidly to changes of pressure.*

A little reflection will show that this compressibility of gases is simply another manifestation of diffusibility. The expansion of a gas under reduced

Fig. 5-2. The volume of a gas varies inversely as the pressure. (It is assumed that there is no friction in the container.)

pressure is brought about by diffusion of the gas as already described. Compression is, in a sense, the reverse of diffusion, and is brought about by application of pressure.

The **thermal expansion** of gases is also a matter of common experience. An automobile tire is more likely to have a blowout on a very hot day than on a cold day. This is because the air in the tire tends to expand and escape when it is heated. Similarly, the warm air over sand or rocks tends to expand, to become less dense, and so rise, creating up-drafts in the atmosphere. Conversely, when gases are cooled they contract. Ultimately, all gases may be converted to liquids or to solids, although some gases do so only at astonishingly low temperatures.

The compressibility of gases, and their thermal expansion, are described respectively by the laws of Boyle and of Charles. Boyle's Law will be considered first.

26. BOYLE'S LAW

If the pressure on a given weight of gas is doubled, the volume will be halved. Or, in other words, **the volume of a given weight of gas varies inversely as the pressure, provided the temperature does not change.** Or, stated

* Robert Boyle spoke of this property as "The Spring of the Air."

still another way, the product of the pressure times the volume of a gas is a constant, provided the temperature is constant. This is **Boyle's Law,** describing the variation of gas volume with change of pressure.

Fig. 5-3. Robert Boyle

Robert Boyle was born in Ireland in 1627. He was the fourteenth child of the Earl of Cork.

Boyle made many discoveries in physics and chemistry. He is remembered chiefly for his work on gases, but he was also the first person to approach a clear understanding of the term "chemical element." His views on the structure of matter are set forth in his celebrated book, "The Sceptical Chymist."

Boyle was one of the founders of the Royal Society of London. He may be regarded as one of the handful of men who established modern science in England.

He died in 1691. *(Bettmann Archive)*

It not infrequently happens that a gas may be collected by displacement of a liquid. A cylinder, shown in Fig. 5-4, is filled with a liquid such as mercury or water, then inverted, still full, over a dish also containing the liquid. Now the gas to be collected is led through a tube under the surface

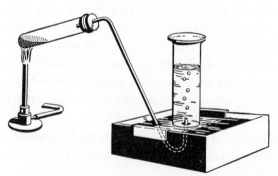

Fig. 5-4. Certain gases may be collected by displacement of water. The gas thus need not come in contact with the atmosphere.

of the liquid in the dish and up into the inverted cylinder. In this way the gas may be collected without having it escape into, or come in contact with, the air. After a convenient amount of gas has been collected, the volume of gas may be measured. But as the volume depends upon the pressure, there would be no object in measuring the volume unless the pressure could also be measured. A simple way to fix the pressure is to raise or lower the cylinder until the liquid level inside the cylinder is even with the level outside. In this way the pressure on the gas, and exerted by the gas, is equal to the pressure of the atmosphere. This is indicated in Fig. 5-5. The volume of the gas is now easily measured, and it remains only to find the pressure exerted by the atmosphere, as this is now equal to the pressure on the gas.

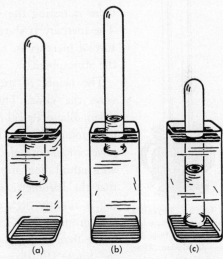

Fig. 5-5. The volume of gas collected varies with the pressure. By adjusting the level of water so that it is the same inside and outside the flask, the pressure on the collected gas is made equal to the atmospheric pressure, as shown in illustration (a).

(a)   (b)   (c)

We are not as a rule aware that the atmosphere constantly exerts a considerable pressure upon us and upon everything around us. It is only when the pressure is greatly altered as in deep-sea diving, or at very high elevations, on mountains or in airplanes, that distress is experienced. The pressure exerted by the air is normally about 15 pounds on every square inch of surface. Over a man's body this pressure amounts to a force of several tons. The existence of this **atmospheric pressure** is demonstrated by taking a tin can and pumping all the air out of it. The can soon collapses completely under the force of the atmosphere on the outside, not counterbalanced by any air inside.

The pressure exerted by the atmosphere is measured by a **barometer,** of which two kinds are in common use, the mercury barometer and the aneroid barometer. The mercury barometer was invented by an Italian scientist, Evangelista Torricelli (1608-1674). In Torricelli's words:

We have made many vessels of glass like those shown as A and B [Fig. 5-6] and with tubes two cubits long. These were filled with quicksilver [mercury], the open end was closed with the finger, and they were then inverted in a vessel where there was quicksilver C; then we saw that an empty space was formed; and that nothing happened in the vessel where this space was formed; the tube between A and D remained always full to the height of a cubit and a quarter and an inch over.*

Fig. 5-6. Torricelli's barometers. These diagrams are from his own description. (After W. S. Magie, A Source Book in Physics, McGraw-Hill Book Company, 1935)

The empty space above the mercury in the tube is often called a "Torricellian vacuum." The mercury rises in the tube to a height of about 29 inches because the atmosphere is pressing down on the mercury in the open vessel. On the surface of this mercury in the open vessel there is resting the weight of 50 miles or more of air. The mercury is shoved up into the tube until the pressure of mercury so supported just equals the pressure of the atmosphere.

The height of mercury in the barometer is not always the same. The distinguished French mathematician, Blaise Pascal (1623-1662), found that on the top of a mountain the mercury level was about 3 inches lower than normal. "This result," he writes, "filled us with admiration and astonishment." Pascal soon found that the barometer reading is slightly higher on the ground floor of a house than at the top of the house. Furthermore, the barometer reading changes slightly from day to day, and upon these changes the science of weather forecasting is largely based.

Aneroid barometers operate on a different principle. A thin hollow drum of metal slightly expands or contracts on changes of atmospheric pressure. This expansion or contraction is communicated to a pointer. The scale over which the pointer moves is generally calibrated in millimeters or inches of mercury, although no mercury is involved in the construction of the aneroid barometer.

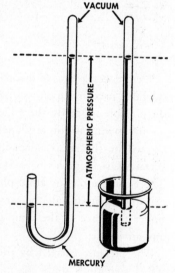

Fig. 5-7. Simple mercury barometers.

In order that measurements on gas volumes may be comparable from day to day and from place to place, it is customary to correct all volumes to the volume which would be occupied by the gas at a certain standard pressure. **Standard pressure** is chosen as the pressure exerted by a column of mercury 760 millimeters (29.9 inches) high.

We shall now proceed to the application of Boyle's Law.

Problem: A sample of nitrogen occupies 280 cc. at a pressure of 845 mm. of mercury. What volume will this •sample of gas occupy if the pressure is changed to 330 mm.? The temperature remains unchanged.

Solution: The new volume, V, is equal to the old volume, 280 cc., corrected for the change of pressure, or,

$$V = 280 \text{ cc.} \times \frac{845 \text{ mm.}}{330 \text{ mm.}} = 717 \text{ cc.}$$

Notice that this solution gives a reasonable answer. The pressure is being lowered; consequently the volume will get larger. The number 717 is larger than 280 by an amount which seems not illogical when the pressure is lowered to less than half its original value.

Problem: Under a pressure of 718 mm. a sample of oxygen occupies 125 cc. What volume will it occupy at standard pressure (S.P.)?

Solution:

$$V = 125 \text{ cc.} \times \frac{718 \text{ mm.}}{760 \text{ mm.}} = 118 \text{ cc.}$$

The pressure this time is raised from 718 mm. to 760 mm. Consequently the final volume will be smaller than 125 cc. The fraction, 718 mm./760 mm., is logical because it is a quantity less than unity. The smaller of the two numbers is the numerator because the volume must diminish if the pressure is raised.

If two or more gases are mixed, their total pressure is the sum of the pressures that each gas would exert if it were alone. This is known as **Dalton's Law of Partial Pressures.** The pressure exerted by each gas in a mixture of gases is said to be the **partial pressure** of that gas. For instance, if the total pressure exerted by a mixture of oxygen and nitrogen is 760 mm. of mercury, and the partial pressure of the nitrogen is 610 mm., then the partial pressure of the oxygen is 760 mm. − 610 mm. = 150 mm.

Dalton's Law of Partial Pressures is of special value in correcting the volume of a gas which has been collected by displacement of water, as described above. Whenever a gas is collected in contact with water, the gas contains some water vapor. The partial pressure of this water vapor depends upon the temperature. In applying Boyle's Law to the correction of gas volumes, we have to consider that the pressure apparently exerted by a gas collected in contact with water is the pressure of the gas itself plus the pressure of the water vapor. The pressure exerted by the *dry* gas may be obtained by subtracting from it the vapor pressure of water at the particular temperature employed. Vapor pressures of water at various temperatures will be found in the Appendix.

Problem: Under 700 mm. of pressure, 275 cc. of oxygen is collected over water, at 23° C. What is the volume of the *dry* gas at standard pressure?

Solution: The vapor pressure of water at 23° C. is about 21 mm. The partial pressure of the oxygen is therefore 700 mm. − 21 mm. Then the corrected volume is

$$V = 275 \text{ cc.} \times \frac{700 \text{ mm.} - 21 \text{ mm.}}{760 \text{ mm.}} = 246 \text{ cc.}$$

27. TEMPERATURE SCALES

There are three different temperature scales in common use. These are Fahrenheit, Centigrade, and Absolute or Kelvin. The **Fahrenheit** scale is the common household and clinical thermometer scale. On this scale the freezing point of water is 32° F. The boiling point of water is 212° F.

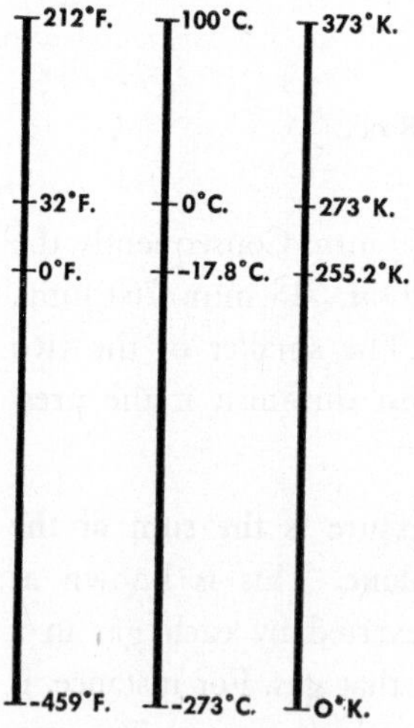

The **Centigrade** scale is fixed at 0° C. for the freezing point of pure water, and 100° C. for the boiling point of pure water. Reference to Fig. 5-8 will show that for 100 Centigrade degrees there are 212 minus 32 or 180 Fahrenheit degrees. Centigrade degrees are obviously larger than Fahrenheit degrees by the fraction $^{180}/_{100}$ or $\%$; that is, 1 Centigrade degree is equal to 1% or 1.8 Fahrenheit degrees. Conversion of Fahrenheit temperatures to Centigrade is accomplished by subtracting 32° from the Fahrenheit temperature, then taking $\%$ of the result.

Fig. 5-8. Temperature scales.

$$°C. = \%(°F. - 32°)$$

Conversely, conversion of Centigrade to Fahrenheit temperatures is given by

$$°F. = (°C. \times \%) + 32°$$

The **Absolute** or **Kelvin** temperature scale is similar to the Centigrade scale in that the divisions on the scale are the same size. But the zero on the Absolute scale is $-273°$ C., the boiling point of water is $373°$ K. Conversion of Centigrade to Absolute temperatures is simply a matter of adding $273°$.

The Fahrenheit scale is, of course, the common scale in English-speaking countries. The Centigrade scale is commonly used in scientific work and is the popular scale in several countries of Europe. The Absolute scale has important theoretical and practical scientific uses. The reasons for choice of the incredibly cold temperature of $-273°$ C. ($-459°$ F.) for the zero Absolute will have to be deferred until the next chapter.

Thermometers are commonly constructed on the principle that liquids expand on heating. Mercury and alcohol (colored) are the liquids generally used. Moderately priced thermometers are generally calibrated at two or more points such as the freezing and the boiling points of water. The intervening space is divided up into the appropriate number of degrees. For accurate work, elaborate corrections are often necessary, especially when the temperature is required within, say, a few hundredths or thousandths of a degree.

Other methods of temperature measurement are available. Sometimes the expansion of a gas is used for special scientific purposes. Thermostats often operate on the bimetallic strip principle. Two unlike metal strips are placed side by side. These metals expand unequally when warmed. The double strip therefore bends to one side or the other to relieve the strain set up. The end of the strip may be connected to a pointer or electrical contact. Other methods used in thermometry are the platinum resistance thermometer; the electrical resistance of platinum, and of most other metals, becomes less as the temperature is lowered. The thermocouple operates on the principle that two unlike metals, such as copper and iron, when placed in contact develop a small electrical potential. The size of this potential depends on the temperature; it may be measured by a sensitive voltmeter, or better, a potentiometer. For very high temperatures optical pyrometers are used. These depend on the color and brightness of an object heated red or white hot.

28. CHARLES'S LAW

If the absolute temperature of a given weight of gas is doubled, the volume will be doubled. Or, in other words, **the volume of a given weight of gas varies directly as the Absolute temperature, provided the pressure does not change.** Or, stated still another way, the volume of a given weight of gas, divided by the Absolute temperature, is a constant: that is, always the same number. This is **Charles's Law,** describing the variation of gas volume with change of temperature. The law was discovered by the French physicist, J. A. C. Charles (1746-1823). Some years later more refined measurements confirming this law were made by J. L. Gay-Lussac (1778-1850), after whom the law is sometimes named.

If the volume of a gas is known at one temperature, Charles's Law enables us to calculate what volume would be occupied by the same weight of gas at another temperature, assuming, of course, that the pressure does not change.

Problem: If the volume of a gas is 150 cc. at 25° C., what would the volume be at 380° C.?

Solution: First convert the temperatures from Centigrade to Absolute, by adding 273° to each. Then 25° C. becomes 298° K., and 380° C. becomes 653° K. The volume changes *directly* as the temperature, so the new volume will be equal to the old volume multiplied by the fraction 653°/298°, or

$$V = 150 \text{ cc.} \times \frac{653°}{298°} = 329 \text{ cc.}$$

Just as it is convenient to have a standard pressure (760 mm.), so it is convenient to have a standard temperature. **Standard temperature** is chosen as 0° C. or 273° K. **Standard conditions,** that is, standard temperature and pressure, is often designated by the letters S.C., or S.T.P. We shall now solve a problem involving both pressure change and temperature change.

Problem: A gas occupies 1000 cc. at 920 mm. pressure and 125° C. What will be the volume at 500 mm. pressure and −20° C.?

Solution: Consider each step separately. The pressure changes by the fraction 500 mm./920 mm. Volume of a gas varies *inversely* as the pressure; hence the volume will change by the fraction 920 mm./500 mm. Neglecting, for the moment, the temperature change, we may write

$$V = 1000 \text{ cc.} \times \frac{920 \text{ mm.}}{500 \text{ mm.}}$$

The temperature changes by the fraction (−20° + 273°)/(125° + 273°), that is, by 253°/398°. Gas volumes change *directly* as Absolute temperature, hence, combining the two operations we write

$$V = 1000 \text{ cc.} \times \frac{920 \text{ mm.}}{500 \text{ mm.}} \times \frac{253°}{398°} = 1170 \text{ cc.}$$

Finally, we shall solve a problem involving pressure change, temperature change, and correction for vapor pressure of water.

Problem: If 475 cc. of oxygen is collected over water at 26° C. and 738 mm., what would be the volume of the dry gas at S.C.?

Solution: The vapor pressure of water at 26° C. is 25 mm.

$$V = 475 \text{ cc.} \times \frac{(738 - 25) \text{ mm.}}{760 \text{ mm.}} \times \frac{273°}{26° + 273°}$$

$$= 475 \text{ cc.} \times \frac{713 \text{ mm.}}{760 \text{ mm.}} \times \frac{273°}{299°} = 407 \text{ cc.}$$

29. PROPERTIES OF LIQUIDS

All gases, when sufficiently cooled, or both cooled and compressed, become liquids. Liquids do not have the compressibility which is characteristic of gases. In fact, the volume of a liquid can be diminished only very slightly even though great extremes of pressure are applied. Similarly, the volumes of liquids do not depend on temperature to anything like the degree shown by gases. To be sure, all liquids show changes of volume—generally expansion, on warming—yet the changes are exceedingly small compared with the changes shown by the volumes of gases.

All liquids have a tendency to evaporate; some, like ether, very rapidly; others, like mercury, so slowly as to be scarcely perceptible. The cause of evaporation is that above a liquid there is always some of the substance present as a vapor, or gas.* Every liquid shows this effect of having some of the substance above it in vapor form. This vapor, in contact with the liquid, has a definite pressure, as do all gases. The pressure of the vapor is a definite value for each temperature, and is called the **vapor pressure** of the liquid. As we have seen, the vapor pressure varies, becoming larger, with increasing temperature. The vapor pressure of water at various temperatures is given in the Appendix.

The reason why liquids evaporate should now be clear. Some of the liquid is present as a vapor. If this vapor diffuses or is blown away, then more liquid will turn to vapor. This process may continue until all the liquid is gone. Whenever a liquid evaporates, heat is absorbed from the liquid and from its surroundings. A drop of ether put on the skin feels very cold because rapid evaporation of the ether takes heat away from the skin. This is the mechanism by which nature tries to keep us cool and comfort-

* The words *vapor* and *gas* are often used interchangeably. Vapor is more frequently used for a substance which, though present as a gas, generally exists as a liquid at room temperature. The word *gas* is more frequently used for a substance like oxygen which only becomes a liquid at very low temperatures.

able in hot weather. Perspiration evaporates from the skin, heat is required for the process, the skin is then left somewhat cooler. It will be found that a reasonable amount of heat will raise the temperature of water to the boiling point, namely 100° C. But to convert this water at 100° C. into steam at 100° C. requires a much larger amount of heat.

Heat is measured in calories. A calorie is the quantity of heat necessary to raise the temperature of one gram of water one Centigrade degree. Or, more precisely, one **calorie** is the heat required to raise the temperature of one gram of water from 14.5° C. to 15.5° C. For most substances other than water it requires less than one calorie to raise the temperature of one gram of the substance one Centigrade degree. The number of calories needed to raise the temperature of one gram of a substance one Centigrade degree is the **specific heat** of the substance. Water has, therefore, by definition, a specific heat of one. The specific heat of benzene is about 0.33, that of gold about 0.031.

To raise the temperature of one gram of water from 0° C. to 100° C. requires 100 calories. To convert this water into steam, without further raising the temperature, requires an additional 540 calories. This heat, necessary to convert one gram of a liquid into a vapor, is called the **latent heat of vaporization.** Thus the latent heat of vaporization of water is 540 calories * per gram, that of mercury is 65 calories per gram, and of helium is only 6 calories per gram.

The vapor pressure of water increases as the temperature is raised. This is true not only of water but of all liquids. If the temperature is raised until the vapor pressure equals the atmospheric pressure, then the liquid starts to bubble and we say it is boiling. **Boiling point** is defined as the temperature at which the vapor pressure is equal to the atmospheric pressure. This definition of boiling point implies that if the atmospheric pressure, as determined by a barometer, changes from day to day, then the boiling point of water must also change. Water boils at 100° C. only if the barometric pressure is equal to 760 mm. of mercury. On a day when the barometer stands at 738.5 mm., the boiling point of water is only 99.2° C. The boiling point of water at various atmospheric pressures is easily found by reference to the Table in the Appendix. In Yellowstone Park, owing to the high elevation and lower pressure, water boils at several degrees below 100° C. On high mountains it is almost impossible to boil eggs because the water may boil well below 90° C. On a flight into the stratosphere, with the barometric pressure only 15 or 20 mm., water will boil and yet not even feel perceptibly warm to the touch.

* The latent heat of vaporization actually changes somewhat as the temperature is changed.

30. PROPERTIES OF SOLIDS

All liquids, if cooled sufficiently, become solids. Some substances, such as carbon, solidify at such high temperatures that little, if anything, is known about these substances in the liquid state. Other substances, such as helium, solidify at such very low temperatures that only fairly recently has their solidification been achieved. Solids resemble liquids in resisting compression. The effect of very high pressures on liquids and solids has been extensively investigated, but pressures of many thousand times normal atmospheric pressure have an almost negligible effect on the volumes of these substances. This is in very sharp contrast to the effect of pressure on the volumes of gases. The very small degree of compressibility shown by liquids or solids must mean that the atoms of these substances are effectively in mutual contact. Any closer approach is strongly resisted by the like electrical forces acting between the electrons. Perhaps in the interiors of distant stars forces may be available to compress atoms still further, but we have, as yet, not mastered this problem on earth.

Many solids melt to the liquid state, if the temperature is sufficiently raised. Melting, or the reverse-process, solidification or freezing, occur at the same temperature and depend merely on whether heat has been added to or taken away from the substance. The melting point is a specific property of a substance and, as such, is often used for the identification of chemical compounds, particularly of organic substances. The melting point of a substance is not greatly changed by changing the pressure. For instance, changing the pressure on water from 760 mm. to 10 mm. changes the melting point only a small fraction of a degree, while the boiling point may in this way be changed from 100° C. to near zero.

In certain circumstances a liquid may be cooled below the freezing point without solidification taking place. If water is cooled, without shaking, it may often be taken down to a temperature of 5 or even 10 degrees below zero Centigrade, the normal freezing point of water. This effect is known as **supercooling**. It is shown by many liquids. If now the water is vigorously stirred, or if a small piece of ice is added to it, the whole sample of water will solidify almost instantly. Supercooled liquids are said to be in a *metastable* state. The reader may wonder if solids may similarly be heated somewhat *above* the melting point without melting taking place. This effect, the reverse of supercooling, does not appear to take place, but sometimes liquids may be heated well above the boiling point without boiling occurring. This is especially true of liquids from which all minute bubbles of air have been removed by centrifuging or by brief application of very high pressure.

It will be recalled that heat, the latent heat of vaporization, is necessary to convert a liquid into a vapor. Similarly heat, the **latent heat of fusion** (melt-

Fig. 5-9. Left, crystals of sodium chloride, halite (*American Museum of Natural History*). Right, crystals of calcium sulfate, calcite (*Chicago Natural History Museum*).

ing), is required to convert a solid into a liquid. For water the latent heat of fusion is 80 calories per gram. This is why a lump of melting ice is far

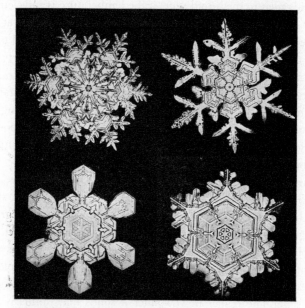

Fig. 5-10. Complicated crystal formation in snowflakes. (*American Museum of Natural History*)

more effective in a refrigerator than the same weight of water at 0° C. The ice may be no colder than the water, but it takes much more heat to melt the ice than it does to raise the resulting water up to room temperature.

Solids have vapor pressures just as do liquids, but the pressures are generally quite small compared with those of liquids. Most people are aware that snow on the ground has a tendency to disappear slowly even though the temperature may continue below freezing. This disappearance of the snow is due to the small but definite vapor pressure of ice. At 0° C. the vapor pressure of ice is 4.6 mm., almost exactly the same as the vapor pressure of water at the same temperature. But for most solids the vapor pressures are too small to be measured at room temperatures.

Some solids have the property, on being heated, of changing directly from a solid to a vapor without first changing to a liquid. Such substances are iodine, carbon dioxide, and calomel. When these substances are cooled, the reverse process takes place, again without formation of a liquid. This process is called **sublimation.** Most substances which undergo sublimation may be liquefied by raising the pressure.

Everyone who lives in a northern climate has seen, in the winter, beautiful patterns on the windows "painted by Jack Frost." Ice and other solids have the remarkable property of forming in regular geometric patterns or **crystals.** Crystals and their attendant effects give rise to some of the most beautiful phenomena in all nature. With few exceptions, all solids form crystals. The study of crystals forms the science of *crystallography,* which, in turn, makes very important contributions to the interlocking sciences of physics, chemistry, metallurgy, and especially mineralogy. Crystals of different substances vary from the submicroscopic to specimens many feet long, such as in the spodumene deposits of the Dakotas. Often in the laboratory, and occasionally in nature, perfect crystals of elements and compounds are formed. More frequently those crystalline substances found in nature are highly complex examples of twinning and multiple growth in such a manner as greatly to confuse the beginner in crystallography. We shall in the following pages have many occasions to refer to crystals and their importance in chemistry.

EXERCISES

A. *Define or explain the following:*

Absolute or Kelvin scale	latent heat of fusion
atmospheric pressure	latent heat of vaporization
barometer	partial pressure
boiling point	standard pressure
calorie	standard temperature
Centigrade scale	sublimation
compressibility	supercooling
crystal	thermal expansion
diffusion	vapor
Fahrenheit scale	vapor pressure

B. *State or explain the following:*

1. Graham's law of diffusion
2. Boyle's Law
3. Dalton's Law of partial pressures
4. Charles's Law
5. What are the states of matter?
6. How do the states of matter differ from each other?
7. What are the characteristic properties of gases?
8. How can a sample of gas be collected at atmospheric pressure but without contact with the atmosphere?
9. Why do most liquids, and even some solids, have a tendency to evaporate?

C. 1. The density of gas A is 1.8 g. per l., that of B 3.4 g. per l. Which will diffuse more rapidly? Explain.
2. The volume of a gas at 720 mm. is 550 cc. What is the volume at Standard Pressure?
3. The volume of a gas at 25° C. is 380 cc. What is the volume at Standard Temperature?
4. The volume of a gas at 45° C. and 600 mm. pressure is 125 cc. What is the volume at −10° C. and 1120 mm. pressure?
5. The volume of a gas collected over water at 21° C. and 738 mm. is 477 cc. What is the volume of the dry gas at S.C. (Standard Conditions of both temperature and pressure)?
6. A sample of nitrogen, collected over water at 23° C. and 765 mm. pressure, occupies 495 cc. What is its volume, dry, under standard conditions?
7. At 300° C. and 1500 mm. pressure a gas occupies 825 cc. At what temperature would it occupy 500 cc. if the pressure is lowered to 900 mm.?
8. At 180° C. and 1125 mm. pressure a gas occupies 235 cc. At what pressure would it occupy 1350 cc. if the temperature is raised to 250° C.?
9. A sample of oxygen, dry, at standard conditions occupies 425 cc. At what total pressure will it occupy 475 cc. over water if the temperature is changed to 20° C.?
10. The density of a gas under standard conditions is 1.429 g. per l. What will the density be at 30° C. and 735 mm., dry?
11. A liter of air under standard conditions weighs 1.293 g. What is the weight of air in a room 5.0 meters long, 5.0 meters wide, and 3.0 meters high, at 23° C. and 750 mm. pressure?
12. How many calories of heat are required to convert 100 g. of water at 20° C. to steam at 100° C.?
13. What is the boiling point of water on a day when the barometer stands at 750 mm.? (This problem should be done by reference to a vapor-pressure table. It cannot easily be done arithmetically.)
14. The density of neon is 0.90 g. per l. (S.C.), that of bromine 7.1 g. per l. What is the ratio of their rates of diffusion?
15. Gas X is found to diffuse 2.7 times faster than gas Y. The latter has a density of 4.15 g. per l. (S.C.). What is the density of gas X (S.C.)?

CHAPTER **MOLECULES**

6

A theory is a tool and not a creed—J. J. Thompson

31. THE KINETIC MOLECULAR THEORY

The properties of gases may be explained by the theory that gases consist of minute particles in constant motion. These minute particles are called **molecules.** This theory accounts in a satisfactory manner for all the properties of gases described in the previous chapter. It is known as the **kinetic molecular theory.** The reader is warned to distinguish sharply in the following discussion between the theory in its various ramifications, and the *experimental*

Fig. 6-1. Cylinders full of different gases are placed mouth to mouth (*left*), and a glass partition separating the gases is removed (*right*). The molecules of each gas begin to diffuse through those of the other, and ultimately form a uniform mixture. The circles in the drawing, representing molecules, are magnified several million times.

observations upon which the theory rests. A scientific theory may or may not be true and it is not a matter of vital importance whether it should ever be proved true. The test of a scientific theory is not so much its ultimate truth as its usefulness in explaining experimental observations and especially in predicting the discovery of new facts.

Two of the outstanding properties of gases are their diffusibility and their compressibility.

Gases diffuse through each other. This seems possible if gases consist of molecules, but not possible if gases must be thought of as continuous elastic fluids. Like individual persons mingling in a crowd, molecules may mingle with other molecules. But a solid block of steel does not readily penetrate another solid block of steel.

Gases diffuse without the application of any external force. The molecules of gases must, therefore, be in constant motion, like a crowd of people sweeping into a room: the crowd seems to move, when actually it is the individuals in the crowd each moving independently.

These gas molecules must be exceedingly small *because they are invisible under the most powerful microscopes.*

Gases are highly compressible: that is, under pressure, the volume of a gas may generally be diminished many times. This must mean that the spaces between the molecules are normally very large as compared with the molecules themselves.

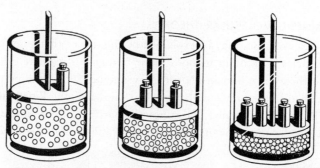

Fig. 6-2. If a gas is compressed, the number of molecules in a given volume is increased. The pressure exerted by these molecules striking the walls is thus also increased. At very high pressures the molecules are effectively in contact with each other and little further compression is possible.

Nevertheless, there must be vast numbers of molecules in any appreciable quantity of gas because in spite of the smallness and lightness of molecules, and in spite of the empty spaces between them, we still find that *samples of gases have appreciable weights. The air in a room weighs many pounds.* The number of molecules necessary to give this weight must be inconceivably large.

If a gas is admitted into a vacuum, it almost instantly fills the whole space. The speed with which the molecules move must therefore be very great.

But *when one gas diffuses through another, the rate of diffusion is much less than when the gas diffuses in a vacuum.* This can only mean that gas molecules must make very frequent collisions. In a vacuum they are free to move rapidly, but in another gas, although the molecules continue to move rapidly, yet their progress is highly irregular because of the many collisions they suffer. People trying to get off a crowded streetcar find their progress much slower than when the car is nearly empty.

Molecules must themselves be almost incompressible, because *under very high pressures a limit is reached above which the gas cannot be further compressed.* At these extremes of pressure the molecules of the gas must be effectively in mutual contact.

The impacts of rapidly moving molecules on the walls of the container produce the effect of a steady pressure. There are so many molecules that no perceptible irregularity is found in the pressure exerted by these molecules. If the volume in which the gas is contained is halved, then the pressure will be doubled because the number of molecules striking the walls will be doubled. Thus Boyle's Law is accounted for by the theory. Or, if two gases are mixed, so long as they do not suffer any chemical changes, the molecules of each gas will strike the walls independently, and the total number of impacts will be the sum of the impacts of each kind of molecules. The total pressure will then be the sum of the pressures exerted by each gas independently, which is Dalton's Law of Partial Pressures.

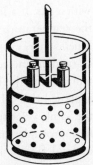

Fig. 6-3. In a mixture of gases the molecules of each gas move independently. The total pressure is thus equal to the sum of the individual pressures.

After these preliminary remarks about the kinetic molecular theory, let us now see what further facts are explained by the theory and, with what, if any, new attributes the molecules must be endowed if they are to account for all the logical deductions which may be made concerning their behavior.

32. MOLECULAR MOTION AND HEAT

If molecules exist and actually move, and with high velocities, then their motion must be completely random. That is, there must never be an occasion when all the molecules rush one way and then turn and rush the other. If this were not so we would be conscious of constant fluctuations in the pressure of the atmosphere. In a closed room it is not possible to detect any fluctuations in pressure even with the most delicate pressure gauges. To be sure, in a wind or inside an air hose the molecules must have a certain directed motion in addition to their random motions. But when the gas is protected from temperature changes or other disturbances, the motions of the molecules must be completely random: that is, at any instant there must be just as many molecules moving in any one direction as in any other.

Furthermore, if the molecules are moving, they must each be possessed of some kinetic energy. Everyone knows that a moving automobile has the ability to do work (or damage) simply because of the facts that it has weight and a certain velocity. Similarly, moving molecules have the ability to do work and this is called **kinetic energy.** It is instructive to see what happens if we increase the kinetic energy of the molecules by stirring them up so that they move faster. This may be done more easily with a liquid than with a gas. If a liquid, or a gas, is very vigorously stirred for several minutes, the temperature rises several degrees. This can only mean that increased kinetic energy is equivalent to increased temperature. Heat is a manifestation of random molecular motion. To state this in another way, the higher the temperature the higher the average velocity of the molecules. It is not to be supposed that all the molecules in any given sample of gas are moving with the same velocity. The velocities of individual molecules at various times may probably range from zero to extremely high values. The majority of molecules will, however, probably have velocities not very far from the average.

The relationship, stated above, of temperature to kinetic energy, raises another question. When a bullet hits an object, its high kinetic energy is immediately partly transformed into heat and partly transferred to kinetic energy of the object struck. It might, therefore, be expected that every time a molecule hit the wall of a flask in which it was confined, that part of its kinetic energy would be transferred to the wall. This could only mean that the molecule was left with less kinetic energy, that is, that the temperature of the gas was diminished. As time went on, the gas would get colder and colder because at every collision with the walls the molecules would lose some of their kinetic energy. Or, to look at the problem in a slightly different way, if the molecules lost some of their kinetic energy they would have to move more slowly and consequently exert less pressure on the walls of the flask. Neither of these effects is found. A gas may be kept sealed up for years without loss of temperature or of pressure.

A possible explanation for this observation is that the molecules are constantly creating new energy to take the place of that lost to the walls of the container. But, after much investigation, scientists have come to the conclusion that **energy,** like matter, **can neither be created nor destroyed.** This is the **Law of Conservation of Energy,** often called the First Law of Thermodynamics.

A preferable hypothesis is that the molecules do not actually lose any energy when they collide with the walls; that the molecules rebound with **perfect elasticity,** taking all their kinetic energy with them. Molecules must, therefore, be able to bounce far better than golf or tennis balls; but to endow molecules with the hypothetical attribute of perfect elasticity seems better than the alternative, which is to deny the Law of Conservation of Energy.

Charles's Law, it will be recalled, states that the volume of a gas varies directly as the Absolute Temperature, provided the pressure remains constant. The pressure exerted by a gas is due to the impacts of moving molecules. If, now, the average velocity of these molecules is raised by heating the gas, the impacts of the molecules will be harder and the pressure will be correspondingly raised. If the pressure is nevertheless maintained constant, then the volume must expand until, although the average molecular impact on the walls is harder, yet there will be fewer molecules striking the walls in a given time. When the temperature of a gas is raised, then either the pressure must go up or the volume must go up. If the latter, then we have the condition covered by Charles's Law.

If a certain volume of gas at $0°$ C. is cooled until the temperature is $-1°$ C., the volume, at constant pressure, will be found by experiment to have shrunk by 1 part in 273. Or if 273 cc. of gas at $0°$ C. is cooled to $-1°$ C., the volume will become 272 cc. In theory, this process could be continued until at $-273°$ C. the gas would have zero volume. In practice all substances solidify before this temperature is reached. Nevertheless it is convenient to consider $-273°$ C. as the **absolute zero** of temperature, and as the zero point on the Absolute scale.* The absolute zero has never been quite reached, although within recent years experimenters have approached it within one thousandth of a degree.

33. PHYSICAL EQUILIBRIUM

When gases are sufficiently cooled they become liquids. There must be attractive forces acting between molecules. Normally, in the gaseous state, these attractive forces are of minor importance. But when the kinetic energy of the molecules is greatly reduced by lowering the temperature, the attractive forces become dominant. The molecules still move, but their movements are greatly restricted compared with those in the gaseous state. Although the molecules in liquids move much more slowly than those in gases, they retain this characteristic that some molecules are, at any instant, moving much more rapidly than others. If a very rapidly moving molecule happens to be near the surface of the liquid, it may fly away to become a gas molecule. The liquid is said to evaporate. Heat is necessary to give molecules sufficient energy to leave the surface of the liquid, and this heat is, of course, the latent heat of vaporization.

If a liquid is evaporating by loss of the most rapidly moving molecules, then the average velocity of the remaining molecules must diminish. If the brightest students in a class are continually being promoted to a more ad-

* More accurate reasoning, based on the energy of the molecules, places the absolute zero at $-273.18°$ C.

vanced class, then the average intelligence of the remainder of the class will go down. If the average velocity of the remaining molecules is diminished, then the liquid will get colder. This is the kinetic molecular explanation of the cooling effect produced by evaporating liquids. If the rate of evaporation, that is the rate of loss of the most rapidly moving molecules, is large, then the cooling effect may be sufficiently pronounced as to freeze the liquid. In this way, water may be frozen if the container is connected to a powerful vacuum pump. In warm climates it is sometimes the practice to put drinking water in porous earthenware jars. The water seeping through

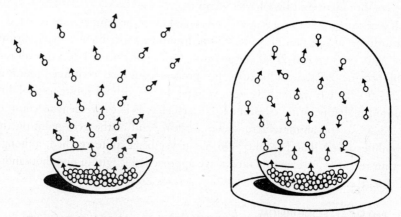

Fig. 6-4. Molecules escape from an open dish and the liquid is said to evaporate. But in a closed container, a condition of equilibrium is set up, and the number of molecules escaping from the liquid is equal to the number returning. The pressure exerted by the vapor molecules under these conditions is called the *vapor pressure.*

the pores evaporates, leaving the remaining water cool. The evaporation of perspiration has a similar effect upon the skin.

If a liquid, instead of being allowed to evaporate into the air, is placed in a closed container, then evaporation will at first proceed as usual. But the molecules in the vapor state are no longer able to escape completely and may in time find their way back into the liquid. After a while a steady state will be reached in which the number of molecules returning to the liquid is exactly equal to the number escaping. We say then that *equilibrium* has been reached. Not only is the number of molecules returning equal to the number escaping but, at any given temperature, the number of molecules and their average velocity in the vapor state is constant. In other words, the pressure exerted by the molecules in the vapor state is constant. This pressure is the *vapor pressure,* to which reference was made in the previous chapter. If now the temperature is raised, the average molecular velocity will be raised. Not only will the vapor-state molecules move more rapidly, but more molecules will have enough energy to escape from the liquid. Both these effects will contribute to raising the vapor pressure, which rises quite sharply with increasing temperature.

This idea of an equilibrium being set up between molecules escaping from and returning to a liquid is of great importance in chemistry. Notice that there is no thought of all motion stopping when equilibrium is reached. On the contrary, great numbers of molecules are moving. The essential point is that the number of molecules escaping from the liquid is exactly equal to the number returning. Such an equilibrium, in which motion is inherent, is often called a **dynamic equilibrium.** When, as in this case, no chemical change is involved, it is referred to as a dynamic **physical equilibrium.**

When liquids are still further cooled, solidification takes place. In solids, molecular motion must be still further restricted but it does not cease entirely. The molecules cannot move about freely but must rather vibrate about certain fixed positions. The fact that solids have definite vapor pressures suggests that even in solids the more rapidly vibrating molecules may escape from the surface to enter the vapor state. Solids, it will be recalled, often form in regular geometric patterns, or crystals. This is reminiscent of the child's box of blocks. If the blocks are thrown in haphazardly, they do not all go into the box. But if time is taken to arrange the blocks in orderly fashion, they all fit in neatly and compactly. Molecules, perhaps, arrange themselves in orderly fashion in the solid state. This could be one of the major differences between the solid state and the liquid state. As we shall see below, this suggested orderly arrangement of molecules in crystals is actually the case.

34. THE BROWNIAN MOVEMENT

The weight of experimental evidence is all heavily in favor of the kinetic molecular theory. Scientists have few doubts concerning the reality of molecules. Indeed, in a few instances, photographs have been obtained of large molecules. But the idea of rapidly moving molecules receives its strongest support from the phenomenon known as the **Brownian movement.**

Robert Brown (1773-1858) was a distinguished Scottish botanist. In his most celebrated experiment he took fine pollen grains, dropped them in water, and then examined them under the microscope. He observed that the pollen grains were in irregular movement, sometimes going one way, sometimes another. Brown soon found that all very finely powdered matter shows this effect. He incorrectly assumed that these moving particles were actually molecules and that he was observing molecular motion. We know now that the fine grains he observed in motion were not molecules but that their

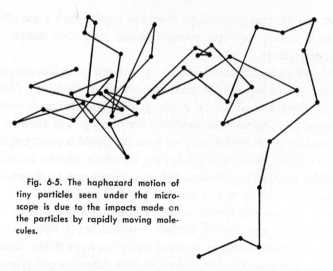

Fig. 6-5. The haphazard motion of tiny particles seen under the microscope is due to the impacts made on the particles by rapidly moving molecules.

motion is due to the impacts of molecules. The observed motions are small and sluggish compared with the darting bullet-like movements of molecules. But the grains of pollen, like elephants struck by machine gun bullets, are jostled back and forth and quiver under the impact of molecular bombardment. No more convincing evidence of molecular motion could be desired.

35. AVOGADRO'S HYPOTHESIS

In 1811, Amadeo Avogadro, an Italian professor of physics, advanced the hypothesis that **equal volumes of gases, under the same temperature and pressure, contain the same number of molecules.** This is now generally ac-

Fig. 6-6. Amadeo Avogadro

Lorenzo Romano Amadeo Avogadro (di Quaregna e di Cerreto) was born in Italy in 1776. He was educated for the law, and practiced for some years. His interests gradually turned toward physics and chemistry and he received an appointment as professor of physics.

Avogadro's famous principle concerning the molecules in gases was published in a monumental memoir in 1811. It was ignored for fifty years.

In 1860 another Italian scientist, Stanislao Cannizzaro (1826-1910), pointed out the extraordinary usefulness of Avogadro's generalization. Modern structural chemistry may almost be said to begin from that date.

But of all this Avogadro knew nothing. He remained teaching quietly until near the end of his life in 1856. (*Bettmann Archive*)

cepted as a law of nature, but in Avogadro's time it was little more than an inspired guess; for that reason we may retain the term "hypothesis."

Avogadro was led to his hypothesis chiefly by consideration of **Gay-Lussac's law of combining volumes.** If a certain volume of oxygen is combined with hydrogen to form steam, it is found that one volume (for instance, 1 liter) of

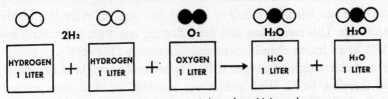

Fig. 6-7. Illustrating Gay-Lussac's law of combining volumes.

oxygen combines with two volumes of hydrogen and that the resulting steam occupies two volumes. It is, of course, assumed that the gas volumes are all measured under the same conditions of temperature and pressure. **Whenever gases interact chemically, or when gaseous products are formed, the ratios of the volumes of these gaseous substances may be expressed as the ratios of small whole numbers.**

$$\text{oxygen} + \text{hydrogen} \rightarrow \text{steam}$$
$$\text{1 volume} \quad \text{2 volumes} \quad \text{2 volumes}$$

The ratio of volumes is 1:2:2. For hydrogen uniting with chlorine, the ratio of small whole numbers is 1:1:2.

$$\text{hydrogen} + \text{chlorine} \rightarrow \text{hydrogen chloride}$$
$$\text{1 volume} \quad \text{1 volume} \quad \text{2 volumes}$$

Let x be the number of molecules of oxygen in 1 liter of the gas. Then, according to Avogadro's hypothesis, 2 liters of hydrogen must contain $2x$ molecules of hydrogen, and 2 liters of steam must contain $2x$ water molecules.

$$\text{1 liter of oxygen} + \text{2 liters of hydrogen} \rightarrow \text{2 liters of steam}$$
$$\text{x molecules} \quad + \quad \text{2x molecules} \quad \rightarrow \quad \text{2x molecules}$$

Dividing through by x, we have:

1 molecule of oxygen + 2 molecules of hydrogen → 2 molecules of steam

Now, according to Dalton's atomic theory, atoms cannot be subdivided; therefore 2 molecules of steam must together contain not less than 2 atoms of oxygen. Hence 1 molecule of oxygen must contain *not less than* 2 atoms of oxygen. On the other hand, a molecule of oxygen has never been found to yield more than two other molecules, each containing oxygen. We conclude that a molecule of oxygen contains *not more than* 2 atoms of oxygen. The formula for molecular oxygen is, therefore, written O_2. This is the form in which the gas oxygen ordinarily occurs.

This deduction of the bimolecular (doubled) formula for oxygen is the first of two major discoveries derived from Avogadro's hypothesis. If the student finds this line of reasoning a trifle obscure, let him not be discouraged. It took the best scientific minds of Europe fifty years to make this relatively simple step. This conclusion and the following one were first clearly stated in 1858 by an Italian chemist, Stanislao Cannizzaro (1826-1910).

The atomic weight of oxygen is 16. The **molecular weight** of oxygen (O_2) must therefore be 32. With this as our standard we shall now proceed to find the molecular weight of any other substance which may be obtained in the gaseous state.

One liter of oxygen at 0° C. and 760 mm. pressure weighs 1.429 grams. One mole of O_2, weighing 32 grams, must therefore occupy (32 g./1.429 g.) $\times$ 1 l. = 22.4 liters. This volume, 22.4 l., is called the **gram molecular volume. It is the volume occupied, under standard conditions, by 1 gram molecular weight, or 1 mole, of the gas.** One mole of any substance, it will be recalled, contains the fabulously large number of 6×10^{23} molecules (more accurately 6.027×10^{23}). Then 22.4 l. of O_2 must contain 6×10^{23} molecules. According to Avogadro's hypothesis, equal volumes of gases contain equal numbers of molecules. Hence 22.4 l. of any gas at standard conditions contains 6×10^{23} molecules, or 1 mole, of that gas. Therefore, in order to find the molecular weight of any substance in the gaseous state we have only to find the weight of 22.4 l. of that substance at 0° C. and 760 mm. pressure. Suppose, for instance, that 22.4 l. of carbon dioxide weighs 44 g. Then a mole of carbon dioxide is 44 g. and the molecular weight is 44. This gives us a marvelously simple and effective method for finding molecular weights. The molecular weights so found are not extremely accurate, but they are sufficiently so for most practical purposes. Experimentally, the method consists of taking a flask of known volume, weighing it empty (vacuum), then filling it with the gas under investigation and weighing once more. The applications of this method for finding molecular weights will be illustrated by a series of problems.

Problem: 1.0 l. of a gas, under standard conditions, weighs 1.35 g. What is the approximate molecular weight of this substance?

Solution: If 1.0 l. weighs 1.35 g., then 22.4 l. will weigh 22.4 $\times$ 1.35 g. = 30.2 g. The molecular weight is 30.2.

It is often convenient to measure the density of a gas at other than standard conditions. In fact, many substances—water, for instance—can only be obtained in the vapor state at elevated temperatures, unless the pressure is made inconveniently low. Carbon tetrachloride is such a substance. It is a liquid under standard conditions. We can, however, obtain the weight and volume as a gas at, say 100° C., then by application of Boyle's and Charles's laws correct the volume to standard conditions and, in this way, find the correct molecular weight.

Problem: A sample of carbon tetrachloride vapor weighs 3.89 g. and occupies a volume of 790 cc. at 100° C. and 743 mm. pressure. What is the approximate molecular weight of carbon tetrachloride?

Fig. 6-8. Bulb for measuring the density of gases.

Solution: First the volume must be corrected to standard conditions,

$$V = 790 \times {}^{273}\!/_{373} \times {}^{743}\!/_{760} = 565 \text{ cc.}$$

This is the volume which, at least in theory, weighs 3.89 g. at standard conditions. We say in theory because if carbon tetrachloride is actually cooled to 0° C. it becomes a liquid.

Now 565 cc. weigh 3.89 g., hence 22.4 liters, or 22,400 cc. would weigh 22,400/565 × 3.89 g. = 154 g. The molecular weight of carbon tetrachloride is 154. Note that we do not compare cubic centimeters with liters, but first convert 22.4 l. to 22,400 cc. It would be just as convenient to convert the 565 cc. to 0.565 l. Then our calculation would be 22.4/0.565 × 3.89 g. = 154 g.

The reader will wonder why we go to the trouble of finding molecular weights this way when all that appears necessary is to find the formula of the substance according to the methods described in Chapter 4, and then find the molecular weight from the formula. The reasons are two: first, we may not have the information necessary to calculate the formula; and second, the methods of Chapter 4 do not always give the correct formula. This will be illustrated by the following problem.

Problem: Hydrogen peroxide contains 94.1 per cent by weight of oxygen, and 5.9 per cent of hydrogen. The molecular weight of hydrogen peroxide as found from the density of its vapor is 34. What is the correct formula for hydrogen peroxide?

Solution:

Element	Parts by Weight	Atomic Weight	Gram-Atoms
O............	94.1	16.0	$94.1/16.0 = 5.9$
H..........	5.9	1.0	$5.9/1.0 = 5.9$

The formula, as found by the above method, is obviously 1 atom of oxygen for 1 atom of hydrogen, or HO. But the formula weight of HO is only $1 + 16 = 17$, whereas the molecular weight is stated to be 34. The correct, molecular, formula is clearly $(HO)_2$ or, as commonly written, H_2O_2. The formula HO gives the correct ratio of atoms in the molecule, but it does not give the total number of atoms in the molecule. Formulas such as HO are commonly called *empirical,* or *simplest,* formulas, as opposed to *correct,* or *molecular,* formulas, such as H_2O_2. Molecular formulas should always be used whenever the substance has a known molecular weight.

The above type of problem is of sufficient importance that it will be illustrated with another example.

Problem: Benzene consists of 92.3 per cent of carbon and 7.7 per cent of hydrogen. It is found that 403 cc. of benzene vapor, at 100° C. and 740 mm. pressure, weigh 1.0 g. What is the correct formula for benzene?

Solution:

Element	Parts by Weight	Atomic Weight	Gram-Atoms
C............	92.3	12.0	$92.3/12.0 = 7.7$
H..........	7.7	1.0	$7.7/1.0 = 7.7$

The ratio of atoms in this compound is clearly 1 to 1, and the empirical formula is CH.

The next step is to find the molecular weight. Correcting the volume to standard conditions,

$$V = 403 \text{ cc.} \times {}^{273}\!/_{373} \times {}^{740}\!/_{760} = 287 \text{ cc. or } 0.287 \text{ l.}$$

Then, 0.287 l. weighs 1.0 g.; therefore 22.4 l. would weigh $22.4/0.287 \times 1.0$ g. $= 78$ g. The molecular weight is 78. The formula weight of CH is $12 + 1 = 13$, which, divided into 78, will go $78/13 = 6$ times. The molecular formula for benzene is, therefore, C_6H_6. When the molecular formula has been found, it is possible to make a somewhat more accurate computation of the exact molecular weight. In the case of benzene, the exact molecular weight is $6 \times (12.00 + 1.008) = 78.048$. This number is more accurate than the value 78 found by vapor density measurements, but we could not have found this more accurate value if we had not known that the molecular weight was approximately 78.

The reader will observe that if we start with the known molecular formula of a substance it is possible to calculate the density of the vapor, or the weight of vapor in any given volume, or the volume of any given weight. This is the reverse of those problems in which the molecular weight is to be found.

Problem: The formula for chloroform is $CHCl_3$. What volume will be occupied, at 120° C. and 700 mm. pressure, by 100 g. of chloroform?

Solution: From the formula, the molecular weight is found to be $12.0 + 1.0 + (3 \times 35.5) = 119.5$. A mole of chloroform is then 119.5 g., and this volume of vapor (assuming it could exist) would, under standard conditions, occupy 22.4 l. Then 100 g. of chloroform would occupy 100 g./119.5 g. $\times$ 22.4 l. = 18.7 l. Correcting for temperature and pressure, we have,

$$V = 18.7 \times {}^{393}\!/_{273} \times {}^{760}\!/_{700} = 29.3 \text{ l.}$$

It must be pointed out that all these computations apply only to those substances which form molecules and which are obtainable as vapors. Many substances decompose before vaporizing. For some of these, another method is available for finding molecular weights provided the substances dissolve in water or other liquids without undergoing chemical change. But many chemical substances do not ordinarily form molecules. Such substances are sodium chloride, calcium carbonate, graphite, diamond, quartz, and numerous others. For such substances the word "molecule" has no meaning. For sodium chloride, for instance, the formula NaCl does not imply that this substance consists of little particles each containing an atom of sodium and an atom of chlorine. But for a "molecular" substance such as ethane, C_2H_6, the existence of such particles or molecules is definitely implied. Molecular substances in general involve electron sharing, or covalence. Electron transfer, or electrovalent, substances do not, in general, form molecules.

36. STOICHIOMETRICAL PROBLEMS INVOLVING GASES

We return now to the problem on p. 58, which was as follows:

Problem: What weight of hydrogen chloride, HCl, is required for the production of 100 g. of chlorine gas, Cl_2, according to the following equation?

$$4HCl + MnO_2 \rightarrow MnCl_2 + Cl_2 + 2H_2O$$

Suppose this problem had read: What *volume* of hydrogen chloride is required for the production of 100 g. of chlorine? The volume of hydrogen chloride is to be measured under standard conditions.

Solution: 100 g. of Cl_2 equal 100/71.0 moles of Cl_2, and, from the equation, 1 mole of Cl_2 may be obtained from 4 moles of HCl. Therefore, 100/71.0 moles of Cl_2 may be obtained from 100/71.0 × 4 moles of HCl. So far this is exactly the method used in solving the problem on p. 58. But now, instead of converting moles of HCl to grams of HCl, by multiplying by 36.5, which is the molecular weight of HCl, we convert directly from moles to liters. This is possible because 1 mole of any gas at standard temperature and pressure occupies 22.4 l. Therefore 100/71.0 × 4 moles of HCl will occupy 100/71.0 × 4 × 22.4 l. = 126 l.

One more problem of this type will be given.

Problem: What volume of oxygen, as collected over water at 18° C. and 752 mm. pressure, can be obtained by the complete decomposition of 250 g. of potassium chlorate? The vapor pressure of water at 18° C. is 15 mm.

Solution: The balanced equation is

$$2KClO_3 \rightarrow 2KCl + 3O_2$$

The formula weight of $KClO_3$ is 122.6; then 250 g. of $KClO_3$ is 250/122.6 moles of $KClO_3$. According to the equation, 3 moles of O_2 are obtainable from 2 moles of $KClO_3$, so that from 250/122.6 moles of $KClO_3$ there will be obtained 250/122.6 × 3/2 moles of O_2. As oxygen is a gas, 1 mole of O_2, at S.C., will occupy 22.4 l.; therefore 250/122.6 × 3/2 moles of O_2 will occupy 250/122.6 × 3/2 × 22.4 l. Correcting for temperature and pressure, this volume of oxygen will occupy

$$V = \frac{250}{122.6} \times \frac{3}{2} \times 22.4 \times \frac{291}{273} \times \frac{760}{752 - 15} = 75.3 \text{ l.}$$

37. HISTORICAL DERIVATION OF ATOMIC WEIGHTS

In Chapter 1 it was shown how atomic weights of the elements may be found by use of the mass spectrograph. Correct atomic weights were actually known long before the mass spectrograph was invented. The method used for this historical determination of atomic weights will be briefly indicated by reference to the element chlorine.

Suppose there is taken a series of compounds containing chlorine. If the atomic weight of chlorine is unknown, then the formulas of these compounds are also unknown. We shall refer to them by name.

First, determine the molecular weight of each substance. This may be done by the method described in Section 35, namely: find the density of the vapor, then calculate the weight of 22.4 l. of vapor as at standard conditions.

Second, determine the percentage of chlorine in each substance. This may be done by straightforward experimental procedures.

Third, calculate the weight of chlorine in one mole of each of the substances. This is found simply by taking the percentage of chlorine and multiplying it by the molecular weight of the substance.

These three steps will be illustrated in Table 4.

TABLE 4

Substance	Molecular Weight	Percentage Chlorine	Weight of Chlorine per Mole of Substance
Hydrogen chloride........	36.5	97.3	35.5
Chlorine dioxide..........	51.5	69.0	35.5
Phosphorus trichloride.....	137.5	77.5	106.5
Phosphorus pentachloride..	208.5	85.0	177.5
Carbon tetrachloride......	154.0	92.2	142.0
Methyl chloride..........	50.5	70.3	35.5

The figures in the final column, giving the weight of chlorine in a mole of substance, are either 35.5 or some simple multiple of 35.5. No molecule in which chlorine is present could contain less than one atom of chlorine; hence it is concluded that 35.5, being the smallest weight of chlorine ever found in a large group of chlorine-containing compounds, must represent the atomic weight of chlorine. If some compound should be discovered to contain only 17.75 g. of chlorine per mole of compound, then we should be forced to regard 17.75 as the atomic weight of chlorine. A similar conclusion would be forced if we found a compound containing, say, 88.75 g. (i.e., $2\frac{1}{2} \times 35.5$) of chlorine per mole of compound. But neither of these contingencies has ever arisen.

38. ELECTRON DIFFRACTION AND MOLECULAR STRUCTURE

The arrangement of atoms in molecules is a subject of great interest for the chemist. If the molecule consists of only two atoms, then there is not very much question about how the atoms are arranged, although it may not be known just exactly how far apart the atoms are. But for more complicated molecules such as ammonia NH_3, nitrous oxide N_2O, and phosphorus oxide P_2O_3, the architectural pattern of the molecule may be quite difficult to visualize. Various lines of experimental evidence lead to definite conceptions about molecular structure. These involve specific heats, X rays, infrared spectroscopy, and several others. About 1931 a young German scientist, R. Wierl, developed an unusually powerful tool for examining the structure of gas molecules. By this means there have become known the distances between atoms in molecules and the angles made by any two atoms with a third. With this information it is possible to make models which, with a very fair degree of accuracy, represent the actual structure of the molecules.

Wierl's method is that of **electron diffraction.** In Chapter 2 reference was made to cathode-ray tubes, in which a stream of electrons is made to pass from one end of the tube to the other. Electrons, in some respects, act more like waves than like individual particles of matter. If they strike or pass through layers of matter, they suffer diffraction in somewhat the same way that light is diffracted in passing through a diffraction grating, or that X rays are diffracted in passing through a crystal. The exact manner in which electrons are diffracted depends upon the arrangement of atoms in the molecule through which the electrons are passing.

The way this experiment is done is to take a special type of cathode-ray tube.* The beam of electrons passes through a cloud of the gas molecules under investigation, then strikes a photographic plate which records the diffracted image of the beam. The cloud of gas molecules is made by slowly evaporating the molecules through a pin-hole in one side of the cathode-ray tube and by freezing them out on the other side by contact with a surface cooled by liquid air at −190° C. The rest of the apparatus is evacuated to the highest possible degree.

water   ammonia   carbon tetrachloride

Fig. 6-9. Models (Fisher-Hirschfelder models) of the molecules of three substances. These models are made up on the basis of information gained from electron diffraction, and other, studies. The relative sizes of the atoms and their geometrical arrangement are probably accurate.

Electron diffraction occurs primarily through scattering of the electron beam by the nuclei of the various atoms which may be in the molecule. This diffraction, or scattering, depends upon the distance between the nuclei of pairs of atoms. The mathematical derivation of these distances lies beyond our scope in this book. But from the photographic record, which consists of a series of diffuse concentric rings, it is possible to compute the distance between any two pairs of atoms in the molecules, and with this information to find the angles made by the various atoms with each other. By this means, as an example, the molecule of carbon tetrachloride, CCl_4, has been carefully studied. It has been verified that the valence bonds of the carbon atom are arranged at the corners of a regular tetrahedron, with the angles between bonds of 109½°. The distance between the nuclei of carbon and chlorine atoms is found to be 1.76 Å. (The abbreviation Å. stands for Ångström Unit. 1 Å. is one one hundred millionth part of a centimeter.) In water the hydrogen atoms are at an angle of 105°, so that H—O⟍$_H$, rather than H—O—H, is the better representation of water molecules. At very high temperatures sodium chloride forms molecules of NaCl in which the interatomic

* R. Spurr and L. Pauling, "The Electron-diffraction Method of Determining the Structure of Gas Molecules," *Journal of Chemical Education,* 18:458 (1941).

distance is 2.51Å. In nitrous oxide the molecule is a straight line N—N—O, but

in ammonia, NH_3, the molecule is umbrella-shaped H. Electron dif-

fraction ranks among the most powerful tools at the disposal of scientists for the study of molecular structure.

39. X RAYS AND CRYSTAL STRUCTURE

In Chapter 2 it was pointed out that X rays are diffracted by crystals. It was shown how this property of crystals was used by Moseley to establish the different wave

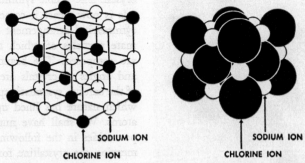

SODIUM ION

CHLORINE ION

SODIUM ION

CHLORINE ION

Fig. 6-10. The arrangement of ions in sodium chloride, as revealed by X-ray diffraction studies, is shown above. The relative positions of the ions are most easily seen in the diagram at the left, but the actual relation of the ions is probably more accurately shown at the right. It will be understood that the diagrams show only a small fragment of the actual crystal.

lengths of X rays emitted by the chemical elements under cathode-ray bombardment.

The diffraction of X rays may also be used for studying the structure of crystals. If a beam of X rays falls on a crystal, the rays may be reflected in such a way that various rays are increased and others diminished in strength or intensity according to the Bragg equation $n\lambda = 2d \sin \theta$ where n is a whole number, λ is the wave length of the X rays, d is the distance between rows of atoms or ions in the crystal, and θ is the angle at which the X rays fall on the crystal. The reflected beam of X rays is generally recorded on a photographic plate or film. The actual results are fairly difficult to interpret, and the mathematical methods for handling the data must be left for more advanced works on crystal structure.* Such methods were first developed by a German scientist, von Laue, about 1912, and have been very greatly improved and expanded by Bragg and Bragg (father and son) in England; by P. Debye, now at Cornell University; and by many others. X-ray diffraction studies are of even greater general utility than electron diffraction studies for chemical identification and other purposes. They are in routine use in laboratories throughout the world.

* G. L. Clark, *Applied X-Rays* (New York: McGraw-Hill, 1940).

The results of such studies show that for crystals such as sodium chloride, the atoms, or rather ions, of sodium and of chlorine are symmetrically arranged in regular order, each sodium surrounded by six chlorines and each chlorine by six sodiums. The X-ray evidence proves that in substances such as these, there can be no such thing as a molecule, unless one wishes to consider the whole mass of the crystal as one giant molecule. This regular arrangement of atoms or ions in crystals is reminiscent of the effect of sprouting corn often seen in a large field in late spring. The sprouts seem to be lined up in endless symmetrical patterns, of course, in two dimensions only, while atoms in crystals are lined up in three dimensions throughout the whole crystal. The visible symmetry of crystals is now clear: it comes from the symmetrical arrangement of the ultimate particles of which the crystals are composed. The beautiful planes and angles of crystals are the result of the careful, systematic spacing with which nature has lined up countless atoms. We shall have numerous opportunities in the following pages to mention the crystalline forms of elements and compounds as they have been revealed by X-ray diffraction.

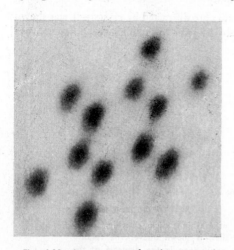

Fig. 6-11. Arrangement of carbon atoms in the molecule of hexamethylbenzene, $C_6(CH_3)_6$, as revealed by photographic analysis of X-ray diffraction results. (Photograph obtained through the courtesy of Dr. M. L. Huggins and the Eastman Kodak Company)

Inspection of Fig. 6-10 will show that in the sodium chloride crystal each sodium ion is surrounded by six equidistant chlorine ions, and that each chlorine is surrounded by six sodiums. The number of equidistant nearest neighbors possessed by any atom, or ion, or group in a substance is called the **co-ordination number.** In sodium chloride both sodium and chlorine have the co-ordination number of six. Co-ordination number is related to the valence, or combining power, of an element and is often referred to as a kind of valence.

EXERCISES

A. *Define or explain the following:*

absolute zero (of temperature)
Brownian movement
co-ordination number
electron diffraction
gram molecular volume
heat (in terms of molecular motion)
hypothesis
kinetic energy

molecular weight
molecule
perfect elasticity
physical equilibrium
temperature (in terms of molecular motion)
theory (as applied to science)

B. *State or explain the following:*

1. Kinetic molecular theory
2. Law of conservation of energy, or first law of thermodynamics
3. Avogadro's hypothesis
4. Gay-Lussac's law of combining volumes
5. In two columns list the various parts of the kinetic molecular theory and the experimental facts which this theory attempts to explain.
6. How does the kinetic molecular theory explain the cooling effect observed during evaporation?
7. What is the relationship between molecules and heat?
8. Prove that the formula for oxygen gas is bimolecular: that is, O_2 rather than O.
9. How were atomic weights of the elements determined before the invention of the mass spectrograph?
10. What kind of information is obtainable through the application of electron diffraction?
11. What are the general principles and results obtained from X-ray diffraction studies?

C. 1. Find the molecular weight of a vapor, 119 cc. of which at 80° C. and 720 mm. pressure weigh 1.05 g.
2. Find the weight of 1000 cc. of carbon tetrachloride vapor, CCl_4, at 150° C. and 760 mm. pressure.
3. What pressure would be exerted by 5.0 g. of acetylene (C_2H_2) vapor at 65° C. in a volume of 100 cc.?
4. What is the density, in grams per liter, of propane (C_3H_8) gas, at standard conditions?
5. A compound of carbon gave, on analysis, the following percentages: C, 30.45; H, 3.83; Cl, 45.69; O, 20.23. The density of the compound was 5.48 times the density of air (1.29 g. per l. at S.C.). What was the formula of the compound?
6. A compound analyzes as follows: C, 37.2 per cent; H, 7.8 per cent; Cl, 55.0 per cent; and 934 cc. of the dry vapor measured at 25° C. and 740 mm. weigh 2.4 g. Find the formula of the compound.
7. At 500° C. and 760 mm. pressure, 5 g. of sulfur vapor occupy 1.239 l. What is the molecular formula of sulfur under these conditions.
8. A sample of anhydrous aluminum chloride weighing 0.2884 g. was heated and yielded 25.2 cc. of vapor collected over mercury as at 18° C. and 765 mm. pressure. What is the formula of aluminum chloride in the vapor state?
9. Find the volume of nitrous oxide, N_2O, obtainable at 25° C. and 720 mm. pressure, from 100 g. of ammonium nitrate. $NH_4NO_3 \rightarrow N_2O + 2H_2O$.
10. What volume of dry air, 21 per cent oxygen, at 27° C. and 760 mm. is required to make 500 g. of chlorine according to the equation: $4HCl + O_2 \rightarrow 2Cl_2 + 2H_2O$.
11. What volume of hydrogen, standard conditions, is obtained by the complete decomposition of 100 g. of ammonia? $2NH_3 \rightarrow N_2 + 3H_2$.

12. What volume (S.T.P.) of hydrogen chloride could be obtained by treating 200 g. of sodium chloride with excess sulfuric acid? $NaCl + H_2SO_4 \rightarrow NaHSO_4 + HCl$.

13. If 5.0 moles of sodium bicarbonate are decomposed by sulfuric acid in a fire extinguisher, find the weight and volume (S.T.P.) of carbon dioxide formed. $2NaHCO_3 + H_2SO_4 \rightarrow Na_2SO_4 + 2CO_2 + 2H_2O$.

14. Twenty grams of a mixture of potassium chlorate and manganese dioxide gave 2.5 l. of oxygen, as collected over water at 22° C. and 740 mm. What percentage of the mixture was potassium chlorate? $2KClO_3 \rightarrow 2KCl + 3O_2$.

15. How many liters of H_2S (S.T.P.) can be obtained by treating 425 g. of ferrous sulfide with excess hydrochloric acid? $FeS + 2HCl \rightarrow FeCl_2 + H_2S$.

16. What volume of oxygen, dry, at 20° C. and 740 mm. pressure is needed to burn 5.0 l. of acetylene, C_2H_2, the acetylene being measured at standard conditions? $2C_2H_2 + 5O_2 \rightarrow 4CO_2 + 2H_2O$.

17. What volume of chlorine, at standard conditions, will be required to change 15 g. of potassium hydroxide into potassium chlorate? $6KOH + 3Cl_2 \rightarrow 5KCl + KClO_3 + 3H_2O$.

18. Compute the ounce-molecular volume of any gas at S.C., expressing the answer in cubic feet. (Ounce-molecular volume is the volume occupied by one molecular weight expressed as ounces. Conversion factors will be found in the Appendix.)

19. The best vacuum achieved in the laboratory is about 10^{-10} mm. of mercury. How many molecules per liter remain in this so-called vacuum (S.C.)?

20. Find the approximate atomic weight of nitrogen from the following data on five gaseous nitrogen compounds.

Compound	Density, g. per l.	% Nitrogen by Weight
Laughing gas...............	1.97	63.6
Nitrogen sesquioxide.........	3.39	36.9
Nitric anhydride............	4.82	25.9
Hydrazine..................	1.43	87.5
Hydrazoic acid..............	1.92	97.8

21. Compare, numerically, the rates of diffusion of carbon dioxide, CO_2, and methane, CH_4.

CHAPTER 7 OXYGEN

That part of the universe to which we have direct access is limited to a thin layer on or near the surface of the earth. In that layer there is more oxygen than any other element: about as much as all other elements taken together. Oxygen is essential to life. Without food, life may persist for a few weeks; without water, for a few days; without oxygen, for only a few moments. Oxygen supports combustion. Flames in air are fed no more by the burning wood, or coal, or gas than they are by the oxygen present in the atmosphere. Oxygen is a constituent of water, the most important of all chemical compounds. Oxygen is the choice for our first detailed consideration of a chemical element.

40. THE DISCOVERY OF OXYGEN

Not infrequently, when a great discovery is made, it turns out that someone else has made the same discovery, but, for one reason or another, the work of the earlier discoverer has not become generally known. This was the case with the discovery of America by Christopher Columbus. Oxygen was known to several ancient philosophers. Reference to a gas believed to be oxygen is found in the writings of Zosimos, a chemist of Egypt, who lived about 250 A.D. In the eighth century A.D. the Chinese philosopher Mao Khoá wrote of *yin* (the weak) and *yang* (the strong) which, combined with fire, are found in air. If charcoal is burned in air, *yin* disappears, but *yang* is left. But these and several other discoveries had no more influence on the course of science than

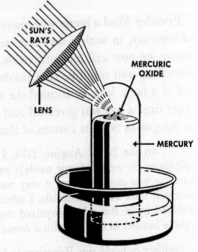

Fig. 7-1. Apparatus used by Priestley in his discovery of oxygen.

the discovery of America by Leif Erikson had on the course of history.

Oxygen was prepared by Carl Wilhelm Scheele, a Swedish chemist, in 1772. Two years later it was prepared independently by an English scientist, Joseph Priestley. Priestley's work was published at once, but Scheele's did not become generally known until 1777. Priestley is often credited with the discovery, but both men made so many chemical discoveries that, even without the discovery of oxygen, their positions are more than secure. We can pay them equal honor for what some scientists regard as the most important single discovery in chemistry.

Fig. 7-2. Joseph Priestley

Joseph Priestley was born in England in 1733. He was educated for, and entered, the ministry. His interest in chemistry arose as a hobby. His political viewpoint was liberal and was at that time considered dangerously radical. His "leftist" writings and speeches so antagonized his neighbors that on one occasion his laboratory was burned by a mob and Priestley was forced to flee for his life.

Of Priestley's several important discoveries his experiments on oxygen were most valuable. They led directly to Lavoisier's classic study on the nature of combustion.

Priestley came to the United States in 1794. He lived at Northumberland in Pennsylvania, where he discovered carbon monoxide. He died in 1804. His home and laboratory equipment have been preserved. (*Bettmann Archive*)

Priestley filled a bottle with mercury, then inverted the bottle in a dish full of mercury, in such a way that no air entered. He took some of the substance we now call mercuric oxide, and inserted this in the bottle so that it floated up and could be seen inside the bottle above the mercury. With the aid of a large lens, he focused the sun's rays on the mercuric oxide. After a short time a gas was given off and partly filled the bottle. Priestley referred to the gas, as was the custom of that time, as "air." In his own words: *

. . . on the 1st of August, 1774, I endeavored to extract air from *mercurius calcinatus per se* [mercuric oxide]; and I presently found that, by means of this lens, air was expelled from it very readily. Having got about three or four times as much bulk as my materials, I admitted water to it, and found that it was not imbibed by it. But what surprised me more than I can well express, was, that a candle burned in this air with a remarkably vigorous flame . . .

Neither Scheele nor Priestley understood the importance of their discovery. Their thinking was handicapped under an erroneous theory about the nature

* *Alembic Club Reprints*, No. 7, Edinburgh, 1901.

of combustion. The importance of oxygen was, however, quickly established by a very great French scientist, Antoine Lavoisier. Lavoisier proved the presence of oxygen in air and established the part played by oxygen in combustion. Lavoisier gave the name "oxygen"; Priestley had called it "dephlogisticated air." But Lavoisier's work was built on that of Priestley and Scheele. The discovery of oxygen was a key to understanding the nature of chemical change. At a single stroke it cleared away the accumulated scientific fallacies of many generations.

41. PRODUCTION OF OXYGEN

Oxygen is easy to obtain from a large variety of chemical compounds which contain oxygen. The industrial production is, however, from the atmosphere, which constitutes an inexhaustible source.

Chemical compounds containing only two elements, one of which is oxygen, are called **oxides.** The oxides of certain metals are readily **decomposed** by gentle application of heat. These metals all belong to the groups of metals which are thought of as being inactive, or which do not very easily combine with other elements. One of these is mercury, the oxide of which, as we have seen, was decomposed by Joseph Priestley. The chemical equation for this reaction is:

$$2HgO \rightarrow 2Hg + O_2$$

A convenient method for collecting this oxygen is by placing the mercuric oxide in a test tube, heating it with a Bunsen burner, and catching the escaping gas in an inverted bottle full of water. The gas is led from the test tube to the bottle by a glass or rubber tube. The mercury released in this process will be found to vaporize and then to liquefy again in the upper, cooler, part of the test tube.

Other oxides which will decompose in this manner are those of gold and silver.

$$2Au_2O_3 \rightarrow 4Au + 3O_2$$
$$2Ag_2O \rightarrow 4Ag + O_2$$

These oxides have the advantage over mercuric oxide that the metal formed is a solid rather than a liquid and is consequently a little easier to handle. Silver oxide is sometimes used for the preparation of small amounts of very pure oxygen.

A fairly large group of other chemical compounds containing oxygen may be decomposed by heat, but the other product is not a metal. Examples of this group are sodium nitrate, potassium chlorate, and lead dioxide. The equations for these reactions are

$$2NaNO_3 \rightarrow 2NaNO_2 + O_2$$
sodium   sodium   oxygen
nitrate   nitrite

$$2KClO_3 \rightarrow 2KCl + 3O_2$$
potassium   potassium   oxygen
chlorate   chloride

$$2PbO_2 \rightarrow 2PbO + O_2$$
lead   lead   oxygen
dioxide   monoxide
          (litharge)

The decomposition of potassium chlorate is especially interesting because, while this reaction proceeds readily at a moderately high temperature, yet it

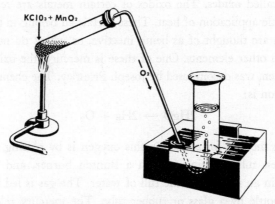

Fig. 7-3. Preparation of oxygen from potassium chlorate plus manganese dioxide as a catalyst.

proceeds much more rapidly if a small amount of another substance is added. This other substance may, for instance, be manganese dioxide, iron oxide, or copper oxide. Manganese dioxide is commonly used. When the reaction is completed, that is, when all the oxygen has been driven off, the manganese dioxide will be found unchanged. But the rate at which the oxygen comes off may be ten or a hundred times as fast when manganese dioxide is present as when no additional substance is added. A substance which changes the rate of a chemical reaction, but is itself not changed, is called a **catalyst.** We shall have many references to catalysts in the following chapters. Another example of catalysis is the decomposition of hydrogen peroxide:

$$2H_2O_2 \rightarrow 2H_2O + O_2$$

At ordinary temperatures this reaction proceeds very slowly, but if a little finely divided platinum, or saliva, or ferric chloride, is added, the decomposition of the hydrogen peroxide becomes very rapid.

It must not be thought that all substances containing oxygen may be decomposed by the application of heat. Perhaps this would be true if sufficiently high temperatures could be reached, but for all practical purposes a substance such as silicon dioxide (quartz or white sand, SiO_2) cannot be decomposed to give oxygen.

Water, of course, contains oxygen, but heat alone is not very satisfactory for its decomposition. Electrical energy will, however, decompose water quite readily. Pure water is not a very good conductor of electricity, but if a little sodium hydroxide or sulfuric acid is added, the water becomes an excellent conductor. Under these conditions hydrogen is given off at the negative pole and oxygen at the positive. The sodium hydroxide, or sulfuric acid, as the case may be, is not changed during this

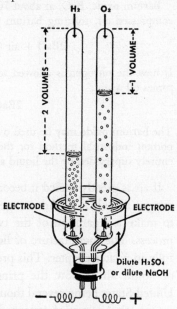

Fig. 7-4. Electrolysis of water to yield hydrogen and oxygen.

process. The **electrolysis** of water is seldom commercially feasible for the production of oxygen—the reason being the cost of electricity—but on a laboratory scale it makes a convenient method for the preparation of small amounts of pure oxygen. The equation is

$$2H_2O \rightarrow 2H_2 + O_2$$

There are numerous other methods for obtaining oxygen. A few of these are given below. These methods have at one time or another all enjoyed some practical or theoretical importance, but at the present time they are seldom encountered outside of the textbooks on inorganic chemistry. Water may be decomposed by heating it with chlorine.

$$2H_2O + 2Cl_2 \rightarrow 4HCl + O_2$$

The product is mixed with hydrogen chloride from which the oxygen could be separated by passing the mixture through lime, the hydrogen chloride being removed by this reagent while the oxygen remains unchanged.

$$CaO + 2HCl \rightarrow CaCl_2 + H_2O$$

Sodium peroxide, treated with water, gives off oxygen.

$$2Na_2O_2 + 2H_2O \rightarrow 4NaOH + O_2$$

Barium oxide, BaO, at about 700°, has the property of taking up oxygen from compressed air, forming barium peroxide, BaO_2.

$$2BaO + air\ (O_2 + N_2) \rightarrow 2BaO_2 + N_2$$

If now the nitrogen is allowed to escape, and the pressure reduced, the oxygen comes off again.

$$2BaO_2 \rightarrow 2BaO + O_2$$

The barium oxide may be used over and over. At one time this was the most important industrial method for the manufacture of oxygen, but it has now been entirely superseded by the liquid air process.

If air is greatly cooled it becomes a liquid. Nitrogen boils at $-195°$ C. and oxygen at $-183°$ C. Advantage of this difference in boiling points is taken to make a separation of the two liquids in what is known as the Linde process. The manufacture of **liquid air** and its uses will be discussed more fully in a later chapter. This process of deriving oxygen from air by the use of liquid air is now the principal industrial method, production in the United States being several thousand tons per day.[*]

One other source of oxygen should be mentioned. Growing plants take in carbon dioxide and give out oxygen. Considering the great quantity of plant life in the world, the amount of oxygen so liberated is very large. This oxygen source is not, of course, a source that could be used commercially. But the fact that oxygen is produced by plant life is of great importance in the chemistry of living matter.

42. PROPERTIES AND USES OF OXYGEN

Oxygen is an odorless, colorless, invisible gas. Its density is slightly greater than air. A convenient way to remember the density of a gas is to recall that 22.4 l. of the gas at S.C. is equivalent to 1 mole. For oxygen, 22.4 l. weighs 32.0 g., therefore 1 l. weighs $1/22.4 \times 32.0 = 1.43$ g. The molecular formula for oxygen is O_2.

It might be expected that the combination of two atoms of oxygen would be a typical example of electron sharing or covalence. But oxygen is almost unique in that the gas is feebly attracted to a magnet, the solid and liquid being quite

[*] *Encyclopedia of Chemical Technology* (New York: Interscience), Vol. 9, p. 718 (1952). This encyclopedia, in fourteen volumes, gives a wealth of information on industrial chemical processes. It may be recommended for examination in connection with any industrial process mentioned in this book.

strongly attracted. This, and other considerations, lead some authorities to think that some of the electrons in a molecule of oxygen are arranged in threes instead of in pairs. This arrangement might be represented

$$:\overset{.}{\underset{.}{O}}:\overset{.}{\underset{.}{O}}:$$

but on this point there is as yet no complete agreement.

Oxygen does not dissolve very much in water. Consequently it is easy to collect oxygen in the usual method by displacement of water. If oxygen were very soluble in, or reacted with, water, this method could not be used. But oxygen does dissolve in water to a slight degree. Under ordinary conditions a liter of distilled water will dissolve about 0.04 g. of oxygen; sea water a little less. This amount of oxygen dissolved in water, although not large, is of great importance for living organisms, such as fish. Without this dissolved oxygen, marine life would be impossible. Everyone knows, or should know, that goldfish do not thrive in water which has been boiled, and from which, as a consequence, all the dissolved oxygen has been removed.

The most significant property of oxygen is the manner in which it supports **combustion**. All substances which burn in air do so much more vigorously in oxygen. A glowing stick of wood instantly bursts into flames, as does a lighted cigarette. Elements such as calcium, sulfur, and phosphorus burn violently in oxygen, producing a brilliant light and a much more rapid evolution of heat than the same substances give while burning in air. Metals, such as iron, which do not usually burn in air may do so in pure oxygen. If an iron wire is heated in a Bunsen burner, then thrust into pure oxygen, it will burn with a great shower of sparks. These substances do not burn so vigorously in air because the oxygen in air is diluted with four times its own volume of nitrogen. The nitrogen does not support combustion and so acts as a damper on the activity of the oxygen.

We commonly speak of oxygen as supporting combustion, but it should be pointed out that oxygen simply acts as one of two substances undergoing chemical combination. A gas flame, of hydrogen or methane, will, of course, burn strongly in oxygen. But if a jet of pure oxygen is led into a jar full of hydrogen or methane and then ignited, the oxygen will appear to be burning in exactly the same way that the other gases normally burn at a jet. If we, by chance, lived in an atmosphere of hydrogen, we should speak of oxygen as being combustible and of hydrogen as supporting combustion.*

A jet of hydrogen burns in oxygen with a very hot flame. This action is

* This experiment of burning oxygen in hydrogen or methane is rather dangerous, and should not be attempted by the inexperienced.

used in the oxy-hydrogen torch which consists of two concentric tubes, the inner one of which delivers oxygen and the outer hydrogen. The hydrogen burns, under these conditions, with a sharp pointed flame hot enough to melt platinum. The temperature of the flame is about 2800° C. If acetylene, C_2H_2, is used instead of hydrogen, the flame is even hotter. Oxy-hydrogen and oxy-acetylene torches are widely used for welding and cutting operations in the fabrication of machinery from steel and other metals. A plate of steel 12 inches thick is easily and cleanly cut with a special oxy-acetylene torch. This application uses most of the oxygen produced commercially.

When liquid oxygen is mixed with combustible matter such as alcohol, gasoline, powdered aluminum, or charcoal, it becomes a powerful explosive. A difficulty in using such explosives is the difficulty in keeping liquid oxygen long enough to get it to the point of application. Such explosive mixtures have found uses in mining, and as explosive or fuel, or both, in long-range military rockets. Other uses for oxygen include the manufacture of synthetic gasoline, the manufacture of nitric acid, and the production of iron from its ore. Oxygen also has very important uses in medicine, especially in surgical anesthesia, in the treatment of pneumonia and heart disease, for high-altitude flying, and for work in mines and submarines. The applications to medicine will be discussed in another section. One should not overlook the fact that most oxygen is used directly from the air in the burning of fuel to heat our homes and offices, to supply energy for innumerable industrial and domestic operations, and as an essential part in the vital processes of every living creature.

43. COMBUSTION

When a substance burns in air, the substance unites with the oxygen of the air. If the substance is, for instance, magnesium, then the process is simply a union of magnesium and oxygen to form magnesium oxide.

$$2Mg + O_2 \rightarrow 2MgO$$

Magnesium oxide is a white, powdery substance. If the original magnesium and oxygen are carefully weighed it will be found that they weigh exactly the same as the magnesium oxide formed. The same kind of reaction occurs with many other substances. The process of uniting with oxygen is called **oxidation,** and the product of oxidation is here called an **oxide.***

---

* The general practice in naming chemical compounds which consist of two elements only is to put the name of the more metallic element first, followed by the name of the less metallic element, the name of which is changed so that it ends in the letters "-ide." In this way the product formed by burning sodium in oxygen is sodium oxide; that by burning aluminum is aluminum oxide.

Carbon burns readily in oxygen. In this case the product, carbon dioxide, CO_2, is a gas. Normally the gas escapes. The carbon, therefore, seems to be disappearing, and at first glance one would think that combustion involves a loss in weight. But if all the carbon dioxide is carefully collected and weighed, it will be found to weigh more than the original carbon. In fact, it will weigh exactly as much as the carbon plus the oxygen with which the carbon combined. This fact, that some oxides are gases and so not easily recognized, originally led to some very erroneous ideas concerning combus-

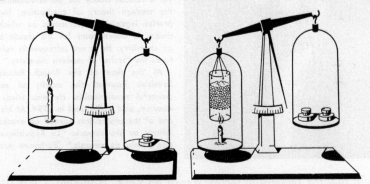

Fig. 7-5. If a candle burns in air it seems to lose weight (left), but if the products of combustion are collected and weighed (as by a mixture of sodium hydroxide and calcium chloride), then the candle is seen actually to gain in weight during combustion (right).

tion. A candle burning obviously burns away and loses weight. But if the products of combustion, in this case carbon dioxide and water, are carefully weighed, their combined weight will be equal to that of the candle plus the oxygen used in the burning.

The apparent, but not real, loss of weight of burning substances led in the seventeenth century to the suggestion that all combustible matter contained a substance which was called **phlogiston**.* A burning substance was thought to emit phlogiston which united with the air. A candle covered with a jar soon goes out. This was thought to result from the air becoming, in a sense, saturated with phlogiston and unable to unite with more. It will be recalled that Priestley called oxygen "dephlogisticated air." He thought he had prepared air from which all phlogiston had been removed, so that, being able to unite with a large amount of phlogiston, this air supported combustion with unusual vigor.

Scheele and Priestley and many other eminent scientists believed in the phlogiston theory and supported it by many arguments and many cleverly

* James B. Conant, *The Overthrow of the Phlogiston Theory: The Chemical Revolution of 1775-1789*. (Cambridge: Harvard University Press, 1950.)

conceived experiments. Most of their experiments are, however, interpreted even better by the modern theory of combustion. Phlogiston was finally over-turned by the celebrated French chemist, Antoine Lavoisier. It must not be

Fig. 7-6. Antoine-Laurent Lavoisier

Lavoisier was born in France in 1743. He had great advantages of family, education, and natural ability. His interests were broad and his discoveries and inventions were many. He is famous chiefly for his establishment of the modern theory of combustion, for the precise ingenious experiments on which the theory is based, and for his classic books on chemistry. He is not infrequently referred to as the "father of modern chemistry."

At the time of the French Revolution, Lavoisier incurred the enmity of several powerful revolutionists. He was tried, con-demned, and guillotined in 1794. At his trial one of the prosecutors earned an everlasting infamy by the remark: "La République n'a pas besoin de savants." (Bettmann Archive)

thought that the phlogiston theory was of no value. Although it was finally disproved, throughout the lifetime of the theory it stimulated many investi-gations into the true nature of combustion and led finally to the idea which we now believe to be true, namely, that combustion is a union with oxygen.

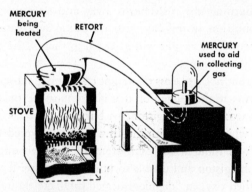

Fig. 7-7. Apparatus used by Lavoisier in his proof that air contains two substances, one of which sup-ports combustion.

The classical experiments of Lavoisier were performed in 1777. He proved that air contains two substances, one of which supports combustion. He proved that Priestley's "dephlogisticated air" is identical with the component of air which supports combustion.

If mercury is gently heated in air or oxygen, it becomes covered with a red powder, mercuric oxide. If, now, this red powder is more strongly heated, it decomposes, yielding mercury and oxygen. Lavoisier gently heated mercury in contact with a definite quantity of air. At the end of twelve days he observed that the air was reduced in volume by about one fifth. The remaining air would not combine with mercury, would not support the combustion of a candle, and quickly suffocated a mouse. The original air was thereby proved to contain two components, one of which supports combustion and one which does not. Now taking the red mercuric oxide formed over the twelve-day period, Lavoisier heated it strongly and collected the gas given off. This gas he found to have the same volume as that lost by the original air in the twelve-day heating. This gas had all the properties of Priestley's "dephlogisticated air," with which it was identical. The inactive component of air was called by Lavoisier "azote," by which name it is still known in France. The name "nitrogen" was suggested by J. A. C. Chaptal in 1823. Lavoisier named the active component of air "oxygen" (acid-producer) from the mistaken belief that all acids contain this gas.

44. DUST EXPLOSIONS AND SPONTANEOUS COMBUSTION

Almost any substance which can be made to burn in air can, under proper conditions, be made to explode. Aluminum metal burns rather slowly even in pure oxygen. But if very finely powdered aluminum, aluminum dust, is mixed with air and then ignited by a match or spark, a very severe explosion will result. Dust explosions result from the rapid union of the combustible dust particles with the oxygen of the air. Such explosions occur fairly often wherever combustible substances are handled under conditions where dusts may be formed. Dust explosions occur most frequently in flour mills and grain elevators, where some very disastrous accidents have taken place. But a surprising variety of substances have been responsible for dust explosions. Some of these are the dusts from cottonseed meal and oil, coal, hard rubber, starch, wood, cork, sugar, chocolate, powdered milk, sulfur, paper, aluminum, and magnesium. The common household practice of emptying the dustpan into the furnace is dangerous because of the possibility of dust explosion.

The quantity of dust in the air to make an explosive mixture is not particularly large. As little as 7 ounces of starch dust per 1000 cubic feet of air will explode. The explosions may be set off by a lighted match, or spark, or by any of the usual causes of fires. Generally there is a primary explosion of small force and having only a local effect, but this is enough to raise dust which has settled on ledges and in corners throughout the building, so that conditions then become just right for the disastrous secondary explosion.

The control of dust-explosion hazards takes advantage of the fact that the explosion is possible only because the finely divided combustible material is intimately mixed with air. If grinding or pulverizing operations are necessary, they may be carried out in an inert atmosphere, such as, for most substances, nitrogen or carbon dioxide. It is not necessary to remove all oxygen but simply to keep the oxygen down below a certain critical level. Other safety measures include properly designed ventilation and "good housekeeping."

Dust explosions are similar in cause and in effects to explosions caused by mixtures of certain gases with air. Coal gas or natural gas or gasoline fumes mixed with air often cause serious explosions. The damage results from the rapid oxidation of the combustible gas which sets up an explosion wave. This explosion wave, which also occurs in dust explosions, exerts great pressure and travels with great speed, sufficient often to blow out the walls of a building.

"Spontaneous combustion" is also a result of uncontrolled oxidation. It sometimes happens that a pile of oily rags, or green hay or green lumber, suddenly bursts into flame. This generally occurs when the combustible material has been piled up without good ventilation. It must be supposed that a slow oxidation sets up and that this generates heat. Normally the heat would be dissipated and no harm would be done. But without adequate ventilation the pile tends to get warmer. Increasing temperature hastens almost all chemical reactions, and the slow oxidation begins to speed up, with still more heat accumulating. Finally the temperature reaches the ignition point. Precautionary measures would include putting such combustible materials in a place where they can do no harm and, in any event, seeing that proper ventilation prevents the accumulation of heat. Large coal piles sometimes catch fire spontaneously. Temperature-recording devices may be inserted deep inside the pile to reveal any tendency toward heating by slow oxidation.

45. PHYSIOLOGICAL PROPERTIES OF OXYGEN

The tissue cells of living organisms have no reserve supply of oxygen. They must therefore be continually supplied with oxygen by the circulation. Animals inhale air from which the oxygen is absorbed through the lungs into the blood. An active man consumes about 30 grams of oxygen per hour. Most of the oxygen in the arterial blood is combined chemically with the blood **hemoglobin.** A small fraction of the oxygen is simply dissolved in the plasma. The blood carries this oxygen to tissues throughout the body and, at the same time, picks up the waste product of tissue oxidation, namely carbon dioxide. The carbon dioxide is finally exhaled from the lungs. The heat liberated in this oxidation process is, of course, the energy for keeping the body warm. In certain circumstances the normal mechanism for supplying oxygen to the tissue cells may not be adequate. In such cases oxygen has important medical applications.

Oxygen is used in the treatment of pneumonia and in some types of heart disease. In pneumonia the state of the lungs is such that the blood is unable to receive its normal amount of oxygen. If the patient breathes air to which pure oxygen is added, the blood is able to obtain an adequate supply, even though parts of the lungs are not working properly. Generally the oxygen content of the air breathed by the patient is about 40 to 60 per cent, instead of the 21 per cent of oxygen in ordinary air. But pure oxygen has been given patients in certain circumstances. For comparatively short periods, at least, pure oxygen seems to have no dangerous effects. The oxygen is administered to the patient with the aid of an "oxygen tent" or by use of a face mask or nasal catheter.

Oxygen has been widely used in medicine in comparatively recent years only, although as early as 1774 Joseph Priestley wrote: "From the greater strength and vivacity of the flame of a candle, in this pure air, it may be conjectured that it might be peculiarly salutary to the lungs in certain morbid conditions. . . ."

It should be pointed out that oxygen does not attack the real cause of pneumonia. What it does is comfort and strengthen the patient until his natural resistance, or drugs, can overcome the infection. But the use of oxygen for these purposes is of great value, and often produces a dramatic relief of symptoms.

Oxygen is useful in the treatment of carbon monoxide poisoning. The transport of oxygen to the tissue cells is facilitated and the poison is swept out of the blood.

In surgical operations oxygen is often used mixed with the anesthetic to insure an adequate supply of oxygen to the cells. Otherwise there would be great danger of the patient's suffocating, especially if the anesthetic is administered by the use of a mask.

The use of oxygen in high-altitude flying is well known. At great elevations the partial pressure of oxygen in the rarefied air is not sufficient to maintain comfort or even consciousness. Oxygen is generally supplied from pressure bottles and is breathed through a face mask.

EXERCISES

A. *Define or explain the following:*

catalysis

catalyst

combustion

decomposition (as applied to a
  chemical compound)

electrolysis

hemoglobin

liquid air

oxide

phlogiston

physiological properties

spontaneous combustion

B. 1. Describe the discovery of oxygen.
    2. From what types of substances may oxygen be easily obtained?
    3. Write balanced equations for the changes taking place when the following substances are heated: mercuric oxide, gold oxide, silver oxide, sodium nitrate, potassium chlorate, lead dioxide.
    4. Write a balanced equation for the catalytic decomposition of hydrogen peroxide.
    5. How did Lavoisier prove the phlogiston theory to be wrong, and establish the modern views of combustion?
    6. What causes dust explosions?
    7. What causes spontaneous combustion?
    8. List the following: (a) physical properties of oxygen (those properties which do not involve a chemical change); (b) chemical properties; (c) physiological properties; (d) uses of oxygen.
    9. Indicate, with the use of a labeled diagram, how water may be decomposed by electricity.

C. 1. There are actually six known isotopes of oxygen. These have mass numbers 14 to 19 inclusive. Show the electronic and nuclear structure of each of these isotopes.
    2. Show electronic arrangement for magnesium oxide, MgO; and for hydrogen peroxide, H_2O_2. The former may be regarded as electrovalent, the latter is more covalent, with the atoms arranged H—O—O—H.
    3. Write formulas for each of the following: barium hydroxide, bismuth oxide, cadmium hydroxide, cobaltous oxide, magnesium hydroxide, and manganous hydroxide.
    4. Name each of the following: CdO, Fe_2O_3, PbO, SnO, and $Ni(OH)_2$.
    5. Complete and balance the following equations:
       a. the reaction of potassium superoxide, KO_2, with water. (This reaction is very like the reaction of sodium peroxide with water to yield oxygen.)
       b. the decomposition of platinum dioxide to platinum and oxygen.
       c. the decomposition of manganese dioxide to Mn_3O_4 and oxygen.
       d. the union of calcium and oxygen to form calcium oxide.
       e. the union of iron and oxygen to form ferric oxide.
       f. the union of cuprous oxide and oxygen to form cupric oxide.

6. Calculate the percentage of oxygen in "white lead," $Pb(OH)_2 \cdot 2PbCO_3$. (This is a double salt the formula weight of which contains one mole of lead hydroxide and two moles of lead carbonate.)

7. A sample of an oxide of gold weighing 2.212 g. was decomposed by heat. The metallic gold obtained weighed 1.972 g. Find the percentage of oxygen in the compound.

8. Compare the density of oxygen with the density of water vapor, at the same temperature and pressure.

9. What volume of oxygen could be obtained as collected over water at $27°$ C. and 765 mm. pressure, by the complete decomposition of (a) 100 g. of gold oxide, Au_2O_3; (b) 100 g. of potassium chlorate, $KClO_3$?

10. What weight of potassium permanganate, $KMnO_4$, is needed to yield 825 cc. of oxygen gas as measured over water at $23°$ C. and 746 mm. pressure? The equation is: $2KMnO_4 \rightarrow K_2MnO_4 + MnO_2 + O_2$.

11. Make an approximate comparison of the weight of air (20 per cent O_2) breathed with the weight of food consumed per day by an average person.

12. How could Lavoisier tell that his "oxygen" was the same as Priestley's "dephlogisticated air"?

13. Lavoisier found that when tin burns in air the product weighs more than the original tin. What property would have to be possessed by phlogiston in order to explain this result?

CHAPTER 8   HYDROGEN

No substance so completely permeates our lives as does water. Water covers a large part of the earth's surface. Water vapor pervades the atmosphere, from which it condenses and falls as the gentle rain from heaven, making possible the growth of vegetation. Water erodes the soil and aids in the leveling of great mountain ranges. Animal tissues consist in large part of water. Without water to drink we soon die. The complete elimination of water from laboratory or industrial apparatus is a matter of very great difficulty. Water has such an intrusive quality that nearly all our chemical reactions take place either in liquid water or else in the presence of water vapor. Indeed, many chemical reactions proceed only in the presence of water. Comparatively rarely do we take the pains to remove completely all traces of water from vessels in which chemical changes are to take place. We turn now to the study of hydrogen, and of its most important compound, water.

46. PRODUCTION OF HYDROGEN

Like oxygen, hydrogen has been known for a long time. Credit for its discovery, or at least its first accurate characterization, is given to Henry Cavendish, who, in 1766, produced hydrogen by the action of acids on various metals such as iron, zinc, and tin.

The name "hydrogen" (water-producer) was given to the element by Lavoisier in 1783. Hydrogen is very widely distributed in nature, particularly in compounds, such as water. It also occurs in all living matter, in most organic compounds, especially in petroleum products, and in many gases found in nature. Traces of hydrogen occur in the atmosphere.

There are available many methods for obtaining hydrogen. Some of these processes are of great commercial value. The electrolysis of water has already been described. The product at the negative pole is very pure hydrogen. Industrially, hydrogen is one of the products obtained by the electrolysis of sodium chloride solution, the other two products being chlorine and sodium hydroxide. "Electrolytic" hydrogen—that is, hydrogen made by electrolysis—is used wherever the cost of electricity is low, and where pure hydrogen is

required. This method produces an appreciable fraction of all commercial hydrogen made.

From water, hydrogen may also be obtained through the use of very active metals at ordinary temperatures, or through the use of moderately active metals at somewhat higher temperatures. For instance, metallic sodium reacts with water in such a way as to liberate hydrogen and to form sodium hydroxide, which remains in solution.

$$2H_2O + 2Na \rightarrow H_2 + 2NaOH$$

This reaction should be tried with care, and with the use of a very small piece of sodium, because the hydrogen mixing with air sometimes explodes and blows the remaining sodium around the room.

An example of a somewhat less active metal is iron. Iron will react with water at ordinary temperatures with the formation of hydrogen and of iron oxide. But this process is very slow. If steam is passed over red-hot iron filings, the reaction is more rapid.

$$3Fe + 4H_2O \rightarrow Fe_3O_4 + 4H_2$$

WATER

SODIUM

Fig. 8-2. Hydrogen collected by the action of sodium on water: $2Na + 2H_2O \rightarrow 2NaOH + H_2$. The sodium soon floats to the surface of the water because it is less dense than water.

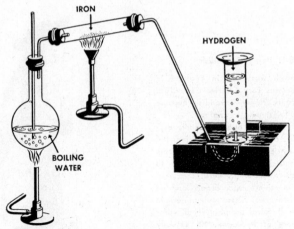

Fig. 8-3. Hydrogen prepared by the action of hot iron on steam: $3Fe + 4H_2O \rightarrow Fe_3O_4 + 4H_2$.

Many metals, of moderate or high activity, will also liberate hydrogen from acids. All acids contain hydrogen, and from many of these the hydrogen is easily obtained. A typical example is the action of hydrochloric acid on zinc. Dilute sulfuric acid would serve as well.

$$Zn + 2HCl \rightarrow ZnCl_2 + H_2$$

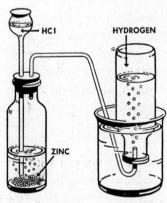

Fig. 8-4. Hydrogen prepared by the action of zinc on hydrochloric acid: $Zn + 2HCl \rightarrow ZnCl_2 + H_2$.

It is a curious fact that very pure zinc does not readily react with acids, but if a little copper, or other relatively inactive metal, is added, the reaction proceeds vigorously. The copper acts as a catalyst. Hydrogen is easily generated by putting some zinc into a bottle and adding hydrochloric acid. But a convenient method for generating definite quantities of hydrogen, and of other gases, is by use of the Kipp generator. The gas is readily collected by displacement of water.

One of the major sources of industrial hydrogen is by the action of steam on red-hot carbon.

$$C + H_2O \rightarrow CO + H_2$$

The products are hydrogen and carbon monoxide, which may be separated by cooling the gas mixture until the carbon monoxide liquefies. Or, alternatively, the mixture of hydrogen and carbon monoxide, which is known as

water-gas, may be mixed with more steam, then passed over a catalyst. The carbon monoxide and steam are converted into carbon dioxide and hydrogen,

$$CO + H_2O \rightarrow CO_2 + H_2$$

from which the former is easily removed by cooling or by absorption in a base such as sodium hydroxide. The catalyst for this process may be a mixture of iron oxide, chromium oxide, and thorium oxide.

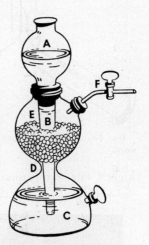

Fig. 8-5. Kipp generator. Hydrochloric acid from A flows through the tube B into the compartment C, then up through the constriction D into the compartment E where it comes in contact with metallic zinc. Hydrogen escapes at F. But if the stopcock F is closed, the pressure of hydrogen in E forces the acid down and away from the zinc, so that the reaction stops.

The Kipp generator is useful for preparing moderate quantities of other gases, such as hydrogen sulfide, as well as hydrogen.

The chief source of industrial hydrogen is the "steam-hydrocarbon" reaction. If, for instance, propane (derived from petroleum) is mixed with steam and passed over a nickel catalyst at high temperature the following reaction takes place:

$$C_3H_8 + 6H_2O \rightarrow 3CO_2 + 10H_2$$

the carbon dioxide then being removed as above.

Commercial hydrogen is sold in steel tanks under high pressure. The annual production is many billions of cubic feet, plus much hydrogen that is produced and used in consecutive operations and hence probably not reported as commercial hydrogen.

47. PROPERTIES AND USES OF HYDROGEN

Hydrogen is a colorless, odorless gas. It has the lowest density of any known substance; a liter of the gas at standard conditions weighs only 0.09 grams. Hydrogen can easily be poured *upwards* from one bottle to another. Because of this low density, hydrogen has long been used for filling balloons. The large difference in density of hydrogen as compared with air (hydrogen is over 14 times less dense) gives it great lifting power. Unfortunately, the highly inflammable nature of hydrogen makes its use hazardous.

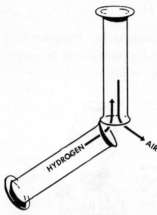

A little arithmetic will show that if 1 liter of hydrogen gas weighs 0.09 g. then 22.4 liters will weigh about 2 g.; the molecular weight must therefore be 2. The atomic weight of hydrogen is 1, hence the formula for ordinary gaseous hydrogen must be H_2.

Liquid hydrogen is a transparent fluid which normally boils at $-252.8°$ C. The freezing point of hydrogen is $-259.18°$ C. or only about 14 degrees above the absolute zero. Hydrogen gas is only very slightly soluble in water.

Fig. 8-6. Pouring hydrogen upward.

The high diffusibility of hydrogen has already been mentioned. Because it has the lowest density of any substance, it also has the highest rate of diffusion. Hydrogen diffuses slowly through rubber, and at elevated temperatures will readily diffuse through iron. The gas is strongly

Fig. 8-7. The German Zeppelin "Hindenburg" burning at Lakehurst, New Jersey, on May 6, 1937. This picture dramatically emphasizes both the lightness and the inflammability of hydrogen gas, with which the Zeppelin was filled. (*Acme Photo*)

adsorbed by several metals, the most noteworthy being palladium. One cubic centimeter of palladium can adsorb over one thousand cubic centimeters of hydrogen gas. The same property is shown by platinum black, a finely divided form of platinum. In this case the heat given off during the adsorption process is sufficient to ignite the hydrogen. This is the principle used in certain gas and cigar lighters.

If a bell is rung in an atmosphere of hydrogen, the note emitted is several octaves above that normally heard. The frequency, or pitch, of a note varies inversely as the square root of the density of the gas. If hydrogen is inhaled, the voice goes up several octaves with very amusing results. The reader is, however, warned that this is a very dangerous experiment. Hydrogen is not poisonous, but impurities sometimes present in hydrogen are poisonous, and the hydrogen may very easily be ignited by a spark or a lighted cigarette. The explosion of a mixture of hydrogen and air in the lungs would invariably be fatal.

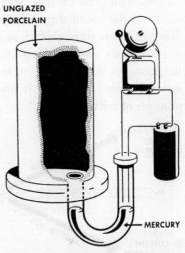

UNGLAZED PORCELAIN

MERCURY

Fig. 8-8. This device is a hydrogen detector. It operates on a principle using the high diffusion rate of hydrogen. If hydrogen gas in the atmosphere comes in contact with the unglazed porcelain cup it diffuses into the cup more rapidly than the air already in the cup can escape. This builds up a little extra pressure in the cup. The extra pressure forces the mercury to move, forming an electric contact, which in turn rings a bell. The device is of value in submarines.

In certain circumstances hydrogen molecules may be broken up into **atomic hydrogen.** This may be done by passing an electric discharge through a tube filled with hydrogen at low pressure, or better, by passing the gas through an electric arc. This second process is used in the atomic hydrogen torch to produce extremely hot flames. With this device, tungsten (melting point 3370° C.) is easily melted. Atoms of hydrogen cannot long exist and at the first opportunity recombine to form molecular hydrogen. A very large amount of heat is given off during this recombination, and it is this heat which contributes to the effectiveness of the atomic hydrogen torch.

Ordinary hydrogen combines with many elements forming compounds which are often of great importance. Some of these compounds are water, ammonia, hydrogen chloride, hydrogen sulfide, methane, and many related substances. Large quantities of hydrogen are used industrially in the manufacture of ammonia and of hydrochloric acid. Hydrogen and oxygen do not combine at ordinary temperatures unless a catalyst is present. But hydrogen burns in air if ignited, and when previously mixed with oxygen or air, it explodes with great violence.

$$2H_2 + O_2 \rightarrow 2H_2O$$

Hydrogen, especially when mixed with air or oxygen, must, therefore, be handled with great caution. Many accidents have been caused through lack of care in the use of these substances. In the writer's own experience a student lost an eye through such an explosion. The inflammability of hydrogen is perhaps its most striking characteristic, a characteristic which led T. Bergmann in the year 1779 to make the rather obvious statement that "inflammable air [hydrogen] is undoubtedly charged with abundance of the principle of inflammability."

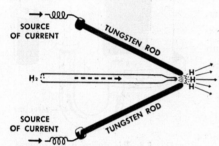

Fig. 8-9. Principle of the atomic hydrogen torch. Hydrogen gas is forced from the center tube through an electric arc where the hydrogen molecules are dissociated (broken up) into hydrogen atoms. As these hydrogen atoms recombine, $2H \rightarrow H_2$, they yield a large amount of heat. Tungsten rods are used to carry the electricity because tungsten can stand the intense heat without melting.

The use of hydrogen in the oxy-hydrogen torch has been described in the previous chapter.

The union of hydrogen with chlorine is also explosive, with this striking difference, that the mixture of gases is stable in the dark but explodes with great violence if illuminated.

$$H_2 + Cl_2 \rightarrow 2HCl$$

Certain metal oxides, such as CuO, when heated in the presence of hydrogen, are converted to metal, water being formed at the same time. Using iron oxide as an example, the equation is

$$Fe_2O_3 + 3H_2 \rightarrow 2Fe + 3H_2O$$

It will be noticed that this is almost exactly the opposite of oxidation. The process is known as **reduction.** The iron oxide is said to have been reduced. Oxidation is the addition of oxygen; reduction is the removal of oxygen. We shall soon have occasion to use a broader definition of oxidation and reduction, but for the present the above will suffice. It will be noted that while the iron oxide is reduced, the hydrogen is itself oxidized to form water. All oxidations are similarly attended with a simultaneous reduction and vice versa. It is often instructive, in a chemical reaction, to pick out the substance oxidized, the substance reduced, the oxidizing agent, and the reducing agent. For instance, in the manufacture of pig iron, iron oxide is heated with carbon. Here the carbon is oxidized.

$$2Fe_2O_3 + 3C \rightarrow 4Fe + 3CO_2$$

The carbon is the reducing agent and the iron oxide is the oxidizing agent.

Hydrogen reduces many oxides, though not all. Aluminum oxide, Al_2O_3, cannot be reduced by hydrogen, but nickel oxide, NiO, is quite easily reduced.

Hydrogen finds many important uses, in addition to those already mentioned. It is used in the manufacture of ammonia, of methanol (methyl alcohol), and of edible fats, such as "Crisco." Large quantities of hydrogen are used as fuel, often mixed with carbon monoxide in the form called "water-gas." Hydrogen is also used in the synthesis of many organic compounds, including artificial or synthetic gasoline. But our description of these uses must be deferred until later chapters.

48. THE COMPOSITION OF WATER

Determination of the composition of water marked a milestone in the history of chemistry. This was done by Cavendish in 1781. Before that time, more than one investigator had noted that moisture is formed when hydrogen burns in air, but no particular attention was paid to the phenomenon. Cavendish exploded one volume of oxygen with two of hydrogen and noted that no gas remained, but that the weight of water formed was equal to the weights of the gases used. Thus it was established that water consists of hydrogen and oxygen, united in the proportions of two volumes of hydrogen to one of oxygen.

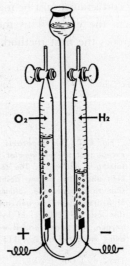

Fig. 8-10. Convenient apparatus for measuring the volumes of hydrogen, and of oxygen, liberated during electrolysis of water acidified with sulfuric acid.

There are three good experimental methods for finding the composition of water, one analytical, that is, by decomposing water, and the other two synthetic, that is, by forming water. The first is the method of electrolysis, which has already been described. (See Fig. 8-10.) If a direct current of electricity is passed through acidified water, hydrogen is liberated at the negative pole and oxygen at the positive. If the apparatus is arranged so that the gases may be collected separately, then the volume of hydrogen will be found to be twice that of the oxygen. For precise work,

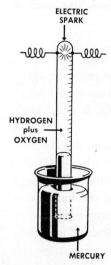

ELECTRIC
SPARK

HYDROGEN
plus
OXYGEN

MERCURY

Fig. 8-11. This diagram illustrates the principle used by Cavendish in finding the composition of water. A certain volume of hydrogen is placed in the tube (called a eudiometer). This hydrogen is then mixed with half as much oxygen (by volume). The gas mixture is exploded by passing an electric spark between the wires shown at the top of the tube. After the explosion no gas remains, but a small quantity of water is found in the tube. The weight of the water equals the combined weights of hydrogen and oxygen admitted to the tube.

corrections must be made for the slight amount of these gases which dissolve in the water. This method gives the composition of water by volume, as does the next method.

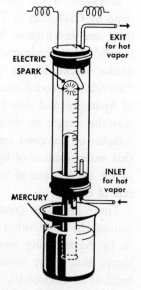

EXIT
for hot
vapor

ELECTRIC
SPARK

INLET
for hot
vapor

MERCURY

Fig. 8-12. This apparatus is similar to that shown in Fig. 8-11 except that the eudiometer tube is surrounded by a jacket containing a hot vapor. The temperature of the eudiometer is thus kept above the boiling point of water. This device makes it possible to compare the volume of steam formed with the volumes of hydrogen and oxygen originally placed in the eudiometer. If (for instance) 200 cc. of hydrogen were mixed with 100 cc. of oxygen, the steam formed would be found to occupy 200 cc., all being measured at, say, 115° C.

If hydrogen and oxygen are mixed in the proportions of two volumes of hydrogen to one of oxygen, and exploded, the water formed will normally appear as a liquid. (See Fig. 8-11.) But if the vessel is surrounded by a heating arrangement, such as a bath of toluene vapor at about 110° C., then the water formed in the explosion will remain as steam. (See Fig. 8-12.) In this way it may be proved that water is formed by the union of two volumes of hydrogen to one of oxygen and that the steam occupies two volumes, provided that all substances are measured at the same pressure and at the same temperature, which must, of course, be above the boiling point of water.

The third method for proving the composition of water gives the weights rather than the volumes involved. If hydrogen is passed over heated copper oxide, the copper oxide is reduced to metallic copper, and water is formed.

$$CuO + H_2 \rightarrow Cu + H_2O$$

If the copper oxide is weighed before the experiment, and the copper is weighed after the reduction, the difference in weight will be the weight of

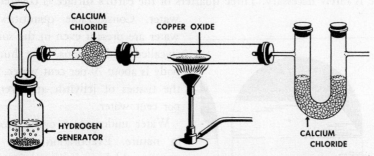

CALCIUM CHLORIDE

COPPER OXIDE

HYDROGEN GENERATOR

CALCIUM CHLORIDE

Fig. 8-13. The composition of water may be found by passing hydrogen (dried over calcium chloride) over a weighed quantity of hot copper oxide: $H_2 + CuO \rightarrow Cu + H_2O$. The water generated in the reaction is collected in a tube full of calcium chloride (*right*), which makes it convenient to weigh the water. The composition of water is then computed from the weight of water formed and from the loss in weight of the copper oxide.

oxygen used. The weight of oxygen used, subtracted from the weight of water formed, will give the weight of hydrogen used. This experiment is performed by placing the copper oxide in a porcelain boat, then carefully weighing the boat plus the copper oxide. The water formed is collected in a weighed tube full of calcium chloride, or some other agent which strongly absorbs water. Hydrogen is passed over the copper oxide and through the calcium chloride tube. The porcelain boat is heated until no further change takes place. The whole apparatus is allowed to cool, then the porcelain boat is weighed again, as is the calcium chloride tube. The data obtained might be as follows:

Copper oxide plus boat before heating.............. 16.452 grams
Copper plus boat after heating.................... 12.030 g.

Weight of oxygen................................ *4.422 g.*

Weight of calcium chloride tube before experiment... 15.907 g.
Weight of calcium chloride tube after experiment.... 20.883 g.

Weight of water............................... *4.976 g.*

Weight of hydrogen (4.976 g. − 4.422 g.)........... *0.554 g.*

Hence, the composition of water by weight is 0.554 g. of hydrogen to 4.422 g. oxygen, or approximately 1 part by weight of hydrogen to 8 parts by weight of oxygen. The most precise determinations give 1.008 parts by weight of hydrogen to 8 parts by weight of oxygen.

49. OCCURRENCE AND PURIFICATION OF WATER

Water occurs in such abundance that its preparation in the usual chemical sense is rarely necessary. Three quarters of the earth's surface is covered by water. Considerable quantities of water are present even in the soil of so-called arid regions. The human body is about 70 per cent water, and the tissues of jellyfish are over 95 per cent water.

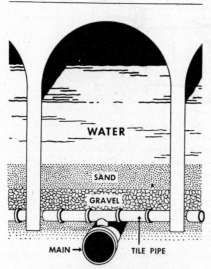

Water undergoes a cyclic process in nature. Evaporation from the oceans and lakes takes water into the atmosphere where, often after transportation over long distances, it condenses and falls to earth as rain or snow. Through the soil and the agency of rivers, the water ultimately finds its way back to the lakes and oceans. During this process the water carries great quantities of silt and of dissolved substances, gradually transforming the shapes and other geographical features of the continents, wearing down mountain ranges, and slowly contributing to the endless series of geological changes.

Fig. 8-14. Purification of water by filtration through sand. The water soaks through the sand and gravel, then into openings in the tile pipe.

Natural water supplies are never perfectly pure although often potable. Rain contains dissolved gases, dust particles, and bacteria. Water which has been in contact with soil or rocks always contains dissolved substances and may also contain organic matter and solid particles in suspension. Sea water contains several per cent of dissolved salts such as sodium chloride, magnesium chloride, and others. Water which contains appreciable amounts of calcium and magnesium salts in solution is called **hard water.** For domestic purposes it is often necessary to "soften" such water. This is done by boiling, by the addition of certain chemicals, or by a process known as *ion-exchange,* as in the Permutit process. But the details of these procedures must be deferred until later.

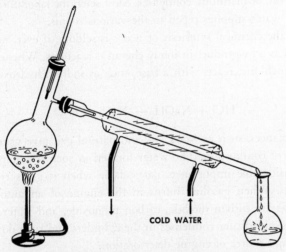

COLD WATER

Fig. 8-15. Purification of water by distillation. Steam from the flask full of boiling water (*left*) is condensed by passage through a narrow tube cooled with water, and then collected in a clean container.

For use in towns and cities, most water supplies have to undergo a **filtration** process to remove suspended solid particles, and a chlorination treatment to kill harmful germs. The water is run into large tanks from which it seeps through layers of sand and gravel. This removes suspended matter and some bacteria as well. Quite frequently the water is treated with alum or aluminum sulfate. Under proper conditions these substances form a gelatinous, slimy precipitate of aluminum hydroxide which falls to the bottom, carrying with it suspended matter and bacteria. Only a small amount of the aluminum sulfate is necessary.

$$Al_2(SO_4)_3 + 6H_2O \rightarrow 2Al(OH)_3 + 3H_2SO_4$$

Chlorination, or the addition of small amounts of chlorine to the water, is standard practice in all large cities. By this means typhoid fever, which used to be very common, has been rendered a comparatively rare disease.

For laboratory purposes very pure water is often required. This may be obtained by **distillation.** The water is placed in a flask to which is attached a condenser. The condenser is cooled with running water. The water in the flask is boiled, and the steam formed is liquefied, or condensed, in the condenser, from which it runs to a clean container. Often it is necessary to distill water repeatedly to obtain the utmost purity. Sometimes various agents have to be added to remove all impurities, and the final distillation is sometimes done with a tin, or platinum, condenser. Most scientific laboratories have special distilled water supplies piped to the various rooms.

Although the chemical synthesis of water is seldom, if ever, necessary, yet water occurs as a by-product in many chemical reactions. Whenever an acid, such as hydrochloric, reacts with a base, such as sodium hydroxide, water is formed.

$$HCl + NaOH \rightarrow NaCl + H_2O$$

Many substances, such as wood, oil, and natural gas, give water as one of the products of combustion. The water formed in such reactions as these is often of considerable importance, particularly when it gives rise to undesirable effects. When gasoline burns in the engine of an automobile, the chief products are carbon dioxide, carbon monoxide, and water. When the engine is cold, this water condenses in the cylinders and runs down into the oil. It is a major source of engine deterioration.

50. PROPERTIES OF WATER

Some of the physical properties of water have already been described. Reviewing these briefly, we recall that water is an odorless liquid, generally considered to be colorless, but perhaps blue or bluish-green in very deep layers. The color of the water in lakes and oceans is at least in part due to reflection from the sky and to the light-scattering effect of small suspended particles. Water freezes at 0° C. and, under 760 mm. pressure, boils at 100° C. The latent heat of fusion is about 80 calories per gram, the latent heat of vaporization 540 calories per gram. The specific heat of water is approximately 1. The density of water is approximately 1 g. per cc., but this actually changes with changing temperature in a most remarkable way. For nearly all substances the density gets smaller as the temperature is raised. For water this is true above 4° C. (more precisely, 3.98°), but between 0° C. and 4° C. the density of water increases with increasing temperature. In other words, the density of pure water reaches a maximum at 4° C. When water freezes there is an increase in volume, resulting in a further decrease of density, amounting to about 10 per cent. Because of this change, ice floats on water, but for most other substances the solid is more dense than the liquid and therefore sinks to the bottom. The fact that ice floats on water is responsible for the existence of icebergs. But if ice did not float on water the lakes and oceans would gradually fill up with ice which would, presumably, not be appreciably melted in summer. This effect would, in turn, have a profound effect on the climate of the whole world. Like other solids, ice forms crystals. Well-formed single crystals of ice are rarely observed, but snowflakes often exhibit multiple crystal formations of extraordinary beauty.*

The molecule of water, it will be recalled, is an essentially covalent structure in which the hydrogen atoms are arranged at approximately right angles to each other.

$$H : \overset{..}{\underset{..}{O}} :$$
$$H$$

Water is an exceptionally good solvent: that is, it dissolves many varieties of other substances. Of course, there are also many substances which do not appreciably dissolve in water. When water is heated very strongly, above a red heat, it begins to dissociate, or decompose, into hydrogen and oxygen. But at lower temperatures water must be regarded as a relatively stable substance.

Water acts on several types of chemical substances. On the more active metals, such as sodium and potassium, the action is vigorous, with formation of hydrogen and the corresponding hydroxide.

$$2K + 2H_2O \rightarrow 2KOH + H_2$$

With chlorine, the final products are hydrochloric acid and oxygen, although other substances may be formed in intermediate steps.

$$2Cl_2 + 2H_2O \rightarrow 4HCl + O_2$$

With certain types of compounds, water produces a change known as **hydrolysis.** This will be illustrated with a single example, although many such reactions are known. If phosphorus pentachloride, PCl_5, is treated with water, the products are hydrochloric acid and phosphoric acid. Hydrolysis is the decomposition of a compound by the use of water.

$$PCl_5 + 4H_2O \rightarrow H_3PO_4 + 5HCl$$

* W. A. Bentley and W. J. Humphreys, *Snow Crystals* (New York: McGraw-Hill, 1931). This book contains several hundred photographs of snowflakes. The reader will be astonished and delighted at the symmetry and variety of these crystals, which rank among the most beautiful of all natural phenomena.

Many chemical compounds, and some elements, have the property of adding water, often to form crystalline substances. An example is copper sulfate, $CuSO_4$. This is a white substance which can add water to form beautiful deep-blue crystals with the formula $CuSO_4 \cdot 5H_2O$. If this crystalline substance is heated, the water is driven off, leaving white anhydrous (no water) copper sulfate again.

$$CuSO_4 \cdot 5H_2O \rightarrow CuSO_4 + 5H_2O$$

These substances containing water are to be considered chemical compounds because the water is present in a definite proportion by weight. The water is often spoken of as "water of crystallization" and the compounds are called **hydrates**. It is customary to write the formulas as shown with a dot before the water, but the formulas might just as well be written as $CuSO_4(H_2O)_5$. Other examples of hydrates are washing soda, $Na_2CO_3 \cdot 10H_2O$; gypsum, $CaSO_4 \cdot 2H_2O$; and Epsom Salts, $MgSO_4 \cdot 7H_2O$. The name "water of crystallization" is not a very good one because many, if not most, solids occur in crystals, whether they contain water or not.

Some substances have a remarkable attraction, or affinity, for water. A few of these are dry calcium chloride, $CaCl_2$; concentrated sulfuric acid, H_2SO_4; and dry phosphorus pentoxide, P_2O_5. These substances are called **drying agents** and are often used to dry gases and other substances. They are capable of reducing the water content of air, for instance, to a remarkably low value.*

51. HYDROGEN PEROXIDE

If a lump of sodium metal is burned in air or oxygen, it is in part converted to sodium peroxide, Na_2O_2. If now this sodium peroxide is added to ice water, or to cold, dilute acid, a peculiar substance, hydrogen peroxide, is formed.

$$2Na + O_2 \rightarrow Na_2O_2$$

$$Na_2O_2 + 2H_2O \rightarrow 2NaOH + H_2O_2$$

$$Na_2O_2 + 2HCl \rightarrow 2NaCl + H_2O_2$$

Hydrogen peroxide is composed of hydrogen and oxygen only, but the proportions in which these elements are present are different from that found in water. Instead of there being two hydrogen atoms for one oxygen atom,

---

* The reader who may care to learn more about water, especially its physical properties, is recommended to look through N. E. Dorsey's *Properties of Ordinary Water-Substance* (New York: Reinhold, 1940). This book contains over 600 pages of carefully edited *facts* concerning water.

as in water, there are two hydrogen atoms for two oxygen atoms. The molecular formula for hydrogen peroxide is H_2O_2. The properties of this substance are quite different from those of water.

Normally, a solution of sulfuric acid yields only hydrogen and oxygen when an electric current is passed through it. But under certain conditions of current, temperature, and amount of sulfuric acid present, the product at the positive electrode is peroxydisulfuric acid, $H_2S_2O_8$. This substance reacts with water yielding sulfuric acid and hydrogen peroxide.

$$H_2S_2O_8 + 2H_2O \rightarrow 2H_2SO_4 + H_2O_2$$

The hydrogen peroxide may be purified by distillation in vacuum. The sulfuric acid may, of course, be used over again in the electrolysis. Ammonium sulfate may be substituted for sulfuric acid in this process. Because of its instability, hydrogen peroxide is not found in appreciable amounts in nature, but very small traces are present in the atmosphere and in rain and snow.

Pure hydrogen peroxide is a colorless liquid, rather syrupy, with a density at $0°$ C. of 1.46 g. per cc. It is dangerously explosive when heated, or when subjected to shock. It also decomposes violently if certain catalysts, such as finely divided platinum, are added to it. The products of decomposition are water and oxygen.

$$2H_2O_2 \rightarrow 2H_2O + O_2$$

Prior to World War II, concentrations of hydrogen peroxide in excess of about 30 per cent in water were considered too dangerous for handling and sale. The hazardous properties associated with this compound are, however, related to traces of impurities which are often present. Hydrogen peroxide is now on the market in concentrations of about 90 per cent. It finds uses in connection with the fueling of rockets, and as an industrial oxidizing agent. Although the compound is no longer considered so dangerous as formerly, it should be remembered that high concentrations are poisonous and that, in contact with the skin, it can produce severe burns.

Ordinary "drug-store" hydrogen peroxide is a 3 per cent solution. This strength may be kept indefinitely provided there is added a trace of acetanilid. Acetanilid, C_8H_9NO, is an organic substance which has the property of inhibiting the decomposition of hydrogen peroxide. Such substances act, in a sense, in an opposite manner to catalysts. They are called **inhibitors**, or sometimes, though incorrectly, *negative catalysts*. All bottles of "drug-store" hydrogen peroxide have on the label a statement to the effect that the contents include about $\frac{1}{10}$ grain of acetanilid. Acetanilid has an effect on hydrogen peroxide which is the reverse of that produced by platinum, manganese dioxide, ferric chloride, saliva, and other catalysts.

In addition to its ability to decompose readily under the influence of catalysts, hydrogen peroxide has several other valuable properties. It is a good oxidizing agent. For instance, sulfurous acid, H_2SO_3, is oxidized to sulfuric acid, H_2SO_4.

$$H_2SO_3 + H_2O_2 \rightarrow H_2SO_4 + H_2O$$

The well-known **bleaching** action of hydrogen peroxide on hair is due to the oxidation of the coloring substances in the hair. One of the most interesting applications of this property is the restoration of "old masters," ancient pictures which have darkened through the centuries until the original picture is scarcely discernible. Most paints contain "white lead," $Pb(OH)_2 \cdot 2PbCO_3$. On exposure to hydrogen sulfide, traces of which are often found in the air of cities, the white lead is slowly converted to lead sulfide, PbS, which is black. This process gradually darkens the picture. Restoration of such pictures may be done by washing the surface with dilute hydrogen peroxide. This does not convert the lead sulfide back to its original form, white lead. But the black lead sulfide is oxidized to another white compound, lead sulfate, $PbSO_4$.

$$PbS + 4H_2O_2 \rightarrow PbSO_4 + 4H_2O$$

In this way the original appearance of the painting is restored.* The oxidizing action of hydrogen peroxide has many other commercial applications in the bleaching of feathers, ivory, silk, and straw.

It is an odd fact that a substance which is such a useful oxidizing agent, may also act as a reducing agent. Hydrogen peroxide acts on silver oxide to produce metallic silver, a typical action of reduction.

$$Ag_2O + H_2O_2 \rightarrow 2Ag + H_2O + O_2$$

The familiar 3 per cent solution of hydrogen peroxide in water is a common household drug. As a germicide it is relatively ineffective, although in this connection it at one time enjoyed considerable popular favor. The solution is effective in cleansing wounds. This action is partly mechanical; the rapid decomposition of the peroxide liberating bubbles of oxygen which tend to remove waste and harmful matter. As a mouth wash, for certain pathological conditions, hydrogen peroxide is often prescribed.

---

* The reader is warned not to try this process on any priceless old masters until such time as he gains some competence as a restorative expert.

The principal uses of hydrogen peroxide are as a raw material for making catalysts for the production of synthetic plastics, and as a propellant fuel in military rockets. The latter use may be illustrated by the reaction between hydrogen peroxide and hydrazine hydrate.

$$2H_2O_2 + N_2H_4 \cdot H_2O \rightarrow N_2 + 5H_2O$$

52. HEAVY WATER *

Water is such a common substance and has been studied in scientific laboratories so thoroughly that most people felt up until 1933 that there was little more to learn about water or about the way it was decomposed by electricity. But that year two scientists, Professor Harold C. Urey (then of Columbia University) and Dr. Edward W. Washburn (of the Bureau of Standards in Washington, D. C.) made a very remarkable discovery. They discovered that when water is being electrolyzed, the water remaining in the container keeps getting denser. Instead of weighing 1.0 grams per cubic centimeter as does ordinary water, this residue of water in the container gradually increases in density until ultimately it weighs over 1.1 grams per cubic centimeter. This material is just as much entitled to the name "water" as is the ordinary water we drink, yet it differs in many ways. It was promptly named **heavy water.**

Experiments soon showed that it was the hydrogen that gave the "heaviness" to heavy water. The way this was proved was as follows: A sample of heavy water was decomposed into hydrogen and oxygen. The hydrogen was then combined again with ordinary oxygen and the water so formed was found to be heavy water. But when the oxygen from the original sample of heavy water was combined with ordinary hydrogen, only ordinary water resulted. It was clear, therefore, that it was the hydrogen that contributed to the peculiar properties of heavy water.

The hydrogen atoms in heavy water weigh twice as much as hydrogen atoms in ordinary water. "Heavy" hydrogen is, therefore, an isotope of hydrogen. It differs from ordinary hydrogen in having a nucleus made up in all probability of one proton and one neutron, instead of one proton and no neutrons as is the case for ordinary hydrogen.

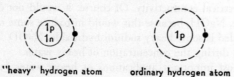

"heavy" hydrogen atom   ordinary hydrogen atom

* *Journal of Chemical Education*, 18:515 (1941), reprinted in part by kind permission of the Editor.

This substance was discovered in 1931 by Professor Urey, who was awarded the Nobel Prize for his work. Generally the different isotopes of an element are not given special names, but the properties of heavy hydrogen are so unique that Professor Urey named it **deuterium,** with the symbol D. Heavy water, therefore, becomes D_2O instead of H_2O. Deuterium is not regarded as a new chemical element, but its discovery was even more important than the discovery of some elements. This is because deuterium at once proved to be such a useful research tool in the scientific laboratory.

The preparation of pure D_2O is an expensive and tedious job. There is only a single cupful of heavy water in nearly four hundred gallons of ordinary water. But, owing to the stimulus given by World War II, the production of heavy water has become a large-scale commercial enterprise, and the price has been reduced to a few cents per gram.

Heavy water differs in many ways from ordinary water. It looks, smells, and tastes like ordinary water, but it is about 10 per cent heavier, or to be exact, its specific gravity at 25° C. is 1.1078 times that of ordinary water. This difference in specific gravity is the easiest way to identify heavy water or to tell what amount of heavy water may be present mixed with ordinary water. Some very sensitive methods have been worked out for measuring very slight changes in specific gravity, and it is possible by this means to detect as little as 1 part in 1,000,000 of heavy water. One of the ways of doing this is to make a little glass float of such weight that it will neither rise nor fall if placed in a tube full of ordinary water. Then if the float is placed in heavy water, it will promptly rise to the surface because the heavy water buoys it up.

Heavy water boils at 101.4° C. instead of 100° C., and it freezes at 3.8° C. instead of 0° C. It is noticeably more viscous, that is, more syrupy, than ordinary water; and it is not possible to dissolve quite so much salt in heavy water as in ordinary water.

Much of the research centered around heavy water has been concerned with deuterium itself rather than with D_2O. Heavy hydrogen, or deuterium, has the formula D_2 and is a gas similar to hydrogen except that it is twice as dense. For research purposes, pure deuterium gas is prepared by passing an electric current through pure heavy water, to which a small amount of sodium hydroxide is added to increase the electrical conductivity. Of course, it would not do to add ordinary sodium hydroxide, NaOH, because this would introduce some ordinary hydrogen. What must be added is some heavy sodium hydroxide, NaOD. This substance can easily be prepared during the concentration of heavy water.

Some of the most important applications of heavy water have to do with its use as an indicator in physiological processes, that is, in the chemical changes taking place in the human or animal body. It is well known that the body consists in large part of water, and the question might arise: when a person drinks a glass of water, are the hydrogen atoms in that water distributed throughout the whole body or are they eliminated at once? Are the hydrogen atoms in the tissues of the body being continually replaced by other hydrogen atoms, or are the body tissues simply washed by the water which is then quickly excreted? Before heavy water was discovered there was no way to approach these problems.

Professor George von Hevesy, in Germany, had a man drink 2 quarts of water containing about ½ per cent D_2O. Heavy water began to appear in the urine only 26 minutes later, but it was not completely eliminated for many days. Taking into consideration all the heavy water eliminated, in urine, through perspiration, and through the lungs, it took about 9 to 10 days for half of the heavy water, and therefore half of the 2-quart test drink, to be eliminated. This does not, of course, mean that the man excreted only 1 quart of water in 10 days, but that it took 10 days to eliminate half the number of actual molecules of water swallowed at the beginning of the experiment. On the average a water molecule stays in the body about 14 days before being eliminated. This is especially interesting because if a person drinks a substance such as methylene blue, the urine is soon strongly colored blue, but the color all disappears—that is, the methylene blue is all eliminated from the body within 43 hours. These experiments show that water swallowed diffuses throughout the whole body and becomes part of the animal tissues before being slowly eliminated. A few hydrogen atoms probably manage to stay in the body many months if not years.

Many similar types of investigations have been and are being carried on in the scientific research laboratories of the world. The most spectacular use of heavy water is in connection with the atomic bomb. Reference to this important use will be made in a later chapter.

EXERCISES

A. *Define or explain the following:*

atomic hydrogen	hard water
bleaching agent	heavy water
chlorination	hydrate
deuterium	hydrolysis
distillation	inhibitor
drying agent	reduction
filtration	water-gas

B. 1. Describe, with appropriate equations, methods for the preparation of hydrogen.
   2. What properties and uses of hydrogen are related to the fact that its density is very low?
   3. List the chemical properties of hydrogen, with appropriate equations.
   4. How can the composition of water be established?
   5. How is water purified?
   6. List physical and chemical properties of water.
   7. Are "hydrates" chemical compounds? Explain.
   8. Describe the preparation and properties of hydrogen peroxide.
   9. How is heavy water obtained? What are its properties and uses?

C. 1. Write complete, balanced equations for the following:

    a. the reaction of barium oxide with oxygen to form barium peroxide, BaO_2.

    b. the reaction of barium peroxide with sulfuric acid to yield barium sulfate and hydrogen peroxide.

    c. the reaction of lithium hydride, LiH, with water to yield lithium hydroxide, LiOH, and hydrogen.

    d. the reaction of potassium metal with heavy water. (This is similar to the reaction of sodium with water.)

    e. the reaction of magnesium metal with dilute hydrochloric acid. (This is similar to the reaction of zinc with dilute hydrochloric acid.)

    f. the reduction of magnetite, Fe_3O_4, with hydrogen to yield iron and water.

    g. the reaction of copper oxide with deuterium gas.

    h. the electrolysis of H_2SO_4 to form $H_2S_2O_8$.

2. A substance has the following percentage composition by weight: lithium, 18.2; aluminum, 71.4; hydrogen, 10.5. What is the simplest empirical formula for the substance?

3. A sample of phosphine gas, PH_3, occupying 720 cc. is decomposed completely to hydrogen and phosphorus vapor. The hydrogen is removed and the phosphorus vapor is found to occupy 180 cc. Both volumes are measured at the same temperature and pressure. What may be said about the molecular formula of phosphorus vapor?

4. Compare the rates of diffusion of hydrogen and uranium hexafluoride, UF_6.

5. What volume of hydrogen could be collected over water at 24° C. and 748 mm. pressure, by the action of excess hydrochloric acid on 100 g. of zinc?

6. What weight of ferric oxide, Fe_2O_3, could be reduced to metallic iron, by the action of 1000 cc. (S.T.P.) of hydrogen?

7. What volume of oxygen (S.C.) could be obtained by the action of a catalyst or heat, to decompose 250 g. of hydrogen peroxide?

8. a. What volume of hydrogen could be collected at standard conditions by the complete reaction of 115 g. of aluminum with excess sodium hydroxide according to the equation:

$$2Al + 2NaOH + 6H_2O \rightarrow 3H_2 + 2NaAl(OH)_4$$

    b. What volume would be occupied by this hydrogen over water at 29° C. and 855 mm. pressure?

9. A sample of "heavy" water is known to have a molecular weight of 20, but it is not certain whether the "heaviness" is due to deuterium as in D_2O or to the oxygen isotope with mass number 18 as in H_2O^{18}. Devise an experiment which you could perform in the laboratory, with relatively simple equipment, to establish this point.

THE CHEMICAL ELEMENTS

9

Only an infinitesimal fragment of the universe may be brought into the laboratory for chemical analysis. The air, the waters of the earth, and a relatively thin layer of rocks and soil are all to which we have direct access. But man has, in effect, transported himself to the center of the earth, to the planets, the sun, and the most distant stars. Combinations of observation and speculation tell something of the chemical composition of matter, wherever it may be.

53. THE EARTH

Accurate chemical analysis is possible on the **atmosphere,** at least up to several miles above the surface of the earth. Such analysis leads to very definite results concerning the composition of air. Air consists about 23 per cent by weight of oxygen, the rest being nearly all nitrogen. But although the total weight of the atmosphere is very great, yet it amounts to a very small fraction of the matter on or near the earth's surface.

The composition of the **hydrosphere,** all the waters of the earth, is also easily determined. Water itself, as we have seen, consists of one part by weight of hydrogen to eight of oxygen. The dissolved salts in sea water contribute about 2.5 per cent to the total weight of the water. But all the oceans, lakes, and rivers together add up to less than 10 per cent of what may properly be considered the crust of the earth.

By far the greater fraction of the earth's accessible crust is the **lithosphere,** the rocky surface extending down beyond the limits of the deepest mines, but certainly no more than a few miles thick. This layer is difficult to analyze with accuracy; rocks and minerals of varying composition are distributed over the earth in a manner far from uniform. Many elements occur, either native or in compounds, in highly restricted deposits in a very few areas. Efforts, therefore, to find the average composition of the earth's crust are not easy. But careful analysis and careful averaging lead to some fairly reliable figures.* Oxygen is by far the most abundant element, making up almost

* F. W. Clarke, *The Data of Geochemistry* (Washington: United States Geological Survey, 1924).

half of the total. Silicon is the next most abundant, amounting to about a quarter of the total, and aluminum and iron follow in order, contributing about 7.5 and 4.7 per cent respectively. The average composition of the earth's crust, including the lithosphere, the hydrosphere, and the atmosphere, is given in the following table derived from F. W. Clarke.

TABLE 5

AVERAGE PERCENTAGE COMPOSITION OF KNOWN TERRESTRIAL MATTER

Element	Abundance	Element	Abundance
Oxygen	49.5	Carbon	0.09
Silicon	25.7	Manganese	0.08
Aluminum	7.5	Sulfur	0.05
Iron	4.7	Barium	0.05
Calcium	3.4	Chromium	0.03
Sodium	2.6	Nitrogen	0.03
Potassium	2.4	Fluorine	0.03
Magnesium	1.9	Zirconium	0.02
Hydrogen	1.9	Nickel	0.02
Titanium	0.6	Strontium	0.02
Chlorine	0.2	Vanadium	0.02
Phosphorus	0.1	All others	0.05

It is a little surprising that oxygen, an element which normally exists as a gas, should be the most abundant. But rocks contain large amounts of oxygen in chemical combination. Even more surprising is the abundance of silicon, an element with which the average person is not familiar. Aluminum, which has been used in large quantities for a relatively short time, is more abundant than iron or copper, which have been known and used for many centuries. The abundance of an element is not necessarily related to its importance to society.

The deepest mines extend only a short distance into the earth. What may be the chemical composition of the earth's interior is largely a matter of speculation. The density of the earth as a whole has been measured. Physicists have done this by finding the mass of the earth from its gravitational attraction, and by computing the volume. The mass divided by the volume gives the density. The density of the earth as a whole is about 5.5 grams per cubic centimeter. This is a surprising result because the average density of the earth's crust, at least of the part we can reach, is only about 2.8. It is clear that the earth's interior must contain material of a much higher density than that on the surface. It has been surmised that the interior of the earth is largely a mixture of metallic iron and nickel. The density of such a mixture is about 7.8, which, averaged with the low density of the lithosphere, could give an over-all density of about 5.5. Evidence that this view of the earth's interior is correct is derived from a study of meteorites, to be described below.

If these speculations are correct, then, taking the earth as a whole, iron is by far the most abundant element, followed by oxygen, silicon, and nickel.

54. OCCURRENCE OF THE ELEMENTS

What *geochemical* condition has caused certain elements to be concentrated in some places and not in others is not well understood. Iron, aluminum, gold, radium, platinum, tungsten, helium, are a few examples of which some countries have an ample supply and some have none.

Some elements are found in the earth's crust in the free or **native** form. That is, they are found free from chemical combination with other elements. Such native elements are oxygen, nitrogen, and helium, among the important gases; gold, silver, copper, platinum, among the important metals; and sulfur and carbon. On the other hand, the great majority of elements is found chemically combined with one or more other elements. The more important metals are frequently found combined with oxygen or sulfur, as the oxide or sulfide. The following list will give an idea of the forms in which some of the important elements are found.

Aluminum: clays; *bauxite,* Al_2O_3
Bromine: in sea water as sodium bromide, $NaBr$
Calcium: *limestone,* chalk, marble, $CaCO_3$
Carbon: *limestone;* all living matter; petroleum; coal
Chlorine: sodium chloride, $NaCl$
Copper: *chalcocite,* Cu_2S; *chalcopyrite,* $CuFeS_2$
Hydrogen: water
Iodine: iodate, $NaIO_3$
Iron: *hematite,* Fe_2O_3; iron *pyrites,* FeS_2
Lead: *galena,* PbS
Magnesium: *dolomite,* $CaMg(CO_3)_2$; in sea water, as $MgCl_2$
Mercury: *cinnabar,* HgS
Nickel: sulfides
Nitrogen: air; *Chile saltpeter,* $NaNO_3$
Oxygen: water; rocks; many minerals
Phosphorus: many rocks, especially *phosphorite,* $Ca_3(PO_4)_2$
Potassium: many rocks; also as chloride, KCl
Silicon: many rocks, as silicate
Sodium: many rocks, as chloride, sulfate, carbonate and silicate, etc.
Sulfur: native; many metal sulfides such as FeS_2

Tin: *cassiterite,* SnO_2
Zinc: *sphalerite,* ZnS

This list is by no means meant to be complete; extended discussion of the occurrence of each element will be found in the appropriate chapters.

It may be wondered why some elements are found free, while others are always found in compounds. The reason is very simple. The more reactive elements, such as phosphorus and chlorine, would not stay in the free state but would immediately react with whatever substance happened to be most convenient, just exactly as they will do in the laboratory if allowed to escape. The moderately inactive metals, such as copper, are sometimes found combined and sometimes free. The least active elements are generally found free.

The different activities of the elements are especially noticeable in the case of the metals. Sodium, for instance, is extremely reactive, and, consequently, is never found in the native condition. Gold, on the other hand, is very often found free because it shows slight chemical activity. Certainly one would not expect to find free those elements which react with water, and only in exceptional circumstances, as in the case of a meteorite, are they so found.

It is possible to arrange the common metals in order of their relative **activities,** and such a list is often of value in predicting the course of chemical reactions. The metals like sodium will obviously be near the top of such a list, and those like gold near the bottom. An easy way to prepare such a list is as follows: if a strip of, say, metallic zinc is placed in a solution of copper sulfate in water, the zinc starts going into solution, and metallic copper begins to appear. This reaction may be represented as follows:

$$Zn + CuSO_4 \rightarrow ZnSO_4 + Cu$$

This is called a **displacement reaction,** and the zinc is said to displace the copper. Zinc is the more active of the two metals. Similarly, copper will displace silver.

$$Cu + 2AgNO_3 \rightarrow Cu(NO_3)_2 + 2Ag$$

It so happens that hydrogen, although a gas, has a definite place in this list. Among the common metals, sodium, calcium, zinc, and iron will displace hydrogen from water or acids.

$$2Na + 2H_2O \rightarrow 2NaOH + H_2$$

But silver will not displace hydrogen in this way; in fact, under certain conditions, hydrogen will displace silver. It will be recalled that in the preparation of hydrogen from water or acids, certain metals could be used but not others. This was simply a question of whether the metal was more or less active than hydrogen. If more active, then the metal could be used to produce hydrogen, but otherwise it could not.

By studying various possible displacement reactions the metals may all be arranged in what might be called an **activity series.** Any element will displace from solution any other element below it in this list. All elements above hydrogen will displace hydrogen from acids, although some do so rather slowly. The metals near the top of the list vigorously displace hydrogen from water. The activity of the metals is also related to the manner in which they combine with oxygen. The metals down to mercury combine directly with oxygen, those near the top of the list do so with great violence. The metals below mercury may be made to combine with oxygen only indirectly. Their oxides, if heated gently, decompose to metal and oxygen. Conversely, the oxides of the metals below chromium are easily reduced to metal by heating the oxides in the presence of hydrogen. The oxides of metals above iron are not reduced by heating them in hydrogen.

It will be observed that the activity series of the metals concisely shows the types of chemical reactions to be expected of each metal, and indicates the probability of any given metal's being found in nature as the free element, or as a compound. The metals at the top of the series are never found free; those at the bottom are often found free. Of course, other

Activity Series of the Metals

potassium
calcium
sodium
magnesium
aluminum
manganese
zinc
chromium
iron
nickel
tin
lead
hydrogen
copper
mercury
silver
platinum
gold

considerations apply to the mode of occurrence of the elements. Sulfur is sometimes found free because the deposits are underground and protected from atmospheric oxidation. Oxygen is found free because, being so abundant, there is not enough oxidizable matter readily available to combine with all the oxygen. Nitrogen is found free because of its inactivity. But all these elements are also found in various states of combination. The only elements which never occur in compounds are the inert gases: helium, neon, argon, krypton, xenon, and radon.

55. METEORITES

I could more easily believe that two Yankee professors would lie than that stones would fall from heaven—Attributed to Thomas Jefferson.

"Falling stars" sometimes land on earth. The origin of such **meteorites** in outer space has been generally accepted for less than 150 years. The third president of the United States seems to have been one of the sceptics.

Every day millions of meteors enter the atmosphere and are burned to dust by the heat of atmospheric friction. A very few reach the earth. In the United States about 25 meteorites are found every year. The average mass of collected meteorites is about 20 kilograms, but they range from several tons down to a few grams. They constitute the only nonterrestrial matter which we can take into the laboratory for examination. These interplanetary visitors are always studied with the greatest of interest. They form a meeting place for chemistry, physics, geology, and astronomy.

There are at least two kinds of meteorites, the metallic kind and the stony kind. There are also many meteorites, the composition of which lies between these two extremes. Metallic meteorites consist principally of iron. The iron content is often about 90 per cent. The only other major constituent is nickel which may range from about 5 to 20 per cent. Other elements found in small amounts include cobalt, phosphorus, sulfur, carbon, copper, and chromium. It will be noticed that these metallic meteorites are very different in composition from the earth's crust, but that they are about the same as has been supposed must be the composition of the earth's interior.

In contrast, the stony meteorites average about 35 per cent oxygen, together with fairly large amounts of iron, silicon, and magnesium. There are also small amounts of most of the other common elements. The composition of these meteorites is therefore much nearer to that of the earth's crust. Indeed, many stony meteorites are, without careful examination, indistinguishable from ordinary stones.

It will be remembered that the isotopes of the elements found on earth are practically always mixed in the same proportions. Or, to state it another way, the atomic weights of the elements as found by chemical methods are always the same. It might be thought that the elements found in meteorites would have their isotopes mixed in different proportions from those found on earth. But the atomic weights of these elements seem to be the same as those found for earthly elements—at least, so far as has been investigated. Perhaps this means that the isotopes are formed in certain proportions no matter where, or under what conditions. Or it may mean that the conditions under which the elements of meteorites were formed may not be very different from those under which our terrestrial elements were formed. Of course, it is not inconceivable that both earth and meteorites were formed at the same time and place.

One of the outstanding characteristics of the metallic meteorites is what is known as the **Widmanstätten figures** (Fig. 9-1). If a surface of metallic meteorite is polished, then etched in dilute acid, there appears a beautiful network of fine lines, suggesting the interlacing of many crystals. This technique is commonly used in metallographic studies. Similar lines are easily produced in several metals, but they have not yet been made on iron-nickel alloys corresponding to the composition of meteorites. To the metallographer the Widmanstätten figures suggest that at one time the meteorite was subject to high temperatures, perhaps about 1000° C., and that cooling took place over many thousands of years. These are the conditions which might be found in the interior of a planet such as the earth. This view is supported by unmistakable evidence that many meteorites must at one time have been liquid.

The stony meteorites are very complex. They often consist of several types of minerals, chiefly well-known silicates such as olivine, $(MgFe)_2SiO_4$; and orthorhombic pyroxenes, $(MgFe)_2Si_2O_6$. A few substances, such as calcium sulfide, are found in meteorites, but do not occur as minerals on the earth. Notably absent from meteorites are water, quartz, and mica. The stony meteorites often contain large spherical grains called chondrules. The origin of these is also a mystery. The chondrules look as though they had at one time been liquid. Nearly all stony

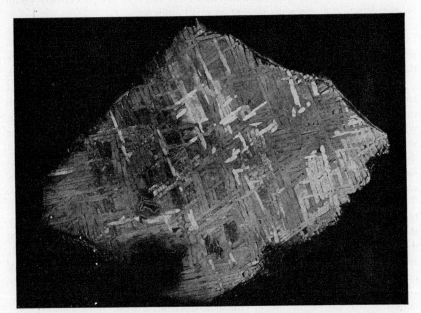

Fig. 9-1. Widmanstätten figures on a meteorite. (*The Chicago Natural History Museum*)

meteorites contain flakes and grains of metallic iron and nickel. A few meteorites are black. This color can be duplicated by heating almost any stony meteorite to 800° C. Perhaps the black stones got too near the sun in their interplanetary wanderings, and so became "scorched."

It will be shown in a later chapter that the age of many rocks may be estimated from a study of the radioactive elements present. The maximum age for the earth has been so investigated and turns out to be about two billion years. Meteorites have been similarly studied. The maximum age found for meteorites is also about two billion years, although some meteorites may be considerably younger.

Speculations concerning the origin of meteorites rank among the foremost of fascinating intellectual pursuits. Perhaps some ancient planet, like the earth, disintegrated, leaving asteroids, meteors, and planetary dust. But such cosmic questions as this we leave for our brother scientists, the astronomers.*

* F. G. Watson, *Between the Planets* (Philadelphia: Blakiston, 1941).

56. THE PLANETS, SUN, AND STARS

It will be recalled from Chapter 2 that the elements, if strongly heated, emit light of various colors. The light may be passed through a spectroscope whereupon it is revealed as being made up of bright lines of various frequencies. The frequencies and arrangement of lines are characteristic for each chemical element. By this art of **spectrochemical analysis** there are revealed the chemical compositions of many substances. Spectroscopes are used in nearly all research laboratories for identifying the elements present in compounds and mixtures; they are particularly useful for the detection of elements present in small amounts.

By the aid of a telescope and a spectroscope it is possible to analyze the light from distant stars. By this means the astronomer, sitting at his ease in the observatory, is able to analyze the most remote galaxy with somewhat less trouble than the chemist, toiling over his evil smells, is able to analyze a piece of mineral.

If the light of the sun is examined with the aid of a spectroscope, a rainbow of colors is perceived. But this rainbow, or continuous spectrum, is interspersed with many dark lines, called **Fraunhofer lines.** The dark lines arise in the following way. If sodium metal is very strongly heated until it vaporizes and glows, the yellow light emitted is found to be due principally to two strong yellow lines in the spectrum. If the sodium vapor is cooled slightly, the yellow lines are no longer visible. Now pass a white light (as from an electric lamp) into the spectroscope, and in the path of this white light place the slightly cooled sodium vapor. The spectrum will be revealed as a continuous rainbow of colors, crossed by two black lines in the yellow region. The position of these black lines is precisely the same as the yellow lines which are found when the sodium vapor is more strongly heated. This dark-line spectrum is called an **absorption spectrum.** It arises from absorption of light by the sodium vapor, which is not heated strongly enough to emit light itself. All the elements, under the proper conditions, show an absorption spectrum which may be used for identifying the elements in the same way that the bright-line, or emission, spectrum is used.

Molecules, as well as atoms, yield spectra, although the number of lines is often much greater and the arrangement more complicated. Molecules also give rise to absorption spectra, under appropriate conditions. It is therefore possible not only to identify the elements present in stars, but to detect the presence of certain molecules. Means are also available for determining the relative abundance of the elements and for estimating their temperatures.

The Moon and the planets emit no light of their own. We see them by reflected sunlight. What we can learn about them is, therefore, largely from their absorption spectra. Sunlight falling upon a planet is partly absorbed. By a study of the frequencies of light undergoing absorption, it is often possible to draw conclusions concerning the composition of the planetary atmospheres. The Moon and Mercury have no atmospheres. Indirect evidence suggests that, with Pluto, they are not very different in composition from the Earth's crust. But Venus and Mars have atmospheres. Because of the much-debated question of possible life on Mars, the compositon of this planet is a matter of extraordinary interest.

Observation of Venus shows extensive cloud-like formations, not unlike our own earthly clouds but considerably thicker. But no water vapor or oxygen can be detected in the atmosphere of Venus. Amounts of these compounds comparable to those found on earth should be fairly easy to detect by their absorption spectra. On the other hand, large amounts of carbon dioxide are detectible. The surface of Venus is probably fairly warm, so that clouds of solid carbon dioxide ("Dry-Ice") are improbable. A current theory is that the atmosphere of Venus consists in large part of formaldehyde, formed by the union of carbon dioxide and water under the influence of ultraviolet light, from the Sun.

$$CO_2 + H_2O \rightarrow CH_2O + O_2$$

The oxygen liberated in this reaction may all be united with the rocks, chiefly iron compounds, on the surface of the planet. This would explain the absence of water vapor and of oxygen. It must be pointed out, however, that the absorption spectrum of formaldehyde has never been found in the atmosphere of Venus. It has been suggested that the formaldehyde may be polymerized: that is, many molecules may join together to form clouds of solid droplets.

$$nCH_2O \rightarrow (CH_2O)_n$$
formaldehyde   polymerized formaldehyde

This would not show the absorption spectrum of formaldehyde; but the whole matter must be regarded as undecided.

The planet Mars does not give any indication of an atmosphere containing oxygen or water vapor. But Mars has well-known polar caps, suggesting very strongly the fall of snow. These caps change with the Martian seasons. There is also fair evidence for the existence of vegetation on Mars. The red color of this planet is probably caused by deserts covered with iron oxide. The abundance of iron oxide could account for the depletion of oxygen in the atmosphere. If life persists on Mars, it must be under conditions much more trying than those on Earth.

The giant planets Jupiter, Saturn, Uranus, and Neptune are very different. The absorption spectra show unmistakable evidence for large quantities of ammonia and methane in the atmospheres of these planets. The planets themselves have densities not greatly different from that of water, and far below the density of the Earth. The temperatures of these planets are very low, in some cases not greatly above the absolute zero. Perhaps their atmospheres consist of clouds of tiny crystals of ammonia, which would solidify at these low temperatures. Water, if present, must be frozen solid and sunk out of sight below the ammonia clouds.

The Sun has proved to be a happy hunting ground for the spectroscopist. The temperature, about 6000° C. on the surface, is such that strong emission spectra are excited. Still further out in the cooler atmosphere, many lines appear in the absorption spectrum. Up to 1937 no less than 62 elements had been identified in the solar atmosphere. The elements missing are not necessarily absent; they may be present in very small amount, or only present in the Sun's interior. It is surprising to find that by far the most abundant element in the Sun's atmosphere is hydrogen, which makes up about 82 per cent by volume of the total. Helium is also abundant, about 18 per cent. All other elements are present in small fractions of 1 per cent. This relative abundance of the elements is in very sharp contrast to that found on the Earth, where oxygen is present in greatest amount.

Most of the stars have roughly the same composition as the Sun, although some-times one element or another seems to be present in greater proportion. There are some stars in which carbon seems to be the most abundant element.

At temperatures a little cooler than the Sun, various types of molecules make their appearance. There is unmistakable evidence in many stars for molecules such as C_2, CH, CN, H_2, OH, TiO, and at still lower temperatures CO. Most of these correspond to substances not, as a rule, considered stable compounds on the Earth, but their reality can be proved and they exist under the special conditions found in the atmospheres of certain stars.

The stars are so far away that their light takes hundreds and thousands of years to reach us. What we learn of their composition is what existed there long ages ago. But such times are generally short in the life history of the stars.

At least twice it has happened that an "element" has been discovered in the Sun or elsewhere in the heavens, and that no corresponding element was known on the Earth. In one case, that of helium, the element was later discovered on the Earth. In another case, that of "nebulium," supposed to be present in distant nebulae, it was later found that the supposed spectrum lines of nebulium were actually due to oxygen under very special conditions. When oxygen was subjected in the laboratory to these conditions, the lines attributed to "nebulium" readily appeared.

In interstellar space, the space between the stars, the amount of matter is in-credibly small. Yet there are dust particles and molecules floating through space, on the average amounting perhaps to less than one molecule per cubic centimeter. This is a "vacuum" almost infinitely superior to any vacuum we can produce in our laboratories. Nevertheless the astrophysicists have detected the presence of various elements and molecules, of which hydrogen is by far the most abundant element, in this very tenuous distribution of matter throughout the known uni-verse. Nature works with the same familiar elements, here on Earth, and in the unfathomable chasms of intergalactic space.*

57. DISCOVERY OF THE ELEMENTS †

The discoveries of oxygen and of hydrogen by Priestley and by Cavendish respectively have been briefly described in the preceding pages. The discov-eries of other elements will be mentioned in due course. But here we shall consider the general circumstances in which elements have been discovered, why some elements have been known for thousands of years and some for scarcely a generation, why the eighteenth and nineteenth centuries saw the discovery of many elements but the twentieth century so far only a few.

The modern concept of a chemical element dates only from the eighteenth century. But a few elements have been known and used since earliest re-

* F. L. Whipple, *Earth, Moon, and Planets* (Philadelphia: Blakiston, 1941).

L. Goldberg and L. H. Aller, *Atoms, Stars, and Nebulae* (Philadelphia: Blakiston, 1943).

† Mary E. Weeks, *The Discovery of the Elements* (Easton, Pa.: *Journal of Chemical Educa-tion*, 1934).

corded history. What we know of the discovery of such elements comes from Biblical allusions, ancient tombs, and the writings of philosophers such as Pliny the Elder (23-79 A.D.).

Gold has been found in Egyptian tombs of prehistoric age. It is probably the earliest metal of which there is any record. The early use of an element is directly related to the ease with which it may be obtained. Gold generally occurs native, and its pleasing appearance and resistance to corrosion are such as to attract the notice of primitive peoples. There is, by contrast, no aluminum in ancient tombs. Aluminum is very difficult to obtain from its minerals: that is, large amounts of energy are required, and the methods for doing this cheaply have been known for relatively few years. Silver, copper, lead, tin, and mercury were also known to the ancients. These metals all occur either in the native form, or else they are quite easily reduced by moderate heating, with or without the addition of charcoal. Carbon and sulfur have been known since prehistoric times. Carbon is always a product of charring wood, and sulfur occurs native in several parts of the world, including the islands of Sicily. It might be argued that the ancients should have known about the element oxygen. Of course, they used oxygen as does every breathing creature, and they sometimes referred to air as an element. But they did not conceive of the air as a mixture containing a substance which supports combustion. Sometimes things are hidden more because they are too obvious rather than because they are too obscure.

Throughout the Dark Ages there were men called **alchemists.** These forerunners of chemistry concerned themselves chiefly with vain efforts to transmute base metals into gold, and to find the elixir of everlasting life. But they made several discoveries which laid the groundwork for the rapid scientific advances of the eighteenth and nineteenth centuries. Among these are the discoveries of arsenic, antimony, bismuth, and phosphorus. The Romans may have known how to prepare antimony but they did not distinguish it from lead. Who discovered the first three of this group of elements is not known, but phosphorus was discovered in 1669 by a German merchant, Hennig Brand (or Brandt). He may be regarded as the first person known to have discovered a chemical element. Phosphorus is not particularly easy to prepare. Its early discovery was, in some respects, a sort of scientific accident.

During the eighteenth and nineteenth centuries the discovery of new elements was greatly accelerated. This was due to the large number of persons who became interested in science, to the growth of general education, and to the discovery of general principles for reducing elements and for testing them. For a time almost every mineral coming to a chemist's hand yielded at least one new element. Particularly was this trend noticeable toward the end of the nineteenth century, after discovery of the family relationships between the elements. These relationships showed the circumstances in which new elements might be found, and indicated what procedures might be most effective in obtaining them. Invention of the spectroscope as applied to chemical analysis placed in the hands of the chemist a very powerful tool for the identification of new elements.

In the twentieth century relatively few new chemical elements have been discovered. This is not because of any faltering in scientific zeal, but rather because the roster of natural elements seems to be about complete. Emphasis has shifted from the discovery of new elements to the artificial production of new elements and to new isotopes of known elements. The discovery of oxygen in the eighteenth century is properly regarded as one of the major achievements in all the history of chemistry. It was scarcely matched until the synthesis of neptunium, plutonium, and other transuranium elements in recent years.

58. THE PERIODIC LAW

Several of the chemical elements show a sort of family resemblance to each other, with respect to their physical and chemical properties. Sodium and potassium are very much alike. Carbon and silicon show close resemblance. Fluorine, chlorine, bromine, and iodine have many "family" characteristics. These resemblances were noted by several early investigators, at least one of whom, an Englishman, J. A. R. Newlands, was ridiculed by some of his scientific colleagues for suggesting in 1866 that the elements might be arranged in family groups.

The atomic number, it will be recalled, is the positive charge on the nucleus of an atom. If the first few elements are arranged in order of increasing atomic number, it will be observed that the elements naturally fall in groups of eight.

$$^2He \quad ^3Li \quad ^4Be \quad ^5B \quad ^6C \quad ^7N \quad ^8O \quad ^9F$$

$$^{10}Ne \quad ^{11}Na \quad ^{12}Mg \quad ^{13}Al \quad ^{14}Si \quad ^{15}P \quad ^{16}S \quad ^{17}Cl$$

Disregarding hydrogen, we find that neon resembles helium, sodium resembles lithium, and so on for each vertical pair of atoms shown. It appears, therefore, that there is something significant about the number eight so far as the atoms are concerned. If now the series of elements is continued, the sequence rapidly breaks down. Chromium is only remotely like sulfur. Iron is not at all like argon.

$$^{18}A \quad ^{19}K \quad ^{20}Ca \quad ^{21}Sc \quad ^{22}Ti \quad ^{23}V \quad ^{24}Cr \quad ^{25}Mn \quad ^{26}Fe$$

However, pursuing the idea a little further, at about number 32, germanium, a resemblance to silicon is noted.

$$^{27}Co \quad ^{28}Ni \quad ^{29}Cu \quad ^{30}Zn \quad ^{31}Ga \quad ^{32}Ge \quad ^{33}As \quad ^{34}Se \quad ^{35}Br$$

Arsenic definitely resembles phosphorus, selenium is much like sulfur, and bromine is very like chlorine. It seems, therefore, that while there is a definite

Fig. 9-2. Dmitri Ivanovitch Mendeleev

Mendeleev was born in Siberia in 1834, the last of a very large family. He was educated at St. Petersburg and abroad, and later became a professor at the University of St. Petersburg. His life was characterized by poor health and hard work.

Mendeleev's Periodic Law is one of the finest generalizations in all science. It ranks with Dalton's atomic theory in breadth and scope. Mendeleev lived to see his work brilliantly confirmed by the discoveries of germanium and gallium, and other elements.

He died in 1907. His genius was recognized by scientists everywhere, both during and after his life. (Bettmann Archive)

set of family relationships among the chemical elements, these relationships are not as simple as they appear at first. It is not very easy to arrange all the elements on a sheet of paper so as to emphasize all the likenesses and unlikenesses among them. But this may be done with a fair degree of success if each vertical (family) group is divided into two subgroups, which may be called A and B subgroups. It is understood that elements in the same group do not necessarily show very close resemblances unless they are also in the same subgroup. For instance, potassium and copper have few points of resemblance; they are, therefore, put in different subgroups, although they both belong in the same main group. The complete table is then as given on the following page.

This is a form of the famous Mendeleev **Periodic Table of the Chemical Elements,** first prepared by the distinguished Russian chemist, Dmitri Mendeleev, in 1868. From this table it is seen that when the elements are arranged in order of increasing atomic number, the elements with similar

TABLE 6

Periodic Table

Series	Group 0	Group 1 A	Group 1 B	Group 2 A	Group 2 B	Group 3 A	Group 3 B	Group 4 A	Group 4 B	Group 5 A	Group 5 B	Group 6 A	Group 6 B	Group 7 A	Group 7 B	Group 8
Series 1															1**H** 1.0080	
Series 2	2**He** 4.003	3**Li** 6.940		4**Be** 9.013		5**B** 10.82		6**C** 12.010		7**N** 14.008			8**O** 16.000		9**F** 19.00	
Series 3	10**Ne** 20.183	11**Na** 22.997		12**Mg** 24.32		13**Al** 26.97		14**Si** 28.06		15**P** 30.98			16**S** 32.066		17**Cl** 35.457	
Series 4	18**A** 39.944	19**K** 39.096	29**Cu** 63.54	20**Ca** 40.08	30**Zn** 65.38	21**Sc** 45.10	31**Ga** 69.72	22**Ti** 47.90	32**Ge** 72.60	23**V** 50.95	33**As** 74.91	24**Cr** 52.01	34**Se** 78.96	25**Mn** 54.93	35**Br** 79.916	26**Fe** 55.85 27**Co** 58.94 28**Ni** 58.69
Series 5	36**Kr** 83.7	37**Rb** 85.48	47**Ag** 107.880	38**Sr** 87.63	48**Cd** 112.41	39**Y** 88.92	49**In** 114.76	40**Zr** 91.22	50**Sn** 118.70	41**Nb** 92.91	51**Sb** 121.76	42**Mo** 95.95	52**Te** 127.61	43**Tc** (99)	53**I** 126.92	44**Ru** 101.7 45**Rh** 102.91 46**Pd** 106.7
Series 6	54**Xe** 131.3	55**Cs** 132.91	79**Au** 197.2	56**Ba** 137.36	80**Hg** 200.61	57-71 *	81**Tl** 204.39	72**Hf** 178.6	82**Pb** 207.21	73**Ta** 180.88	83**Bi** 209.00	74**W** 183.92	84**Po** 210	75**Re** 186.31	85**At** (210)	76**Os** 190.2 77**Ir** 193.1 78**Pt** 195.23
Series 7	86**Rn** 222	87**Fr** (223)		88**Ra** 226.05		89**Ac** 227.0		90**Th** 232.12		91**Pa** 231		92**U** † 238.07				

* Rare earth elements 57 to 71: La, Ce, Pr, Nd, Pm, Sm, Eu, Gd, Tb, Dy, Ho, Er, Tm, Yb, Lu.
† Transuranium elements 93-98: Np, Pu, Am, Cm, Bk, Cf.

properties are found at recurrent, though not equal, intervals. The intervals, or periods, are, disregarding hydrogen, made up of eight, eight, eighteen, eighteen, and thirty-two elements. In other words: **the properties of the elements are a periodic function of the atomic numbers. This is the Periodic Law,** generally regarded as one of the most important generalizations in chemistry.

The Periodic Table, in the form shown, consists of nine vertical groups numbered zero to eight, and of seven horizontal series. Family resemblances among the elements are found only in the vertical groups. It will be noticed that Groups 1 to 7 have A and B subgroups, and that Group 8 consists of three series of three elements each. The subgroups do not start until the fourth series is reached. Hydrogen is placed in a series of its own. Many other characteristics of the Table will be described later.

When we say that the properties of the elements are a periodic function of the atomic numbers, we mean that a given specific property such as hardness or activity changes from element to element just as business cycles of prosperity and depression occur through the years. But the periodicity of the elements is far more regular than any table of business cycles. We shall illustrate the periodicity of the elements with two properties, the melting points and the valences. But it must be emphasized that nearly all specific physical and chemical properties of the elements show this periodicity.

Let us plot on graph paper the melting points of the elements with the atomic numbers on the horizontal axis and melting points on the vertical (Fig. 9-3). We start with extremely low temperatures for hydrogen ($-259°$ C.) and helium ($-272°$ C.), rise through lithium ($186°$ C.), beryllium ($1350°$ C.), boron ($2300°$ C.), and carbon ($3500°$ C.), then fall precipitously to nitrogen ($-210°$ C.), oxygen ($-218°$ C.), fluorine ($-223°$ C.), and neon ($-249°$ C.), then rise again through sodium ($97.5°$ C.), magnesium ($651°$ C.), and silicon ($1420°$ C.). This cyclic or periodic variation is repeated through all the elements. The periodicity is not perfect—a few elements seem to be misplaced—but in general the results are highly significant. Such a periodicity could not arise accidentally. It must be the result of some underlying, fundamental recurring feature in the structure of the atoms.

Another periodic property is the valence. Nearly all the chemical elements unite with oxygen, and such formulas as SO_3, CO_2, Al_2O_3, and P_2O_5 are very common. Suppose we arbitrarily assign to each of the elements an **oxidation state,** defined as follows: *

---

* Some authors use the term "oxidation number," others use "valence number," in the same sense in which we shall use the term "oxidation state."

(a) the algebraic sum of the oxidation states in any formula must equal zero.

(b) the oxidation state for a free (uncombined) element is zero.

(c) the oxidation state of oxygen in a compound is minus two, except in peroxides (and superoxides).

Then for sulfur in SO_3 the oxidation state is $+6$, for carbon in CO_2 it is $+4$, for aluminum in Al_2O_3 it is $+3$, and for phosphorus in P_2O_5 it is $+5$. These

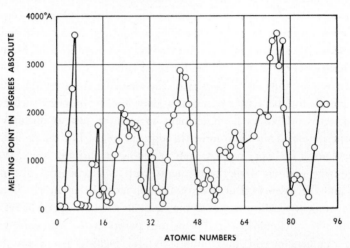

Fig. 9-3. The Periodic Law illustrated by a plot of atomic numbers versus melting points of the elements.

oxidation states should not be confused with the charges on the ions as shown in Table 3, p. 47. When the ion is derived from a single atom, as Cl^-, Na^+, Al^{+++}, and $S^=$ the charge on the ion is the same as the oxidation state; but in the sulfate ion, $SO_4^=$, the oxidation state of the sulfur is $+6$. The oxidation state of an element may be found if there is known the formula of a compound containing that element. For instance, the oxidation state of nitrogen in nitric acid, HNO_3, is $+5$; that of manganese in permanganic acid, $HMnO_4$, is $+7$. The oxidation states are somewhat arbitrary numbers which do not necessarily have any significance so far as atomic or molecular structure is concerned, but their usefulness will become increasingly obvious.

If now the first few elements in the Periodic Table are assigned their oxidation states, as found from the formulas of the oxides, it will be seen that these states show a periodicity not unlike that shown by the melting points.

Element	H	He	Li	Be	B	C	N	O	F
Oxide	H_2O	—	Li_2O	BeO	B_2O_3	CO_2	N_2O_5	—	—
Oxidation State	+1	0	+1	+2	+3	+4	+5	..	..

Element		Ne	Na	Mg	Al	Si	P	S	Cl
Oxide		—	Na_2O	MgO	Al_2O_3	SiO_2	P_2O_5	SO_3	Cl_2O_7
Oxidation State		0	+1	+2	+3	+4	+5	+6	+7

Several of the elements show different oxidation states in different compounds. The above listing shows only those oxides in which the maximum oxidation state is found. It will be noted that the oxidation state of an element, so found, generally corresponds to the number of the group to which the element belongs in the Periodic Table. For instance, silicon is in Group 4 in the table; the oxidation state of silicon is +4 in the oxide SiO_2. The element vanadium similarly is in Group 5. It shows an oxidation state of +5 as in the oxide V_2O_5.

In combination with hydrogen the elements mentioned above show sometimes the same oxidation state as they do when combined with oxygen, but more often the state is different. This is shown by the following listing of some hydrides.

Element	He	Li	Be	B	C	N	O	F
Hydride	—	LiH	BeH_2	B_2H_6	CH_4	NH_3	H_2O	HF
Oxidation State	0	+1	+2	+3	−4	−3	−2	−1

Element	Ne	Na	Mg	Al	Si	P	S	Cl
Hydride	—	NaH	MgH_2	Al_2H_6	SiH_4	PH_3	H_2S	HCl
Oxidation State	0	+1	+2	+3	−4	−3	−2	−1

Here, although the periodicity is different, yet it is well defined, changing in regular steps from element to element. In these valency changes as in the periodicity of physical properties there is a suggestion of some underlying periodicity in the structure of the various atoms.

When Mendeleev first proposed the Periodic Table, he suggested several different forms in which the Table might be written. There have been endless modifications advanced since Mendeleev's time. Some of these are elaborate and are in three dimensions. Most of such tables are so cumbersome as to lose their usefulness. Only one form of the Table will be given, other than that already presented. This, shown on the inside back cover, is called the "long form." Instead of having A and B subgroups, the elements are spread out across the table. This eliminates the rather unsatisfactory subgroups but fails to bring out the resemblances between, say, titanium and germanium. Many teachers of chemistry prefer the long form of the table. For most physical purposes and for some chemical purposes it is definitely to be preferred to the "short form." No one has yet devised a "perfect" form for the Periodic Table; nor is there much expectation, or need, that anyone should.

59. SIGNIFICANCE OF THE PERIODIC LAW

When Mendeleev first proposed the Periodic Table in 1868, there were over a dozen blank spaces where elements now appear. One of the reasons Mendeleev's work is so highly esteemed is that he boldly predicted the existence and discovery of new elements, and he stated in detail what the properties of these new elements would be. Within a few years Mendeleev's predictions were brilliantly realized, especially by the discoveries of the elements germanium, scandium, and gallium. His predictions and their subsequent fulfillment will be illustrated by reference to germanium, which Mendeleev called **eka-silicon** (Es). Equally successful predictions were made for other undiscovered elements.

TABLE 7

PROPERTIES OF EKA-SILICON PREDICTED BY MENDELEEV

	Eka-silicon (Es) *Predicted by Mendeleev* *in 1871*	*Germanium (Ge)* *Discovered by Winkler* *in 1886*
Atomic weight.........	72	72.6
Density..............	5.5	5.35
Atomic volume........	13	13.5
Color................	dirty gray	grayish-white
Action on strong heating	yields EsO_2	yields GeO_2
Effect of water.........	none	none
Effect of acids.........	slight	HCl has no effect
Effect of alkalies.......	slight	KOH solution has no effect, but fused KOH has
Properties of oxide.....	refractory; density 4.7; more basic than SiO_2 but less than SnO_2	refractory; density 4.703; feebly basic
Properties of chloride...	$EsCl_4$ will boil below 100° and have a density of 1.9 at 0° C.	$GeCl_4$ boils at 83° and has a density of 1.887 at 18° C.
Organo-metallic compounds	$Es(C_2H_5)_4$ will boil at 160° and will have a density of 0.96	$Ge(C_2H_5)_4$ boils at 163.5° and has a density of 0.99

Mendeleev was able to make these predictions by considering the properties of the elements surrounding the blank space, now filled by germanium. The atomic weight must lie between that of zinc, 65.38, and that of arsenic,

74.91. (Gallium had not been discovered in 1871.) It was clear that the atomic weight of germanium must be nearer that of arsenic than that of zinc. Hence 72 is a reasonable guess. The formula of germanium compounds must be similar to those of other elements in the group. The formula for silicon oxide is SiO_2, hence the formula for germanium oxide should be GeO_2. Similar lines of reasoning were used in all the predictions.

In 1869 not a single member of the inert gas family (Group 0) was known, and Mendeleev could not have had any way of predicting the existence of this group. But when helium and argon were discovered, the existence of Group 0 became obvious and very intensive search was made for the other members of the group. This search was successful, but some of these gases, especially krypton and xenon, are so rare that their discovery might have been delayed many years had it not been for the guidance of the Periodic Table.

Until fairly recently there were four blank spaces in the Periodic Table. These were for the elements with atomic numbers 43, 61, 85, and 87. Claims have been made for the discovery of all these elements and the discoveries seem to have been verified. With the discovery of these elements, the Periodic Table is complete from elements 1 to 98. One of its major achievements has been the direction it has given research toward the discovery of new elements.

Another way in which the Periodic Table has been useful is in the study of the physical and chemical properties of the elements and their compounds. For instance, when radium was discovered, it was not immediately clear whether its atomic weight should be 113 and whether it should have a chloride with the formula RaCl, or whether the atomic weight should be 226 and the chloride $RaCl_2$. But there was a vacancy in the Periodic Table right under barium, which forms a chloride $BaCl_2$, and for the element belonging to this blank space an atomic weight of 113 was impossible, while 226 was entirely reasonable. In this way the atomic weight of radium was quickly established.

Another of the many ways in which the Table is useful may be illustrated by the study of catalysts. When a chemist finds that a certain element or compound is useful as a catalyst, he frequently investigates the catalytic action of other elements near by in the Periodic Table. In this way Haber was led to the use of iron as a catalyst in the synthesis of ammonia. Similarly, Midgley and his colleagues were led to the use of tetraethyllead as an antiknock in gasoline.

So far as the average chemist and student of chemistry are concerned, the principal use of the Periodic Table is in the systematization of knowledge.

Many facts, otherwise unrelated, are brought together so as to ease the burden on the memory. For instance, if we wished to know the formula for molybdic acid, we need only note that molybdenum is in Group 6 of the Table and that sulfur is also in this Group. The formula for sulfuric acid is H_2SO_4, that for molybdic acid must be H_2MoO_4. Or, if we wish to know the solubility in water of radium sulfate, we need only remember that in Group 2, calcium sulfate is moderately soluble, strontium sulfate less so, barium sulfate still less—hence radium sulfate must dissolve in water to an extremely slight degree.

In spite of the very great importance of the Periodic Table it must not be thought that the Table alone can solve all chemical problems, or that the Table is without defects. There are several shortcomings in the Table. When Mendeleev proposed the Table the atomic numbers of the elements were not known. Mendeleev arranged the elements in order of increasing atomic *weight,* and his statement of the Periodic Law was that the "physical and the chemical properties of the elements vary as periodic functions of their atomic weights." It will be noticed that in four instances, argon-potassium, cobalt-nickel, tellurium-iodine, and thorium-protactinium, the elements are not arranged in order of increasing atomic weight. Before the discovery of atomic numbers this situation caused a good deal of discussion. It was suspected that the atomic weights reported for these elements might be in error. We know now that the atomic weights are merely averages of the weights of the several isotopes present. In the cases mentioned, the abundance of the various isotopes is such that the elements with the higher atomic numbers happen to have slightly lower atomic weights. This difficulty is, therefore, easily resolved when once the fundamental nature of atomic numbers is understood.

Another difficulty arises in connection with the place of hydrogen. Some authors put hydrogen above lithium in Group 1; others put it above fluorine in Group 7. But there is no satisfactory place for this element. Still another difficulty arises with the elements known as **rare earths.** There are fifteen of these elements, starting with lanthanum (57) and ending with lutetium (71). These elements are all so much alike that it is often very difficult to separate them from each other. They are sometimes left out of the table entirely. They act so much like a single element that we have chosen to place them all together in Group 3, under yttrium.

But in spite of these difficulties, the Periodic Law stands as one of the great monuments of science. Particularly is this clear when we see, as in the next section, how the groups and periods of the Table foreshadowed the brilliant twentieth-century developments in the field of atomic structure.

60. THE PERIODIC LAW AND THE ELECTRONIC STRUCTURE OF THE ELEMENTS

It will be recalled from Chapter 2 that the electrons in atoms are shown by the data of spectroscopy to be arranged in various energy levels. The distribution of electrons in the atoms of all the elements was shown in Table 2 (p. 30). It was shown in Chapters 2 and 3 that the electrons in the highest normal energy level are those primarily concerned in valence. If we list the elements of the first few series (as in Table 8), we find that there is a close relationship between the highest oxidation state shown by each element and the number of electrons in the highest normal energy level for that element.

TABLE 8

RELATION OF OXIDATION STATES TO ELECTRON DISTRIBUTION

Element	He	Li	Be	B	C	N	O	F
Oxidation state in highest oxide	0	1	2	3	4	5	..	..
Electrons in 2nd energy level	0	1	2	3	4	5	6	7
Element	Ne	Na	Mg	Al	Si	P	S	Cl
Oxidation state in highest oxide	0	1	2	3	4	5	6	7
Electrons in 3rd energy level	0	1	2	3	4	5	6	7

It will be clear that the reason the valences of the elements show a periodic variation is that the numbers of electrons in the highest energy levels in the various atoms show a periodic change from one to eight and then back to one again. The inert gases—helium and neon (and argon)—have their outermost energy levels filled by (respectively) 2, 8, and 8 electrons. This accounts for the fact that the second and third series each have eight elements. There is just room in each level for eight electrons and hence for eight different elements, before building has to start in the next highest energy level.

The various groups of elements in the Periodic Table show their "family" resemblances because all the elements of a group have the same number of electrons in the highest normal energy level, and this is the level which largely determines the properties of the element. In Group 1 the metals lithium, sodium, potassium, rubidium, and cesium all have a single electron in the highest level, although these elements have very different numbers of electrons in lower levels. These elements all have an oxidation state of +1 and they form a typical family of elements. In Group 2 the elements beryllium, magnesium, calcium, strontium, barium, and radium all have two electrons in the highest normal level, and they all have an oxidation state of +2. In Group 7 the elements fluorine, chlorine, and iodine have seven electrons in the outermost level. It will be recalled that these elements often form ions, and hence compounds, by gaining, rather than by losing or sharing, an electron. The formulas for ionic compounds of this group are all similar: as for instance, in the case of the potassium salts, KF, KCl, KBr, and KI.

As we proceed through the Periodic Table, various complexities arise. The series become longer, and the elements often have numerous oxidation states. This is due to the complicated way in which the various energy levels can hold electrons. In the rare earth group of elements, the chemical and physical properties of these elements may be thought of as remaining practically constant while electrons are being built into an inner energy level. But, in general, the family resemblances of the Periodic Table are now easily explained. They arise because each member of a "family" has the same number of electrons in its highest normal energy level.

EXERCISES

A. *Define or explain the following:*

absorption spectrum
abundance (as applied to a chemical element)
activity (as applied to a chemical element)
alchemy, alchemists
atmosphere
displacement reaction
eka-silicon
Fraunhofer lines
geochemistry, geochemical
hydrosphere

lithosphere
metallography
meteorite
native element
occurrence (as applied to a chemical element)
oxidation state
Periodic Table
rare earths
spectrochemical analysis
Widmanstätten figures

B. 1. State the Periodic Law
  2. What are the three or four most abundant elements on the earth's crust, and what is their approximate percentage abundance?
  3. What are some of the forms in which some common elements (e.g., Al, C, Cl, Cu, H, Fe, Hg, N, O, Si, and S) occur in nature?
  4. What, in general, is the composition of meteorites?
  5. What means are available for studying the composition of the sun, the planets, and the distant stars? What conclusions have been reached?
  6. What determines, in general, whether an element occurs free or in compounds?
  7. What is meant by "activity series of the metals," and what experiments could be performed to arrange the elements in such a series?
  8. What is meant by the "periodicity" of the properties of the elements?
  9. What are the uses and achievements of the Periodic Law and Periodic Table?

10. What are the weaknesses of the Table?
11. What relationships exist between position in the Periodic Table and arrangement of electrons in the atom?

C. 1. Show products to be expected for each of the following:
    a. Mn + 2HCl →
    b. Zn + MnCl$_2$ →
    c. 3H$_2$ + 2AuCl$_3$ →
    d. Ca + NiCl$_2$ →
    e. Ni + CaCl$_2$ →

2. By reference to the Periodic Table list by symbol the following:
    a. the two elements most like rubidium, Rb.
    b. the atomic number of tantalum, Ta.
    c. two pairs of elements in which the order of increasing atomic number is not the order of increasing atomic weight.
    d. the probable formula for zinc telluride.
    e. the element with atomic number 19, 81, 7, 55.
    f. elements (X) which might be expected to form an oxide X$_2$O$_5$, X$_2$O$_7$, X$_2$O$_3$, XO, X$_2$O.
    g. elements (Z) which might be expected to form a hydride H$_4$Z, H$_2$Z, HZ, H$_3$Z.
    h. the arrangement of electrons in scandium, Sc.

3. Show oxidation states for the element in black letters in each of the following formulas: **Ca**O, **Ti**O$_2$, **Sb**$_2$O$_3$, **W**O$_3$, H**I**, **Ge**H$_4$, H$_2$**Se**, H$_2$**Se**O$_3$, **Zn**(OH)$_2$, H$_3$**P**O$_4$, **Y**(OH)$_3$, **K**, **S**$_2$, **Cl**$_2$.
4. Write formulas for the compounds formed by hydrogen with the elements of atomic numbers 33, 35, 52, and 20.
5. Write formulas for some compounds formed by oxygen with the elements Bi, Ba, Nb, Hf, Ac, Rb, Kr, and Mn.
6. Is there any property of the atoms which is *not* periodic?
7. The atomic weights of three elements increase in the order X, Y, and Z. The element Y has the following arrangement of electrons: 2, 8, 8, 3. The atomic number of X is 12 less than that of Y, and the atomic number of Z is twice that of Y. Identify the elements and show the arrangement of electrons in X and Z.

CHAPTER **CHEMISTRY AND ENERGY**

10

The energy of molecules and its relationship to what is called "heat" have already been discussed in Chapter 6. But energy in various forms is associated with all chemical changes. Chemistry is the science of matter and its transformations. Every transformation of matter is paralleled by a transformation of energy. The burning of wood, or coal, or gasoline, the growth of vegetation, the manufacture of steel—all involve changes of energy. Sometimes, as in the burning of coal, energy is liberated. Sometimes, as in the growth of vegetation, energy is absorbed. The transformation of energy is no less important than the transformation of matter.

61. DIFFERENT KINDS OF ENERGY

Energy is defined as the ability to do work. A waterfall, when properly harnessed, has the ability to illuminate a city, move streetcars, manufacture aluminum, and to do a host of useful tasks. But one soon sees that all forms of energy may be divided into two classes. The falling water at Niagara Falls has the ability to do work because of the fact that it is moving. Such energy is called **kinetic energy;** it is always associated with motion. But the water at the top of the Falls also has energy. It is certainly possessed of energy because it very soon performs its work. But the energy is of a rather different form than the kinetic energy. The energy of the water at the top of the Falls is energy of position rather than of motion. Such energy is called **potential energy.**

This distinction between kinetic and potential energy is very clear in connection with chemical reactions. An exploding bomb has terrific kinetic energy, enough to sink a battleship. But that energy must also have been in the bomb in the form of potential energy before it exploded. The potential energy is a property of the T.N.T., or other explosive, with which the bomb is loaded. It does not become kinetic energy until the bomb is detonated. Similarly, at a gas station, we buy potential energy in the convenient form of the mixture called "gasoline." In the car engine this potential energy is converted to kinetic energy, or the energy of motion.

Both kinetic energy and potential energy are found in several different forms. There is, for instance, **mechanical energy,** such as we associate with a falling body, or a moving train, or, for that matter, with the motion or position of any visible or tangible object. **Thermal,** or heat, **energy** is, as we have seen, associated with the random motions of the molecules. **Electrical energy** is associated with the motions or relative positions of the charged fundamental particles, the electrons and protons. A current of electricity in a wire is a stream of electrons coursing through the metal. Finally there is a fourth kind of energy, **electromagnetic energy,** of which light is an example. This electromagnetic energy seems not necessarily to be associated with matter in any form. However, the precise nature of electromagnetic energy is not known. Apart from the fact that it possesses certain properties both of matter and of waves or vibrations completely divorced from matter, its nature continues to elude the best scientific minds. Radio waves, infrared heat waves, visible light, ultra-violet rays, X rays, and *gamma* rays from radioactive substances are all examples of electromagnetic energy. The various relationships between these and the other forms of energy make up an important part of the science of physics.

62. ENERGY AND CHEMICAL CHANGE

Practically all transformations of matter, that is, chemical changes, involve simultaneous energy changes. All forms of energy may be found associated with different chemical reactions. Sometimes the energy is required to bring about the desired chemical change. For instance, heat and light are required to bring about the union of carbon dioxide and water into the carbohydrate substance of trees and other vegetation. At other times, as in the burning of wood, heat is liberated. Reactions which require the addition of heat are called **endothermic;** those that liberate heat are called **exothermic.** When energy is required to bring about a chemical change, as in growing a tree, the energy merely stays as potential energy within the wood until such time as the tree is cut down and burned. The majority of chemical reactions involve heat, rather than other forms of energy; and exothermic reactions are most common among those chemical changes familiar to us.

Forms of energy other than heat are also often found associated with chemical change. Mechanical energy may be utilized to grind substances together to bring about their chemical reaction. Explosions, on the other hand, produce mechanical energy. Electrical energy is produced in dry cells or storage batteries during chemical changes within the cell. Electricity is also used in many industries such as copper and lead refining and in the manufacture of chlorine, to bring about desired chemical changes. Electromagnetic energy, in the form of light, is produced during many chemical reactions. The light is produced along with heat in the burning of wood, coal, oils, and gases; and without heat in such processes as that employed by the firefly. Light also brings about the explosive union of hydrogen and chlorine to form hydrogen chloride; light affects photographic plates or films; and most important of all, light is essential to the growth of most forms of vegetation.*

When we realize the large amount of potential energy in gasoline or in a thimbleful of nitroglycerine, it is of interest to know just where in the molecules this energy resides. It seems most likely that this energy is electrical. The molecules consist of atoms, which, in turn, consist of positive and negative electricity, together with some neutrons. In some cases the arrangement of electrical charges will be so symmetrical, or at least so lacking in what might be called "electrical strain" within the molecule, that the substance is very stable, and, as in the case of silica, SiO_2, much energy must be applied in order to break the various parts of the molecule away, that is, to decompose the substance.

On the other hand, a case might be imagined where the protons and electrons had been forced into such highly strained positions that almost any other configuration would be preferable, or rather, have less energy. Such may be the case in, say, nitrogen triiodide, NI_3, which explodes at the merest touch. Some authors consider chemical energy as a distinct form, like electric and thermal energies, but from what has been said it will be clear that chemical energy is, at least in part, a special kind of electrical potential energy.

63. ENERGY SOURCES

Energy in its various forms is indispensable to life and to civilization. It is worthwhile, therefore, to think about the primary sources of energy available to us. Although energy may be obtained from a host of different sources, the primary source is the sun. The sun's light and heat are responsible for other energy sources such as water power, coal, oil, and firewood. The one exception is the energy associated with radioactive transformations. Such energy may contribute something toward the warmth of the earth.

Where the sun gets its energy has been a favorite subject of debate among scientists for many years. It seems most likely, at present, that the sun's great energy comes from atomic transmutations on a grand scale, hydrogen being

---

* A very beautiful demonstration of "cold-light" may be performed by mixing solutions of hydrogen peroxide and potassium ferricyanide with 3-amino-phthalhydrazide. The light persists for several minutes and is bright enough to read by.

transmuted to helium with the simultaneous liberation of tremendous quantities of energy in the form of heat and light. Such an explanation involves serious modification of the laws of Conservation of Mass and of Energy. There is, however, ample evidence that such transmutations do take place, and many have been duplicated in the laboratory. There seems no other possible source of the vast quantities of energy poured by the sun into space. The sun is large enough to keep up this enormous production of heat and light for many millions, if not billions, of years. Ultimately, however, it must burn down, and the sun and earth return to utter cold and desolation.

The sun's rays are used directly as a source of energy for the growth of almost all vegetation. But otherwise man makes little direct use of the sun's energy, preferring to use the secondary sources which are generally in more convenient form. Water power is one of these sources. Formerly, water power was used directly in such operations as grinding grain in flour mills. Now it is most frequently converted to electrical energy to be used in innumerable ways. Water power has its source in the sun. The energy of the sun provides the latent heat of vaporization necessary to evaporate water from oceans and lakes. This water vapor is condensed and falls as rain on various parts of the earth. Ultimately it finds its way back to the oceans and lakes by way of rivers in which the hydroelectric plants are erected. The supply of hydroelectric energy is assured so long as severe changes in climate do not occur.

Coal is another important source of energy. This energy too came originally from the sun. Coal, as most people know, is formed by the decay, under suitable conditions, of great forests which once flourished on the earth. The supply of coal is limited but seems sufficient for many years to come.

One of our greatest sources of energy at the present time is petroleum (literally, "rock-oil"). Gasoline and other products from petroleum are used to operate automobiles, ships, trains, and for many other purposes. The original source of the petroleum is not known with any certainty. However, it is reasonably sure that this important source of energy was formed through the agency of the sun. The supply of petroleum is decidedly limited. Even though new oil fields are being found and more economical methods of treatment are being devised, it is probable that in much less than one hundred years petroleum will be a curiosity. That need not, however, occasion much alarm because products like gasoline may be obtained from coal and from oil shale; and alcohol, which is reasonably satisfactory as a motor fuel, may be made from corn and other farm products. It is, moreover, entirely possible that new inventions may make the gasoline engine, as we know it, quite obsolete.

It should not be overlooked that all animals, including man, are possessed of the ability to do work. This energy is, as always, originally derived from the sun through vegetation which serves as the primary food for both herbivorous and carnivorous animals.

64. THERMOCHEMICAL EQUATIONS

It will be recalled that heat is measured in calories, and that a calorie is the amount of heat necessary to raise the temperature of one gram of water one Centigrade degree. The heat lost or gained in a chemical reaction is often indicated in the equation by such a notation as follows:

$$C + O_2 \rightarrow CO_2 + 95,000 \text{ cals.}$$

This equation may be read: "The union of carbon and oxygen is an exothermic reaction, in which 12 g. of carbon unite with 32 g. of oxygen to form 44 g. of carbon dioxide, with the liberation of 95,000 calories of heat." Often the kilocalorie (kcal.) is used instead of the calorie to measure large quantities of heat. One kilocalorie equals one thousand calories.

An example of an endothermic reaction is the formation of carbon disulfide from carbon and sulfur:

$$C + 2S \rightarrow CS_2 - 19,600 \text{ cals.}$$

This equation is sometimes written:

$$C + 2S + 19,600 \text{ cals.} \rightarrow CS_2$$

the calories being transposed with change of sign. Equations such as the above are called **thermochemical equations.** They differ from ordinary equations only in that they show the quantity of heat involved in the reaction.

Beginners sometimes have difficulty in understanding the significance of the words "exothermic" and "endothermic." If a reaction is exothermic, heat is given out. The reacting mixture and its surroundings will probably become warm. Coal, burning in a furnace, is a good example of an exothermic reaction; the heat liberated in the reaction of coal plus air heats up the remaining coal and the furnace itself, as well as supplying warmth for the whole building. But endothermic reactions tend to cool off the reacting substances. The mixture and container may actually feel cool to the touch. Most chemical reactions stop if they become cool. Hence to keep an endothermic reaction going it is necessary to supply heat. In the manufacture of carbon disulfide, heat must continually be supplied by an external source; otherwise the reaction would quickly stop.

The quantities of heat liberated or absorbed in a chemical reaction are found by placing weighed amounts of the reagents in a **calorimeter.** A calorimeter is an insulated chamber supplied with a sensitive thermometer for accurate observation of the heat change taking place. The heat given off, say, in the burning of carbon to carbon dioxide could be found by placing a weighed amount of carbon in the calorimeter, together with a substance which will readily give up oxygen, or with an arrangement for the intro-

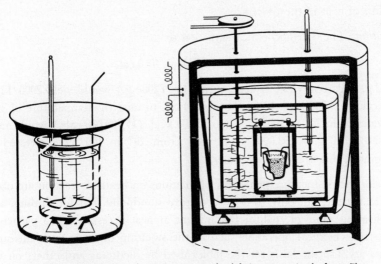

Fig. 10-1. Calorimeters. The apparatus on the *left* is a very simple form. The reacting substances may be placed in the test tube. As the reaction proceeds, the water in the inner beaker will become warmer (if the reaction is exothermic). From the increase of temperature, the weight of water, and the specific heat of water, the number of calories liberated in the reaction may be calculated. The apparatus at the *right* is a more elaborate calorimeter, in which the reacting materials are ignited by an electrically heated wire.

duction of oxygen gas. The carbon is then ignited by a spark or other means. The heat given off is generally absorbed in a weighed amount of water. The specific heat of water is, of course, known. From the weight of water and the rise in temperature of the water it is possible to calculate the quantity of heat liberated by the burning carbon. With a few corrections, the heat of the reaction, or the heat of combustion, of the carbon may then be calculated.

Problem: The heat of combustion of aluminum is about 7.4 kcal. exothermic per gram of Al. Write the thermochemical equation for the reaction.

Solution: The ordinary equation is

$$4Al + 3O_2 \rightarrow 2Al_2O_3$$

and the atomic weight of aluminum is 27. If 1 g. of Al burns to liberate 7.4 kcal., then 4×27 g. of Al would liberate $4 \times 27 \times 7.4$ kcal. = 798 kcal. The thermochemical equation is therefore

$$4Al + 3O_2 \rightarrow 2Al_2O_3 + 798 \text{ kcal.}$$

Problem: How much water would be raised in temperature from 20° to 100° C. by the combustion to carbon dioxide of 2.0 kg. of carbon, assuming no loss of heat in the process?

Solution: The thermochemical equation is

$$C + O_2 \rightarrow CO_2 + 95 \text{ kcal.}$$

If 12 g. of carbon yield 95 kcal., then 2 kg. (2000 g.) would yield $2000/12 \times 95$ kcal. = 15,800 kcal. It would take 80 cal. to raise the temperature of 1 g. of water from 20° to 100° C. Then 15,800 kcal. (15,800,000 cals.) would raise $15,800,000/80$ g. = 198,000 g. of water from 20° to 100° C. Expressed in kilograms, this is 198 kg. of water.

Calorimetric measurements and calculations on heats of reaction are often of great value, not only from a theoretical standpoint, but for finding, say, the heating value of coal, or the amount of heat necessary for a particular industrial chemical operation such as the smelting of iron. Such measurements are also the basis for the tables used by dietitians and others on the calorie value of foods.

It is of interest to know that the amount of heat change per gram in the formation of a given substance from its elements is a perfectly definite quantity dependent in no way upon the method of preparation or upon the intermediate steps in the procedure. For instance, if a gram of iron slowly corrodes in air to ferric oxide, the number of calories liberated is the same as when a gram of iron burns brilliantly in pure oxygen, provided the final product is the same. In one case the heat is liberated slowly over many days, while in the other it is all liberated in a few seconds. The same result would be achieved if the iron were first converted into another substance entirely, say, ferric nitrate, and then reconverted to the ferric oxide. In the same way the heat of combustion of sugar is shown to be almost exactly the same whether measured in a calorimeter in the usual way, or developed through the digestive processes in a man. This last method involves placing a man in a specially designed insulated room which serves as a large calorimeter. The man is then fed a certain weight of sugar. Accurate instruments record the heat liberated from the man during the conversion of the sugar in the man's body to carbon dioxide and water.

The fact that the heat of formation of a substance from its elements does not depend on the method of preparation makes possible the indirect calculation of such heats without the necessity for a direct calorimetric determination. This will be illustrated by a calculation of the heat of formation of carbon monoxide from the elements carbon and oxygen according to the equation:

$$2C + O_2 \rightarrow 2CO$$

It has been found experimentally that the combination of carbon with oxygen to form carbon dioxide is exothermic, as given above, and that the combustion of carbon monoxide is also exothermic in accordance with the equation:

$$2CO + O_2 \rightarrow 2CO_2 + 135 \text{ kcal.}$$

Writing:

$$2C + 2O_2 \rightarrow 2CO_2 + 190 \text{ kcal.}$$

and:

$$2CO + O_2 \rightarrow 2CO_2 + 135 \text{ kcal.}$$

by subtraction: $2C + 2O_2 - 2CO - O_2 \rightarrow 2CO_2 - 2CO_2 + 55 \text{ kcal.}$

whence: $2C + O_2 \rightarrow 2CO + 55 \text{ kcal.}$

The heat of formation of carbon monoxide is thus found to be 55/2 kcal. = 27.5 kcal. per mole.

65. REACTION VELOCITY

It is common experience that some chemical reactions, such as the explosion of dynamite, proceed at very high speed, while others, such as the rusting of iron, take place very slowly. This notion of reaction velocity, or speed of reaction, is so important as to require precise definition. **Reaction velocity** may be defined as the number of moles of substance reacting in unit time per unit volume. Thus, if there were 3 moles of a gas present in a 1-liter flask, and if 0.1 mole of the gas were decomposed in 1 second, then the reaction velocity might be stated as 0.1 mole per second per liter.

Of great importance are the factors which influence reaction velocity. If it takes a week to make a ton of fertilizer, or for the paint on a car to dry, the processes are plainly not very practical. But if the reactions involved can be speeded up to take place in an hour or less, the processes may be commercially feasible. On the other hand, if the disintegration of rubber tires, or the souring of face cream, can be retarded, then the value of these products may be correspondingly increased. Study of the factors influencing reaction velocity make up a part of what is called "chemical kinetics," an important branch of chemistry.

These factors are (1) *the nature of the reactants,* (2) *the concentration of the reactants,* (3) *the temperature of the reactants,* and (4) *the presence of catalysts.* Certain other factors are of minor importance.

The *nature of the reactants* is of prime importance in fixing the rate of chemical reaction. Magnesium will burn vigorously in air, while iron ordinarily will not burn at all. Just why this difference should exist is not clearly understood. It doubtless is connected with the number and arrangement of the electrons in the various substances, but direct experiment is the only way known at present for finding which types of substances will react rapidly and which slowly.

The influence of *concentration* on reaction velocity is easily demonstrated by the action of hydrochloric acid on zinc. With very dilute acid the reaction is scarcely perceptible, but as the strength of the acid is increased, the reaction becomes more and more vigorous. It is, in general, found that **the velocity of a chemical reaction varies with the concentration of the reacting substances.** This statement is known as **the Law of Mass Action.** Supposing we have a hypothetical reaction,

$$A + B \rightarrow C + D$$

the Law of Mass Action states that if the concentration of A or of B or of both is increased—that is, if more of these substances are put into a given volume—then the velocity of the reaction will be increased. The concentration of the products C and D will not affect the velocity of the reaction as written. The reason why reaction velocity varies with concentration of reactants becomes clear when we consider the following: reaction between two molecules can only be expected to take place when the molecules collide, or at least when they come within "striking distance" of each other. If the concentration is low, the chances of collision are slight, but as the concentration rises, the chances of collision, and of reaction, become correspondingly greater. Consequently the reaction velocity increases.

Somewhat related to this effect of concentration is the influence of the nature and extent of surface available for the reaction between a solid and a liquid or a gas. A lump of metallic iron oxidizes in air very slowly, but an extremely fine iron powder catches fire in air.* The effect of large surface area contributes to the explosion of powdered materials in "dust" explosions, as described in an earlier chapter. In a similar way, reaction velocity is often

---

* Such material is called "pyrophoric" iron. It is made by reducing iron oxide or iron oxalate at a temperature only a little above room temperature.

influenced by intimacy of contact. Two substances such as mercury and sulfur placed together do not react rapidly, but if they are ground together with the aid of a mortar and pestle, they unite fairly quickly. In brief, atoms and molecules react more quickly the larger their numbers which are allowed to come in close contact in a given time.

The next effect on reaction velocity to be considered is that of *temperature*. For almost all reactions, the velocity is increased as the temperature is raised. Many reactions, such as the decomposition of potassium chlorate, proceed very slowly or not at all at room temperature, but become vigorous on warming. Increasing the temperature is, therefore, a convenient method for speeding up a reaction. In general, the speed of the reaction is increased two- or three-fold for every ten-degree rise of temperature.

At first glance it might be thought that this increase in reaction velocity might be related to the fact that at higher temperatures, molecules move more rapidly and hence collide more vigorously. This idea is not quite correct; it cannot account for the fact that reaction velocity increases two or three hundred per cent for a ten-degree rise while the speed of the molecules increases only three or four per cent for a similar temperature rise. The true explanation is more probably somewhat as follows: At any temperature the molecules are not all moving at the same velocity. Some are

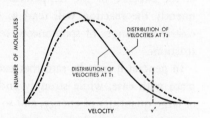

Fig. 10-2. Raising the temperature from T_1 to T_2 (say from 300° C. to 310°) may increase the average molecular velocity only a few per cent. But the number of molecules moving fast enough (v') to react chemically has been doubled.

moving very rapidly and some very slowly. Probably only the faster-moving molecules collide with sufficient energy to bring about an "effective" collision, that is, a collision resulting in a chemical change. It will be recalled that in evaporation only the most rapidly moving molecules get away. If the temperature is raised a few degrees there is a small increase in the average kinetic energy of all the molecules, but there may be a very great increase in the number of molecules which now have sufficient energy to make an effective collision. Increase of temperature increases the velocity of almost all chemical reactions, not because the average kinetic energy of the molecules is increased, but because more molecules reach a velocity high enough to enter into a chemical change.

It should now be clear why exothermic reactions are more familiar to us, and why endothermic reactions are usually found under special conditions in laboratory or plant. When a reaction gives off heat, that heat goes to warm up the products, the surroundings, and the remaining reactants. Consequently, the reaction speeds up with evolution of still more heat. Hence the reaction very quickly goes to completion, that is, all the reactants are used up. The reaction is self-sustaining, in the sense that once it has started no more heat need be applied from external sources. This is very obvious in the combustion of wood when a house burns down. The heat emitted serves only to hasten the complete destruction of the house. Of course, if the reaction proceeds slowly enough so that the heat may be conducted away without appreciably warming the reactants, then no rapid reaction may ever take place. This effect is often seen in "spontaneous combustion" as described in an earlier chapter. If the heat of the slow oxidation in a pile of oily rags is allowed to accumulate, the reaction will speed up until flames burst out. But if the heat is dissipated by adequate ventilation, no fire need occur. By contrast with all this, endothermic reactions require the absorption of heat. Unless supplied externally, as from a Bunsen burner, this heat can only come at the expense of the temperature of reactants and surroundings. Consequently the reaction will tend to slow down and stop entirely. There is clearly no danger of spontaneous combustion in the case of an endothermic reaction.

In general it may be said that exothermic reactions may be made to take place with ease, while strongly endothermic reactions require the addition of large quantities of energy, and so are correspondingly difficult. This is one reason why the production of aluminum has been commercially possible for less than fifty years, while copper has been used since prehistoric times. The reaction

$$2Al_2O_3 \rightarrow 4Al + 3O_2 - 798,000 \text{ cals.}$$

requires an immense amount of energy, while the corresponding reaction for copper

$$2CuO \rightarrow 2Cu + O_2 - 69,800 \text{ cals.}$$

requires less than ten per cent as much. Even at the present time aluminum plants have to be built adjacent to the largest sources of hydroelectric energy, such as Niagara Falls.

The fourth factor which influences reaction velocity is the presence of *catalysts*. The effect of foreign substances on the speed of chemical reactions is very interesting and is often of great practical value. When potassium chlorate is heated, oxygen is slowly evolved. But if a little manganese dioxide, MnO_2, is added to the potassium chlorate, the reaction becomes much more rapid. At the end of the experiment the manganese dioxide may be recovered unchanged. Similarly, as one step in the manufacture of sulfuric acid the reaction

$$2SO_2 + O_2 \rightarrow 2SO_3$$

proceeds, under ordinary circumstances, very slowly. But in the presence of metallic platinum the reaction becomes fast enough to be a very important commercial process. Such substances, which increase the velocity of chemical reactions without themselves being altered, are called *catalysts*. This statement must suffice for the definition of a catalyst, although a complete definition might take many pages. The mechanism by which catalysts speed up reactions is not well understood; there are probably very different mechanisms for different types of chemical reactions. Sometimes the catalyst may work by forming an intermediate compound which breaks down easily, reforming the catalyst. Sometimes the catalyst may adsorb the reactants, thereby effectively increasing their concentration. Still other mechanisms have been suggested, but these, for the moment, lie beyond us.

Certain living organisms secrete catalysts, more frequently called *enzymes*, which play a vital part in supporting life as, for instance, in the digestion of food. Further reference will be made to enzymes when we come to study biochemical processes, that is, the chemistry of living matter.

Some substances act in a manner to retard the velocity of reaction. Hydrogen peroxide decomposes fairly rapidly under ordinary circumstances, but when mixed with a trace of acetanilid it becomes quite stable and may remain fresh on the druggists' shelves for many months. Substances such as this are often called "negative catalysts"; more properly they are referred to as "inhibitors."

66. REVERSIBLE REACTIONS

It very often happens that the products of a given chemical reaction are themselves able to react, forming once more the original reactants. A good example is the action of steam on hot iron.

$$3Fe + 4H_2O \rightarrow Fe_3O_4 + 4H_2$$

This reaction has often been used for the commercial production of hydrogen. Now, if hydrogen is passed over hot iron oxide, the products are metallic iron and steam.

$$Fe_3O_4 + 4H_2 \rightarrow 3Fe + 4H_2O$$

This is an example of a *reversible* reaction. Such reactions are indicated by a double-arrow notation.

$$3Fe + 4H_2O \rightleftarrows Fe_3O_4 + 4H_2$$

Many, if not most, chemical reactions are reversible. A few other examples are the action of oxygen on hydrogen chloride,

$$O_2 + 4HCl \rightleftarrows 2H_2O + 2Cl_2$$

the formation of hydrogen iodide from the elements,

$$H_2 + I_2 \rightleftarrows 2HI$$

and the formation of ammonia.

$$N_2 + 3H_2 \rightleftarrows 2NH_3$$

67. CHEMICAL EQUILIBRIUM

The existence of reversible reactions gives rise to what is known as "chemical equilibrium." Suppose we consider a hypothetical reversible reaction,

$$A + B \rightleftarrows C + D$$

and examine what happens as the reactants are brought together.

At first, the only reaction will be between A and B because no C and D will yet have been formed. As the reaction proceeds, the concentrations of both A and B will become smaller and smaller so that the reaction as written in the right-hand direction will become slower and slower. This is, of course, in agreement with the Law of Mass Action, that the velocity of a reaction depends on the concentration of the reactants. At the same time, however, the concentration of C and D will be increasing because they are being formed in the reaction of A and B. As soon as the concentrations of C and D become appreciable they will start reacting, with the result that A and B are formed again. As long as the concentrations of C and D are increasing, the reaction as written in the left-hand direction will become faster. Ultimately, there will come a time when the speed of the right-hand, or forward, reaction is exactly balanced by the speed of the left-hand, or reverse, reaction. The concentrations of all four substances will then remain constant, and *equilibrium* will be said to have been reached. Note that both forward and reverse reactions are still going on, even though the concentrations of reactants and products do not change.

It is not to be supposed that equilibrium is reached when all the substances are present in equal amount. The relative amounts and concentrations of each substance present at equilibrium are very different for different reactions, and for the same reaction under different conditions. It will be noticed that chemical equilibrium is not unlike the state of physical equilibrium which may exist between a liquid and its vapor.

The reaction of iron and steam to form iron oxide and hydrogen offers a good example of chemical equilibrium. If iron and water are placed in a container and heated to a suitable temperature (300° or 400° C.), analysis, after a short time for the attainment of equilibrium, would show the presence of iron, steam, iron oxide, and hydrogen. The total amounts and concentrations of these four substances would not then change provided external conditions such as temperature and pressure did not change. But the two reactions would nevertheless be proceeding continuously.

68. RULE OF LE CHATELIER

From what has been said, it should be clear that the concentrations of all substances in a chemical equilibrium will remain constant only so long as

Fig. 10-3. Henri Louis Le Chatelier

Le Chatelier was born in France in 1850. He was trained in mathematics and chemistry by his father, who was an engineer, and he later attended the Sorbonne in Paris. In 1908 he was appointed to the professorship of inorganic chemistry at the Sorbonne.

Le Chatelier is known to chemists for the principle which bears his name. He is, however, equally well known for his contributions to metallurgy and metallography. He constantly urged a close relationship between pure "academic" chemistry and applied "industrial" chemistry.

Le Chatelier lived until 1936. He once wrote that "the most striking characteristic of great men is their zeal for work." (*Journal of Chemical Education*)

the two reaction velocities involved remain equal. If one reaction should be speeded up, then obviously, some of the substances present would increase in concentration at the expense of others, until a new equilibrium could be set up. The displacement of chemical equilibria is often of very great importance for the economical production of industrial chemicals. Chemical equilibria are found to be displaced according to certain laws which are included in the Rule, or Principle, of **Le Chatelier,** which may be stated: **if a system** (a set of reacting substances) **at equilibrium is subjected to a stress, the equilibrium will be shifted in such direction as to reduce the stress.** By stress is meant a change of conditions such as concentration, temperature, or pressure. The effect of each of these will be considered in turn.

Returning to the reaction

$$3Fe + 4H_2O \rightleftarrows Fe_3O_4 + 4H_2$$

let us consider the effect of increasing the *concentration* of, say, the steam. This will result in increasing the velocity of the forward reaction without directly affecting the reverse reaction. The result will, therefore, be more iron oxide and more hydrogen, and, of course, less iron. It is plain that if steam be continually pumped into the reaction chamber, a large amount of hydrogen will be produced and most of the iron used up. Notice, however, that exactly the same effect could have been produced by diminishing the concentration of hydrogen. In this case the speed of the reverse reaction would have been decreased, resulting in a shift of the equilibrium in the direction of more hydrogen and iron oxide, and less of iron and steam. In the industrial process, steam is continually blown into the chamber and it sweeps the hydrogen out into suitable containers. The steam concentration in the reaction chamber is thereby kept high, and the hydrogen concentration low. If we regard these changes of concentrations as stresses, then the equilibrium shifts in such direction as to reduce the stress. In this case the equilibrium shifts so as to diminish the increased steam concentration and to build up the depleted hydrogen concentration.

The effect of changing the *temperature* of an equilibrium mixture depends on which of the reversible reactions is exothermic. A good example is the formation of ammonia.

$$N_2 + 3H_2 \rightleftarrows 2NH_3 + heat$$

The union of nitrogen and hydrogen to form ammonia is strongly exothermic, while the reverse reaction must, of course, be endothermic. According to Le Chatelier's Rule, if the temperature is raised, the equilibrium will shift in such a direction as to reduce the stress, that is, to cool the mixture off by using up the additional heat. The equilibrium of the above reaction will, therefore, be shifted in the direction of less ammonia and of more nitrogen and hydrogen. In order to make the industrial production of ammonia feasible by this process, it is necessary to work at as low a temperature as is possible, consistent with getting the reaction to go at all.

The effect of *pressure* on a system at equilibrium may be illustrated by the same reaction, of nitrogen and hydrogen to form ammonia. It will be recalled that, at constant temperature, the pressure exerted by a gas or a mixture of gases is proportional to the total number of gas molecules present. If now the stress of increased pressure is placed on this system, the equilibrium will be shifted in such direction as to diminish the total number of molecules present. Notice that in the equation as written

$$N_2 + 3H_2 \rightleftarrows 2NH_3$$

there are twice as many molecules when only nitrogen and hydrogen are present as when these have been completely converted to ammonia. For every two molecules of ammonia there are one of nitrogen and three of hydrogen. The effect of increased pressure will therefore be to shift the equilibrium in the direction of more ammonia. When this process is carried out industrially, pressures up to a thousand or more times atmospheric pressure are actually used. But in such an equilibrium system as

$$H_2 + Cl_2 \rightleftarrows 2HCl$$

change of pressure would have no effect because there are the same number of molecules no matter which reaction predominates. Notice, also, that this effect of pressure applies only to gases. In the reaction of iron and steam to form hydrogen and iron oxide, change of pressure has no effect on the iron or on the iron oxide, because, these substances being solids, they cannot be appreciably compressed.

It remains to discuss the effect of a *catalyst* on chemical equilibrium. It will be recalled that catalysts may markedly change reaction velocities. It is found by experiment that catalysts never displace a condition of equilibrium. Catalysts may, and often do, change the velocity of both forward and reverse reactions in a system at equilibrium, but both reaction rates are always affected to precisely the same degree. Catalysts may hasten the attainment of equilibrium, and are often used for that purpose. But they do not shift the equilibrium, that is to say, they do not change the concentrations of reactants or products, once equilibrium has been reached.

The important industrial reaction

$$2SO_2 + O_2 \rightleftarrows 2SO_3 + 45,200 \text{ cals.}$$

will be used to show how the principles outlined above are used to make this reaction commercially successful. This reaction is used in the manufacture of the industrially important chemical, sulfuric acid. The reaction between sulfur dioxide and oxygen is immeasurably slow at room temperature. But if the temperature is raised to speed up the reaction, the reverse reaction is speeded still more, the equilibrium is displaced far to the left, and the yield of sulfur trioxide is negligibly small. However, by the use of platinum as a catalyst, the reaction is speeded up to a satisfactory rate while the temperature is kept low enough to insure a satisfactory yield of sulfur trioxide. Actually a temperature of about 400° C. is generally used. The student should try to distinguish clearly between the actual *condition* of equilibrium and the *rate of attainment* of that equilibrium. Both concepts are vitally important to an understanding of chemistry. Study of reaction rates is often called "chemical kinetics"; study of chemical equilibria is called "chemical thermodynamics." These two subjects together make up a large part of an important branch of science called "physical chemistry."

69. EQUILIBRIUM CONSTANT

Suppose that p molecules of substance A react with q molecules of substance B to yield r molecules of C and s molecules of D according to the equation:

$$pA + qB \rightleftharpoons rC + sD$$

then it is found experimentally that at equilibrium:

$$\frac{[C]^r \times [D]^s}{[A]^p \times [B]^q} = K$$

Where $[C]^r$ stands for the concentration of C raised to the power r, and the other terms have a similar meaning. The concentrations are generally given in moles per liter. The constant K is known as the equilibrium constant. For a reaction such as the union of nitrogen and hydrogen to form ammonia

$$N_2 + 3H_3 \rightleftharpoons 2NH_3$$

the equilibrium constant is given by

$$\frac{[NH_3]^2}{[N_2] \times [H_2]^3} = K$$

It is possible to derive the equilibrium constant on a theoretical basis. This will be done for a very simple, idealized, case:

$$A + B \rightleftharpoons C + D$$

as follows:

The velocity v_1 of the reaction between A and B is, according to the principle of mass action,

$$v_1 = k_1[A] \times [B]$$

or, in words, the velocity of this reaction is proportional to the product of the concentration of A times that of B. The constant k_1 is simply the proportionality constant which might, in part, reflect the fact that only a few of the collisions between A and B molecules are effective in bringing about a chemical reaction.

Similarly, the velocity of the reverse reaction, v_2, is given by

$$v_2 = k_2[C] \times [D]$$

By definition, equilibrium is the condition in which the velocity of the forward reaction is equal to the velocity of the reverse reaction, namely, $v_1 = v_2$. Hence, at equilibrium:

$$k_1[A] \times [B] = k_2[C] \times [D]$$

and rearranging:

$$\frac{[C] \times [D]}{[A] \times [B]} = \frac{k_1}{k_2} = K$$

one constant divided by another constant being, of course, equal to a third constant.

The equilibrium constant is of great value in calculating the yields of products to be expected in chemical reactions; some applications of this will be given later. It may be noted that while the equilibrium constant is derived by equating reaction velocities, it in itself tells us nothing concerning the speed with which equilibrium may be reached.

EXERCISES

A. *Define or explain the following:*

calorimeter	exothermic
chemical equilibrium	kinetic energy
concentration	mechanical energy
electrical energy	potential energy
electromagnetic energy	reaction velocity
endothermic	reversible reaction
energy	thermal energy
equilibrium constant	thermochemical equation

B. 1. State the Law of Mass Action
    2. State the Rule of Le Chatelier
    3. Derive from fundamental principles an expression for the equilibrium constant for the hypothetical reaction:

$$A + B \rightleftharpoons C + D$$

    4. What are the principal sources of energy?
    5. List some examples of energy associated with chemical change.
    6. What explanation may be offered for the fact that the velocity of chemical reaction generally increases quite rapidly as the temperature is raised?
    7. List, with appropriate examples, the factors which influence reaction velocity.

C. 1. The following equation represents the exothermic reaction of acetylene with oxygen to form carbon monoxide and water.

$$2C_2H_2 + 5O_2 \rightarrow 4CO_2 + 2H_2O + 624 \text{ kcal.}$$

State the exact quantitative meaning of the equation in moles and calories, then in grams and calories.

    2. Ammonia burns in air as follows:

$$4NH_3 + 3O_2 \rightarrow 2N_2 + 6H_2O \text{ (liquid)} + 364 \text{ kcal.}$$

Calculate the heat of combustion per gram of ammonia.

    3. From the following two reactions:

$$CO_2 + Ca(OH)_2 \rightarrow CaCO_3 + H_2O + 30.5 \text{ kcal.}$$

and

$$CaO + H_2O \rightarrow Ca(OH)_2 + 11.5 \text{ kcal.}$$

Find the heat of the reaction

$$CaO + CO_2 \rightarrow CaCO_3$$

    4. If increased temperature raises the reaction velocity of both forward and reverse reactions in equilibrium, how does it happen that increased temperature always shifts the equilibrium?
    5. If a catalyst, and increase of temperature, both speed up a reaction velocity, what difference does it make which one is used? Explain fully.
    6. If a reaction is driven more nearly to completion by increase of temperature, what may be said of the heat effect associated with the reaction?
    7. In the water-gas reaction

$$C + H_2O \rightleftharpoons CO + H_2$$

what will be the effect of blowing a large excess of steam over the heated coke? Explain.

    8. Consider the following five systems in equilibrium (all substances may be considered as gases):

(1) $2NO + O_2 \rightleftharpoons 2NO_2 + heat$

(2) $N_2 + O_2 \rightleftharpoons 2NO - heat$

(3) $N_2 + 3H_2 \rightleftharpoons 2NH_3 + heat$

(4) $H_2 + I_2 \rightleftharpoons 2HI - heat$

(5) $2CO + O_2 \rightleftharpoons 2CO_2 + heat$

a. List those systems in which increase of pressure has no effect on the equilibrium.

b. List those in which increase of temperature has no effect on the equilibrium.

c. List those in which addition of a catalyst has no effect on the equilibrium.

9. What, approximately, is the increase of velocity of a chemical reaction which may be expected in raising the temperature from $0°$ C. to $100°$ C.?

10. Write expressions for the equilibrium constants for the following reactions (all substances may be considered gases):

(1) $CO + H_2O \rightleftharpoons CO_2 + H_2$

(2) $2H_2 + O \rightleftharpoons 2H_2O$

(3) $2H_2O + 2Cl_2 \rightleftharpoons 4HCl + O_2$

11. Three different reactions have the following equilibrium constants: 10^{12}, 1, and 10^{-28} respectively. State if these reactions at equilibrium have yielded (1) scarcely any product, (2) virtually all reactant has been used up, or (3) reactant and product are present in roughly equal proportions.

CHAPTER

11 SOLUTIONS

Solutions fill the oceans, solutions are running in our veins . . .
—Svante Arrhenius

In nature, a pure chemical element is a rare occurrence. Almost always the elements are combined or mixed. In the latter case, the mixture may be heterogeneous, as in soils, clays, sands, and rocks, where the individual components of the mixture are easily recognizable—if not by the naked eye, then by a microscope; or the mixture may be homogeneous, as in the air and the water, where the components of the mixture are not so readily identified. Those chemical reactions with which we are familiar, either in the laboratory or in industry, occur, in a very large percentage of cases, not between pure elements or compounds, but between elements and compounds in solution. This is true also of the air we breathe, of the food we eat and digest, and of many other processes taking place in the animal body. This chapter and the next will be devoted to the physical and chemical properties of solutions.

70. PROPERTIES OF SOLUTIONS

Sand mixed with water quickly settles to the bottom of the container, as does clay. Very fine clay may take several hours to settle out, but there need never be the slightest doubt that what we have is a mixture, because the components of the mixture can easily be identified as clay and water. The mixture, as anyone can see, is made of water plus little particles of clay. A mixture of sugar and water is, however, quite different. The sugar dissolves, up to a certain point, in the water, and we cannot see the individual particles of sugar after dissolving has taken place. This is true no matter how powerful a microscope is used; and the sugar never settles out like the clay, no matter how long we wait. The sugar is said to be in **solution.** The sugar solution differs from the clay or sand suspension in being *optically homogeneous,* that is, it appears on visual observation to be the same all the way through. The clay suspension, on the other hand, is obviously optically inhomogeneous because the individual clay particles are visible. From the

176

standpoint of molecules we might say that the sugar molecules are free to move in the water, independently of each other. The molecules of a dissolved substance are, therefore, not unlike the molecules of a gas. They move as individuals rather than as large aggregates of molecules. But in a suspension the molecules are aggregated together in vast numbers to form visible lumps of solid matter.

If solutions are optically homogeneous it may be inquired how solutions differ from chemical compounds. Recalling the definition of a chemical compound, that the elements are present in a definite proportion by weight, we see that a major distinction between solutions and compounds is that the composition of a solution may vary; that of a compound may not. It is possible to make a sugar solution containing a very little sugar, or a fairly large amount of sugar. The composition of a chemical compound cannot be so altered without destroying the compound.

The substance which, like sugar, is dissolved in another, such as water, is called the **solute.** The water, in this case, is called the **solvent.** These terms are convenient, and, in many instances, there is no ambiguity as to which substance is the solute and which the solvent. But water may be dissolved in alcohol, or alcohol in water, in any proportion. Under such circumstances the terms solute and solvent tend to lose their meaning.

There are many different types of solutions. Gases may dissolve in other gases. The air, which may be thought of principally as oxygen dissolved in nitrogen, is an example of a gas dissolved in a gas. Gases dissolve in liquids, as, for instance, air dissolved in water, or carbon dioxide dissolved in water to form soda water. In a few cases gases dissolve in solids. Hydrogen can dissolve to a considerable extent in the metal palladium. Liquids dissolving in other liquids form one of the commonest classes of solutions. Alcohol in water, acetic acid in water, mixtures of hydrocarbons in gasoline, many other examples will come to mind. Solids dissolved in liquids form another important class of solutions. Salt in water, sugar in water—we shall present innumerable examples of such solutions in later chapters. Solutions of solids in other solids are also well known. **Alloys,** consisting of two or more metals, often are formed by a process of solid-solution. Brass, for instance, is a solution of copper and zinc.

Common experience shows that sugar in a cup of coffee will remain at the bottom undissolved unless the coffee is stirred. The rate at which solution takes place depends very greatly on the thorough mixing of solute and solvent. The normal processes of diffusion will, in time, result in complete solution taking place even without stirring, but it may require many days or months. The density of solutions is often greater than that of the pure solvent. This fact is often used where large quantities of a solid must be dissolved. Let us say that a solution of copper sulfate is required. If the copper sulfate is simply placed at the bottom of the container and covered with water, solution will be very slow. But if the copper sulfate is placed on a perforated ledge near the top of the solvent, then as the solution is formed, it sinks because of its high density. In this way mixing is promoted, although no outside source of energy is needed to operate a mechanical stirrer. Increased rates of solution are also produced by heating, but the principal effect is again that of mixing, brought about by convection currents.

A finely ground powder dissolves more rapidly than the same weight of solute in one solid lump. This is because the rate of solution depends upon the surface of solute exposed to the solvent. A finely powdered substance has a much greater surface area than the same weight in one piece.

Many persons have the impression that, say, a pint of one liquid added to a pint of another will produce a quart of mixture. This is not generally true. If a pint of alcohol is added to a pint of water the volume of the solution produced is considerably less than a quart. This is, presumably, because the mixture of alcohol and water leaves less space between adjacent molecules than do either of these substances alone.

71. CONCENTRATION

A solution of sugar in water may contain a small quantity of sugar or it may contain a relatively large amount. In the first case the solution is said to be dilute, in the second concentrated. These terms, however, are not sufficiently precise for most purposes. We must have exact methods of stating what degree of concentration any given solution may possess. There are several methods for expressing the **concentration** of solutions. One method is by the use of percentages. If, for instance, 100 g. of a solution contained 13 g. of sodium chloride, we might say that the concentration of the solution was 13 per cent by weight. Percentage concentration by weight means the weight of the solute per 100 g. of solution (not of solvent). Concentration percentages by volume rather than by weight are also frequently used when both solute and solvent are liquids, as for alcohol and water. Notice that the percentage by weight and the percentage by volume need not have the same numerical value for a given solution unless, as rarely happens, the solute and solution have the same density.

For much chemical work the concentration of solutions is expressed, not as percentages, but rather as moles of solute per liter of solution. A mole, it will be recalled, is a formula weight expressed as grams. Thus a mole of sodium chloride is 58.5 g. This weight of sodium chloride dissolved in exactly 1 liter of solution (*not of solvent*) is said to be a 1-**molar solution** of sodium chloride. A 1-molar solution is often abbreviated to 1M. The use of molar concentrations will be illustrated by several problems.

Problem: What weight of sugar, $C_{12}H_{22}O_{11}$, is required to make a liter of 1M sugar solution?

Solution: The formula weight of sugar is 342. A mole of sugar therefore weighs 342 g. It will take 342 g. of sugar to make 1 liter of 1M sugar solution.

It is particularly important to notice that molar solutions refer to *moles of solute per liter of solution*. This is not the same as moles of solute per liter of solvent. A liter of sugar solution does not necessarily contain a liter of water, just as, it was pointed out above, a quart of alcohol-water solution is not formed by mixing a pint of alcohol and a pint of water. To make a 1M solution of sugar, or of other solute, use is made of a volumetric flask (Fig. 11-1). A volumetric flask has a rather large body and a narrow neck. On the neck there is etched a mark such that when the flask is filled to the mark, the amount of liquid contained is a definite volume, such as 1 liter. To make a liter of 1M solution of sugar, weigh out 342 g. of sugar and place this in a 1-l. volumetric flask. Fill the flask about three-quarters full of water, then shake the flask until all the sugar is dissolved. Add more water,

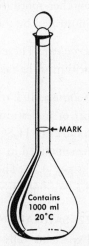

Fig. 11-1. Volumetric flask.

with frequent shaking, until the solution reaches the mark on the neck of the flask. You then have 1 l. of 1M sugar solution. Notice that this operation is not the same as weighing out 342 g. of sugar and adding to it 1 l. of water.

Problem: What weight of magnesium nitrate, $Mg(NO_3)_2$, is contained in 1.8 l. of 0.63M solution?

Solution: The formula weight of $Mg(NO_3)_2$ is 148. Therefore 1 l. of 1M $Mg(NO_3)_2$ solution would contain 148 g. Then 1.8 l. of 1M $Mg(NO_3)_2$ solution would contain 1.8 × 148 g., and 1.8 l. of 0.63M solution would contain 1.8 × 148 g. × 0.63 = 168 g.

Problem: What is the molar concentration of a solution which contains 200 g. of HCl in 6.5 l. of solution?

Solution: A mole of HCl is 36.5 g. In 6.5 l. of 1M HCl there would be 6.5 × 36.5 g. Then 200 g. of HCl in 6.5 l. of solution is only 200 g./(6.5 ×

36.5 g.) = 0.84 moles per liter. The concentration of the solution is 0.84M. Observe that the symbol M does not represent "moles"; it means "moles of solute per liter of solution."

A solution, the concentration of which is definitely known, is said to be *standardized*, and is referred to as a *standard solution*. Methods for the standardization of solutions will be developed further in the next chapter.

It fairly often occurs that from a standard solution it is desired to prepare another more dilute standard solution. The method for doing this will be illustrated by the following problem.

Problem: There is available a quantity of 6.0M H_2SO_4. What volume of this acid must be taken to prepare 10 l. of 2.5M H_2SO_4?

Solution: 10 l. of 2.5M H_2SO_4 contain 10×2.5 moles of H_2SO_4. This number of moles must, therefore, be taken from the 6M solution. By definition, 6 moles of H_2SO_4 are contained in 1 l. of 6M solution; hence 1 mole would be contained in $\frac{1}{6}$ l., and 10×2.5 moles would be contained in $10 \times 2.5 \times \frac{1}{6}$ l. = 4.2 l. The desired 10 l. of 2.5M H_2SO_4 may then be made by taking 4.2 l. of 6M H_2SO_4 and diluting this until the volume is 10 l.

72. SATURATION

Experience tells us that there is a limit to the amount of sugar which may be dissolved in water. After this limit is reached, it is not possible to get more sugar in solution no matter how long the mixture is stirred, unless the temperature or other conditions are changed. Additional sugar added simply lies undissolved, at the bottom of the container. The sugar is said to have a definite solubility in water, that is, there is a definite limit to the weight of sugar which may be dissolved in a given quantity of water. The term **solubility** means the amount of solute which may be dissolved in a given amount of solvent.

Some substances, such as sugar, are highly soluble in water, that is, rather large quantities may be brought into solution. Others, such as barium sulfate, are soluble to such an exceedingly slight degree that they are commonly said to be insoluble, although a truly insoluble substance probably does not exist. Degree of solubility is determined not only by the nature of the solute, but also by the solvent. Sulfur readily dissolves in carbon disulfide, but it is practically insoluble in water. Furthermore, the solubility of most substances depends on the temperature, and, especially for gases, it also depends on the pressure.

Degree of solubility may be expressed in several different ways. A convenient method is that already described for molar concentrations. A definite quantity of solution may be shaken with an excess of solute until no more solute goes into solution. A sample of solution might then be analyzed to find how many moles of solute are present per liter of solution. Other ways of expressing solubilities are in grams of solute per liter or per 100 g., of solution, or grams of solute per liter, or per 100 g., of solvent. Still other ways will suggest themselves.

A solution which has been shaken with excess solute until no further dissolving takes place is said to be a **saturated** solution. The concentration of a saturated solution is the solubility of the solute at the particular temperature employed. A condition of saturation implies the existence of a physical equilibrium not unlike that described already for the pressure exerted by a vapor in contact with its liquid phase. When a solution is saturated, particles of the excess solute are continually going off into the solvent, but particles are also crystallizing out of solution to become solid again. When these opposing processes take place at equal rates, the condition of equilibrium is reached, and then we say that the solution is saturated. A saturated solution is defined as a solution in which the dissolved solute is in equilibrium with excess undissolved solute.

With a few exceptions, most solids become more soluble as the temperature is raised. This effect can give rise to the peculiar phenomenon known as supersaturation. Sodium thiosulfate, photographer's "hypo," is a typical example of a substance which is much more soluble at high temperatures than at low. If a saturated solution of this compound is prepared at, say, 100° C., there will be in solution several times as much solute as would be the case at room temperature. Now suppose that this saturated solution at 100° is filtered from excess solute, then allowed to cool down to room temperature. It might be expected that the solute would crystallize out so that a saturated solution would be maintained at whatever the temperature happened to be. This is not always the case. Careful cooling, in the absence of shaking or of dust particles, often results in the solution's reaching room temperature with no crystallization having taken place. The solution in this condition contains several times as much solute as does a saturated solution at the same temperature. The solution is said to be **supersaturated.**

Supersaturation is not an equilibrium condition. It resembles in certain respects the condition known as supercooling. Such states are called metastable. If to the supersaturated solution there is added a single tiny crystal of the solid solute, the crystal will grow rapidly and in a few seconds all the excess solute will have crystallized out. Sometimes the supersaturation is broken by shaking the flask, or by scratching the inside of the flask with a glass rod. Occasionally supersaturations are difficult to overcome. This is especially true when the solute is a substance which has never been prepared before, and of which there is, of course, no "seed" crystal available for starting crystallization.

73. THE SEPARATION OF DISSOLVED SUBSTANCES

The separation of a solution into its components is one of the commonest of operations and one of the most useful. A very large number of substances are prepared or purified through the agency of a solvent, which must, at one step or another, be efficiently removed. Several methods are available for this operation. The particular method used depends on the nature of the solution.

The separation of mixed gases is commonplace in the preparation of such gases as oxygen or nitrogen for sale. The cheapest way to separate these gases is to liquefy them first, then to have them undergo fractional distillation. The problem then becomes, however, essentially the separation of two liquids, and will be considered below. In some instances solutions of one gas in another may be separated by taking advantage of their different rates of diffusion. This is most efficient when the molecular weights of the two gases are quite different, as in the cases of hydrogen and carbon dioxide. For lack of better methods diffusion has been tried, with success, in the separation of isotopes. Chemical methods are available for the separation of certain types of gases. For instance, oxygen may be separated from nitrogen by passing the mixture over hot copper. The oxygen unites with the copper to form copper oxide,

$$2Cu + O_2 \rightarrow 2CuO$$

while the nitrogen passes over unchanged. An effect not unlike this occurs in the respiration of air by animals. The oxygen of the air is combined with hemoglobin in the blood and so transported to the tissues. The nitrogen is not so combined and is immediately exhaled along with the waste products, carbon dioxide and water vapor.

The separation of gases from liquids is generally easily achieved by boiling the solution. Air may be completely removed from water by boiling the water for a few moments. It is a general rule that gases become less soluble in liquids as the temperature is raised. In this way ammonia may be expelled from water by boiling the solution. In some cases, such as hydrogen chloride in water, complete removal of the gas is not possible. The solution of hydrogen chloride in water, namely hydrochloric acid, is said to form a constant boiling mixture. Gases may also be removed from liquids by reduction of the pressure. The solubility of a gas in a liquid is approximately described by **Henry's Law,** which is that **the weight of gas which will dissolve in a liquid is directly proportional to the pressure of the gas above the liquid.** Consequently if the pressure is reduced to a very low value, the gas tends to come out of solution. This effect is easily demonstrated by putting some tap water in a test tube and connecting the tube to a vacuum pump. Bubbles of air form on the glass where the air comes out of solution.

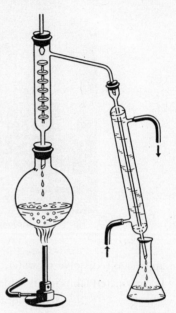

Liquids are often separated from other liquids by **fractional distillation.** This is possible when the two, or more, liquids have different boiling points. The greater the difference between the boiling points, the more easily is the mixture separated.

Separation of liquids in this way has been developed to a fine art, particularly in the petroleum industry. The process involves heating the liquids and allowing the vapors to pass through a fractionating column. In this column, which may be simply a glass tube, or which may be packed with rods or glass helices or wire gauze or the like, part of the mixed vapor is condensed and runs back into the flask from which it is vaporized again. In this way there is set up a coun-

Fig. 11-2. Apparatus for fractional distillation on a laboratory scale. The fractionating column, above the round-bottomed flask (*left*), aids in the separation of substances having different boiling temperatures. Those substances having lower boiling points tend to reach the condenser first.

tercurrent flow; vapor goes up and liquid flows down. This action brings about separation of the different components of the mixture and these components may be taken off, as desired, at the top of the fractionating column. Generally a condenser is attached near the top of the column. In the laboratory, very efficient columns have been devised only a few feet high, but for industrial use on a large scale such fractionating columns make up a large proportion of the landscape in the neighborhood of an oil refinery.

Another method for separating liquids is the process known as **extraction.** This will be described in relationship also to the separation of a solid from a liquid.

Iodine dissolves in water to give a brown solution. This iodine may be removed from the water in the following way: Carbon tetrachloride does not

Fig. 11-3. Fractionating columns used in petroleum indus-try.

appreciably dissolve in water, but it is itself an excellent solvent for iodine. If carbon tetrachloride is added to an iodine solution in water, the carbon

Fig. 11-4. Separa-tory funnel. Immisci-ble liquids may be separated by allow-ing the lower layer to drain through the stopcock.

tetrachloride sinks to the bottom because of its higher density. If now the mixture is vigorously shaken, the io-dine in large part dissolves in the carbon tetrachloride layer, forming a beautiful purple solution. This solution of iodine in carbon tetrachloride may be removed from the remaining water solution, preferably by the aid of a separatory funnel (Fig. 11-4), which has a convenient out-let at the bottom. If now a second quantity of carbon tetra-chloride is added to the water solution, and shaken, prac-tically all the iodine will be removed from the water. By repeated use of this extraction, or partition, process the quantity of a substance in solution may be made negli-gibly small. The use of extraction depends on having a solute which is soluble in two solvents, and on these two solvents being *mutually immiscible,* that is, not appreci-ably soluble in each other. Extraction is used in the manu-facture or purification of many natural and synthetic chemical compounds. It has also important applications in metallurgy.

One of the most obvious methods for separating a solid from a liquid is by **distillation.** This has already been described in the purification of water for special purposes. The solution is simply boiled and the pure water vapor is condensed for use. The solid residue remains in the distilling flask.

Still another extremely useful method of separation is that of **crystallization.** This is probably the commonest of all methods used in the purification of chemical compounds. Every solid has, of course, a definite solubility in each solvent. If part of the solvent is removed by evaporation, then the excess solute will tend to crystallize out. Or, if the solute is much more soluble hot than cold, the solution may be prepared at an elevated temperature and then allowed to cool. As the solution cools, supercooling being avoided, crystals of the solute will appear. Crystallization may be so conducted that very little of the solute is lost through remaining in solution. When crystallization appears to be complete, or nearly complete, the remaining solution, sometimes called mother-liquor, may be poured off, leaving the pure crystals.

The separation of a solid in solution in another solid is a common operation in metallurgy. Sometimes the solid solution may be melted and separated by extraction. Sometimes electrochemical methods are employed, as in the electrorefining of copper. Such separations in alloys are familiar practices in analytical laboratories where, say, silver is separated from nickel by dissolving the alloy in acid, then precipitating the silver as silver chloride, which may be filtered from the nickel which remains dissolved.

74. MOLECULAR WEIGHTS IN SOLUTION

It will be recalled that the molecular weights of vapors may be obtained from the weight of 22.4 l. of the vapor under standard conditions. There is another method which is applicable to substances which can be obtained in solution.

During cold weather it is common practice to sprinkle salt on sidewalks to melt the layer of ice which makes walking hazardous. The action of the salt is to lower the freezing temperature of the water to a point where the ice melts. It is a general rule that a solution freezes at a lower temperature than does the pure solvent; also, that the lowering of the freezing point so produced is proportional to the weight of solute present in a given weight of solvent. If 10 g. of solute in 100 g. of water make a solution which starts to freeze at $-2.0°$ C., then 20 g. of the same solute in the same weight of water will lower the freezing point to $-4.0°$ C. Furthermore, it is found that this lowering of the freezing point of solutions is proportional to the number of moles of solute dissolved in a given weight of water. For instance, one mole of sugar dissolved in 1000 g. of water lowers the freezing point to $-1.86°$ C. One mole of alcohol in 1000 g. of water also lowers the freezing point to $-1.86°$ C. This, then, offers a method of finding the molecular weights of dissolved substances.

Problem: A solution contains 25 g. of a substance in 298 g. of water. The freezing point of the solution is $-3.0°$ C. What is the molecular weight of the substance?

Solution: 298 g. of solvent contain 25 g. of solute; then 1.0 g. of solvent would contain $^{25}\!/_{298}$ g. of solute, and 1000 g. of solvent would contain $^{25}\!/_{298} \times 1000$ g. = 84 g. of solute.

The freezing point is lowered from $0°$ to $-3.0°$, that is, it is lowered 3.0 degrees.

$1.86°$ is the lowering which would be produced by 1 mole of solute in 1000 g. of water; therefore, $3.0°$ is the lowering which would be produced by 3.0/1.86 moles of solute in 1000 g. of water.

Now, 3.0/1.86 moles equals 84 g., or 3.0/1.86 $\times$ gram-molecular weight = 84 g., so that the gram-molecular weight = $84 \times 1.86/3.0 = 52$ g., and the molecular weight is 52.

The quantity $1.86°$ is called the **molecular depression constant** for water. It is the freezing point lowering when 1 mole of solute is dissolved in 1000 g. of water. For other solvents the molecular depression constant is different; for instance, for benzene it is $5.12°$.*

The lowering of the freezing point is not the only property by which solutions differ from pure substances, and it is not the only property which may be used to find the molecular weight of a dissolved substance. It will be recalled that the vapor pressure of a liquid rises sharply with increasing temperature. Fig. 11-5 shows the vapor pressure of a pure liquid plotted against temperature, and it also shows the vapor pressure of a solution similarly plotted. It will be noted that at any given temperature the vapor pressure of the solution is less than that of the pure solvent. The depression of the vapor pressure is related to the number of moles of solute present, and may be used to find the molecular weight of dissolved substances, although the method is somewhat more complicated than the freezing-point method.

It will be recalled that the boiling point of a liquid is the temperature at which the vapor pressure becomes equal to the atmospheric pressure. Suppose the atmospheric pressure to be any given value, such as 760 mm., then the vapor pressure of the solution does not reach this value until the tem-

---

* A solution containing one mole of solute in 1000 g. of solvent is called a **molal** solution. Note that this is not the same as a *molar* solution.

perature has been raised some distance above the normal boiling point of
the pure solvent. This is a direct consequence of the fact that the vapor
pressure of the solution is at all temperatures lower than that of the pure
solvent. The molecular elevation of the boiling point is a definite quantity
related to the molecular weight of the solute, just as is the molecular depression constant. For water the molecular elevation constant is 0.52°. One mole
of solute dissolved in 1000 g. of water raises the boiling point 0.52°. The

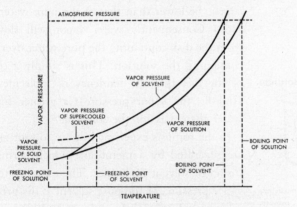

Fig. 11-5. Vapor pressure plotted against temperature for a
pure solvent, for supercooled solvent, and for solid solvent. The
vapor pressure for a solution is also shown. It will be noted
that the vapor pressure of the solution is less than that of the
pure solvent at any given temperature, and that this results in
the solution having a lower freezing point and a higher boiling point. The curves are exaggerated a little for the sake of
clearness.

boiling point of a liquid is, of course, dependent on the barometric pressure
which changes from time to time. The elevation of the boiling point is not
quite so convenient for molecular weight determinations as is the lowering
of the freezing point. Nevertheless, both methods have frequent applications.

75. OSMOSIS

The phenomenon of osmosis was discovered in 1748 by the Abbé Nollet. The
end of a glass tube is tightly covered with a piece of animal membrane, or
parchment paper. Inside the tube there is placed a solution of sugar in water.
The tube, containing the solution, is then dipped into pure water so that the
membrane is covered on one side by the solution, on the other by water. It
will now be observed that the level of liquid in the tube slowly moves up as
water diffuses through the membrane into the solution. After a time a condition of equilibrium will be reached, and the height to which the water in
the tube reaches is a measure of the **osmotic pressure** of the solution.

Several explanations for this effect have been advanced. The effect is closely related to the lowering of the vapor pressure of solutions as described in previous sections. A popular explanation is as follows: Suppose two dishes are placed in an evacuated chamber, one dish containing a concentrated solution of, say, sulfuric acid or of calcium chloride, the other pure water. The vapor pressure of the solution will, of course, be lower than that of the pure water. (See Fig. 11-7.) Consequently water vapor will slowly diffuse from the dish containing the pure water over to the dish containing the solution. This is simply a consequence of the fact that the tendency of molecules to escape (that is, the vapor pressure) is greater for the pure water than it is for the solution.

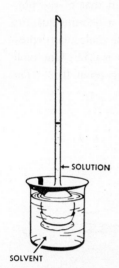

← SOLUTION

SOLVENT

Fig. 11-6. Osmosis experiment. The osmotic pressure is indicated by the height to which the solution rises in the tube.

In the osmosis experiment, pure solvent and solution are separated by a membrane which permits the diffusion of solvent molecules. The escaping tendency, or vapor pressure, of the pure solvent is the greater; hence solvent molecules diffuse through the membrane into the solution faster than they diffuse in the reverse direction. After some pressure is built up, the two processes tend to come to equilibrium.

Osmosis has been the subject of considerable study. Pressures have been developed up to several hundred atmospheres. A very effective membrane

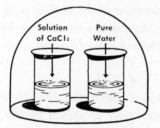
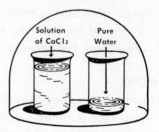

Fig. 11-7. An experiment to prove that the vapor pressure over a solution is less than that over the pure solvent. Beakers containing, respectively, pure water, and concentrated calcium chloride solution, are placed under an evacuated glass bell-jar. After some days it will be found that water has moved from one beaker to the other.

may be made by depositing copper ferrocyanide in the pores of unglazed porcelain. The osmotic pressure, like freezing-point lowering and vapor-pressure lowering, depends on the number of moles of solute present, and so may be used for molecular weight determinations, although it is not so convenient for this purpose as the other methods.

Major interest in osmosis lies in biology. Osmosis is the mechanism by which salts and food molecules in solution are transported from the blood to the tissue cells. The cells of the animal body have varying degrees of permeability to different substances, and upon their proper functioning health and life depend. The flow of sap through plants is also maintained and regulated by osmosis. It is well known that pure water injected into the

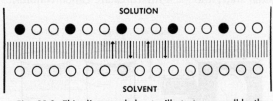

SOLUTION

SOLVENT

Fig. 11-8. This diagram helps to illustrate a possible theoretical explanation of osmosis. On one side of the membrane there is pure solvent with, of course, a definite vapor
pressure. On the other side of the membrane there is a
solution, with a lower vapor pressure. The molecules of
solvent are, therefore, able to "evaporate" through the
membrane more readily in the direction: solvent → solution.

blood stream of an animal may cause death. The reason for this is clearly seen under a microscope. The cells of the blood contain solutions and these solutions are normally at or very near equilibrium with the blood fluid. If blood cells are put in pure water, the water flows into the cells which swell up and burst, or swell to the extent that pigment (hemoglobin) escapes. The cells are said to have undergone **hemolysis,** a condition which in an animal may be fatal. If, on the other hand, blood cells are placed in a concentrated solution of sodium chloride, water diffuses out through the cell membrane, and the cells shrink and have a wizened appearance.

A solution of sodium chloride which has the same osmotic pressure as the solution in healthy blood cells is often used in biology for perfusion experiments, or for injection into the circulatory system to replace loss of blood, although blood plasma and whole blood are more frequently used for this latter purpose now. Such a salt solution is called a **"physiological salt solu-tion,"** or a "normal saline solution." It contains 0.9 to 1.0 per cent of sodium chloride. The well-known Ringer's solution, a solution containing 0.75 per cent of salt, is used for experiments on the heart of the frog. The osmotic pressure of frog's blood is much lower than that of human blood.

76. COLLOIDS

True solutions are optically homogeneous, the solute does not settle out, and the freezing point and other properties show characteristic changes. Mechanical suspensions, on the other hand, rapidly settle out, as does sand from water; the individual particles are readily discerned; and the freezing point and other properties are generally those of the pure liquid.

There is a borderline between these two categories of mixtures. The particles may be too small to settle out or to be visible, but too large for the mixture to be considered a true solution. Matter in this condition is said to be in the **colloidal state,** and such mixtures are called **colloids.**

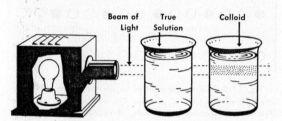

Fig. 11-9. The Tyndall effect (diagrammatic).

Colloid particles are not visible to the unaided eye, but they may be made visible by the ultramicroscope. A beam of light shining through a true solution, free from dust particles, is practically invisible because there is nothing in the solution to reflect light into the observer's eye. But a beam of light shining through a colloid is clearly visible because the tiny colloidal particles, although themselves invisible, reflect light to the observer. This effect is often seen when sunlight enters a darkened room through a small hole in a shade. The beam of light is brilliantly visible because of reflection from colloidal dust particles suspended in the air. The same effect renders visible the beam from a searchlight. This property of colloids is known as the **Tyndall effect.** If the beam of light is focused by a lens, and a microscope is placed directly above the focal point, then the colloidal particles become visible as tiny dancing specks of light. This arrangement is called an ultramicroscope. The movement of the particles is, of course, the Brownian movement. The fact that colloids show the Brownian movement is a further distinction between colloids, true solutions, and mechanical mixtures.

It might be expected that, in time, colloids would settle out, and, for one reason or another, some of them do. But colloidal gold prepared by Michael Faraday over a hundred years ago is still in the colloidal state. There appear to be at least three reasons why colloidal particles do not settle out.

First, the particles are small enough to show the Brownian movement. This continued erratic motion prevents the particles from collecting in aggregates and from falling, under the influence of gravity, to the bottom of the con-

Fig. 11-10. Photograph of the Tyndall effect in a colloid.

tainer. The effect is like that of gusts of wind preventing a piece of paper from falling to the ground. *Second,* the colloidal particles are electrically charged and all the particles of a given colloid have the same charge. Like

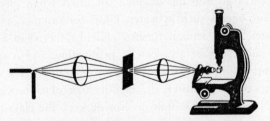

Fig. 11-11. Principle of the ultramicroscope. An intense light is sharply focused on a drop of colloidal material. The colloid particles may then be seen under an ordinary microscope as tiny specks of light.

electric charges repel each other. The particles are thus prevented from collecting in larger aggregates. *Third,* not infrequently it is found that films form around the colloidal particles. These films may, for instance, be of gelatin, which acts to prevent coagulation of the particles. Prevention of coagulation is one of the principal factors tending to keep the colloidal particles from settling out. If the particles can grow by one particle adhering to another, then the particles will soon be too large for the Brownian movement, and once the Brownian movement stops, settling out will be rapid.

Substances may be prepared in the colloidal state by several methods. Such substances must, of course, be relatively insoluble in the mixture which is to be used. Otherwise the colloid will simply pass into true solution. Colloids may be prepared either by breaking down, or dispersing, massive portions of matter to the dimensions where colloidal effects appear, or they may be

prepared by starting with dissolved substances and building up, or condensing, colloidal particles from the individual atoms or ions of which they are composed. Colloid particles are very small, yet they each contain many thousands or millions of atoms or molecules.

Dispersion, as a method of preparing colloids, is often practiced with a colloid mill, a mechanical device which grinds particles to colloidal size. Another way of doing this, especially for the prepara-

Fig. 11-12. Bredig arc.

tion of colloidal metals, is to take two wires of the substance, say, gold or platinum, connect them to an electrical circuit, and bring the wires in momentary contact under water. The electric arc which forms tears little particles of the metal away and some of these are of the proper dimensions to form a colloid. The method is referred to as the **Bredig arc.**

Many substances go into the colloidal condition when placed in contact with appropriate agents such as water. Glue, for instance, is often said to dissolve in water, but it actually forms a colloid rather than a true solution. The water is said to act by a process of **peptization,** and is spoken of as a peptizing agent. Sodium hydroxide acts as a peptizing agent on many substances. In the ceramic industry, the manufacture of chinaware and porcelainware, small amounts of sodium hydroxide keep the clays in a fluid, colloidal, condition without the use of excess water. The clays may thus conveniently be molded for firing without the shrinkage and distortion attendant upon the use of much water.

Colloids of one liquid in another, such as oil and water, are generally difficult to keep any length of time. But they may be stabilized by the use of **emulsifying agents.** Such agents form a protective film over the colloidal particles. Soap will emulsify a mixture of oil and water, and yolk of egg will emulsify a mixture of olive oil and vinegar as in mayonnaise.

The **condensation** methods for colloid preparation involve starting with a solution. Gold colloid may be prepared by addition of a mild reducing agent, such as tannin, to a dilute gold chloride solution. A beautiful red-gold or blue-gold colloid results. The color depends on the size of the particles, which, in turn, depends on the conditions under which the reduction is carried out. Colloidal arsenic sulfide is prepared by adding hydrogen sulfide to arsenous oxide, As_2O_3.

$$As_2O_3 + 3H_2S \rightarrow As_2S_3 + 3H_2O$$

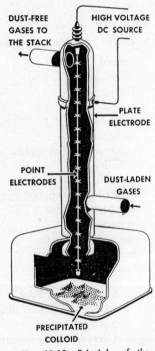

DUST-FREE GASES TO THE STACK

HIGH VOLTAGE DC SOURCE

PLATE ELECTRODE

POINT ELECTRODES

DUST-LADEN GASES

PRECIPITATED COLLOID

Colloidal ferric hydroxide is made by hydrolyzing ferric chloride. A dilute solution of ferric chloride in water is simply boiled for a few moments. The red colloid results.

$$FeCl_3 + 3H_2O \rightarrow Fe(OH)_3 + 3HCl$$

It is sometimes necessary to break down the colloidal state, in order to separate the constituents. This is done by neutralizing the electric charges which normally aid in preventing settling. Suppose the particles are all negatively charged. This charge may be neutralized by adding to the colloid an ion carrying a strong positive charge. Barium chloride, $BaCl_2$, for instance, or even better, aluminum sulfate, $Al_2(SO_4)_3$, would be effective in breaking down a negative colloid. If, on the other hand, the charge on the colloid is positive, then an ion with a strong negative charge should be added. Such ions are contained in sodium sulfate, Na_2SO_4, or better, sodium phosphate, Na_3PO_4. A negative colloid will neutralize a positive colloid.

Fig. 11-13. Principle of the Cottrell Precipitator.

This principle of neutralizing the electric charges on colloids is applied in the **Cottrell Precipitator.** Smokes are examples of *aerosols,* or colloids formed in air. In various industries, smokes produced incidental to chemical operations may be objectionable or may carry away valuable by-products. Such smoke particles may be recovered by having the flue gases pass through chambers containing highly charged wires or chains. The smoke particles collect on these wires, fall to the floor of the chamber, and are easily taken away for treatment. Such installations produce quite startling results, and often pay for themselves in a very short time.

A large number of industrial and household problems are related in one way or another to colloids. Almost any substance may be prepared or may occur in the colloid state. Colloid chemistry ranks among the important branches of chemistry. Its study is essential for an understanding of many problems in agriculture, petroleum, metallurgy, preparation of food, dyeing, road making, photography, water treatment, sewage disposal, rubber, dairy products, paints, soaps, inks, and many others.

EXERCISES

A. *Define or explain the following:*

aerosol	molar solution
alloy	molecular depression constant
Bredig arc	optically homogeneous
colloid	osmosis
colloid mill	peptization
concentration	physiological salt solution
condensation (as applied to colloids)	saturated solution
	solubility
crystallization	solute
dispersion (as applied to colloids)	solution
emulsifying agent	solvent
extraction	suspension (as applied to a chemical system)
fractional distillation	
hemolysis	supersaturated solution
immiscibility	Tyndall effect

B. 1. State Henry's Law.
   2. How do solutions differ from compounds? How do they resemble compounds?
   3. Give specific examples of different types of solutions, such as gas in liquid, liquid in liquid, etc.
   4. Describe the steps necessary to prepare 1 liter of one molar solution of any solute in any solvent.
   5. What methods are available for separating the components of a solution?
   6. With the aid of a simple experiment demonstrate that the vapor pressure over a sugar solution is less than that over pure water at the same temperature.
   7. What is the basis for the statement that "supersaturation is not an equilibrium condition"?
   8. Show diagrammatically the relation between vapor pressure of a pure solvent and a solution, especially in the neighborhood of boiling and freezing points.
   9. Describe, with a suitable diagram, a possible explanation for the phenomenon of osmosis.
   10. What methods are available for the preparation of colloids?

11. How do colloids differ from true solutions?

12. Why do not colloids settle out?

13. How may colloids be coagulated?

C. 1. What weight of magnesium perchlorate, $Mg(ClO_4)_2$, is required for 300 cc. of $1.8M$ solution?

2. What volume of $12M$ H_2SO_4 is required for the preparation of 15 l. of $0.10M$ solution?

3. How many moles of solute are present in each of the following solutions? (a) 240 cc. of $3.5M$ $BaCl_2$; (b) 240 cc. of $3.5M$ HNO_3; (c) 240 cc. of $3.5M$ of an unknown solute?

4. What volume of $1.38M$ HNO_3 solution will contain 8 g. of nitrogen?

5. What volume of $3.35M$ Na_2SO_4 contains the same weight of solute as 125 cc. of $1.25M$ solution?

6. What volume of $2.60M$ $BaCl_2$ contains the same number of moles of solute as 2.10 liters of $1.75M$ LiCl solution?

7. To what volume must $6.0M$ HCl be diluted in order for it to be $0.60M$?

8. To what volume must 25 cc. of $6.0M$ HCl be diluted in order for the solution to be $0.85M$?

9. What volume of $4.5M$ H_2SO_4 must be diluted to prepare 100 cc. of $1.00M$ solution?

10. What is the molar concentration of a hydrochloric acid solution which contains 28.1 per cent HCl by weight, and which has a density of 1.14 g. per cc.?

11. Find the molecular weight of a substance 3.2 g. of which dissolved in 65 g. of water lowers the freezing point to $-1.05°$ C.

12. What freezing-point lowering would be produced by 200 g. of methyl alcohol, CH_3OH, dissolved in 1000 g. of water?

13. What is the molecular weight of a non-electrolyte, 3.25 g. of which dissolved in 50 g. of water depresses the freezing point to $-2.90°$ C.?

14. What is the concentration of a water solution of sugar ($C_{12}H_{22}O_{11}$) which freezes at $-1.00°$ C.

15. What weight of benzene as solvent would be required to dissolve 10 g. of naphthalene ($C_{10}H_8$) so that the solution would freeze at $+1.0°$ C.? Molecular depression constant for benzene is $5.12°$. Normal freezing point is $5.4°$ C.

16. A solution has the following composition: 650 g. water; 25 g. $C_{12}H_{22}O_{11}$; 5.0 g. $C_6H_{12}O_6$; 2.0 g. $C_3H_8O_3$; find the freezing point of the solution.

17. What weight of ethyl alcohol, C_2H_6O, must be added to 1 l. of water to make an automobile radiator "anti-freeze" which will not freeze above $0°$ F.?

18. The molecular depression constant for naphthalene is $6.9°$. When 0.154 g. of acetanilide is dissolved in 9.83 g. of naphthalene, the freezing point of the solvent is lowered $0.805°$. What is the molecular weight of acetanilide?

19. Pure cyclohexane freezes at $6.0°$ C.; 20 g. of benzene (C_6H_6) in 1.0 kg. of cyclohexane freezes at $1.0°$ C. At what temperature would a solution containing 1.3 moles of benzene in 500 g. of cyclohexane freeze?

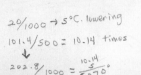

20. The molecular depression constant for water is 1.86°. If 2.7 g. of a substance is dissolved in 100 g. of water it is found that the freezing point of the solution is $-1.10°$ C. Suppose that another sample of the *solute* is vaporized at 100° C. and 760 mm. What will be the density of the vapor in grams per liter at that temperature and pressure?

21. How would you prepare a saturated solution of a substance which is less soluble hot than cold?

22. A water solution freezes at $-1.86°$ C. Is this a "molar" solution? Explain.

23. Is a saturated solution necessarily a concentrated solution?

24. In the text it is stated that a finely powdered substance has a much greater surface area and hence will dissolve more rapidly than the same weight of substance in one solid piece. Compare the surface areas of a solid cube 1 cm. on a side, with the same weight of sample divided into cubes 0.001 cm. on a side.

IONIZATION

12

---

*This is either a dissolution of the mutual involutions of the atoms, or
a similar dispersion of the unsentient elements*—Marcus Aurelius

The theories of science rank among the major achievements of the human
mind. These theories are a matrix which at once support and are supported
by the innumerable experimental observations which make up the descriptive
body of natural philosophy. Science, especially physical science, consolidates
its position from time to time by some stroke of intellectual genius, which,
like lightning, illuminates a vast panorama of hitherto unrelated facts. Such
theories are the Atomic Theory, the Kinetic Molecular Theory, and the
Theory of Atomic Periodicity.

The life history of theories in science is not infrequently the same. An
accumulation of facts becomes sufficient for some genius like Dalton, or
Avogadro, or Mendeleev to see the pattern linking all these facts together.
The theory is stated. The theory is eagerly tested and debated, sometimes not
without acrimony and ridicule for the discoverer. The theory withstands all
tests and proves its usefulness in elucidating a host of new facts and new
ideas. The discoverer's position is secure and he takes his place among the
very great of science. But sooner or later an occasional fact is found at
variance with the theory. An increasing number of observations, often of a
more refined sort, cannot be explained by the theory. Such new observations
were not possible earlier because more refined measuring devices had not
been invented, or hitherto unsuspected phenomena had not been discovered.
Finally, the theory in its original form must be abandoned. Sometimes the
theory, after long years of faithful service, is thrown out forever; this was
the fate of the Phlogiston Theory. More frequently, the theory must be restated. The original claims for it may have been too broad. But, reshaped and
with its limitations understood, the theory may be established more firmly
than ever, and may become a veritable foundation stone in the edifice of
natural knowledge. In this position stand those theories mentioned above.
To them we must add the Theory of Electrolytic Dissociation, or Ionization,
first stated by the distinguished Swedish scientist, Svante Arrhenius.

77. SOLUTIONS OF ELECTROLYTES

It will be recalled that the freezing-point depression of a solvent was used in the previous chapter to find the molecular weight of a solute. In general, it was shown that the freezing-point depression and the boiling-point elevation are proportional to the total concentration of solute molecules. This method for finding molecular weights, excellent though it is in many cases, fails to give correct results for several types of solutions.

The substance sodium chloride, NaCl, will serve as an example. From inspection of the formula it might be assumed that 1 mole of sodium chloride dissolved in 1000 g. of water would lower the freezing point 1.86°, which is the molecular depression constant for water. Actually, the freezing point is lowered about 3.5°, almost twice as much as anticipated. This *anomalous depression of the freezing point* is found for several large groups of compounds dissolved in water, or in a few other solvents. By contrast, benzene and certain other solvents generally give normal freezing-point depressions, even though the same solute may give an "anomalous" depression in water.

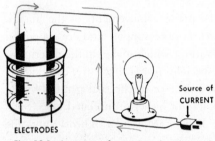

Fig. 12-1. Apparatus for testing the electrical conductivity of solutions.

Solutions which give these unusually large freezing-point depressions are characterized in another way. *They all conduct the electric current.* Such substances which, when dissolved, form electrically conducting solutions are called **electrolytes.** Electrolytes are divided into three important classes of chemical compounds: acids, bases, and salts. It should be pointed out that substances may conduct electricity in more than one way. A metal such as copper conducts electricity with no observable chemical change. Such a conductor is called a *metallic* conductor. The conductivity of electrolytes is, on the other hand, always attended with chemical changes, as in the decomposition of water by the electric current. This kind of electrical conduction is generally called *electrolytic,* as opposed to metallic. The conductivity of solutions of electrolytes is easily demonstrated by connecting an electric light in series with two strips of metal, preferably nickel or platinum. These strips are dipped into a beaker containing the solution under investigation. If the solution conducts electricity, the lamp will light up. The degree of electrical conductivity of the solution may be estimated very roughly by the brightness of the lamp. It may be added that substances which dissolve to form conducting solutions often show electrical conductivity when they are melted or fused, even though no water may be present.

Solutions which show anomalous freezing points, and electrical conductivity, differ from solutions of nonelectrolytes in yet a third way. It will be recalled that most chemical reactions have measurable velocities; even the reaction rate of explosions is measurable, although very high. But reactions between solutions of electrolytes appear to be *instantaneous*. If solutions of sodium chloride and silver nitrate are mixed, a white precipitate is formed at once. If dry copper nitrate and dry ammonium carbonate are mixed, nothing happens until the mixture is heated. Then a brown gas appears and the mixture slowly turns black. But if solutions of these two substances are mixed, a green precipitate appears instantly. Solutions of electrolytes often act as if all molecules present reacted in the same fraction of a second.

In general, molecules react only when they have appropriate energies. Molecules having sufficient energy to react are said to be activated. Normally, in reacting mixtures, relatively few molecules are thus activated, although by raising the temperature, the number of activated molecules may be increased. But solutions of electrolytes act as though all particles present are activated, and as though no further absorption of energy is necessary for reaction to take place.

Electrolytes differ from nonelectrolytes in at least three major respects. Any explanation of these differences must account for these three categories of observable facts. To repeat: any theoretical explanation for the differences between electrolytes and nonelectrolytes must explain: (1) the anomalous depression of the freezing points, (2) the electrical conductivity, and (3) the existence of instantaneous reactions. A theory to account for all these facts was advanced by Arrhenius in the year 1887.

78. THE ARRHENIUS THEORY

Arrhenius suggested that conducting solutions contain electrically charged particles produced by dissociation (breaking up) of the electrolyte. Such charged particles are called **ions.** The process is called **ionization.** These ions are identical with the ions described in a preliminary way in Chapter 3 as being produced by the gain or loss of electrons from atoms or groups of atoms. At the time Arrhenius advanced his theory, nothing was, of course, known of electrons or of atomic structure.

In the case of a water solution of sodium chloride, it is assumed that the ions of sodium and of chlorine become, under the influence of the water, free to move independently and so give rise to the electrical conductivity of the solution. Notice that the theory does not claim the existence in solution

Fig. 12-2. Svante Arrhenius

Arrhenius was born in Sweden in 1859. He was educated at the University of Upsala. His doctorate thesis was the essence of his famous theory of electrolytic dissociation, or ionization. The cold reception his professors gave this thesis is mentioned in the text.

In 1905 Arrhenius became director of the Nobel Institute in Stockholm. In addition to his work in solutions of electrolytes, he made important contributions to the study of chemical reaction velocity. He exerted a tremendous influence on the development of physical chemistry.

In later years the interests of Arrhenius changed to bacteriology and to astronomy, and to the popularization of science. He died in 1927. (Bettmann Archive)

of free sodium metal or of free chlorine gas. These substances are very reactive and sodium reacts violently with water, forming sodium hydroxide and hydrogen. Rather, the theory claims the existence of the charged par-

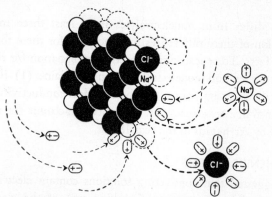

Fig. 12-3. Diagrammatic representation of how a crystal of sodium chloride may dissolve in water. The ions of sodium and of chlorine in the crystal attract water molecules which have the effect of reducing the electrical attraction between adjacent oppositely charged ions. These ions then drift away independently under the influence of the Brownian movement.

ticles, which, in the case of sodium, we now believe to be atoms of sodium minus one electron, and, in the case of chlorine, atoms of chlorine plus one electron.

Let us now see how well this theory explains those experimental facts it was designed to explain. In the first place, the existence of electrical conductivity is explained because the ions, being charged, are attracted toward oppositely charged electric poles. The motion of electrically charged particles constitutes an electric current. Thus, at least in a qualitative way, the Arrhenius theory explains the electrical conductivity of solutions of electrolytes.

With regard to the anomalous freezing-point depression, it was pointed out that the depression is about twice what would be expected by inspection of the formula for sodium chloride. It will be recalled that in all cases involving nonelectrolytes, the freezing-point depression is proportional to the concentration. The suggestion, therefore, is that a mole of sodium chloride actually contains two moles of particles. The mole of sodium chloride breaks up into a mole of sodium ions plus a mole of chlorine ions. Each of these contributes to depressing the freezing point. The total depression is therefore about twice that to be expected if no dissociation had taken place. Hence the Arrhenius theory of ionization explains the anomalous freezing-point depressions.

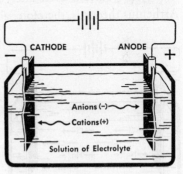

Fig. 12-4. Oppositely charged ions move in opposite directions under the influence of an electric current.

Finally, let us consider the high reaction velocities shown by solutions of electrolytes. Solutions of sodium chloride and of silver nitrate appear to react instantaneously, with the formation of a white precipitate of silver chloride. If this reaction is written

$$NaCl + AgNO_3 \rightarrow \underline{AgCl} + NaNO_3$$

it is difficult to see why the reaction should be instantaneous any more than, say, the slow reaction between the same substances dry, when they are rubbed together in a mortar. It would appear that for reaction to take place, first the sodium chloride and the silver nitrate would have to decompose, and then the several fragments would have to reassemble to form silver chloride and sodium nitrate. It is hard to understand how this could be a very rapid process. If, however, the substances in solution are present as ions, then the reason for the great speed of the reaction becomes clear.

$$Na^+ + Cl^- + Ag^+ + NO_3^- \rightarrow \underline{AgCl} + Na^+ + NO_3^-$$

The only real change taking place has been the union of each silver ion with a chloride ion. The ions are already present ready to react when the solutions are mixed, and no decomposition or input of energy is needed before the silver ions and chloride ions combine. The sole actual change taking place could very well be represented by the equation

$$Ag^+ + Cl^- \rightarrow \underline{AgCl}$$

because the sodium ions and the nitrate ions do not take any actual part in the reaction. Evidence that the sodium ions and nitrate ions are present unchanged is easily found in the fact that the final solution will still conduct the electric current even after the silver chloride has been removed. The Arrhenius theory is, therefore, able to explain the existence of instantaneous

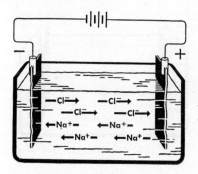

Fig. 12-5. Under the influence of an electric current, a solution of sodium chloride soon is found to have sodium ions collecting around the negative pole (cathode), while chlorine ions collect around the positive pole (anode). Some chlorine may actually bubble off from the surface of the anode.

reactions, as well as the electrical conductivity, and the anomalous freezing-point depression.

While the Arrhenius theory explains or correlates those experimental facts it claims to explain, it should not be accepted as a true picture of nature until we can investigate more fully what the properties of ions may be, and see if certain logical deductions from the theory can be fulfilled experimentally.

If solutions of electrolytes contain ions rather than molecules, then surely all solutions containing, say, copper should have the same color, because the copper will be in the same form, that is, as an ion, in all such solutions. Solutions of copper nitrate, copper chloride, and copper sulfate should all have the same color. Similarly, all permanganates, containing the ion, MnO_4^-, should have the same color; as should all nickel salts. That this is actually true is excellent evidence in favor of the theory. Dilute solutions of copper (Cu^{++}) salts are blue, permanganates are purple, nickel salts are green.

Furthermore, if the ions are really charged particles of matter comparatively free to move about in the solution, then it ought to be possible to separate these oppositely charged particles. It is well known that opposite electric charges attract each other. If, therefore, two wires are placed in a beaker containing a solution of an electrolyte, and if these wires are connected to the opposite poles of a battery or electric generator, then it might be expected that the ions would migrate to the proper wire, that is, the negative ions would migrate to the positive pole and vice versa. (See Fig. 12-5.) Returning for a moment to our solution of sodium chloride, we ought to find the chlorine ion migrating to one pole and the sodium to the other.

This may be tested very easily, and experiment actually shows that the chlorine will begin bubbling off the surface of the positive pole, or anode, while sodium ions collect around the negative pole, or cathode. Because of this behavior negative ions are called **anions,** and positive ions **cations.** This effect of ionic migration may be shown very beautifully by using as electrolyte copper permanganate, $Cu(MnO_4)_2$, instead of sodium chloride. (See Fig. 12-6.) The copper ion is blue and permanganate ion is purple. A solution of copper permanganate is colored purple because the permanganate ion is an unusually rich purple. If a solution of copper permanganate is placed in a U-tube, and the surface of the solution is covered with some colorless electrolyte such as nitric acid, suitable elec-

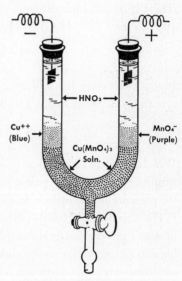

Fig. 12-6. Migration of ions demonstrated by electrolysis of copper permanganate solution.

trodes may be placed in the nitric acid without disturbing the colored solution. When the current is turned on, the blue color of the copper ions will soon make its appearance around the cathode, while the purple of the permanganate will creep up around the anode. This is excellent confirmatory evidence for the existence of ions.

Thus, with respect to at least two logical deductions, the Arrhenius theory is amply supported by direct observation. As we shall see, the theory receives further support from a great array of additional experimental facts.

79. ACIDS, BASES, AND SALTS

If hydrogen chloride, HCl, is dissolved in benzene the solution will not conduct electricity. Presumably the molecules of hydrogen chloride remain as such in this solvent. But if hydrogen chloride is dissolved in water, the solution becomes an excellent conductor; this can only mean that ions are present in the water solution.

Various suggestions have been made as to what kind of ions are present in the water solution. The simplest view is that the hydrogen chloride molecules dissociate into hydrogen ions and chloride ions.

$$HCl \rightleftarrows H^+ + Cl^-$$

There is considerable evidence that the hydrogen ions unite with water molecules to form $H^+(H_2O)$ or H_3O^+, which are called hydronium ions.

$$H^+ + H_2O \rightleftarrows H_3O^+$$

Perhaps therefore the ionization of hydrogen chloride should be written as a reaction between hydrogen chloride and water.

$$HCl + H_2O \rightleftarrows H_3O^+ + Cl^-$$

Whichever way is correct will not affect our discussion, and we shall use the simpler representation unless for some reason it is necessary to emphasize the presence of the hydronium ions.

The excellent electrical conductivity of this solution of hydrogen chloride in water proves that many ions are present, that is, that the reaction equilibrium point lies far to the right as the equation is written, and that there are relatively few hydrogen chloride molecules present. But when this solution is boiled, hydrogen chloride gas escapes. This proves that the reaction is actually reversible as written, and that as soon as the hydrogen chloride molecule concentration is diminished, by boiling the gas off, hydrogen ions and chloride ions continue combining to form more molecules.

All that really happens in the ionization of hydrogen chloride is that an HCl molecule yields up a hydrogen ion, H^+, to a water molecule. Recall that a hydrogen ion is a hydrogen atom which has lost its only electron. A positive hydrogen ion is simply a proton. It may be said, therefore, that when hydrogen chloride dissolves in water, a proton is transferred from the hydrogen chloride molecule to the water molecule.

There are many substances which readily give up hydrogen ions. Such substances are called **acids.** Common examples are H_2SO_4, HNO_3, and H_3PO_4, sulfuric, nitric, and phosphoric acids respectively. *An acid may be defined as a substance which is capable of giving up a hydrogen ion.*

Many acids, such as hydrochloric, nitric, and sulfuric, form highly conducting solutions in water. They are called strong acids. But some acids in water are only fair conductors of the electric current. Acetic acid, CH_3CO_2H, is an example.

$$CH_3CO_2H \rightleftarrows H^+ + CH_3CO_2^-$$

acetic acid molecule $\rightleftarrows$ hydrogen ion + acetate ion

This can only mean that relatively few ions are formed. The acetate ion must hold on to the hydrogen ion, so that comparatively few hydrogen ions and acetate ions are present at any time, although large numbers of acetic acid molecules may be present. Another way of expressing this is to say that the equilibrium favors the substance on the left side of the equation as written.

It will be recalled that chemical equilibrium may be displaced by changing the concentration of one or more of the reacting substances. In the ionization reaction of acetic acid, if one of the ions on the right could be removed, then the speed of reaction toward the left would be greatly diminished and soon practically all the acetic acid molecules would have lost protons and become ions. It might be said that the reaction had gone to completion toward the right. It is easy to lower the concentration of one or more of the ions in a system at equilibrium. The hydrogen ion readily combines with hydroxide ions, OH^-, to form water.

$$H^+ + OH^- \rightleftarrows H_2O$$

The equilibrium for this reaction of hydrogen and hydroxide ions lies very far to the right. Addition of hydroxide ions to an acetic acid solution would, therefore, have the effect of displacing the ionization of acetic acid molecules toward the right until no more acetic acid molecules remain, and the solution would contain only acetate ions and water.

Of course, it is not possible simply to add hydroxide ions to the solution of acetic acid because it is impossible to have a substance containing only negative or only positive ions. But many substances contain hydroxide ions together with an appropriate number of positively charged ions. A good example is sodium hydroxide which is made up of the ions Na^+ and OH^-. The sodium ion need in no way interfere with the reaction, and the sole function of the hydroxide ions is to accept a proton, with consequent formation of water. Any substance, such as sodium hydroxide, which is capable of providing hydroxide ions is called a **base**. Owing to the fact that it is the hydroxide ion which accepts a proton from an acid, it might be more logical to call the hydroxide ion the base and to forget about the sodium ion. But, at least for the present, it will be more convenient to call a base any substance, such as NaOH, KOH, or $Ca(OH)_2$, which can supply hydroxide ions. These examples are respectively sodium hydroxide, potassium hydroxide, and calcium hydroxide.

Whenever an acid is mixed with a base, a vigorous reaction takes place and a considerable amount of heat is liberated. The reaction of hydrochloric acid with potassium hydroxide is a good example. This reaction is often represented as follows:

$$HCl + KOH \rightarrow KCl + H_2O$$

However, the reaction is poorly represented by such an equation which does not indicate the presence of any ions. A better representation is

$$H^+ + Cl^- + K^+ + OH^- \rightarrow K^+ + Cl^- + H_2O$$

and perhaps still better representation would indicate hydronium ions instead of H^+.

When an acid reacts with a base, the process is called **neutralization.** Notice that the only real change taking place in neutralization is the union of a hydrogen ion with a hydroxide ion to form water. If this is actually true, then every neutralization reaction between a strong acid and a strong base should give off the same amount of heat for every mole of water formed, regardless of what acid and base are used. This has been shown experimentally to be true, as is seen from the following thermochemical equations.

$$HCl + KOH \rightarrow KCl + H_2O + 13,800 \text{ cals.}$$

$$HNO_3 + NaOH \rightarrow NaNO_3 + H_2O + 13,800 \text{ cals.}$$

$$H_2SO_4 + Ca(OH)_2 \rightarrow CaSO_4 + 2H_2O + 27,600 \text{ cals.}$$

In the last equation twice as much water is formed per mole of acid or base, hence twice as much heat is liberated.

From these results it may be said that the formation of water from hydrogen ions and hydroxide ions is an exothermal reaction liberating 13,800 calories of heat per mole of water formed. For weak acids such as acetic acid, or weak bases such as ammonium hydroxide, the situation is more complicated because some of the energy is used to complete the ionization of the neutral molecule.

If an acid is neutralized by a base, it sometimes happens that the two ions left unite to form an insoluble compound. This is the case for sulfuric acid and barium hydroxide.

$$H_2SO_4 + Ba(OH)_2 \rightarrow BaSO_4 + 2H_2O$$

The barium sulfate forms at once as a white precipitate. For many other acids and bases the ions simply remain as independent particles and no precipitate forms. This is the case for hydrochloric acid uniting with sodium hydroxide. We can, of course, regard this mixture as simply a solution of sodium chloride in water, which it is.

$$HCl + NaOH \rightarrow NaCl + H_2O$$

In any event, by evaporating the water the compound remaining may always be crystallized and obtained for examination. The potassium chloride, KCl; sodium nitrate, $NaNO_3$; and calcium sulfate, $CaSO_4$, shown above are examples. Such substances are called **salts.** Salts are almost always substances which are formed by electron transfer, or electrovalence (see Chapter 3). Salts may conveniently be defined either through their mode of preparation, or through the nature of the valence forces operating in the compound. *A salt is, therefore, a compound which is formed, together with water, by the action of an acid on a base.* Or, alternatively, *a salt is a compound which is formed essentially by electron transfer.*

Acids, bases, and salts make up the classes of substances called electrolytes. They all have the property of forming electrically conducting solutions. They form three categories of chemical compounds of major importance both from the theoretical and the practical viewpoints.

80. TITRATION

Suppose that to a beaker partly full of dilute acid there is slowly added some dilute base. At first there will be in the beaker an excess of acid, but after a time the amount of base present will be more than enough to neutralize all the acid originally present. There will then be an excess of base in the beaker. There must, of course, be a point at which all the acid has been neutralized, yet no appreciable excess of base has been added. That point is called the *neutral point,* or *end point,* of the reaction. At the end point neither hydrogen ions nor hydroxide ions are present in excess.

Determination of the precise end point of a neutralization reaction is possible with the use of **indicators.** These are complex organic compounds which have the property of turning one color when placed in acid and another in base. The change of color is often very sharp, as little as one drop of excess acid or base being sufficient to bring about the color change. Common indicators are litmus (red in acid, blue in base), phenolphthalein (colorless in acid, red in base), and methyl red (red in acid, yellow in base).

A measured quantity of an acid, or base, may easily be placed in a beaker or flask by the aid of a pipette. This is a glass tube which has a mark on the stem. If the pipette is filled to the mark, then drained into a flask, a definite quantity of liquid will be delivered. Pipettes are often calibrated to deliver exactly 10 cc. Base solution may now be added to this acid in the flask by the use of a burette. The burette is a long tube carefully marked off in divisions, generally a total of 50 cc. with divisions at every 0.1 cc. With the aid of the burette, and an appropriate indicator, it is possible to find exactly how much base solution is necessary to neutralize a given volume of acid

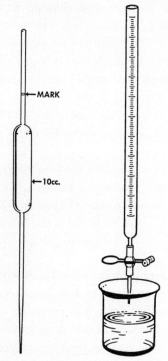

MARK

10cc.

Fig. 12-7. Pipette.   Fig. 12-8. Burette.

solution, or *vice versa*. This operation is called **titration;** it forms part of that branch of chemistry called volumetric quantitative analysis. If the concentration of an acid is known, it is possible by titration to find the concentration of a base.

Problem: What weight of sodium hydroxide will be required to neutralize 25 cc. of 0.50*M* sulfuric acid?

Solution: Always write a balanced equation for the reaction,

$$2NaOH + H_2SO_4 \rightarrow Na_2SO_4 + H_2O$$

If the acid is 0.50*M*, then 1000 cc. contains 0.50 moles of H_2SO_4, so that 25 cc. would contain $\frac{25}{1000} \times 0.50$ moles of H_2SO_4.

According to the equation, 1 mole of H_2SO_4 neutralizes 2 moles of NaOH, therefore $\frac{25}{1000} \times 0.50$ moles of acid would neutralize $\frac{25}{1000} \times 0.50 \times 2$ moles of NaOH. As 1 mole of NaOH is equal to $(23 + 16 + 1)$ g. $= 40$ g., the weight of NaOH required to neutralize 25 cc. of 0.50*M* H_2SO_4 is

$$\frac{25}{1000} \times 0.50 \times 2 \times 40 \text{ g.} = 1.0 \text{ g. of NaOH}$$

Problem: What is the molar concentration of a nitric acid solution, 75 cc. of which neutralize 30 cc. of 1.2*M* Ca(OH)$_2$ solution?

Solution:

$$Ca(OH)_2 + 2HNO_3 \rightarrow Ca(NO_3)_2 + 2H_2O$$

The amount of Ca(OH)$_2$ reacting is

$$\frac{30}{1000} \times 1.2 \text{ moles}$$

According to the equation, 1 mole of $Ca(OH)_2$ neutralizes 2 moles of HNO_3. The amount of nitric acid required to neutralize $^{30}\!/_{1000} \times 1.2$ moles of calcium hydroxide is then,

$$^{30}\!/_{1000} \times 1.2 \times 2 \text{ moles of } HNO_3$$

This number of moles of HNO_3 is contained in 75 cc. of acid solution, therefore 1000 cc. of acid solution would contain

$$^{1000}\!/_{75} \times {}^{30}\!/_{1000} \times 1.2 \times 2 \text{ moles}$$
$$= 0.96 \text{ moles of } HNO_3$$

If 0.96 moles are contained in 1000 cc., then the concentration of the solution is $0.96M$.

A demonstration which neatly illustrates several of the points in this section is the neutralization of barium hydroxide with sulfuric acid.

$$Ba(OH)_2 + H_2SO_4 \rightarrow \underline{BaSO_4} + 2H_2O$$

It so happens that the salt formed, barium sulfate, is insoluble in water and precipitates at once. If suitable electrodes are placed in the reaction vessel, it will be possible to observe the electrical conductivity of the mixture as the reaction proceeds, while a drop or two of indicator will show when the acid and base are exactly neutralized.

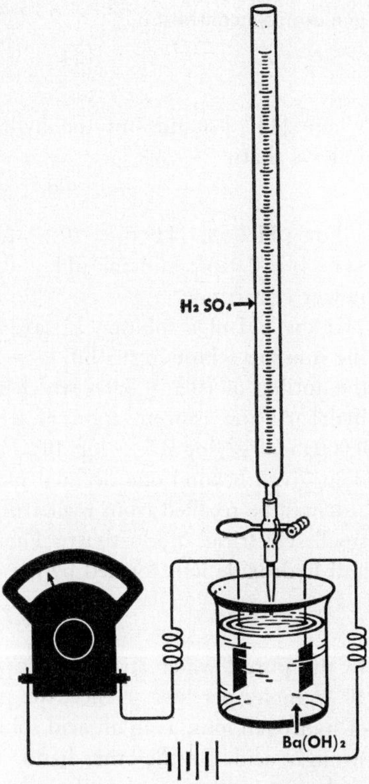

The barium hydroxide solution is placed in the beaker, and the dilute sulfuric acid is added from a burette. At first in the beaker there are only barium ions and hydroxide ions, Ba^{++} and OH^-. The solution will, therefore, be strongly basic and the electrical

Fig. 12-9. Apparatus to demonstrate change of electrical conductivity during neutralization of barium hydroxide by sulfuric acid.

conductivity will be high. As the sulfuric acid is added, the reaction taking place will be

$$Ba^{++} + 2OH^- + 2H^+ + SO_4^= \rightarrow \underline{BaSO_4} + 2H_2O$$

When the base is exactly neutralized there will, therefore, be almost no ions in solution. The beaker will contain only water and a precipitate of solid barium sulfate. Water is almost a nonconductor of electricity, and solid salts do not conduct appreciably. At the exact end point the electrical conductivity of this mixture will fall to practically zero, proving that no ions are present. At the moment the conductivity falls, the indicator will be changing color. Then as the next drop of acid is added the conductivity will start to rise again because ions from the excess acid will be present.

81. pH AND THE IONIZATION OF WATER

The concentration of hydrogen ions in solution is often represented by a convention known as pH. This term is defined as the negative logarithm of the hydrogen ion concentration.

$$pH = - \log [H^+] = \log \frac{1}{[H^+]}$$

where $[H^+]$ stands for the hydrogen ion concentration in moles per liter. It follows that

$$[H^+] = 10^{-pH} = 1/10^{pH}$$

For pH $= 8$, $[H^+] = 10^{-8}$ moles per liter or $0.00000001M$; for pH $= 2$, $[H^+] = 0.01M$; and for pH $= 0$, $[H^+] = 1M$, because ten raised to the zero power equals one.

If the pH of a solution is, say, 2.6 then $[H^+]$ is most conveniently found as the number whose logarithm is -2.6, that is as the antilog of -2.6. This equals the antilog of $(0.4 - 3.0)$, which is 0.0025; hence, $[H^+] = 0.0025M$. Or, if the hydrogen ion concentration of a solution is $0.00035M$, then the pH $= - \log 0.00035 = -(\log 3.5 + \log 10^{-4}) = -(0.54 - 4) = 3.5$. Values of pH are seldom given beyond one decimal place.

It will be recalled from earlier discussion that pure water has a definite, though small, electrical conductivity. This slight conductivity is due to hydrogen ions and hydroxide ions formed by the reversible reaction

$$H_2O \rightleftarrows H^+ + OH^-$$

In the purest water at room temperature the concentration of hydrogen ions is 10^{-7} moles per liter. Hence, the pH of pure water is 7. A higher concentration of hydrogen ions, as in an acid solution, will give a lower pH. A pH of 3 is quite strongly acid. On the other hand, a basic solution will have a higher pH because if the concentration of hydroxide ions is raised, the concentration of hydrogen ions must be correspondingly diminished. It will be noted from the equilibrium constant

$$\frac{[H^+] \times [OH^-]}{[H_2O]} = K$$

that water is so slightly ionized that its own concentration may be taken as constant. With only negligible error we may write

$$[H^+] \times [OH^-] = K_i$$

It so happens that K_i in this expression is, at room temperature, equal to 1.0×10^{-14}. If $[H^+]$ is raised, as by adding an acid, then for K to remain equal to 10^{-14} it is necessary for $[OH^-]$ to diminish correspondingly, and vice versa.

The pH method for representing hydrogen ion concentration is a convenience and is widely used. The pH of blood is normally about 7.4, that of the gastric fluid in the stomach about 3 to 4, of sea water 8.2, and of milk of magnesia 10.5.

82. NORMAL SOLUTIONS

It has been noted that the formulas of some acids such as hydrochloric, HCl, have only one hydrogen atom which ionizes and is consequently replaceable in a neutralization reaction. Other acids such as sulfuric, H_2SO_4, have two replaceable hydrogen atoms, while some such as phosphoric, H_3PO_4, have three. Similarly, some bases such as sodium hydroxide, NaOH, have one replaceable hydroxide ion, while others such as calcium hydroxide, $Ca(OH)_2$, have two.

This distinction is the basis of another method for describing the concentration of acids, bases, and salts. The formula weight of an acid, divided by the number of replaceable hydrogen atoms in the formula is called the equivalent weight of the acid. Similarly, the formula weight of a base, divided by the number of replaceable hydroxide ions in the formula is called the equivalent weight of the base. Examples of equivalent weights of some acids and bases are:

Substance	Formula	Formula Weight	Equivalent Weight
Hydrochloric acid......	HCl	36.5	36.5
Sulfuric acid..........	H_2SO_4	98.1	49.0
Phosphoric acid........	H_3PO_4	97.0	32.3
Sodium hydroxide.......	NaOH	40.0	40.0
Calcium hydroxide.....	$Ca(OH)_2$	74.1	37.0

Just as a mole is a formula weight expressed as grams, a gram-equivalent weight is an equivalent weight expressed as grams. A **normal solution** is one which contains one gram-equivalent weight of solute per liter of solution. It will be clear that for hydrochloric acid and for sodium hydroxide a molar (M) solution and a normal (N) solution are exactly the same but that a one molar sulfuric acid solution is twice as concentrated as a one normal sulfuric acid solution.

Normal solutions are convenient for persons having to do large numbers of titrations. The convenience will be illustrated by the following problem.

Problem: What volume of $0.30N$ acid is required to neutralize 10 cc. of $2.5N$ base?

Solution: As the base is $2.5/0.30$ times as concentrated as the acid it will require $(2.5/0.30) \times 10$ cc. $= 83$ cc. of acid to neutralize the base.

Notice that in the above problem the answer is the same no matter what acid or what base is under consideration.

The idea of normal solutions may also be applied to salts and to reactions involving oxidation and reduction but the method is less used now than formerly. Do not confuse normal solutions with a "normal saline solution," which is a solution containing about 1 per cent of sodium chloride in water, and is much used in biology.

83. MODERN THEORIES OF ELECTROLYTES

The Arrhenius theory of ionization was received at first with little favor. Arrhenius worked out this theory as part of his thesis for the doctor's degree, but he was so sure that his professors would not approve that he stated his conclusions in a roundabout manner. In Arrhenius' words:

I had, in this manner, deduced a rather large number of different properties which had not been explained before; but I must say that this circumstance made no very great impression upon my professors in Upsala.

I came to my professor, Cleve, whom I admire very much, and I said: "I have a new theory of electrical conductivity as a cause of chemical reactions." He said: "That is very interesting," and then said "Good-bye." He explained to me later, when he had to pronounce the reason for my receiving the Nobel prize for that work, that he knew very well that there are so many different theories formed, and that they are all almost certain to be wrong, for after a short time they disappear, and, therefore, by using the statistical manner of forming his ideas, he concluded that my theory also would not last very long.*

Opposition to the Arrhenius theory was both active and passive. But gradually the overwhelming success of the theory converted all, or almost all, the doubters. Arrhenius received nearly all the high honors which the scientific world bestows upon its most distinguished members. His theory, once considered too obscure for inclusion in undergraduate chemistry courses, now occupies a position of major importance in any elementary presentation of the subject.

But early in the twentieth century, observations began accumulating to the effect that the Arrhenius theory might be in need of revision. To understand these difficulties we must return to the original postulates made by Arrhenius. His theory may be summarized as follows:

(1) In appropriate solvents, acids, bases, and salts dissociate into electrically charged particles.

(2) In dilute solution electrolytes are almost entirely dissociated into ions: that is, there are few molecules of solute remaining.

(3) In more concentrated solutions the ions are in equilibrium with the undissociated molecules of solute, as may be illustrated by the reversible reaction

$$NaCl \rightleftarrows Na^+ + Cl^-$$

The third postulate has not been emphasized in this discussion until now. It is with this postulate that the difficulties arise.

If an equilibrium exists between ions and undissociated molecules, then it should be possible to find to what extent ionization has progressed in any given solution, that is, to find what fraction of the solute is in the form of ions, and what remains as molecules.

* *Journal of American Chemical Society*, 34:353 (1912).

There are two principal ways of making this calculation, one from the depression of the freezing point, and the other from a careful study of the electrical conductivity of the solutions. The details of these calculations lie, unfortunately, beyond us. But the difficult point, for the Arrhenius theory, is clear; the two methods of calculating degree of ionization do not give the same result. Table 9 shows the per cent ionization of sodium chloride calculated by the two methods. The discrepancy is obvious.

TABLE 9

PER CENT APPARENT IONIZATION OF SODIUM CHLORIDE IN SOLUTION

Molar Concentration of NaCl	Per Cent Apparent Ionization by Freezing-Point Method	Per Cent Apparent Ionization by Conductivity Method
0.01	93.8	93.6
0.1	87.5	85.2
0.5	81.5	77.4
3.0	95.5	54.6
4.5	115.1	43.4

From M. C. Sneed and J. L. Maynard, *General Inorganic Chemistry* (New York: D. Van Nostrand Co., Inc., 1942. By permission).

The chief difficulties with the Arrhenius theory may be summarized as follows:

(1) For many electrolytes, different methods of obtaining the degree of ionization do not agree.

(2) The important effect of the solvent molecules in promoting solution and ionization is not explained.

(3) The effect of oppositely charged ions on each other is not considered.

Numerous attempts have been made to amplify or alter the Arrhenius theory of ionization. Some of these have been fairly successful. The best known of these newer theories is that of Debye and Hückel. The Debye-Hückel theory, in brief, postulates that strong electrolytes, including nearly all salts, are 100 per cent ionized. The properties of such solutions are dependent in part on solvent molecules attaching themselves to the ions, and on the effects of oppositely charged ions clustering about each other. The idea of 100 per cent ionization for strong, good-conducting electrolytes is, of course, supported by X-ray evidence on the existence of ions in the solid state, and by the theoretical views expressed in Chapter 3 concerning the nature of the valence forces in electrovalent types of compounds.

No theory of electrolytes has proved entirely satisfactory. The Arrhenius theory, for all its weakness, marks a turning point in the history of science. With it, there came into being physical chemistry, the borderline field between chemistry and physics. No understanding of solutions is possible without the groundwork of theory laid by Arrhenius. His position among the great of science is assured.

EXERCISES

A. *Define or explain the following:*

acid H^+ (capable of giving up H^+)   ionization

anion *negative ion (goes to anode)*   metallic conduction

base OH^- (capable of giving up OH^-)   neutralization

burette   neutral point or end point (as applied

cation *positive ion (goes to cathode)*   to reaction of acid and base) *all acid neutralized*   *no excess of base*

electrolyte   normal solution

electrolytic conduction   pH

electrolytic dissociation   pipette

hydronium $H^+(H_2O)$ or H_3O^+ salt *compound formed by acid + base*

indicator   titration

ion

B. 1. What experimental facts must be explained by any theory of electrolytes?
    2. What is the Arrhenius ionization theory?
    3. How does the Arrhenius theory explain the facts of Question 1?
    4. What is the present status of the Arrhenius theory?
    5. What is the difference between a weak and a strong acid?
    6. Why does the neutralization of a strong acid with a strong base always result in the same quantity of heat being liberated per mole of water formed?

C. 1. Find the weight of substance indicated to prepare one liter of each of the following: $0.50M$ $HClO_4$, $0.50N$ H_2SO_4, $1.3N$ $Ba(OH)_2$, $2.5M$ $Ba(OH)_2$.
    2. What weight of potassium hydroxide will be needed to neutralize 50 cc. of $0.65M$ nitric acid? $HNO_3 + KOH \rightarrow KNO_3 + H_2O$ $\ell \times M = milles$ *moles*
    3. What volume of $0.30M$ sodium hydroxide solution will be needed to neutralize 10 cc. of $0.18M$ sulfuric acid?
    4. If 23.2 cc. of sodium hydroxide solution is needed to neutralize 10 cc. of $0.44M$ hydrochloric acid, what is the molar concentration of the base?
    5. It requires 18.5 cc. of NaOH solution to neutralize 10 cc. of $0.55M$ HCl solution. What is the concentration of the base in (a) moles per liter, (b) grams per liter?
    6. It requires 17.6 cc. of $1.12M$ H_3PO_4 to neutralize 50 cc. of $Ca(OH)_2$ solution. What is the concentration of the base in (a) moles per liter, (b) grams per liter? $3Ca(OH)_2 + 2H_3PO_4 \rightarrow Ca_3(PO_4)_2 + 6H_2O$.
    7. How many grams of KOH are required to neutralize 22 cc. of oxalic acid which contains 0.95 moles of $C_2O_4H_2$ per liter? $2KOH + C_2O_4H_2 \rightarrow C_2O_4K_2 + 2H_2O$.

8. What volume of $0.50M$ $AgNO_3$ is required to precipitate as $AgCl$ all the chlorine in 1.0 g. of NaCl?

9. What volume of $1.05M$ $Ba(OH)_2$ solution is required to neutralize 50 cc. of $0.75M$ H_2SO_4? What weight of $BaSO_4$ will be formed?

10. How many liters of dry carbon dioxide at standard conditions will be liberated by the action of 150 cc. of $1.5M$ HCl on excess limestone?

11. A solution is made up by mixing 50 cc. of $0.75M$ KOH and 33 cc. of $0.65M$ H_2SO_4. The solution is then diluted to 1000 cc. What is the molar concentration of acid (or of base) which remains not neutralized?

12. What volume of $1.15N$ sulfuric acid is needed to neutralize 23.3 cc. of $1.88N$ potassium hydroxide (KOH) solution?

13. Find the pH of the following solutions:
   a. A solution containing 0.0001 moles per liter of hydrogen ion.
   b. A $0.0005M$ solution of the strong base, $Ba(OH)_2$.
   c. A $0.3M$ solution of the strong acid, HCl.

14. The concentration of hydroxide ions may be represented by the expression pOH, which has a meaning exactly analogous to pH. If in a water solution the pH is 9, what is the pOH?

15. Give the hydrogen ion concentration in moles per liter for solutions having a pH = 3; pH = 8.5.

16. A $0.1M$ acid solution is reported as having a pH of 3. What explanation may be offered?

17. Write formulas for the following salts: ammonium chloride, barium sulfate, calcium oxalate, chromic sulfate, cupric sulfide, ferrous sulfate, potassium permanganate, silver nitrate, sodium hypochlorite, sodium bicarbonate, strontium nitrate.

18. Name each of the following: $Al_4(SiO_4)_3$, $SbCl_3$, $Ba(NO_2)_2$, Bi_2S_3, CaF_2, $CuCl_2$, $PbBr_2$, MgI_2, $Hg(NO_3)_2$, Ag_2S, AgI, $NaHCO_3$, $NaClO_3$, $Zn(NO_3)_2$.

19. When Arrhenius presented his theory it was argued that sodium could not be present in a solution of sodium chloride in water, because sodium is known to react with water to yield hydrogen and sodium hydroxide. What is the fallacy in this objection?

20. Using electron diagrams, show the difference between sodium atom and sodium ion, aluminum atom and aluminum ion, bromine atom and bromide ion, sulfur atom and sulfide ion, sulfide ion and sulfate ion.

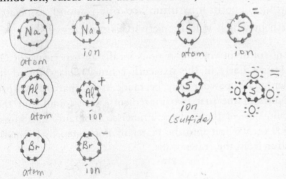

SULFUR AND RELATED
13 ELEMENTS

															H	He
Li	Be	B											C	N	O	F	Ne
Na	Mg	Al											Si	P	S	Cl	A
K	Ca	Sc	Ti	V	Cr	Mn	Fe	Co	Ni	Cu	Zn	Ga	Ge	As	Se	Br	Kr
Rb	Sr	Y	Zr	Nb	Mo	Tc	Ru	Rh	Pd	Ag	Cd	In	Sn	Sb	Te	I	Xe
Cs	Ba	La-Lu	Hf	Ta	W	Re	Os	Ir	Pt	Au	Hg	Tl	Pb	Bi	Po	At	Rn
Fr	Ra	Ac	Th	Pa	U-												

Quickly, O! Dame, bring fire that I may burn sulfur, the cure of ills—The *Odyssey* of Homer.

84. PRODUCTION OF SULFUR

Sulfur, the brimstone of the ancients, is widely distributed in nature, both as the free element and in the form of metallic sulfides and sulfates. Iron pyrites, a sulfide of iron with the formula FeS_2, is one of the commonest of minerals, as is gypsum, or calcium sulfate. Many, if not most, of the commercially valuable metals such as zinc, lead, copper, and silver are, more frequently than not, found combined with sulfur. Great deposits of the element sulfur are found in certain parts of the world, particularly in Texas and Louisiana. This sulfur may have been formed through the action of water containing petroleum as a reducing agent on dissolved calcium and magnesium sulfates. The more important deposits of sulfur are often found associated with regions of the earth in which volcanic activity is notable.

The occurrence of sulfur in volcanic regions recalls an experience of Cortez in his conquest of Mexico. Early in the sixteenth century Cortez found his army short of gunpowder. Black powder may be made from charcoal, saltpeter, and sulfur. Ample supplies of the first two ingredients were found, but the sulfur proved more difficult. One of the soldiers, Francisco Montano, had himself lowered in a basket 400 or 500 feet into the crater of Popocatepetl. From this position he scraped sulfur from the crater walls.

A large proportion of the world's sulfur is produced by the Frasch process. This is the process used in the southern United States. The sulfur is found as the element several hundred feet below the surface, and under layers of clay and limestone. The nature of the deposits and the poisonous gases present make it impossible for men to work in shafts such as are used in ordinary mining operations. In the Frasch process the sulfur is melted in the ground and pumped to the surface as a liquid. This procedure is possible because the sulfur melts at about 113° C., only a few degrees above the normal boiling point of water.

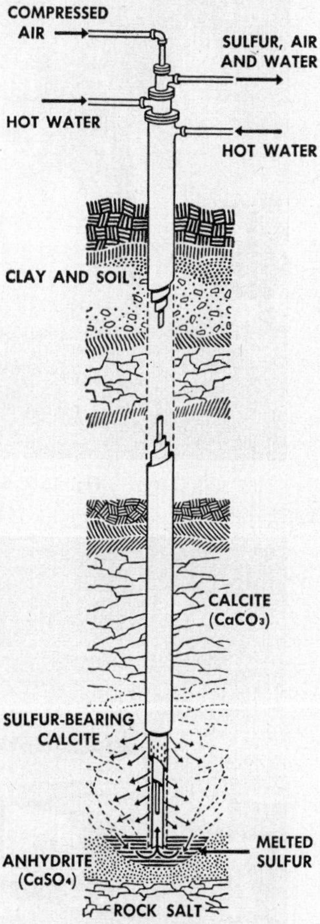

Three concentric pipes are sunk into the ground, the outermost about 6 inches in diameter and the innermost 1 inch. (See Fig. 13-1.) It will be recalled that the boiling point of water rises with increasing pressure. At a pressure of 100 lbs. per square inch, the water may be heated to 170° C. This is well above the melting point of the sulfur. This superheated water is forced down the space between the outermost and the intermediate pipe. The water melts the sulfur in the ground. Then compressed air is pumped down the innermost pipe. This air mixes with the molten sulfur, forming a froth which is forced up and emerges in the space between the innermost and the intermediate pipes. A fourth pipe with a diameter of about 8 inches is sometimes used to carry additional superheated water. The liquid product (Fig. 13-3) is collected in large bins where it solidifies into veritable mountains of yellow sulfur

Fig. 13-1. Diagrammatic representation of the Frasch process. The discharging sulfur is seen in Fig. 13-3.

(Fig. 13-4), containing many thousands of tons. The sulfur is very pure and requires no further processing for most uses.

The Louisiana sulfur deposits were discovered in Calcasieu Parish in 1865. Every attempt to mine the sulfur ended with failure, often with disastrous accidents, until Herman Frasch developed his unique process. He applied for his first sulfur-mining patent in 1890. His first efforts were accompanied by many difficulties, all of which he solved. Frasch was an American chemical

Fig. 13-2. Sulfur wells, as seen from the surface.

Fig. 13-3. Liquid sulfur discharging into a vat where it will solidify and be stored prior to being shipped.

engineer who was well known for successful developments in petroleum and related fields before he undertook the sulfur problem. The excitement and satisfaction attending the first attempt to produce sulfur by the Frasch process are described in Frasch's own words:

When everything was ready to make the first trial, which would demonstrate either success or failure, we raised steam in the boilers, and sent the superheated water into the ground without a hitch.

Fig. 13-4. Sulfur being loaded into a railroad car for shipment.

After permitting the melting fluid to go into the ground for twenty-four hours, I decided that sufficient material must have been melted to produce some sulphur. The pumping engine was started on the sulphur line, and the increasing strain against the engine showed that work was being done. More and more slowly went the engine, more steam was supplied, until the man at the throttle sang out at the top of his voice, "She's pumping!" A liquid appeared on the polished rod, and when I wiped it off I found my finger covered with sulphur. Within five minutes the receptacles under pressure were opened and a beautiful stream of the golden fluid shot into the barrels we had ready to receive the product. After pumping for about fifteen minutes the forty barrels we had supplied were seen to be inadequate. Quickly we threw up embankments and lined them with boards to receive the sulphur that was gushing forth; and since that day no further attempt has been made to provide a vessel or a mold into which to put the sulphur.

When the sun went down we stopped the pump to hold the liquid sulphur below until we could prepare to receive more in the morning. The material on the ground had to be removed, and willing hands helped to make a clean slate for the next day. When everything had been finished, the sulphur all piled up in one heap, and the men had departed, I enjoyed all by myself this demonstration of success. I mounted the sulphur pile and seated myself on the very top. It pleased me to hear the slight noise caused by the contraction of the warm sulphur, which was like a greeting from below—proof that my object had been accomplished. Many days and many years intervened before financial success was assured, but the first step towards the ultimate goal had been achieved. We had melted the mineral in the ground and brought it to the surface as a liquid. We had demonstrated that it could be done.

This was especially gratifying as the criticisms I had received from technical papers and people who had heard of what I was attempting to do had been very adverse. Everyone who expressed an opinion seemed to be convinced that this thing could not be done, one prominent man offering to eat every ounce of sulphur I ever pumped. A fair illustration of public opinion is the remark of the mail boy who drove me to the railroad the morning after our first pumping. He said: "Well, you pumped sulphur sure, but nobody believed it but the old carpenter, and they say he's half crazy."

This severe criticism, while not agreeable, did not carry very much weight with me. I felt that I had given the subject more thought than my critics, and I went about my work as best I could, thoroughly convinced that he who laughs last, laughs best.*

85. PROPERTIES AND USES OF SULFUR

Under normal conditions sulfur is a yellow solid. Contrary to popular opinion, it has no odor. At room temperature, sulfur occurs in the rhombic

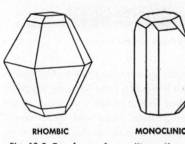

RHOMBIC   MONOCLINIC

Fig. 13-5. Two forms of crystalline sulfur.

form. This name is derived from the shape of the crystals, well-formed examples of which may be made by dissolving sulfur in carbon disulfide and allowing the solution to evaporate slowly. *Rhombic* sulfur is the stable form of sulfur up to 96° C. Above this temperature the crystals tend to become long and needle-shaped. This form of sulfur is called *monoclinic*. Rhombic sulfur melts at 112.8° C. and monoclinic sulfur at 119.25°. If monoclinic sulfur is cooled below 96° C., it slowly reverts to the rhombic form.

The peculiar property of an element existing in more than one form is called **allotropy**. Allotropy is a property possessed by many elements, a conspicuous example of which is carbon. Carbon occurs as charcoal, graphite, and diamond, but there is nothing but carbon in each of these substances. Similarly, oxygen occurs as ordinary oxygen or as ozone. These substances

---

* *Journal of Industrial and Engineering Chemistry*, 4:137 (1912).

are very different in nearly all their properties, yet they may easily be converted from one to another without the addition or taking away of any other element. The differences found in allotropic modifications, or allotropes, of an element seem to be due to the method in which the atoms of the element are arranged and combined with each other.

Sulfur is outstanding for the large number of allotropic modifications it forms. There are at least four, and probably more, forms in addition to the rhombic and the monoclinic. When sulfur is melted it forms a pale yellow fluid. At somewhat higher temperatures the liquid turns almost black and so viscous that it will not pour out of an inverted vessel. As the temperature is raised still higher, the liquid becomes less viscous and finally boils at 444.6° C. If the liquid near its boiling point is poured into cold water, a very peculiar rubbery mass is formed. This is called *plastic sulfur*. Plastic sulfur gradually reverts to rhombic sulfur at room temperature, and, of course, loses its plastic properties. With the addition of phosphorus sulfide, or of certain other substances, plastic sulfur may be kept for fairly long periods. At one time it was thought that a synthetic rubber substitute might be made in this way.

The vapor of sulfur at moderate temperatures has the formula S_8. On further heating, these large molecules tend to break down, mostly to S_2. Dissolved sulfur also has the formula S_8.

Although sulfur is normally a solid and oxygen is a gas, the chemical actions of the two elements are often similar. This is, of course, to be expected from the position of the two elements in the Periodic Table, and from the corresponding similarity in the arrangement of electrons in the atoms.

Sulfur combines readily with nearly all metals. With iron, for instance, the action is vigorous, yielding ferrous sulfide.

$$Fe + S \rightarrow FeS$$

Sulfur burns in air with a small blue flame. In oxygen the action is considerably more vigorous. The product in each case is sulfur dioxide.

$$S + O_2 \rightarrow SO_2$$

With hydrogen, sulfur combines slowly at somewhat elevated temperature, yielding hydrogen sulfide.

$$H_2 + S \rightarrow H_2S$$

With carbon, strongly heated, sulfur forms carbon disulfide.

$$C + 2S \rightarrow CS_2$$

In normal times the annual world production of sulfur is about 12,000,000 tons. By far the larger part of this is used in the manufacture of sulfuric acid, the uses of which will be described later. A small percentage of all sulfur is used directly as the element. Finely powdered sulfur acts as a **fungicide** (fungus destroyer) on fruit trees and vines. Considerable amounts are sprayed on grape vines.

The vulcanization of rubber, a process discovered by Goodyear in 1839, consists of heating crude rubber and sulfur. The product gains desirable strength and elasticity in this process, and also loses the stickiness which is characteristic of crude rubber.

Sulfur is also used directly in the manufacture of certain types of cements and dyes, of black gunpowder for fireworks displays, and of matches. The extremely low electrical conductivity of sulfur makes it useful for insulating purposes. But all these uses, although important, require only a small fraction of the sulfur which goes into the manufacture of sulfur dioxide and sulfuric acid.

86. SULFUR DIOXIDE

When sulfur burns in air or in oxygen, the product, as already pointed out, is sulfur dioxide.

$$S + O_2 \rightarrow SO_2$$

This is a typical oxidation in which the oxidation state of the sulfur goes from zero to plus four. Sulfur dioxide may also be prepared in other ways, two of which will be mentioned. If copper is treated with dilute sulfuric acid, no reaction takes place, but if the sulfuric acid is concentrated and hot, sulfur dioxide is liberated.

$$Cu + 2H_2SO_4 \text{ (conc., hot)} \rightarrow CuSO_4 + SO_2 + 2H_2O$$

Notice that in this reaction the oxidation state of sulfur changes from +6 to +4, while that of the copper changes from 0 to +2. The sulfur undergoes a process in this reaction which is in a sense the reverse of that in the first equation, in which the sulfur oxidation state is changed from 0 to +4. *When the oxidation state is raised, we say that oxidation has taken place; when it is lowered the substance is said to be reduced.* In the action of copper on hot, concentrated sulfuric acid the sulfur in the sulfuric acid is reduced from an oxidation state of +6 to +4, while the copper is oxidized from 0 to +2. These definitions of oxidation and reduction are broader than those previously given, but the broader definitions are more useful. *Oxidation is an increase of oxidation state, reduction is the reverse.* Notice that so far as the copper is concerned, it merely changes from a neutral atom to a positively charged ion, with the simultaneous liberation of two electrons.

$$Cu^0 \rightarrow Cu^{++} + 2 \text{ electrons}$$

In this particular case, at least, oxidation might be defined as a *loss of electrons*.

Another convenient method for making sulfur dioxide is to treat sodium sulfite, Na_2SO_3, or sodium bisulfite, $NaHSO_3$, with dilute hydrochloric or sulfuric acid.

$$Na_2SO_3 + 2H_2SO_4 \rightarrow 2NaHSO_4 + H_2O + SO_2$$

$$NaHSO_3 + HCl \rightarrow NaCl + H_2O + SO_2$$

Sulfur dioxide is also often formed as a by-product in smelting operations.

Sulfur dioxide is a colorless gas with a very strong, sharp, choking odor. It is highly poisonous, but under normal conditions accidental breathing of the gas rarely occurs. This is because the powerful odor of the gas gives ample warning of its presence.

Under moderate pressure, or at somewhat lowered temperature, sulfur dioxide becomes a colorless liquid.

Many of the important chemical properties of sulfur dioxide are concerned with the solution of the gas in water. Pure sulfur dioxide is used chiefly in the manufacture of sulfuric

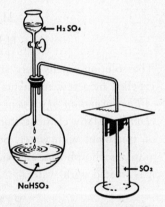

Fig. 13-6. Generation of sulfur dioxide, $NaHSO_3 + H_2SO_4 \rightarrow NaHSO_4 + H_2O + SO_2$.

acid, and in mechanical refrigerators. But its use for the latter purpose is being superseded by less poisonous substances. Sulfur dioxide gas is also applied as a disinfectant. Its use for this purpose, particularly for infected buildings, goes back many thousands of years, as is obvious from the quotation with which this chapter starts. But at the present time sulfur dioxide is being displaced by more effective substances.

The reader may wonder why some compounds are called dioxides and some peroxides, although in the formulas SO_2 and BaO_2 there is considerable superficial resemblance. The reason for this distinction is as follows: any compound containing two oxygen atoms would normally be called a dioxide, but some dioxides have the property of forming hydrogen peroxide, which has unique oxidizing properties. If SO_2 is treated with dilute sulfuric acid, no reaction occurs. But if BaO_2 is treated with dilute sulfuric acid, hydrogen peroxide is liberated.

$$BaO_2 + H_2SO_4 \rightarrow BaSO_4 + H_2O_2$$

The hydrogen peroxide so formed is easily identified by its oxidizing properties. An oxide which, when treated with dilute acid, forms hydrogen peroxide is called a **peroxide.** Other compounds, the formulas of which contain two atoms of oxygen, are generally called dioxides. There are differences in the mode of linkage between the atoms in peroxides and dioxides.

Sulfur dioxide dissolves to a considerable extent in water. The solution so formed consists in part of sulfurous acid.

$$SO_2 + H_2O \rightleftarrows H_2SO_3$$

Sulfurous acid is a weak acid which ionizes to a slight degree into bisulfite ion, HSO_3^-, and to an even smaller degree to sulfite ion, $SO_3^=$.

$$H_2SO_3 \rightleftarrows H^+ + HSO_3^-$$

$$HSO_3^- \rightleftarrows H^+ + SO_3^=$$

The solution smells very strongly of sulfur dioxide, all of which may be expelled by a few moments' boiling.

The formation of an acid by the oxide of an element serves to classify the element. Many elements form oxides which, like that of sulfur, give acids on treatment with water. Such elements are called **nonmetals.** Another example is phosphorus, an oxide of which, P_2O_5, yields phosphoric acid when it is treated with water.

$$P_2O_5 + 3H_2O \rightarrow 2H_3PO_4$$

In contrast to the nonmetals, certain other elements give oxides which, in water, form bases. Examples are sodium and calcium.

$$Na_2O + H_2O \rightarrow 2NaOH$$

$$CaO + H_2O \rightarrow Ca(OH)_2$$

Elements, the oxides of which form bases with water, are called **metals.** This distinction between metals and nonmetals is often used as a definition of these two classes of elements. As we shall see later, however, there are other properties which also serve to distinguish one class of elements from another.

Sulfur is capable of exhibiting several different oxidation states from -2 to $+6$. Because of this the sulfur in sulfurous acid, with an oxidation state of $+4$, is capable of being either oxidized or reduced. A typical case of oxidation occurs when sulfurous acid is shaken with air, especially with the addition of a drop of cupric chloride as a catalyst. The sulfurous acid is oxidized to sulfuric acid, the oxidizing agent being, of course, the oxygen of the air.

$$2H_2SO_3 + O_2 \rightarrow 2H_2SO_4$$

The principal use of sulfurous acid is as a bleaching agent. Large quantities are used in the bleaching of delicate substances such as silk, paper, straw, or wool, which would be injured by more vigorous agents such as chlorine. As a preservative for fruits and vegetables, sulfur dioxide is effective but it is not harmless. Pure-food laws require that sulfur dioxide be almost entirely absent from the final product.

Sulfurous acid reacts with bases to form bisulfites and sulfites. With sodium hydroxide the reactions are as follows:

$$H_2SO_3 + NaOH \rightarrow NaHSO_3 + H_2O$$
sodium bisulfite

$$H_2SO_3 + 2NaOH \rightarrow Na_2SO_3 + 2H_2O$$
sodium sulfite

As previously pointed out, all sulfites and bisulfites give sulfur dioxide when they are treated with acid.

The "sulfite" process for the manufacture of paper pulp involves the compound calcium bisulfite, $Ca(HSO_3)_2$, which dissolves the lignin from wood, leaving relatively pure cellulose, from which paper is made.

87. SULFURIC ACID

Sulfur dioxide has the approximate electron configuration shown.

sulfur dioxide

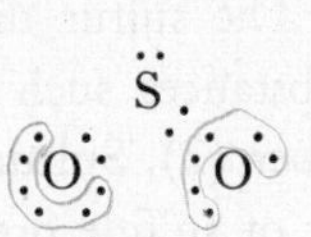

Sulfur dioxide easily takes on another atom of oxygen to form sulfur trioxide, a probable electron configuration of which is also shown.

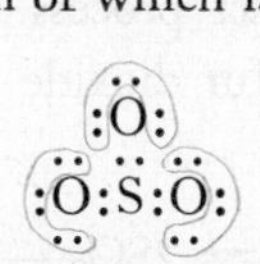

$$\overset{+4}{SO_2^{-4}} + O_2 \rightarrow \overset{+6}{SO_3^{-6}}$$

sulfur trioxide

In other words, sulfur dioxide is easily oxidized, the oxidation state of the sulfur changing from +4 to +6.

Sulfur trioxide, SO_3, is not of itself especially important, but when added to water it forms sulfuric acid, H_2SO_4, one of the most important of all industrial chemicals.

There are two main processes for the manufacture of sulfuric acid, the contact process (Fig. 13-7) and the lead-chamber process. Of these, the first will be described.

In the contact process there are three principal steps, represented by the following equations:

(1) $$S + O_2 \rightarrow SO_2$$

(2) $$2SO_2 + O_2 \rightleftarrows 2SO_3$$

(3) $$SO_3 + H_2O \rightarrow H_2SO_4$$

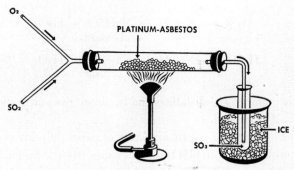

Fig. 13-7. Laboratory demonstration of the contact process for making sulfur trioxide. $2SO_2 + O_2 \rightarrow 2SO_3$.

The first step involves the burning of sulfur, as already described for the preparation of sulfur dioxide. The sulfur dioxide so obtained is generally quite pure with respect to substances such as dust and especially arsenic which interfere with step number (2). Sulfur dioxide is sometimes obtained as a by-product in the roasting of sulfide ores. Such sulfur dioxide is often used in the manufacture of sulfuric acid, but it generally requires a careful purification process before it may be so used.

The second step in the contact process is the step of greatest interest, namely, the oxidation of the sulfur dioxide to sulfur trioxide. This reaction is exothermic. $Cu^{++} + S^{--} \rightleftarrows CuS$

$$2SO_2 + O_2 \rightleftarrows 2SO_3 + 44,400 \text{ cal.}$$

At room temperature the reaction proceeds so slowly that it would take almost forever to get enough sulfur trioxide to be useful. If the temperature is raised, the reaction will proceed more rapidly. But because the reaction is exothermic, heat will drive the equilibrium to the left. The yield of sulfur trioxide will, therefore, be cut down until the process is no longer economically feasible. The manufacturer of sulfuric acid faces this dilemma: if the temperature is moderate, the yield of sulfur trioxide is theoretically large, but it takes too long to get it. On the other hand, if the temperature is high, the reaction proceeds rapidly enough but the yield of sulfur trioxide is

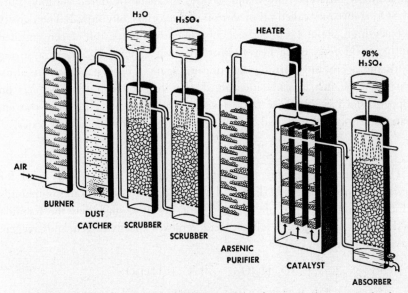

Fig. 13-8. Industrial production of sulfuric acid by the contact process. At the far left, sulfur is burned in air to form sulfur dioxide, which is then thoroughly purified in a dust catcher, two scrubbers, and an arsenic purifier. The mixture of sulfur dioxide and air is then passed over the catalyst, where the heat from the exothermic reaction $2SO_2 + O_2 \rightarrow 2SO_3$ is used to warm incoming gases. Finally the sulfur trioxide is absorbed in concentrated sulfuric acid.

negligible. In these circumstances the only thing to do is to use a moderate temperature and to use a catalyst which will speed up the reaction. A catalyst cannot, of course, alter the equilibrium.

A catalyst often used for this process is platinum; vanadium pentoxide or other vanadium compounds are also widely used. A mixture of carefully purified sulfur dioxide and air is passed over finely divided platinum. The most efficient temperature is about 400° C. Under these conditions nearly all the sulfur dioxide is oxidized to sulfur trioxide.

The third step in the contact process would appear to be simply a matter of adding the sulfur trioxide to water, but mechanical reasons make it quite difficult. It is simpler and quite effective to add the sulfur trioxide to concentrated sulfuric acid, and then to add water to the mixture until the desired concentration for the market is reached.

Annual production of sulfuric acid runs into many millions of tons. Much acid is used over and over again in industrial processes, so that the total tonnage of sulfuric acid handled is very large indeed.

The reasons why sulfuric acid is so important are twofold: first, it will do so many different things, and second, it can be produced cheaply. Pure H_2SO_4, sometimes called oil of vitriol, is a colorless, oily liquid. The density is fairly high, about 1.8 g. per cc.; consequently a bottle full of concentrated sulfuric acid feels quite heavy. Pure, or nearly pure, H_2SO_4 is a strong oxidizing agent and a strong dehydrating agent. The first property is illustrated by the fact, already mentioned, that hot concentrated acid acts on copper, which is otherwise fairly resistant to attack by acids. Hot, concentrated sulfuric acid will oxidize sulfur, forming sulfur dioxide, and water.

$$S + 2H_2SO_4 \rightarrow 3SO_2 + 2H_2O$$

The dehydrating action of concentrated sulfuric acid is often used for drying air, or other gases. The acid will also take water from compounds which contain hydrogen and oxygen. For instance, sugar has the formula $C_{12}H_{22}O_{11}$; concentrated sulfuric acid removes the hydrogen and oxygen, leaving nothing but carbon.

$$C_{12}H_{22}O_{11} \rightarrow 12C + 11H_2O$$

The water, so removed, probably combines chemically with the H_2SO_4, forming a hydrate. This marked dehydrating action of sulfuric acid results in the charring, or even the ignition, of wood or paper. It is also responsible, in part, for the very severe action of concentrated sulfuric acid on the skin and flesh. Acid on the clothing, skin, or in eyes should always be flushed off instantly with very large quantities of water. *Do not hesitate a moment but get the affected part under an open faucet.*

When sulfuric acid takes up water, a large quantity of heat is liberated. The effect of this is to make the mixture hot, often too hot to handle. If a few drops of water are added to concentrated sulfuric acid, part of the water is converted to steam, which may result in the acid's spitting around in a very dangerous manner. If, however, the acid is slowly added to water, no dangerous spitting occurs. It is important to remember this because many dangerous burns, especially in the eyes, have been received by people who add water to acid rather than acid to water. This applies only to powerful dehydrating agents such as sulfuric acid. Hydrochloric and nitric acids do not behave in this way.

Dilute sulfuric acid behaves as a typical acid. It ionizes into bisulfate ions, HSO_4^-, and sulfate ions, $SO_4^=$.

$$H_2SO_4 \rightleftarrows H^+ + HSO_4^-$$

$$HSO_4^- \rightleftarrows H^+ + SO_4^=$$

It is a strong acid, reacting vigorously with the more active metals, such as zinc, to give hydrogen and zinc sulfate;

$$Zn + H_2SO_4 \rightarrow ZnSO_4 + H_2$$

and, of course, it readily neutralizes bases such as sodium hydroxide.

$$2NaOH + H_2SO_4 \rightarrow Na_2SO_4 + 2H_2O$$

Sulfuric acid also has properties conferred on it by the sulfate ion. For instance, with barium salts, sulfuric acid forms insoluble barium sulfate.

$$BaCl_2 + H_2SO_4 \rightarrow \underline{BaSO_4} + 2HCl$$

Barium sulfate is insoluble in acids, the formation of this white precipitate being a good test for the sulfate ion.

Because of its fairly high boiling point, in the neighborhood of 300° C., sulfuric acid can be used to displace other, lower-boiling acids. For instance, the treatment of sodium chloride with concentrated sulfuric acid yields hydrogen chloride which, in water, forms hydrochloric acid.

$$NaCl + H_2SO_4 \rightarrow NaHSO_4 + HCl$$

or

$$2NaCl + H_2SO_4 \rightarrow Na_2SO_4 + 2HCl$$

Sulfuric acid also has useful properties as a catalyst. A large number of organic reactions take place in the presence of sulfuric acid added either as a dehydrating agent, as a catalyst, or as both.

To summarize, the importance of sulfuric acid depends on its varied usefulness and its low cost. Its properties include action as acid, sulfate, catalyst, oxidizing agent, and dehydrating agent. It is sold in various concentrations and purities, from fairly dilute water solution, to solutions containing an excess of SO_3 in pure H_2SO_4. Such mixtures, called **"oleum"** or pyrosulfuric acid, $H_2S_2O_7$, are very powerful and useful reagents.

In peacetime most of the tonnage of sulfuric acid goes into fertilizer manufacture. Very large amounts are also used in the manufacture of explosives, such as T.N.T., and for other chemicals. The iron and steel industry uses large amounts for the *pickling* of sheets before galvanizing or electroplating. Other large users are petroleum, coal products, paints, textiles, and cellulose film. It is not infrequently said that the industrial importance of a nation may be estimated from its annual production of sulfuric acid.

88. SULFATES

It will be recalled that sulfuric acid in water ionizes to form hydrogen ions, bisulfate ions, HSO_4^-, and sulfate ions, $SO_4^=$. The arrangement of atoms in the sulfate ion may be indicated structurally by a formula such as shown.

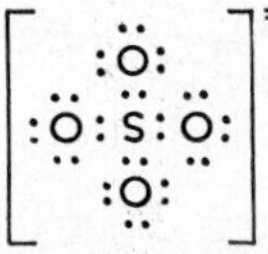

$$
\begin{bmatrix}
\ddot{O}: \\
:\ddot{O}:S:\ddot{O}: \\
:\ddot{O}:
\end{bmatrix}^=
$$

sulfate ion

This ion may combine with positive ions to form compounds. With one hydrogen ion the substance formed is, of course, the bisulfate ion, or with two hydrogen ions, the compound is hydrogen sulfate or sulfuric acid.

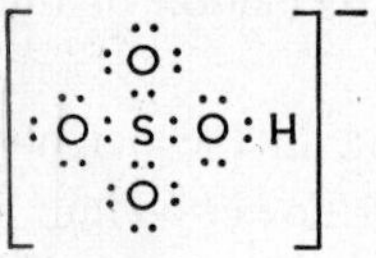

$$
\begin{bmatrix}
:\ddot{O}: \\
:\ddot{O}:S:\ddot{O}:H \\
:\ddot{O}:
\end{bmatrix}^-
\qquad
H:\ddot{O}:S:\ddot{O}:H
$$

bisulfate ion 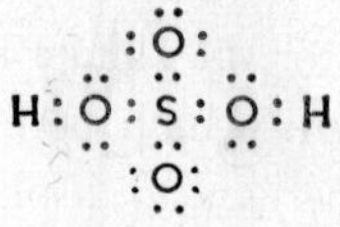   sulfuric acid

It should be emphasized once more that these electronic structures are formal representations rather than true pictures of what the substances look like.

The sulfate and bisulfate ions can combine with many positive ions. For instance, with sodium ion the products are respectively sodium sulfate and sodium bisulfate.

$$2Na^+ + SO_4^= \rightarrow Na_2SO_4$$
sodium sulfate

$$Na^+ + HSO_4^- \rightarrow NaHSO_4$$
sodium bisulfate

Sodium sulfate occurs in nature as the mineral *thenardite* in parts of the United States, Canada, and Siberia. It is also a by-product in some industrial chemical operations, such as the manufacture of hydrogen chloride from sodium chloride and sulfuric acid.

$$2NaCl + H_2SO_4 \rightarrow Na_2SO_4 + 2HCl$$

Sodium sulfate is a moderately important article of commerce. It is used in the manufacture of the cheaper grades of glass and of coarse wrapping paper. Compounds related to sodium sulfate are potassium sulfate, K_2SO_4, and ammonium sulfate, $(NH_4)_2SO_4$. Both are used extensively as fertilizers. Magnesium sulfate, $MgSO_4$, is well known as the heptahydrate, $MgSO_4 \cdot 7H_2O$, or Epsom salts. It has a very disagreeable taste and a powerful purgative action. Industrially, considerable tonnages are used in the manufacture of paints and soaps, in tanning and dyeing, and in the treatment of cotton fabrics.

Calcium sulfate, $CaSO_4$, occurs in nature in the anhydrous form, but more commonly as the dihydrate, $CaSO_4 \cdot 2H_2O$, or *gypsum*. Certain types of the dihydrate are known as alabaster. Gypsum has a number of uses and is an important article of commerce. In various forms it is used in cement, as a corrector for alkaline soils, in the manufacture of tile, wallboard, glass, terra cotta, pottery, and various types of plaster.

When gypsum is heated to about $125°$ C., it loses part of its water of hydration, forming the hemihydrate, $(CaSO_4)_2 \cdot H_2O$.

$$2CaSO_4 \cdot 2H_2O \rightarrow (CaSO_4)_2 \cdot H_2O + 3H_2O$$

This substance is known as **plaster of Paris,** and is a white powder. When mixed with water it reverts to gypsum in a few minutes.

$$\underset{\text{plaster of Paris}}{(CaSO_4)_2 \cdot H_2O} + \underset{\text{water}}{3H_2O} \rightarrow \underset{\text{gypsum}}{2CaSO_4 \cdot 2H_2O}$$

The gypsum crystals grow rapidly, interlacing throughout the mass until the final product is a comparatively hard, solid block. This is how plaster casts are made. As the reaction takes place, the gypsum expands slightly so that a very sharp impression is made. This makes the plaster method particularly useful in statuary production, such as making a bronze statue from a clay model, and also in making artificial dentures.

Barium sulfate, $BaSO_4$, occurs as the mineral *barite*. This compound is highly insoluble in water and is, accordingly, easily prepared by mixing any soluble barium salt such as the nitrate with any substance which gives sulfate ions.

$$Ba(NO_3)_2 + H_2SO_4 \rightarrow BaSO_4 + 2HNO_3$$

The ionic change taking place is simply

$$Ba^{++} + SO_4^{=} \rightarrow BaSO_4$$

Most barium sulfate is used in drilling deep oil wells; its high density aids in controlling gas pressures. Other uses are as a filler in paper, ceramics, and oilcloth, and as permanent white pigment in paints, cosmetics, and glass.

Considerable quantities of barium sulfate are used in **lithopone.** This is a white paint body formed by reacting solutions of zinc sulfate and barium sulfide.

$$BaS + ZnSO_4 \rightarrow BaSO_4 + ZnS$$

Both zinc sulfate and barium sulfide are soluble in water, but both barium sulfate and zinc sulfide are insoluble. Lithopone has the advantage over white lead paints in that it is not discolored by hydrogen sulfide. Barium sulfate is also used for X-ray examination of the gastrointestinal tract.

Aluminum sulfate, $Al_2(SO_4)_3$, does not occur in nature, but it may be prepared by the action of sulfuric acid on aluminum hydroxide. The salt is generally crystallized with eighteen molecules of water, $Al_2(SO_4)_3 \cdot 18H_2O$. Aluminum sulfate hydrolyzes in water.

$$Al_2(SO_4)_3 + 6H_2O \rightarrow 2Al(OH)_3 + 3H_2SO_4$$

It is used in fixing dyes, and in the purification of water. As previously pointed out, the gelatinous aluminum hydroxide formed by hydrolysis of aluminum sulfate adsorbs and carries away solid impurities and some bacteria.

If solutions of potassium sulfate and aluminum sulfate are mixed and then evaporated, there appear colorless crystals of a double salt. The formula of this double salt is $KAl(SO_4)_2 \cdot 12H_2O$. This compound is ordinary **alum.** Alum is used in the manufacture of paper, in purifying water, and in dyeing. There are many different types of alums, formed by replacing the potassium by another ion with a charge of plus one, or by replacing the aluminum by some other ion with a charge of plus three. The sulfur is also capable of replacement. Sodium aluminum alum, $NaAl(SO_4)_2 \cdot 12H_2O$, is used in some types of baking powders.

In addition to these oxy-acid salts of sulfur, one other will be mentioned. If sodium sulfite solution is boiled with sulfur, there is formed a solution of sodium thiosulfate, $Na_2S_2O_3$.

$$Na_2SO_3 + S \rightarrow Na_2S_2O_3$$

The hydrate, $Na_2S_2O_3 \cdot 5H_2O$, is well known as photographer's **hypo.**

89. SULFIDES

When hydrogen is passed over, or bubbled through, heated sulfur some combination takes place to form hydrogen sulfide, H_2S.

$$H_2 + S \rightarrow H_2S$$

This method of preparation is, however, not very satisfactory. Better results are obtained by treating any metallic sulfide with dilute acid. For general laboratory use iron sulfide is treated with dilute hydrochloric acid.

$$FeS + 2HCl \rightarrow FeCl_2 + H_2S$$

A Kipp generator is convenient for this purpose. The hydrogen sulfide so obtained is not very pure. When higher purity is desired, calcium sulfide may be used.

$$CaS + 2HCl \rightarrow CaCl_2 + H_2S$$

Hydrogen sulfide is a colorless gas with a highly offensive odor. The odor is that of rotten eggs, in which the gas is generated from the sulfur in the yolks. This gas is exceedingly poisonous. Its toxicity is approximately the same as that of hydrogen cyanide, which is generally considered to be among the most toxic gases known. Although hydrogen sulfide has a very unpleasant, nauseating smell, the nose becomes accustomed to the odor in time, until the gas seems much less objectionable than at first. This is one of the chief dangers because it is then possible to breathe a dangerous or fatal dose without being aware of anything wrong. The gas acts to produce unconsciousness, with little or no warning. Persons overcome with the gas must be removed to the fresh air with utmost speed.

Hydrogen sulfide is not a very stable compound; moderately elevated temperatures result in its complete decomposition to hydrogen and sulfur. Hydrogen sulfide burns in air with the formation of sulfur dioxide and water,

$$2H_2S + 3O_2 \rightarrow 2SO_2 + 2H_2O$$

but if a cold dish is held in the flame, free sulfur is deposited as a yellow spot on the dish.

$$2H_2S + O_2 \rightarrow 2H_2O + 2S$$

Hydrogen sulfide tarnishes most metals, even fairly inactive ones like silver, in the presence of air. The tarnish consists of the sulfide of the metal. With sulfur dioxide in the presence of a little moisture, hydrogen sulfide gives free sulfur and water.

$$2H_2S + SO_2 \rightarrow 3S + 2H_2O$$

This reaction is thought to contribute to the formation of free sulfur in volcanic regions.

Hydrogen sulfide dissolves in water to a moderate degree. The resulting solution has slight acid properties, owing to the small ionization to form hydrosulfide ion, HS^-, and sulfide ion, $S^=$.

$$\overset{+}{H_2}\overset{=}{S} \rightleftarrows H^+ + \overset{+}{H}\overset{=}{S}$$

$$\overset{+}{H}\overset{=}{S} \rightleftarrows H^+ + S^=$$

Hydrogen sulfide in water is, therefore, sometimes called hydrosulfuric acid. Like other acids it has the property of neutralizing bases, with the formation of sulfides. Many metallic sulfides are insoluble.

Hydrogen sulfide can act as a reducing agent. For instance, with ferric chloride in acid solution, the oxidation state of the iron is reduced from $+3$ to $+2$, while the sulfur goes from -2 to zero.

$$2FeCl_3 + H_2S \rightarrow 2FeCl_2 + S + 2HCl$$

An important use of hydrogen sulfide is found in qualitative analysis for the metal ions. It so happens that not only are many sulfides insoluble in water, but their colors are often quite distinctive. For instance, copper sulfide is black, cadmium sulfide is yellow, antimony sulfide is orange, zinc sulfide is white.

$$CuCl_2 + H_2S \rightarrow CuS + 2HCl$$

$$CdCl_2 + H_2S \rightarrow CdS + 2HCl$$

$$2SbCl_3 + 3H_2S \rightarrow Sb_2S_3 + 6HCl$$

$$ZnCl_2 + H_2S \rightarrow ZnS + 2HCl$$

Many metal sulfides may also be prepared by direct combination of the elements. If iron powder and sulfur are heated together, the mass glows for a moment and is converted to iron sulfide.

$$Fe + S \rightarrow FeS$$

The same is true of many other metals, some of which, like aluminum, combine with sulfur with almost explosive violence.

It should be pointed out again that many elements occur in nature as the sulfide. Sulfides of iron, copper, lead, and zinc are very common as minerals, and in some cases constitute the most important natural mineral resource of these metals.

90. SELENIUM

Directly under sulfur in Group 6 of the Periodic Table there appears the element selenium. This element was discovered by Berzelius in 1817 and called selenium from the Greek word *selenos,* meaning the moon. The element is found associated with sulfur in relatively small quantities.

Like sulfur, selenium has several allotropic forms. There are two red monoclinic forms, a metallic form, and an amorphous form. Like sulfur, selenium is a solid at room temperature. The metallic form has the peculiar property of changing its electrical conductivity on exposure to light. Selenium is, therefore, used to make light-sensitive cells, but other types of photo-electric cells are used more frequently. Selenium is widely used in rectifiers for converting alternating current (A.C.) to direct current (D.C.).

In its chemical properties, selenium closely resembles sulfur, as would be inferred from its position in the Periodic Table. Thus, it burns in air to form selenium dioxide, which is a white solid.

$$Se + O_2 \rightarrow SeO_2$$

There are two common acids of selenium: a rather unstable selenous acid, H_2SeO_3, and selenic acid, H_2SeO_4, which closely resembles sulfuric acid. The corresponding salts—such as sodium selenite, Na_2SeO_3, and sodium selenate, Na_2SeO_4—are also well known.

Metals combine with selenium to form selenides. For instance, powdered iron combines with powdered selenium to form iron selenide,

$$Fe + Se \rightarrow FeSe$$

in a manner exactly analogous to the formation of iron sulfide. If a metallic selenide is treated with dilute acid, hydrogen selenide is formed.

$$FeSe + 2HCl \rightarrow FeCl_2 + H_2Se$$

Hydrogen selenide is an extremely poisonous gas, which will precipitate many metal selenides from solution.

$$Pb(NO_3)_2 + H_2Se \rightarrow PbSe + 2HNO_3$$

It will be clear that selenium is both chemically and physically very much like sulfur. There are, however, differences between the two elements. Thus selenites and selenates are more easily reduced than sulfites and sulfates. Hydrogen selenide is somewhat less stable than hydrogen sulfide. But this pair of elements serves as an excellent example of how, through knowing the chemical properties of one element, it is possible to predict the properties of other elements adjacent to it and in the same group of the Periodic Table.

Selenium is used principally in the manufacture of glass to eliminate the greenish color caused by iron. It is also used for making ruby glass and red pigments. Considerable amounts are used in the production of rubber.

Selenium is poisonous in all its compounds, particularly so in the reduced, selenide form. The element occurs in the soil of various regions in the United States. In certain circumstances selenium enters into growing vegetation in the same way that sulfur normally takes part in the growth of plants. This seems to be particularly true when the soil is poor in sulfur and relatively rich in selenium. The vegetation does not appear to be greatly affected, but animals and humans eating such vegetation are often severely poisoned. In man the early symptoms are general debility and a persistent halitosis, as of garlic. More severe symptoms include mental disorders and scaling of the skin. Animals often show an erosion of the bones in the legs, with hoof abnormalities, and anemia. Death often results.

Selenium poisoning is found especially in parts of South Dakota and Wyoming. It will be recalled that at the famous battle called Custer's Last Stand a relief expedition failed to reach General Custer in time. It has generally been thought that this was in part due to timidity or lack of aggressiveness on the part of the officer commanding the relief expedition. He, however, in his official report blamed a peculiar sickness which affected his horses. Some truth to this story is lent by the fact that the route of the relief expedition lay through seleniferous regions.

Below selenium in the Periodic Table lie the elements tellurium and polonium. Tellurium is well known but has few uses. Its chemical properties resemble those of selenium. Polonium is a very rare, radioactive element.

91. EQUATION WRITING

There is no easy method for writing equations. But each equation involves several steps and it is possible to give some rules covering some of the steps. The several steps are:

1. Knowing the reactants and products.
2. Expressing these in formulas.
3. Balancing the equation.

The course of a chemical reaction can, in general, be found only by experiment. All the equations in this book are the result of someone's careful experimentation. The student must realize that this phase of chemistry calls for much memorization. It is true that trained chemists often predict the course of reactions with astonishing accuracy, but it is always direct experiment which establishes the facts. Valuable new reactions are not infrequently discovered quite by accident. For knowing the reactants and products the student must have recourse to texts, reference books, and experimentation. There are, however, a few general considerations which may be helpful.

a. Direct combination, or synthesis, is often used in the preparation of compounds. For instance, sulfur dioxide may be prepared by the direct union of sulfur and oxygen.

b. Decomposition often yields elements as in $2HgO \rightarrow 2Hg + O_2$; or other compounds as in $NH_4NO_3 \rightarrow N_2O + 2H_2O$.

c. Double decomposition between salts in solution seems to involve a change of partners as in $NaCl + AgNO_3 \rightarrow AgCl + NaNO_3$, but if this reaction is written in the form of the ions which are known to be present, $Na^+ + Cl^- + Ag^+ + NO_3^- \rightarrow AgCl + Na^+ + NO_3^-$, the reaction is seen to be merely a kind of synthesis, $\overline{Ag^+ + Cl^-} \rightarrow \underline{AgCl}$. It is more instructive to write as ions all substances which are chiefly present as ions in solution.

d. In an ionic reaction whenever it is possible for a precipitate to form, as in the example above, the reaction generally occurs. Similarly, when it is possible for a gas to be liberated, this generally occurs, as in the reaction:

$$Na_2SO_3 + 2HCl \rightarrow 2NaCl + H_2O + SO_2$$

The same is true of many reactions in which a substance only slightly ionized may be formed. This occurs in neutralizations such as:

$$NaOH + HCl \rightarrow H_2O + NaCl$$

the reaction going virtually to completion to the right because water is only very slightly ionized.

e. Whenever an oxidizing agent is mixed with a reducing agent there is a probability of reaction, as in the oxidation of sulfurous acid to sulfuric acid by oxygen. It will be noted that most examples of synthesis and of decomposition involve oxidation and reduction, as do displacement reactions such as the displacement of copper from copper sulfate solution by the action of metallic zinc.

In many reactions, particularly those which occur between ions in solution, various ionic groups such as sulfate ($SO_4^=$), nitrate (NO_3^-), and perchlorate (ClO_4^-) retain their identity. The formulas of these important ions and others given in Table 3 (p. 47) should be memorized as they are encountered in the text or laboratory.

Expressing the reactants and products in formulas also calls for a substantial burden on the memory. If the substance is ionic (electrovalent) then the formula is simply a combination of ions as given in Table 3, with due regard for the fact that the resultant charge on the formula must add to zero. Thus the formula for bismuth ferrocyanide is made up of Bi^{+++} and $Fe(CN)_6^{\equiv}$. The least common multiple of three and four is twelve. It will require four Bi^{+++} ions with a total charge of $+12$ to balance three $Fe(CN)_6^{\equiv}$ ions with a total charge of -12. The formula is then $Bi_4[Fe(CN)_6]_3$.

With respect to covalent compounds it is probably best to attempt memorization of the formulas whenever the compounds are encountered. In most compounds it is possible to assign oxidation states to all the elements present, although sometimes this procedure has to be rather arbitrary. When this is done, care must be taken, as in dealing with ionic substances, to see that the sum of the oxidation states of the various elements in the formula of the compound adds to zero. Rules for assignment of oxidation states were given on p. 148. In a substance such as sodium thiosulfate, $Na_2S_2O_3$, it is difficult to know what should be done about the two sulfur atoms. If they both have the same oxidation state it must be $+2$, but other possibilities are $+4$ and zero, and $+6$ and -2. In the cases of simple ions such as Na^+ and $S^=$ the oxidation states are equal to the charges on the ions, but in many other cases they are little more than arbitrary numbers assigned as an aid to memory and as an aid in balancing equations as shown below.

Equations which do not involve oxidation and reduction rarely offer difficulty in balancing. But when oxidation and reduction occur the equation may be quite troublesome. Two examples will be given of a method which is useful.

The first example will be the catalytic oxidation of ammonia by oxygen to form nitric oxide and water.

(1) Show oxidation states of all elements taking part in the reaction. (An element not combined with another element is considered to have an oxidation state of zero.)

$$N^{-3}H^{+1}_3 + O^0_2 \rightarrow N^{+2}O^{-2} + H^{+1}_2O^{-2}$$

It will be noted that only nitrogen and oxygen undergo a change of oxidation state in this reaction. The hydrogen remains unchanged.

(2) The nitrogen is oxidized from -3 to $+2$, a change of $+5$. The oxygen is reduced from 0 to -2, a change of -2.

(3) Oxidation must always be accompanied by, and equal to, reduction. The gain by the nitrogen must equal the loss by the oxygen. The least common multiple of 5 and 2 is 10. It is, therefore, necessary to take two nitrogen atoms, each going from -3 to $+2$, to balance five oxygen atoms, each going from -2 to 0. Provisionally the equation is:

$$2NH_3 + 2\tfrac{1}{2}O_2 \rightarrow 2NO + 3H_2O$$

(4) The equation may be cleared of the fraction by multiplying everything by two:

$$4NH_3 + 5O_2 \rightarrow 4NO + 6H_2O$$

In many oxidations and reductions the charge may be thought of as a loss or gain of electrons respectively. For instance, when Cu^0 is oxidized to Cu^{++} it is clear that two electrons are lost. The change of oxidation state may be considered in terms of loss and gain of electrons, if it is so desired. In some reactions oxidation and reduction take place with no very obvious loss or gain of electrons. For that reason, the purely arbitrary method of assigning oxidation states is presented here.

This section will conclude with one more example of the method for balancing oxidation-reduction equations. The reaction is the production of chlorine from hydrochloric acid by the action of potassium permanganate.

(1) Show the oxidation states of all elements which undergo oxidation or reduction. In the following example these elements are chlorine and manganese.

$$HCl^{-1} + KMn^{+7}O_4 \rightarrow Cl^0_2 + KCl^{-1} + Mn^{+2}Cl_2^{-1} + H_2O$$

(2) The chlorine is oxidized from -1 to 0, a net change of $+1$. But it will be noted that some of the chlorine undergoes no oxidation but is simply used as Cl^{-1} to form KCl and $MnCl_2$.

(3) The manganese is reduced from $+7$ to $+2$, a net change of -5.

(4) The total gain of oxidation states must equal the total loss; hence it will be necessary to take 5 chlorine, in the form of HCl, and 1 manganese, in the form of $KMnO_4$. As a tentative equation we then have:

$$5HCl + KMnO_4 \rightarrow 2\tfrac{1}{2}Cl_2 + ?KCl + ?MnCl_2 + ?H_2O$$

But this involves $2\tfrac{1}{2}Cl_2$, which may be cleared to a whole number by taking 10HCl and $2KMnO_4$:

$$10HCl + 2KMnO_4 \rightarrow 5Cl_2 + ?KCl + ?MnCl_2 + ?H_2O$$

(5) Now note that $2KMnO_4$ will yield $2KCl + 2MnCl_2$ for which a total of 6 chlorine will be required. These 6 chlorine undergo no oxidation. We add these 6 chlorine to the 10 chlorine which do undergo oxidation, and the complete balanced equation is then:

$$16HCl + 2KMnO_4 \rightarrow 5Cl_2 + 2KCl + 2MnCl_2 + 8H_2O$$

EXERCISES

A. *Define or explain the following:*

allotropy	metal
alum	nonmetal
dehydrating	oleum
dioxide	oxidation
fungicide	peroxide
gypsum	pickling (of metal)
iron pyrites	plaster of Paris
lithopone	reduction

B. 1. Indicate procedures and all equations for the following:

  a. Frasch process (no equation)

  b. preparation of iron sulfide, sulfur dioxide, hydrogen sulfide

  c. preparation of carbon disulfide

  d. rhombic, monoclinic, and plastic sulfur (no equation)

  e. $Cu + 2H_2SO_4$ (hot, conc.) $\rightarrow$ $Cu\,SO_4 + SO_2 + 2H_2O$

  f. $2Na_2SO_3 + 4HCl \rightarrow 4NaCl + 2SO_2 + 2H_2O$

  g. $SO_2 + H_2O \rightarrow$ H_2SO_3

  h. ionization of sulfurous acid (2 steps) $H_2SO_3 \rightleftharpoons H^+ + HSO_3^-$ $HSO_3^- \rightleftharpoons H^+ + SO_3^=$

  i. oxidation of sulfurous acid $2H_2SO_3 + O_2 \rightarrow 2H_2SO_4$

  j. reaction of sulfurous acid with a base $H_2SO_3 + NaOH \rightarrow NaHSO_3 + H_2O$

  k. a bisulfite plus an acid

  l. contact process for sulfuric acid $S + O_2 \rightarrow SO_2 \mid 2SO_2 + O_2 \rightarrow 2SO_3 \mid SO_3 + H_2O \rightarrow H_2SO_4$

  m. $S + 2H_2SO_4$ (hot, conc.) $\rightarrow$ $3SO_2 + 2H_2O$

  n. sugar plus hot concentrated sulfuric acid $C_{12}H_{22}O_{11} (+ H_2SO_4) \rightarrow 12C + 11H_2O$

  o. ionization of sulfuric acid (2 steps) $H_2SO_4 \rightleftharpoons H^+ + HSO_4^- \mid HSO_4^- \rightleftharpoons H^+ + SO_4^=$

  p. "setting" of plaster of Paris $(CaSO_4)_2 \cdot H_2O + 3H_2O \rightarrow 2CaSO_4 \cdot 2H_2O$

  q. hydrolysis of aluminum sulfate $Al_2(SO_4)_3 + 6H_2O \rightarrow 2Al(OH)_3 + 3H_2SO_4$

  r. preparation of sodium thiosulfate $Na_2SO_3 + S \rightarrow Na_2S_2O_3$

  s. burning of hydrogen sulfide (2 reactions) $2H_2S + 3O_2 \rightarrow 2SO_2 + 2H_2O$
  $2H_2S + O_2 \rightarrow 2H_2O + 2S$

   t. $2H_2S + SO_2 \rightarrow$ 3 S + 2 H₂O
   u. ionization of hydrogen sulfide in water (2 steps) H₂S
   v. reducing action of H_2S on ferric chloride
   w. precipitation of metal sulfides by H_2S
   x. preparation of selenium dioxide, hydrogen selenide, lead selenide

2. Explain the necessity for using a catalyst in the contact process for manufacture of sulfuric acid.
3. List properties of sulfuric acid and account for its industrial importance.

C. 1. If concentrated hydrochloric acid is added to a cold, saturated solution of sodium sulfate, a precipitate of sodium chloride appears. Explain.
2. What volume of air (S.C.) is necessary to prepare 1000 kg. of sulfuric acid by the contact process?
3. Show analogies between oxygen, sulfur, and selenium on the basis of: (a) electronic structure, and (b) chemical and physical properties.
4. Sodium sulfide and magnesium sulfide are examples of ionic (electrovalent) compounds; hydrogen sulfide and carbon disulfide are examples of covalent compounds. In calcium sulfate both types of valence forces are to be found. Write probable electronic diagrams for all five substances.
5. The molecule S_2, like O_2, is attracted to a magnet. Write a possible electronic diagram for S_2.
6. In some of the following substances the sulfur can act only to be oxidized (and hence the substance can only be a reducing agent). In others the reverse is true. Which of the following could act only as reducing agents, which only as oxidizing agents, and which as both? H_2S, SO_3, SO_2, S(free), Na_2SO_3, H_2SO_4.
7. The density of rhombic sulfur is 2.06 g. per cc., that of monoclinic is 1.96 g. per cc. Discuss the effect of pressure on the equilibrium

$$S(rhombic) \rightleftarrows S(monoclinic)$$

8. Sulfur vapor is believed to have the formula S_8 at moderate temperatures, and S_2 at higher temperatures. Describe an experiment by which this information could be verified.
9. Sulfurous acid is said to be a weak acid, sulfuric acid fairly strong. What is the experimental criterion for this distinction?
10. Show the oxidation state of each element in the following group of substances and ions: H_2, O_2, H_2O, HCl, HNO_3, $NaNO_3$, Na_2CO_3, CO_2, CS_2, Na_2SO_3, PbO_2 (a dioxide), $SO_4^=$, ClO_4^-, NH_4^+, NO_3^-, NH_4NO_2, $H_4P_2O_7$, Na_2MnO_4, $Zn(ClO_4)_2$, $Na_2Cr_2O_7$.
11. Consider the following:
   a. $CuO + H_2 \rightarrow Cu + H_2O$
   b. $Cl_2 + 2Br^- \rightarrow Br_2 + 2Cl^-$
   c. $Ag^+ + Zn \rightarrow Zn^{++} + Ag$
   d. $H_2SO_4 + NaNO_3 \rightarrow HNO_3 + Na_2SO_4$
   e. $KMnO_4 + MnSO_4 + H_2O \rightarrow MnO_2 + K_2SO_4 + H_2SO_4$
   f. $CuSO_4 + NaOH \rightarrow Cu(OH)_2 + Na_2SO_4$

g. Na_2O_2 (a peroxide) $+ CrCl_3 + NaOH \rightarrow Na_2CrO_4 + NaCl + H_2O$
h. $Al + Cl_2 \rightarrow Al_2Cl_6$
i. $Pb(NO_3)_2 + H_2S \rightarrow PbS + HNO_3$
j. $FeS + O_2 \rightarrow Fe_2O_3 + SO_2$

Show oxidation states for all atoms in the above equations, indicate which reactions involve oxidation and reduction, and balance all equations.

12. Balance the following:

a. $HNO_3 + KI \rightarrow KNO_3 + NO + I_2 + H_2O$
b. $PbO_2 + Pb + H_2SO_4 \rightarrow PbSO_4 + H_2O$
c. $NH_4NO_2 \rightarrow N_2 + H_2O$
d. $Sn^{++} + 2Fe^{+++} \rightarrow 3Fe^{++} + Sn^{++++}$
e. $PbO_2 + H^+ + Mn^{++} \rightarrow Pb^{++} + MnO_4^- + H_2O$

13. In some of the above equations (Question 12) an element acts in more than one way so far as oxidation or reduction is concerned. Point out in which reactions this is true and in each of such cases list: (a) what is oxidized, (b) what is reduced, (c) the oxidizing agent, and (d) the reducing agent.

12.
a.
$$8 \overset{+1}{H} \overset{+5}{N} \overset{-2}{O_3} + 6 \overset{+}{K} \overset{-}{I} \longrightarrow 6 \overset{+1}{K} \overset{+5}{N} \overset{-2}{O_3} + 2 \overset{+2}{N} \overset{=}{O} + 3 \overset{0}{I_2} + 4 \overset{+}{H_2} \overset{=}{O}$$

gain 3 e
(reduced)

lose 1 e$\times 2 = 2e$
oxidized

b.
$$\overset{+4}{Pb} \overset{-2}{O_2} + \overset{0}{Pb} + 2 H_2 \overset{-2}{SO_4} \longrightarrow 2 \overset{+2}{Pb} (SO_4) \overset{-2}{} + 2 H_2 O$$

gain 2 e
reduced

lose 2 e
oxidized

c.
$$(\overset{-4}{N} \overset{+1}{H_4} \overset{+4}{N} \overset{-2}{O_2}) \longrightarrow \overset{0}{N_2} + 2 \overset{+}{H_2} \overset{=}{O}$$

gains 4 e
reduced

loses 4 e
oxidized

d. $2 Sn^{++} + 2 Fe^{+++} \longrightarrow 3 Fe^{++} + Sn^{++++}$

e.
$$5 \overset{+4}{Pb} \overset{-2}{O_2} + 4 H^+ + 2 Mn^{++} \longrightarrow 5 Pb^{++} + 2 \overset{+4}{M} n O_4^- + 2 H_2 O$$

gain 2 e
reduced

lose 2 e
oxidized

CHAPTER 14 CHLORINE AND RELATED ELEMENTS

H																	He
Li	Be	B											C	N	O	F	Ne
Na	Mg	Al											Si	P	S	Cl	A
K	Ca	Sc	Ti	V	Cr	Mn	Fe	Co	Ni	Cu	Zn	Ga	Ge	As	Se	Br	Kr
Rb	Sr	Y	Zr	Nb	Mo	Tc	Ru	Rh	Pd	Ag	Cd	In	Sn	Sb	Te	I	Xe
Cs	Ba	La-Lu	Hf	Ta	W	Re	Os	Ir	Pt	Au	Hg	Tl	Pb	Bi	Po	At	Rn
Fr	Ra	Ac	Th	Pa	U-												

In Group 7, subgroup B, of the Periodic Table there appear five elements. These are fluorine, chlorine, bromine, iodine, and astatine. These elements are called the **halogens,** from a Greek word meaning "salt-producer." With metals such as sodium they all form compounds not unlike ordinary table salt. The halogens constitute one of the most obvious family groups in the Periodic Table. With the exception of astatine they are all industrially important. Chlorine ranks with the most important of all chemical elements.

Reasons for the family resemblances found among the halogens become clear when we consider the arrangement of electrons in these atoms. In the highest normal energy level they all have seven electrons. They can each add one electron to form a negative ion with a minus one charge.

$$:\!\ddot{\text{C}}\text{l}\cdot \ + \ e \ \rightarrow \ :\!\ddot{\text{C}}\text{l}\!:^{-1}$$

chlorine atom + electron → chloride ion

This negative ion is then able, by electrostatic attraction, to combine with other ions, such as that of sodium, Na^+, to form typical salts, of which sodium chloride is one.

Although fluorine is the first halogen in the Periodic Table, we shall start with the most important, which is chlorine.

92. PRODUCTION OF CHLORINE

Chlorine was discovered by the Swedish chemist Carl Wilhelm Scheele in 1774. It was not, however, until about 1809 that the nature of chlorine as a chemical element was proved. Scheele and other distinguished scientists of the time believed chlorine to be a compound containing oxygen.

Chlorine occurs widely distributed on the earth. It never is found as the free element because its chemical activity is very high. But in the form of chlorides it is found in very extensive deposits. Sea water, salt brines, and salt beds are all important sources of chlorine. Most industrial chlorine in the United States is produced from salt brines in the region centering around Lake Erie.

Fig. 14-1. Carl Wilhelm Scheele

Scheele was born in Sweden in 1742. His early life was characterized by poverty and by a disinterested love of chemical experimentation. At the age of fourteen he was apprenticed to an apothecary, and this gave him the opportunity he needed for reading such technical books as were available, and for doing experiments.

Although he made no important theoretical advances, the list of his discoveries is long. Some of his discoveries, such as that of oxygen, were made independently by other workers at about the same time. His discoveries include chlorine, ammonia, hydrogen chloride, arsenic acid, hydrogen fluoride, glycerine, milk sugar, and lactic acid. He also invented many new chemical processes.

Scheele died in 1786. His life can remind us that there are unknown continents still to be discovered in natural science. (*Photo obtained through courtesy of Dr. Ralph E. Oesper, University of Cincinnati*)

In sodium chloride, the chief source of industrial chlorine, the chlorine is in the form of the chloride ion. Production of chlorine is, therefore, essentially a problem of removing an electron from the ion so that an atom of chlorine is formed.

$$:\overset{..}{\underset{..}{Cl}}: \quad \rightarrow \quad :\overset{..}{\underset{..}{Cl}} \cdot \quad + \quad e$$

chloride ion → chlorine atom + electron

Two chlorine atoms then combine to form a molecule of chlorine gas. The molecule of chlorine, Cl_2, is a typical substance formed by covalence, or electron sharing.

$$:\overset{..}{\underset{..}{Cl}} \cdot \quad + \quad \cdot \overset{..}{\underset{..}{Cl}}: \quad \rightarrow \quad :\overset{..}{\underset{..}{Cl}}:\overset{..}{\underset{..}{Cl}}:$$

chlorine atom + chlorine atom → chlorine molecule

It is clear that the main problem in chlorine production is removal of the electron from the ion. Removal of electrons is oxidation, according to the more general definition of that process. The oxidation state of the chlorine must be changed from minus one, as in Cl^-, to zero, as in Cl_2^0.

Removal of electrons may be achieved by the use of chemical oxidizing agents, of which oxygen, lead dioxide, and potassium permanganate are examples; or it may be done by **electrochemical oxidation.** The chemical method is often used for small-scale laboratory preparation of chlorine; the electrochemical method is a common industrial process.

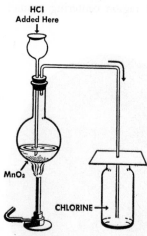

HCl
Added Here

MnO₂

CHLORINE →

Fig. 14-2. Generation of chlorine: $MnO_2 + 4HCl \rightarrow MnCl_2 + Cl_2 + 2H_2O$.

The chemical oxidation of a chloride is illustrated by the passage of hydrogen chloride, HCl, together with air over a catalyst at an elevated temperature. Notice that the chlorine is oxidized, while the oxygen is reduced.

$$4HCl + O_2 \text{ (air)} \rightleftarrows 2Cl_2 + 2H_2O$$

This reversible reaction, known as the Deacon process, was at one time the chief commercial producer of chlorine.

A similar oxidation is caused by manganese dioxide.

$$4HCl + MnO_2 \rightarrow MnCl_2 + Cl_2 + 2H_2O$$

Here the manganese changes oxidation state from four to two. If so desired, the hydrogen chloride may be generated in the same reaction mixture from sodium chloride and sulfuric acid.

$$NaCl + H_2SO_4 \rightarrow NaHSO_4 + HCl$$

If, therefore, we mix sodium chloride, sulfuric acid, and manganese dioxide, chlorine will be given off on gentle heating. A complete equation for this reaction might be written:

$$2NaCl + MnO_2 + 3H_2SO_4 \rightarrow 2NaHSO_4 + MnSO_4 + Cl_2 + 2H_2O$$

This reaction is also convenient for the laboratory preparation of chlorine. Other oxidizing agents which may be used include potassium dichromate, potassium permanganate, lead dioxide, sulfur trioxide, and concentrated nitric acid. Some of these have applications in the industrial production of chlorine.

It will be recalled that when acidified water is electrolyzed, the water decomposes, producing hydrogen at the cathode ($-$), and oxygen at the anode

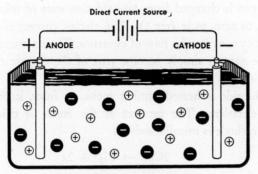

Direct Current Source

ANODE   CATHODE

Fused Sodium Chloride contains
equal numbers of Anions (Cl⁻)
and of Cations (Na⁺)

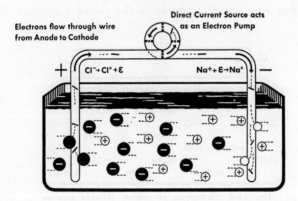

Electrons flow through wire
from Anode to Cathode

Direct Current Source acts
as an Electron Pump

$Cl^- \rightarrow Cl^\circ + \varepsilon$ $Na^+ + \varepsilon \rightarrow Na^\circ$

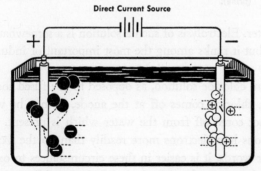

Direct Current Source

Chlorine Atoms combine to form
Chlorine gas (Cl₂) which bubbles
off near the Anode

Sodium appears as bright silvery
liquid metal near the Cathode

Fig. 14-3. Electrolysis of fused sodium chloride.

(+). The oxygen is changed from an oxidation state of minus two, which it has in H_2O, to zero, as in free O_2. The electric current is able to do this because electricity consists of a flow of electrons. The electrons which may be taken from the oxygen simply become part of the electric current flowing through the wires.

If sodium chloride is heated until it melts, or **fuses,** it becomes a good conductor of electricity. The product at the anode is chlorine, and the product at the cathode is metallic sodium.

$$2Cl^- \rightarrow Cl_2{}^0 + 2\epsilon$$

$$Na^+ + \epsilon \rightarrow Na^0$$

This is an important industrial method for the production of both chlorine and sodium. But even more important is the use of a solution of sodium

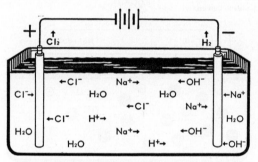

Fig. 14-4. Electrolysis of sodium chloride solution (brine).

chloride in water. Electrolysis of such a solution is a somewhat more complicated process, but it ranks among the most important of industrial chemical operations.

When sodium chloride solution, as opposed to dry fused sodium chloride, is electrolyzed, chlorine comes off at the anode. It may be wondered why oxygen does not come off from the water which is present. The reason is that chloride ions lose electrons more readily than do the oxygen atoms in water. In other words, it is easier in these circumstances to oxidize chlorine from an oxidation state of -1 to 0, than it is to oxidize oxygen from -2 to 0. When both are present in a process, there is a competition between chlorine and oxygen as to which will lose electrons more easily. The chlorine wins.

At the cathode, or negative, pole there are two products. One is hydrogen gas and the other is a solution of sodium hydroxide. It may be wondered why metallic sodium does not appear at the cathode. But, as at the anode, there is also a competition taking place at the cathode. The competition is between hydrogen ions from the water and sodium ions from the sodium chloride. Each can take on electrons to become, in the one case, hydrogen gas, and, in the other, metallic sodium.

$$2H^+ + 2\epsilon \rightarrow H_2$$

$$Na^+ + \epsilon \rightarrow Na^0$$

It is, however, easier to put an electron into a hydrogen ion than it is into a sodium ion. The hydrogen wins this competition.

If part of the hydrogen is removed from water, the remainder is simply the hydroxide ion,

$$H_2O \rightleftarrows H^+ + OH^-$$

which, together with the sodium ions present, forms a solution of sodium hydroxide.

The electrolysis of sodium chloride, or **brine,** solution is easily demonstrated by dipping two platinum electrodes into the solution and allowing a direct current to flow for a few moments. Chlorine is evolved at the positive

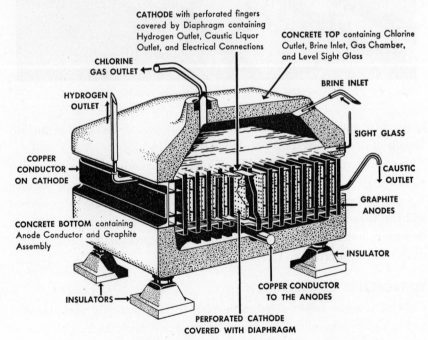

Fig. 14-5. Hooker cell for electrolytic production of chlorine from brine.

pole. Bubbles of hydrogen come off at the negative pole. The fact that sodium hydroxide is also formed around the negative pole is shown by adding a few drops of an indicator solution. The indicator will quickly show the presence of a base in the vicinity of the cathode.

The industrial electrolysis of brine makes use of several types of cells for the efficient utilization of the electric current and the convenient separation

Fig. 14-6. Installation of Hooker cells.

of the three marketable products, chlorine, hydrogen, and sodium hydroxide. Details of one of these cells are shown in Fig. 14-5.

In normal years, annual world production of chlorine is several million tons, a large portion of it being obtained electrolytically. Although chlorine is a gas, it is easily liquefied under pressure. In spite of its highly poisonous and corrosive action, it is shipped under pressure as an article of commerce in steel cylinders and tank cars. With adequate precautions there is little danger in this procedure.

93. PROPERTIES OF CHLORINE

Chlorine is a gas, yellowish-green in color. It has a powerful choking odor, and is highly poisonous. The density of the gas is fairly high; 22.4 liters at standard temperature and pressure weigh 71.99 g. The atomic weight of chlorine is 35.457; the formula for the molecule of chlorine gas must, therefore, be Cl_2.

Chlorine is fairly easily liquefied by cold or by increased pressure, or both. Under normal atmospheric pressure the boiling point of the liquid is $-33.7°$ C. The liquid is yellow. Chlorine is moderately soluble in water. The solution called "chlorine-water" is a common laboratory reagent. As will be shown later, a reversible chemical reaction takes place between chlorine and water.

Chlorine is one of the most reactive of chemical elements. It combines directly with most elements, and indirectly with all but a very few. It shows an astonishing variety and versatility in its various states of combination.

With hydrogen, chlorine combines to form hydrogen chloride.

$$H_2 + Cl_2 \rightarrow 2HCl + 44,060 \text{ cal.}$$

This exothermic reaction takes place with a powerful explosion when the mixture of gases is exposed to bright light as from the sun or from a piece of burning magnesium ribbon. In the dark the mixture of gases may be kept a long time without a perceptible change.

This reaction of hydrogen and chlorine under the influence of light is an example of a photochemical reaction. In this particular reaction the energy of the light is apparently necessary to initiate the change, although once the reaction is started it proceeds violently to completion. An explanation of this action is found in what is called a **chain reaction** mechanism. The first step seems to be the absorption of light by a chlorine molecule, with the formation of chlorine atoms.

$$Cl_2 + \text{light} \rightarrow Cl + Cl$$

This step is called the primary photochemical process and is the only step in which light is necessary.

The next step is for a chlorine atom to react with a hydrogen molecule, yielding a hydrogen chloride molecule and a hydrogen atom.

$$Cl + H_2 \rightarrow HCl + H$$

The hydrogen atom then reacts with another chlorine molecule, forming a hydrogen chloride molecule and a chlorine atom.

$$H + Cl_2 \rightarrow HCl + Cl$$

This chlorine atom then reacts with another hydrogen molecule, and so on, until all the hydrogen and chlorine molecules are used up. This concept of chain reactions has proved very useful in the study of chemical change. It is noteworthy that a very small quantity of air mixed with the hydrogen and chlorine completely stops the explosive reaction between these two gases. The air acts as negative catalyst, or inhibitor. Presumably the air does this by reacting with either the hydrogen atoms or the chlorine atoms and thus stopping the chain reaction. As there are only relatively few hydrogen atoms and chlorine atoms in existence at any instant, it does not take much impurity such as air to react with all of them. In this way the chain is broken and the reaction comes to a stop. The action of catalysts and inhibitors has been greatly cleared up by the concept and study of chain reactions.

It is also clear from this that when we write an equation such as $H_2 + Cl_2 \rightarrow 2HCl$ we do not tell much about the actual mechanism of the change, but rather simply state the initial and final substances present. To present the complete picture of what happens in a chemical reaction is often exceedingly difficult, and has, in fact, been achieved in only a very few cases.

If a burning jet of hydrogen is put into a jar full of chlorine, the hydrogen will continue to burn. The product is, of course, hydrogen chloride. This demonstration proves that chlorine may often support combustion just as well, if not better, than oxygen. The demonstration is somewhat dangerous because of the possibility of explosion.

Chlorine reacts vigorously with many metals. A thin sheet of copper, warmed slightly and thrust into chlorine, burns vigorously, with the formation of cupric chloride.

$$Cu + Cl_2 \rightarrow CuCl_2$$

Similarly, powdered antimony catches fire when sprinkled into chlorine. The product is antimony trichloride.

$$2Sb + 3Cl_2 \rightarrow 2SbCl_3$$

Dry liquid chlorine does not attack steel; hence steel cylinders and tank cars may be used for transporting this substance. However, if the chlorine is moist it will attack the steel.

Chlorine also combines vigorously with many nonmetals, of which phosphorus will serve as an example. With an excess of phosphorus, the product is phosphorus trichloride. With excess of chlorine, phosphorus pentachloride is formed.

$$2P + 3Cl_2 \rightarrow 2PCl_3$$

$$PCl_3 + Cl_2 \rightleftarrows PCl_5$$

If chlorine or chlorine water is added to a solution of sodium or potassium bromide, the characteristic reddish-brown color of free bromine appears. This is a reaction of displacement similar to the displacement of a metal by a more active metal, such as copper by zinc.

$$Cu^{+2}SO_4 + Zn^0 \rightarrow Zn^{+2}SO_4 + Cu^0$$

The equation for the displacement of bromine by chlorine might be written:

$$2NaBr + Cl_2 \rightarrow 2NaCl + Br_2$$

but it will be remembered that in the case of copper and zinc, the only real change taking place is represented by the ionic equation:

$$Cu^{++} + Zn^0 \rightarrow Zn^{++} + Cu^0$$

We may, therefore, write

$$2Br^- + Cl_2^0 \rightarrow 2Cl^- + Br_2^0$$

as representing the displacement of bromine by chlorine.

It will be noted that in this reaction the bromide ion, Br^-, loses one electron, and each chlorine atom gains one. The bromine is oxidized and the chlorine is reduced. The chlorine must obviously be a better oxidizing agent than the bromine.

Chlorine is also able to displace iodine from iodides,

$$2KI + Cl_2 \rightarrow I_2 + 2KCl$$

and bromine is able to displace iodine from iodides,

$$2KI + Br_2 \rightarrow I_2 + 2KBr$$

but bromine cannot displace chlorine from chlorides, and iodine cannot displace either chlorine or bromine from chlorides or bromides, respectively. These elements thus form a series of decreasing activity, not unlike the activity series for the metals.

These several reactions form convenient tests for bromide and iodide. A solution is suspected of containing, say, sodium iodide. To this solution in a test tube there are added a few drops of chlorine water. Iodine, if present, will appear as a brown color in the solution. If now a little carbon tetrachloride or chloroform is added, this solvent will extract the iodine in the form of a characteristic rich purple solution, proving the presence of iodine. Under the same conditions, bromine imparts a yellow to reddish-brown color to the carbon tetrachloride.

With water, chlorine undergoes a reversible reaction to form hydrochloric acid and hypochlorous acid.

$$Cl_2^0 + H_2O \rightarrow HCl^{-1} + HCl^{+1}O$$

chlorine + water → hydrochloric acid + hypochlorous acid

That is to say, chlorine water is not only a solution of chlorine in water. It consists, in part, of two acids formed by interaction of the chlorine with the water. Notice that the chlorine itself is both oxidizing and reducing agent.

One atom of chlorine is reduced to an oxidation state of minus one, the other is oxidized to a state of plus one in hypochlorous acid. This mixture is a good bleaching agent. The properties of hypochlorous acid will, however, be deferred until later.

The reactions presented above by no means exhaust the chemical properties of chlorine. Many other compounds containing chlorine will be described later. It should be pointed out that chlorine is a typical nonmetal. Its oxides dissolve in water to form acids.

Breathing chlorine is always dangerous. Fortunately its powerful suffocating odor gives ample warning of its presence. Only under unusual circumstances do fatalities result, but in World War I the surprise use of chlorine by the Germans caused 15,000 casualties in a few hours. Of these, about 5000 were fatal.

94. USES OF CHLORINE

The use of chlorine in water purification * has already been mentioned in Chapter 8. This procedure was first introduced in Belgium in the year 1902. At the present time the great majority of people in the United States drink chlorinated water. By this means there has been achieved a great measure of control over water-borne bacteria, especially over those which cause the diseases typhoid fever, dysentery, and cholera.

Various water sources require various degrees of chlorination. Those with a high organic content often require much more chlorine than relatively pure well or spring water. The object in general is to have the water reach the consumer with somewhere between a trace and 0.1 to 0.2 parts per million of chlorine. The exact amount needed to control disease-producing bacteria is established by a continuous testing procedure carried out by all properly operated water works. In order to achieve this concentration of chlorine, it is necessary to add a somewhat larger quantity of chlorine, perhaps one part per million or even more, to the water from the intake. This excess chlorine is partly used up in killing bacteria and in other ways.

Chlorine does not kill all bacteria; some are particularly resistant to its action. But it appears that most, if not all, disease-producing bacteria are killed. Besides killing bacteria, the chlorine performs other functions such as removing tastes and odors, helping to keep filter beds clean, and improving the processes used for removal of color in the water. The cost of doing all this is estimated at less than one cent per person per year, surely a remarkable bargain in public health. The urgency of proper chlorination for drinking water is shown by what occurred in Milwaukee one day in 1916. An

* H. E. Babbitt and J. J. Doland, *Water Supply Engineering* (New York: McGraw-Hill, 1939).

attendant at the water works turned off the chlorination machinery for eight hours. It happened that the water was heavily polluted. The results were 50,000 to 60,000 cases of enteritis, 400 to 500 cases of typhoid, and 40 to 50 deaths.

The largest user of chlorine is the **bleaching** industry. Natural or synthetic material nearly always contains matter which imparts to it a gray or brown color. Very large tonnages of chlorine are used to bleach this undesired color out of textiles and paper. The action is one of oxidation, a colorless compound being produced. Not all textiles are treated with chlorine because the action is vigorous and wool and silk are damaged by its use. For these substances sulfur dioxide is often used as the bleaching agent.

In wartime very large amounts of chlorine are used for a host of essential products. Some is used in the bleaching of cotton linters for smokeless powder. For this reason chlorine was scarce during World War II. During the war the paper used in magazines and books was not the glistening white to which we had been accustomed. The reason for this was that insufficient chlorine was available for adequately bleaching the paper. Bleaching by chlorine does not take place in the absence of water. The bleaching agent is not, strictly speaking, the chlorine itself, but is rather the hypochlorous acid formed by reaction of the chlorine with water.

Chlorine has a multitude of uses in the preparation of other substances. Many of these will be described in due course. A few examples are carbon tetrachloride, the chlorides of sulfur, phosphorus chloride, tin tetrachloride, hydrogen chloride, chlorsulfuric acid, and many others. Among the uses of chlorine there may be mentioned the recovery of tin from "tin cans." Tin cans are made of sheet steel with a thin coating of tin to prevent corrosion. Tin is scarce enough, and was especially so during World War II, so that recovery of the tin from used tin cans was necessary. One of the ways of doing this is to pass chlorine over the cans. The tin combines with chlorine to form tin tetrachloride, which is a liquid with a boiling point of 114° C.

$$Sn + 2Cl_2 \rightarrow SnCl_4$$

This substance is, therefore, easily removed from the remaining iron by gentle heating.

Chlorine was introduced as an agent of chemical warfare by the Germans in 1915. Its use for this purpose was based on several factors, the most important of which is its high toxicity. In order to be effective as a poison war gas, a substance must not only be very poisonous but must be dense enough so that it is not immediately dissipated into the air. It must also be capable of being produced on a large scale. Chlorine has a high density, being about two-and-a-half times as dense as air. It is also produced on a very large scale by all industrial nations. Before World War I Germany had almost a world monopoly on chemical industry.

The use of chlorine by the Germans, aided by the element of surprise, achieved a great success from the German point of view. This might even have had a decisive effect if the Germans had exploited it boldly. But the Germans underestimated the effect of the first gas attack and did not take full advantage of it. Defensive measures were quickly found. At first these measures consisted only of a strip of cotton bandage soaked in sodium thiosulfate. This was worn over the mouth and nose during a gas attack. It is said that so great was the urgency on the Allied side that every front-line soldier was supplied with one of these primitive masks in less than two weeks after the first gas attack.

More elaborate gas masks soon became available; these were completely effective against chlorine, and at the present time chlorine, as an agent of chemical warfare, is obsolete. More effective poison gases became available, and better protective means were discovered. Chemical warfare is one of the few horrors which the world was spared in World War II. But if it had broken out, the Allied Nations were more than adequately prepared to meet it.

95. HYDROCHLORIC ACID

When hydrogen and chlorine unite, the product is a gas, hydrogen chloride.

$$H_2 + Cl_2 \rightarrow 2HCl$$

A solution of hydrogen chloride in water is called hydrochloric acid. An old name for hydrochloric acid is "muriatic acid"; this name is still often used in industry.

In recent years an increasingly large amount of hydrochloric acid has been made through direct synthesis from hydrogen and chlorine. These gases are, of course, derived from the electrolysis of brine. The acid so formed is unusually pure.

An older method, until fairly recently the only large-scale producer of hydrochloric acid, is the treatment of sodium chloride with concentrated sulfuric acid. Sodium chloride is chosen because it is the cheapest chloride available, and sulfuric acid because it combines cheapness with a fairly high boiling point.

If concentrated sulfuric acid is added to sodium chloride, the products are hydrogen chloride and sodium bisulfate.

$$2 NaCl + H_2SO_4 \xrightarrow{(dil.)} Na_2SO_4 + 2HCl$$

$$NaCl + H_2SO_4 \text{ (conc.)} \rightleftarrows HCl + NaHSO_4$$

This reaction is reversible, as may readily be shown by passing hydrogen chloride into a saturated solution of sodium bisulfate. When this is done, sodium chloride crystallizes from solution. However, hydrogen chloride is a gas, not very soluble in concentrated sulfuric acid, and the boiling point of sulfuric acid is high, about 338° C. If the mixture is warmed, the gaseous hydrogen chloride is driven off, while the high-boiling sulfuric acid remains behind. The reaction equilibrium is, therefore, displaced to the right until only sodium bisulfate remains.

As performed in the laboratory, this is generally the only reaction which takes place. But industrially it is more economical to treat the sodium bisulfate with more sodium chloride. Then on heating the mixture to redness the following reaction takes place:

$$NaCl + NaHSO_4 \rightleftarrows Na_2SO_4 + HCl$$

There is a good market for both hydrochloric acid and for sodium sulfate. Demand for the latter is particularly great from glassworks.

There is another reaction which, while not of much industrial importance, is interesting from a scientific viewpoint. This is the hydrolysis of certain types of chlorides. If phosphorus trichloride is treated with water it hydrolyzes to give hydrogen chloride and phosphorous acid.

$$PCl_3 + 3H_2O \rightarrow 3HCl + H_3PO_3$$

Sodium chloride will not undergo this type of reaction, but a few other chlorides such as silicon tetrachloride, titanium tetrachloride, and aluminum chloride do it readily.

Hydrogen chloride is a colorless gas with an exceedingly sharp suffocating odor. The gas is poisonous but the odor is so pronounced that injuries from breathing it are rare. This gas is very soluble in water. As measured at standard temperature and pressure, 1 liter of water will dissolve 503 liters of hydrogen chloride. The solution is, of course, concentrated hydrochloric acid.

It might be thought that, as hydrogen chloride is a gas, it could all be removed by boiling the solution. This is not the case. When the concentration of hydrogen chloride in water reaches about 20 per cent (at 760 mm. pressure), the solution distills over unchanged. Such a solution is called a **constant-boiling mixture** because the temperature, as well as the composition, remains constant until all the acid is distilled.

Hydrogen chloride dissolved in water is a typical strong acid, second only to sulfuric acid in importance. The solution has an exceedingly sharp, sour taste; it turns litmus red; it reacts with the more active metals; and it conducts electric current. The products of electrolysis are hydrogen at the cathode and chlorine at the anode. The reaction with zinc is typical of the action of hydrochloric acid on the more active metals. The products are hydrogen and zinc chloride.

$$Zn + 2HCl \rightarrow H_2 + ZnCl_2$$

This, it will be recalled, is a common laboratory preparation method for hydrogen.

Hydrochloric acid neutralizes bases, as do other acids. The reaction with, for instance, potassium hydroxide is

$$\underset{base}{KOH} + \underset{acid}{HCl} \rightarrow \underset{salt}{KCl} + \underset{water}{H_2O}$$

or, written in ionic form:

$$K^+ + OH^- + H^+ + Cl^- \rightarrow K^+ + Cl^- + H_2O$$

In gaseous form, hydrogen chloride is undoubtedly a covalent type of compound, formed by electron sharing between hydrogen and chlorine.

$$H \!:\! \overset{..}{\underset{..}{Cl}} \!:$$

It has, however, some of the characteristics of an electrovalent compound, and these manifest themselves when hydrogen chloride is dissolved in water. The solution becomes a good conductor of electricity, presumably owing to formation of chloride ions and hydronium ions.

$$HCl + H_2O \rightarrow Cl^- + H_3O^+$$

As usual, we shall ignore the hydronium ion and consider it to be simply a hydrogen ion, H^+, except where circumstances require otherwise.

By contrast with this behavior in water solution, hydrogen chloride dissolved in benzene does not conduct the electric current, nor does it have the other properties generally ascribed to acids. This is presumably because in a solvent such as benzene, the hydrogen chloride remains dissolved simply as the HCl molecule, and does not react with the benzene to form ions, as it does with water.

The principal uses of hydrochloric acid are in making other chemicals; other large users include the "pickling" of sheet steel prior to galvanizing, tinning, or enameling. Large amounts are used in the manufacture of glue, textiles, dyes, foods, and soap. A dilute solution of hydrochloric acid is a normal constituent of gastric juices.

96. SODIUM CHLORIDE

Total annual world production of sodium chloride runs into tens of millions of tons. Along with coal, petroleum, air, water, limestone, and some others, sodium chloride is a major raw material and natural resource.

Those who know Niagara Falls only as a scenic wonder may be surprised to learn that the industries in that area consume about 400,000 tons of common salt per year. These industries are located where they are because of the vast power development at the Falls, the great salt fields in the Lake Erie region, and the proximity to potential customers.

Let us consider a typical chemical industry consuming limestone, sodium chloride, and coal, and follow through some of the operations and products derived directly or indirectly from the sodium chloride alone.

The brine is pumped from far below the surface of the earth. Part of it goes to electrolytic cells where the products are hydrogen, sodium hydroxide, and chlorine. The hydrogen is used in the plant, or sold, possibly for the synthesis of ammonia. The sodium hydroxide is purified, dried, and sold for use in such industries as production of other chemicals, rayon, cellophane, textiles, petroleum, pulp and paper, and soap. The chlorine is dried, liquefied by compression, and sold for use in chemical production, paper, sanitation, and textiles.

Another part of the brine is treated with ammonia, then with carbon dioxide. There is formed a precipitate of sodium bicarbonate, and a solution of ammonium chloride. The ammonium chloride is treated with calcium hydroxide to yield ammonia for use over again, and calcium chloride which is used for dust control, ice removal, skidproofing, concrete construction, refrigeration, air drying, coal treatment, and freezeproofing fire barrels.

The sodium bicarbonate is partly purified for sale. It is used for baking powder, pharmaceuticals, foods, and fire extinguishers. The remainder of the sodium bicarbonate is converted to sodium carbonate and is sold for use in glassmaking, chemicals, pulp and paper, metallurgy, and textiles. But part of the sodium carbonate is treated with calcium hydroxide to form pure calcium carbonate. This is used in paper, paint, rubber, printing ink, pharmaceuticals, and foods.

These are only a fraction of the astonishing ramifications of a small part of one chemical industry.

97. OXY-ACIDS AND SALTS OF CHLORINE

It will be recalled that chlorine reacts reversibly with water to form hydrochloric acid and hypochlorous acid.

$$Cl_2 + H_2O \rightleftarrows HCl + HClO$$

Hypochlorous acid is one of a series of oxy-acids of chlorine, that is, acids which contain oxygen. These acids, their formulas, and the oxidation states of the chlorine are shown in Table 10, together with the sodium salt of each acid.

TABLE 10

Oxy-Acids and Salts of Chlorine

Name	Formula	Oxidation State of Cl	Sodium Salt
Hypochlorous acid...	HClO	+1	sodium hypochlorite, NaClO
Chlorous acid........	HClO$_2$	+3	sodium chlorite, NaClO$_2$
Chloric acid.........	HClO$_3$	+5	sodium chlorate, NaClO$_3$
Perchloric acid.......	HClO$_4$	+7	sodium perchlorate, NaClO$_4$

Some of these acids and salts are of considerable importance. This table will also illustrate the common method for naming oxy-acids and salts. The commonest acid, which at one time happened to be *chloric,* is given the ending *-ic.* The salts derived from this acid have the ending *-ate.* The acids with smaller proportions of oxygen are called *-ous,* and *hypo -ous,* respectively, with the corresponding salts, *-ite,* and *hypo -ite.* The acid with a greater proportion of oxygen is given the name *per -ic,* and the salt *per -ate.* It will be recalled that salts of sulfuric acid are sulf*ates,* and salts of sulfurous acid are sulf*ites.*

Hypochlorous acid is the agent responsible for the bleaching action of moist chlorine. It is a very weak acid, that is, it gives a low concentration of hydrogen ions in solution. It is, however, a useful oxidizing agent; in fact, that is the property upon which its bleaching action depends. The acid is never prepared pure because it decomposes whenever an attempt is made to concentrate the solution. A dilute solution of the acid may be made by treating calcium hypochlorite with an acid. Even such a weak acid as carbonic will serve this purpose.

$$Ca(ClO)_2 + H_2CO_3 \rightarrow CaCO_3 + 2HClO$$

The calcium carbonate formed may be removed by filtration.

Hypochlorous acid has the property of decomposing under the action of sunlight, yielding oxygen and hydrochloric acid.

$$2HClO \rightarrow 2HCl + O_2$$

If chlorine water is exposed to sunlight it gradually decomposes, because, with continued removal of the hypochlorous acid, the equilibrium is continually shifted to the right side of the equation as written. The final products are nothing but hydrochloric acid, and oxygen, which normally escapes.

$$2Cl_2 + 2H_2O \rightleftarrows 2HCl + 2HClO \rightarrow 4HCl + O_2$$

When chlorine is passed into a cold solution of a hydroxide one of the products formed is a hypochlorite.

$$Cl_2 + 2NaOH \rightarrow NaCl + NaClO + H_2O$$

This is the principal way in which sodium and calcium hypochlorites are made. A dilute solution containing sodium hypochlorite is sold under the name Zonite for use as an antiseptic. Carrel-Dakin solution, widely used in World War I for the prevention of infection, is a dilute solution of sodium hypochlorite. The mixture formed by the addition of chlorine to a sodium hydroxide solution is naturally a strong bleaching agent because of the hypochlorite present. It is prepared on a very large scale for industrial bleaching operations. Calcium hypochlorite, used also as a bleach and as a disinfectant, has almost entirely replaced "bleaching powder" which was once a very common article of commerce, often found in the household.

When chlorine is passed into a cold solution of sodium hydroxide, the products are sodium chloride and sodium hypochlorite, but if this reaction mixture is allowed to become warm, the reaction yields sodium chlorate instead of sodium hypochlorite.

$$3Cl_2 + 6NaOH \rightarrow 5NaCl + NaClO_3 + 3H_2O$$

Sodium and potassium chlorates are important articles of commerce. Chloric acid solution may be made by treating barium chlorate with sulfuric acid, but there is not very much occasion for preparing this acid.

$$Ba(ClO_3)_2 + H_2SO_4 \rightarrow \underline{BaSO_4} + 2HClO_3$$

Sodium and potassium chlorates are good oxidizing agents. Their use is attended with some danger because traces of acid mixed with chlorates produce the explosive gas, chlorine dioxide, ClO_2. Similarly, chlorates mixed with oxidizable substances, such as charcoal, magnesium, or sulfur, may produce very powerful explosions. These chlorates are used in matches, explosives, and fireworks. They are also used to some extent as weed killers, although this is a rather dangerous practice.

It will be remembered that a useful laboratory preparation of oxygen consists of heating potassium chlorate, especially in the presence of a catalyst such as manganese dioxide or ferric oxide.

$$2KClO_3 \rightarrow 2KCl + 3O_2$$

If potassium chlorate is cautiously heated, in the absence of a catalyst, most of it is converted into potassium perchlorate, together with some potassium chloride.

$$4KCl^{+5}O_3 \rightarrow 3KCl^{+7}O_4 + KCl^{-1}$$

Industrially sodium perchlorate is made by electrolysis of sodium chlorate solution. The reaction is often said to be represented by the following equation, although it is probably more complicated.

$$NaClO_3 + H_2O \xrightarrow{\text{(electrolysis)}} NaClO_4 + H_2$$

Of several methods for producing perchloric acid, one is to treat sodium perchlorate solution with hydrogen chloride. If the solution is concentrated,

$$NaClO_4 + HCl \rightarrow HClO_4 + \underline{NaCl}$$

sodium chloride precipitates and may be removed by filtration. Perchloric acid is an important article of commerce. It is a strong acid and a powerful oxidizing agent. When highly concentrated it is dangerously explosive, but moderately dilute solutions are safe.

98. BROMINE

This element was discovered in 1824 by a French chemist, A.-J. Balard. As not infrequently happens, other scientists had previously worked with the element. At the time Balard's discovery was announced, a celebrated German chemist, Justus von Liebig, actually had a bottle full of bromine on his laboratory shelf. Liebig thought it was a compound of chlorine and iodine.

The name bromine is derived from a Greek word meaning "stench." The element is appropriately named. Because of its great chemical activity, the element does not occur free in nature. It is fairly widely distributed as the bromides of sodium, potassium, and magnesium, but in small amounts compared with chlorine.

Until about 1924 adequate amounts of bromine for industrial and scientific use were derived chiefly from the Stassfurt salt beds in Germany and from the brines of the Lake Erie region. At that time increasingly large amounts of bromine became necessary for the treatment of gasoline. The only source large enough appeared to be the ocean, which contains about 300,000 tons of bromine (as bromide ion) per cubic mile of water. This is not a large concentration of bromine. It works out at only a few cents' worth of bromine per ton of water to be treated. Nevertheless it is at present our chief source of bromine. The annual production of bromine from sea water is now many millions of pounds.

The chief chemical reaction involved in the extraction of bromine is the familiar one of oxidation. The bromine must be oxidized from an oxidation state of minus one as in the bromide, Br^-, ion, to a state of zero, as in free bromine, Br_2^0.

A convenient, cheap oxidizing agent is chlorine. Sea water is treated with chlorine to liberate the bromine.

$$2Br^- + Cl_2 \rightarrow Br_2^0 + 2Cl^-$$

The dilute sea-water solution of bromine is then blown with air. The air sweeps the bromine and excess chlorine out of the water. The mixed gases are then reduced with sulfur dioxide, reoxidized with more chlorine, and finally the bromine is purified by fractional distillation. For satisfactory operation of this process it is necessary to treat the raw, incoming sea water with a little sulfuric acid to establish the proper hydrogen-ion concentration.

The use of sea water as a source of raw material captures the imagination. For thousands of years the sea has been a source of salt. But it also contains inexhaustible supplies of many other valuable substances. The only trouble is that the concentrations are low and the extraction processes expensive. In recent years magnesium has been produced economically from the ocean. It will be interesting to see what product comes next.

On a laboratory scale, bromine is often prepared by the same methods which are used for chlorine. If sodium bromide is mixed with manganese dioxide and sulfuric acid, bromine is liberated.

$$2NaBr + MnO_2 + 3H_2SO_4 \rightarrow Br_2 + 2NaHSO_4 + MnSO_4 + 2H_2O$$

Bromine is a reddish-brown liquid, but its boiling point is only 58.78° C.; consequently it vaporizes easily to form a reddish-brown gas. The gas has a high density, as might be expected from the formula Br_2 and the fairly high atomic weight of bromine. The gas tends to lie heavily along a floor, and to flow into any depression. The reactions of bromine are very similar to those of chlorine. It reacts with many metals and nonmetals to form bromides. It dissolves in water and, to a certain extent, forms hypobromous acid, HBrO. On the whole, bromine is less active than chlorine, but it is nevertheless a dangerous substance to handle. On the skin it quickly makes painful burns. Breathed in large amount it is fatal. A very slight amount of the gas breathed causes a burning, heavy sensation in the throat and chest. This sensation, which causes considerable distress and may lead to hospitalization, often persists for days.

Bromine unites with hydrogen to form hydrogen bromide. This substance is a gas resembling hydrogen chloride in most of its properties. In water it forms hydrobromic acid. It is a better reducing agent and it is less stable than hydrogen chloride. It will be recalled that hydrogen chloride may be prepared by treating sodium chloride with sulfuric acid. It might be thought that a similar method would serve for hydrogen bromide, but this is not the case. If sodium bromide is treated with concentrated sulfuric acid the products are free bromine, sulfur dioxide, sodium sulfate, and water. Hydrogen bromide is sometimes prepared on a laboratory scale by the hydrolysis of phosphorus tribromide.

$$PBr_3 + 3H_2O \rightarrow H_3PO_3 + 3HBr$$

Phosphorus tribromide is conveniently prepared by adding bromine to a mixture of red phosphorus and wet sand. The formation of the tribromide and the subsequent hydrolysis take place smoothly. The purpose of the sand is to slow down the reaction. The principal industrial preparation of hydrogen bromide is, however, through direct union of hydrogen and bromine.

The principal use of bromine is in the treatment of gasoline. Gasoline burns more efficiently in an automobile engine when the rate of explosion is slowed down by the addition of tetraethyllead, $(C_2H_5)_4Pb$. The lead so introduced tends to foul the spark plugs unless there is added a few drops of ethylene dibromide, $C_2H_4Br_2$. The amount of ethylene dibromide per gallon of gasoline is quite small, but the amount of gasoline used is so very great that large tonnages of bromine are required. Hence the necessity arose for large-scale production, which was only possible by the sea-water extraction process.

Bromine and its compounds also have considerable use in the synthesis of other substances in industry and in the laboratory. Silver bromide is used extensively in photography.

The bromides of sodium, potassium, calcium, and ammonium are used in medicine. They have a sedative action and are used, often indiscriminately, to quiet the nerves and to promote sleep. The use of bromides by the layman for these purposes is to be discouraged. A type of poisoning called **bromism** results from continued excessive use of bromides. This in no sense is to be confused with the poisoning produced by the free element bromine. Bromism may appear in the form of a rash, followed by severe nervous and mental symptoms. In some psychopathic hospitals a fairly large fraction of all patients admitted are found to be suffering from bromism. The bromides have a place in medicine, but they should not be taken except under a doctor's direction.

The use of bromides for producing sleep has resulted in adoption of the word "bromide" in quite a different sense. A tedious or dull remark is often said to be a "bromide."

99. IODINE

Iodine was discovered in 1811 by a French chemist, Bernard Courtois. The element is named from a Greek word meaning "violet," because iodine vapor is that color. Iodine is not so active as chlorine and bromine, but is, nevertheless, too active ever to occur in nature as the free element. Iodine is found in very small amounts in sea water as the iodide ion, I^-; and as calcium iodate, $CaIO_3$, mixed with sodium nitrate, or Chile saltpeter. Chile had at one time practically a world monopoly on iodine. The element also occurs in seaweed, and in certain animal organs, particularly the thyroid gland.

Iodine is readily liberated from iodides by methods similar to those used for bromine. Treatment of sodium iodide with chlorine, or with bromine, results in rapid displacement of the iodine. The reaction may be regarded as a removal of an electron from the iodide ion by the more active chlorine or bromine.

$$2I^- + Cl_2 \rightarrow I_2 + 2Cl^-$$

Iodine may also be prepared from iodides through the oxidizing action of manganese dioxide in the presence of sulfuric acid. The reaction is exactly parallel to methods for the preparation of chlorine and bromine.

$$2NaI + MnO_2 + 3H_2SO_4 \rightarrow MnSO_4 + 2NaHSO_4 + I_2 + 2H_2O$$

Iodine is purified by a process known as **sublimation.** Most solids when heated first turn to liquid, then to vapor. Cooling reverses these steps. Iodine is an example of a fairly small group of substances which turn directly from solid to vapor without any liquid being formed whether the element is being heated or cooled. The iodine is said to sublime. If impure iodine undergoes sublimation, many impurities are removed, just as they are often removed by the process of distillation.

At the present time fairly large amounts of iodine are produced in the United States from oil-well brines. During World War I iodine was so scarce that plants were established on the West Coast for extraction of the element from seaweed. Annual consumption of iodine in the United States averages between one and two million pounds.

Iodine is a black solid with almost a metallic luster. But in spite of its appearance it cannot be considered a metal. It does not conduct electricity, and its oxides are acidic. As previously mentioned, gentle heating of iodine produces a violet vapor. The element dissolves to a slight extent in water, forming a brown solution. It dissolves to a much greater extent in benzene, carbon tetrachloride, chloroform, and related solvents, in all of which it forms a rich purple solution. Iodine also dissolves readily in a water solution of an iodide. For instance, an aqueous potassium iodide solution dissolves large quantities of iodine. Presumably this is due to the formation of a so-called "addition" compound between the iodine and the iodide,

$$KI + I_2 \rightarrow KI_3$$

or, written in ionic form:

$$I^- + I_2 \rightarrow I_3^-$$

Iodine is a good oxidizing agent and is a fairly active element. Nevertheless it is decidedly less active than the other common halogens. It is displaced from iodides by chlorine and bromine, and it undergoes oxidation to higher valence states as in iodic acid, HIO_3, and the iodates. When iodine vapor is mixed with hydrogen and passed over a catalyst, a little hydrogen iodide is formed. This reaction is endothermic and not too satisfactory, but it is the chief industrial method for the preparation of hydrogen iodide. Another way to prepare this substance is by hydrolysis of phosphorus triiodide.

$$PI_3 + 3H_2O \rightarrow H_3PO_3 + 3HI$$

This reaction is, of course, analogous to a method for the preparation of hydrogen bromide. The red phosphorus and iodine may be mixed in a flask to which water is added slowly.

Hydrogen iodide dissolves in water to form hydriodic acid. This is a strong acid and a useful reducing agent. It has the characteristic sharp suffocating odor possessed also by hydrogen chloride and hydrogen bromide.

While iodine has a very sharp smell, it is not nearly so dangerous as chlorine or bromine. The element itself is poisonous when taken internally, but the danger from breathing the fumes is much less than is the case for the other halogens.

In the laboratory, iodine is used as a standard oxidizing agent. It is also used as a sensitive test for starch. When starch comes in contact with iodine a bluish-black color is formed. This color may be due less to a definite chemical compound than to a colloidal effect. In any event, the development of this color makes a good test for starch or, conversely, for iodine. The test may also be adapted for certain oxidizing agents. For instance, if a piece of paper is dipped into a starch solution, then into potassium iodide (which has no effect on starch), then the action of any oxidizing agent is to convert the iodide to iodine, which in turn gives the black color with the starch.

The most important use of iodine and its compounds is in medicine. The element has two principal medical uses: as a germicide, and in the treatment of certain thyroid conditions.

Iodine is a very strong agent against bacteria. It is one of the oldest germicides and it remains one of the best. It is generally used as a tincture, that is, a solution of iodine and sodium or potassium iodide dissolved in ethyl alcohol. Ordinary household iodine solutions contain only a few per cent of the element, but are none the less highly effective. It should be pointed out that the element iodine is the germicidal agent and that sodium and potassium iodides have no such action.

The other major use of iodine in medicine is in connection with the thyroid. This gland, situated at the front of the neck, secretes a compound called thyroxin. Thyroxin contains iodine. Failure of the gland to function properly, either through lack of iodine in the diet, or for other causes, produces such conditions as goiter, cretinism, myxedema, and other very grave diseases. Lack of iodine in food often results in goiter. For this reason, iodine in the form of potassium iodide is now commonly added to common table salt. A person requires only about 75 milligrams of iodine per year, but there can be no question that this addition to the diet has markedly decreased the incidence of goiter. This is particularly true in the Great Lakes region of the United States, where the natural iodine content of the soil is low.

100. FLUORINE

Although this element stands above chlorine in the Periodic Table, it has been deferred until last. Until a few years ago, fluorine was not a very important element. Its chemistry was diffi-
cult and not well understood. There were few uses which required a large tonnage of the element. This situation has greatly changed, especially during the years of World War II. The most spectacular use of fluorine is in the compound uranium hexafluoride which made possible the atomic bomb.

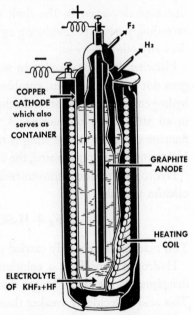

Fig. 14-7. Cell for production of fluorine. (After W. N. Jones, *Inorganic Chemistry*, Blakiston Company, 1947. By permission)

Compounds of fluorine have been known for a long time and the existence of the element has been understood for many years. Credit for the first preparation of the free element is generally given to a celebrated French chemist, Henri Moissan. In 1886 he electrolyzed a solution of potassium hydrogen fluoride, KHF_2, in liquid anhydrous hydrogen fluoride, HF. The name "fluorine" is derived from a Latin word meaning "to flow" because of the use of calcium fluoride as a flux in metallurgical operations.

Fluorine is certainly one of the most active, if not *the* most active, of elements known. It never occurs free in nature, but in various minerals it is fairly widely distributed. These minerals are fluorite, or fluorspar, which is calcium fluoride, CaF_2; cryolite, $AlF_3 \cdot 3NaF$; and fluorapatite or calcium fluophosphate, $Ca_5F(PO_4)_3$.

The element is prepared by electrolysis of a molten mixture of KF and HF. The temperature need not be high, and there are several satisfactory procedures which operate near room temperature. The relative amounts of KF and HF must, however, be controlled fairly accurately. These substances and the fluorine which is liberated attack nearly all materials which might be used for a container. But copper is satisfactory for this purpose because it becomes covered with a layer of copper fluoride which prevents further attack. Several commercial fluorine generators use a special grade of steel. The fluorine appears, of course, at the positive electrode, while hydrogen comes off at the negative.

Fluorine is a pale yellow gas with an odor that somewhat resembles that of chlorine. Fluorine is dangerously poisonous. The element combines violently with almost all other elements, except the inert gases. With hydrogen, fluorine explodes, even in the dark and at low temperatures. Fluorine is an exceedingly powerful oxidizing agent. It gains an electron more readily than does any other element.

Fluorine does not dissolve in water in the same way that the other halogens do; it does, however, combine vigorously with water, forming oxygen, hydrogen fluoride, and several other products. Carbon can be made to ignite in an atmosphere of fluorine. A convenient method of telling whether a fluorine generator is operating is to hold a cigarette near the fluorine outlet. If fluorine is being generated, the cigarette will ignite with a sharp explosion.

Hydrogen fluoride is conveniently prepared by the action of sulfuric acid on calcium fluoride.

$$CaF_2 + H_2SO_4 \rightarrow CaSO_4 + 2HF$$

This reaction is generally carried out in a lead or platinum dish.

Hydrogen fluoride is a colorless gas with a sharp odor. It is extremely dangerous to breathe. The gas dissolves in water to form hydrofluoric acid. This acid is decidedly weaker than hydrochloric, but it possesses the unique property of being able to dissolve glass. The acid is an important article of commerce. It is sold for laboratory use in plastic bottles. Great care should be taken in handling hydrofluoric acid. It produces very painful, slow-healing burns.

The action of this acid on glass will be illustrated by equations for the reactions on silica and on calcium silicate. Glass itself is a complex mixture of silicates not readily represented in an equation. In both reactions an interesting feature is formation of the gas silicon tetrafluoride.

$$SiO_2 + 4HF \rightarrow SiF_4 + 2H_2O$$

$$CaSiO_3 + 6HF \rightarrow CaF_2 + SiF_4 + 3H_2O$$

Hydrofluoric acid is used to "etch" glass. If the glass is covered with a layer of paraffin wax which is partly cut away in any desired design, then hydrofluoric acid will react with that part of the glass which has been uncovered.

The major uses of hydrogen fluoride and hydrofluoric acid at the present time are as a catalyst in the production of aviation gasoline, and in the manufacture of synthetic cryolite for the metallurgy of aluminum.

Large tonnages of calcium fluoride are used in the metallurgical and ceramic industries, and numerous compounds containing fluorine have come on the market in recent years. Among these may be mentioned dichlorodifluoromethane, CCl_2F_2, or Freon-12, which is used in refrigeration. Increasing amounts of fluorine are being used in the manufacture of certain plastics. Extremely small amounts of fluorides in drinking water seem to have a favorable effect on the incidence of dental caries. For this reason, traces of soluble fluorides are sometimes added to municipal water supplies in regions where the natural water is deficient in this element.

EXERCISES

A. *Define or explain the following:*

brine	electrochemical oxidation
bromism	halogens
chain reaction	photochemical reaction
chlorination	sublimation
constant boiling mixture	tincture of iodine

B. 1. Indicate procedures and all equations for the following:
 a. oxidation of a chloride by (1) air, (2) MnO_2.
 b. electrolytic production of chlorine from (1) fused chloride, (2) brine.
 c. production of hydrogen chloride (1) by synthesis, (2) from a chloride and sulfuric acid, (3) by hydrolysis.
 d. reactions of chlorine with (1) a metal; with (2) a nonmetal.
 e. displacement reactions shown by (1) chlorine, (2) bromine.
 f. action of chlorine on water.
 g. reactions of hydrochloric acid (1) on Al, Zn, Cu, (2) on a base.
 h. chlorine water in sunlight.
 i. preparation of sodium hypochlorite from brine.
 j. decomposition of potassium chlorate by heat (two equations).

k.   preparation of perchloric acid from a perchlorate.
l.   preparation of bromine from a bromide.
m. preparation of hydrogen bromide by (1) synthesis, (2) hydrolysis.
n.   preparation of iodine from an iodide.
o.   preparation of hydrogen iodide by (1) synthesis, (2) hydrolysis.
p.   production of fluorine from a fluoride.
q.   preparation of hydrogen fluoride by (1) synthesis, (2) reaction of sulfuric acid on a fluoride.
r.   action of hydrogen fluoride on silica, SiO_2.

C. 1. Identify the following as essentially ionic (electrovalent) or essentially covalent types of compounds: F_2, HBr, $NaClO_4$, NaI, SiF_4.

2. Show probable arrangement of electrons in (a) hypochlorous acid, (b) CCl_2F_2, and (c) calcium fluoride (a salt). Note that the usual method of writing HClO is misleading so far as the arrangement of atoms is concerned.

3. Why cannot a chemical oxidation process be used for the production of fluorine?

4. Chlorine and bromine are common impurities in iodine. The iodine may be purified by mixing it with potassium iodide, then heating. What is the basis for this purification process?

5. Iodine, atomic number 53, has a lower atomic weight than tellurium, atomic number 52. What explanation can be offered?

6. The formula for hydrogen fluoride is sometimes written H_2F_2. What experiments could be performed to gain evidence on this point?

7. The dry hydrogen halides are poor conductors of electricity even though they may be liquefied. The aqueous solutions are good conductors. Why?

8. Hydrofluoric acid attacks glass, but hydrochloric does not. How can we say that hydrochloric is a stronger acid?

9. If the reaction of sodium chloride and sulfuric acid is reversible, how can hydrogen chloride be prepared efficiently by this process?

10. Assuming that a very large city uses about a billion kilograms of water per day, what tonnage (1 ton is roughly 1000 kg.) of sodium chloride must be used to supply the necessary chlorine at a chlorination rate of 1 part per million?

11. Write balanced equations for the following reactions:
a. $HCl + PbO_2 \rightarrow PbCl_2 + ?$
b. $Br_2 + SO_2 + H_2O \rightarrow$
c. $KBr + I_2 \rightarrow$
d. $H_2O + Br_2 \rightarrow HBrO + ?$
e. $MgCl_2 + H_2SO_4 \rightarrow$
f. $Ca(OH)_2 + Cl_2 \xrightarrow{cold}$

12. Write formulas for the following: aluminum iodide, calcium chlorite, chromic chloride, cuprous chloride, mercurous chloride, sodium chlorite, zinc perchlorate.

13. Name the following: $BaBr_2$, $BiCl_3$, $Ca(ClO_4)_2$, $CoCl_2$, $FeCl_3$, $Ni(ClO_4)_2$.

14. Chlorine added to water soon produces an equilibrium $Cl_2 + H_2O \leftrightarrows HCl + HClO$, but if (a) the mixture is exposed to sunlight, or (b) a base is added, the reaction goes virtually to completion. Explain these effects.
15. In the electrolysis of sodium chloride solution what would be the result if the usual products at cathode and anode were allowed to mix? What would the result be if the products were allowed both to mix and to get warm?

NITROGEN AND RELATED ELEMENTS

B subgroup

A subgroup

																H	He
Li	Be	B											C	N	O	F	Ne
Na	Mg	Al											Si	P	S	Cl	A
K	Ca	Sc	Ti	V	Cr	Mn	Fe	Co	Ni	Cu	Zn	Ga	Ge	As	Se	Br	Kr
Rb	Sr	Y	Zr	Nb	Mo	Tc	Ru	Rh	Pd	Ag	Cd	In	Sn	Sb	Te	I	Xe
Cs	Ba	La-Lu	Hf	Ta	W	Re	Os	Ir	Pt	Au	Hg	Tl	Pb	Bi	Po	At	Rn
Fr	Ra	Ac	Th	Pa	U-												

Group 5 in the Periodic Table has, in the A subgroup, the elements vanadium, niobium, tantalum, and protactinium. Of these elements we shall have little more to say. But the B subgroup contains several elements of major importance, and all merit some attention. These elements are nitrogen, phosphorus, arsenic, antimony, and bismuth. These elements show a striking gradation of properties from the nonmetals, nitrogen and phosphorus, to the metal, bismuth. In spite of this gradation there are very close resemblances in all these elements. In no other group in the Periodic Table is there to be found a more regular and yet such a far-reaching change as we go from element to element.

Our attention will be first directed to nitrogen, which ranks along with oxygen, sulfur, and chlorine, as among the most important of all chemical elements.

101. NITROGEN

Nitrogen seems first to have been characterized by a Scottish scientist, D. Rutherford (not to be confused with Lord Rutherford, the physicist, who lived about a hundred years later). D. Rutherford published a Latin manuscript in 1772; the manuscript contained this passage:

By the respiration of animals, healthy air is not merely rendered mephitic [that is, charged with carbon dioxide], but it also suffers another change, for, after the mephitic portion is absorbed by a solution of caustic alkali, the remaining portion is not rendered salubrious, and, although it occasions no precipitate in lime-water, it nevertheless extinguishes flame, and destroys life.

Rutherford's "phlogisticated air," as he called it, was studied by Scheele and by Lavoisier. The latter called it *azote*,* by which name it is still known in France. The name "nitrogen" was suggested by J. A. C. Chaptal in 1823. Derivation of the name is from the Greek word *nitron* (saltpeter), from which nitrogen may be obtained.

About 80 per cent of the atmosphere consists of nitrogen. Every square mile of the earth's surface has above it millions of tons of nitrogen. This atmospheric nitrogen constitutes an inexhaustible source. Nitrogen is indispensable for fertilizers and for explosives. Toward the end of the nineteenth century it was feared that available supplies of nitrogen for these uses would soon be exhausted unless means were found for extracting and using nitrogen from the air. But about 1913 there was developed a process for the use of atmospheric nitrogen, and since that time the supply has been limited only by the capacity of the ammonia and nitric acid manufacturing plants. No shortage of raw material has since occurred or ever will occur. Production capacity in the world is several million tons per year.

Other sources of nitrogen are **saltpeter** or potassium nitrate, KNO_3, the supply of which is very limited, and **Chile saltpeter,** or sodium nitrate, $NaNO_3$. Extensive deposits of this latter substance are found in northern Chile. They constitute an important source of nitrogen. Still other substances which yield appreciable supplies of nitrogen compounds are coal and animal residues.

It should be pointed out that nitrogen is an essential constituent of all living matter. The cells of animal tissues contain nitrogen in complicated compounds called proteins. Nitrogen is not only necessary for animal and plant growth, but it is produced by the decay of animal and plant tissues.

Nitrogen may be prepared by heating ammonium nitrite, NH_4NO_2.

$$NH_4NO_2 \rightarrow N_2 + 2H_2O$$

This compound is, however, not very stable. It is convenient to make the ammonium nitrite as required by mixing sodium nitrite and ammonium chloride.

$$NaNO_2 + NH_4Cl \rightarrow NH_4NO_2 + NaCl$$

Some care must be taken not to heat this mixture very strongly because ammonium nitrite sometimes decomposes violently. The nitrogen prepared

---

* The word "azote" means, literally, "no life." The prefix is retained in such terms as azide, hydrazoic acid (HN_3), and azobenzene.

by this reaction is relatively pure, except of course for the water formed simultaneously. The water is easily removed by passing the gas mixture over a drying agent such as anhydrous calcium chloride.

Nitrogen may also be prepared from air. The chief substance to be removed is oxygen. If air is passed over hot copper, the oxygen forms copper oxide while the nitrogen passes on unchanged.

$$O_2 + 2Cu \rightarrow 2CuO$$

$$N_2 + Cu \rightarrow \text{no reaction}$$

This is a convenient method for small-scale preparation of rather impure nitrogen. Carbon dioxide and water vapor, both of which are present as

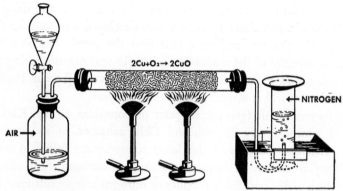

Fig. 15-1. Preparation of nitrogen from air. Air is slowly passed over heated copper. The nitrogen so obtained contains impurities.

impurities, may be removed by passing the gases through sodium hydroxide, and then over anhydrous calcium chloride, or some similar combination of reagents.

$$CO_2 + 2NaOH \rightarrow Na_2CO_3 + H_2O$$

But nitrogen so prepared from air contains other impurities, the nature of which will be discussed in the next chapter.

The large-scale industrial preparation of nitrogen is achieved from air by a process of liquefying the air, then separating its constituents by fractional distillation. The nitrogen and the oxygen are separated in the same operation and both of these elements have important commercial applications. The details of the liquid air process will be given in the next chapter.

Nitrogen is a colorless, odorless gas. The boiling point is $-195.8°$ C. At still lower temperatures it becomes a white solid. The formula for the gas is N_2, and the electronic configuration may be represented as follows:

:N:::N:

Considered as an element, nitrogen is relatively inert. It combines with other elements slowly and with difficulty. A reason for this lies in the large amount of energy necessary to break up the nitrogen molecule into separate atoms. But nitrogen in its compounds is just the opposite; it becomes one of

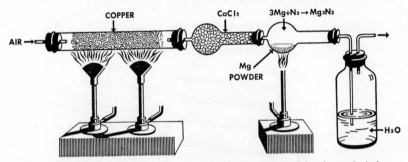

Fig. 15-2. Preparation of magnesium nitride. Nitrogen prepared by the method shown in Fig. 15-1 is dried over calcium chloride, then passed over heated magnesium. The bottle at the extreme right serves to indicate the rate of flow of gas, and to prevent reverse flow of air.

the most active of elements. For instance, nearly all important explosives contain nitrogen.

Nitrogen does not burn or support combustion. Under certain conditions it combines slowly with a few elements such as oxygen and hydrogen. With some of the more active metals such as magnesium, it unites slowly at elevated temperatures, forming salts called *nitrides*.

$$3Mg + N_2 \quad \rightarrow \quad Mg_3N_2$$
magnesium nitride

But in spite of this relative inertness in the elementary condition, nitrogen is one of the most interesting of all elements.

By far the largest proportion of industrial nitrogen goes into the manufacture of fertilizers and explosives. A small quantity is used to create an inert atmosphere for operations which cannot be carried out in air because of oxidation produced by the oxygen in air.

102. AMMONIA *

This gas ranks among the most important of all chemical compounds. It occurs in nature as the result of decaying animal and vegetable matter, but

---

* The name "ammonia" is said to be derived from "salt of ammon" [ammonium chloride] obtained by fourth century B.C. Egyptians from camel dung, near the temple of Jupiter Ammon.

apparently not otherwise, except possibly in the atmospheres of distant planets.

On a small scale the gas may be formed by treating an ammonium salt such as ammonium chloride, NH_4Cl, with any strong base, such as sodium hydroxide, NaOH.

$$NH_4Cl + NaOH \rightarrow NH_3 + NaCl + H_2O$$

Any ammonium salt and any strong base may be substituted for those given.

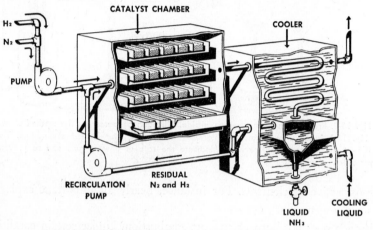

Fig. 15-3. Flow diagram for the Haber synthesis of ammonia.

The most important industrial method for ammonia production is the **Haber process.** The history of this process also illustrates the profound effect of scientific discovery on world affairs.

If nitrogen and hydrogen are heated together, a reversible reaction takes place, yielding a small percentage of ammonia.

$$N_2 + 3H_2 \rightarrow 2NH_3 + 21,880 \text{ cals.}$$

The reaction at ordinary temperatures is so slow as to be useless. It will be noticed that the reaction is exothermic. Hence, according to Le Chatelier's Law, an increase of temperature will reduce the yield of ammonia. Increase of pressure will, however, increase the yield of ammonia, and use of a catalyst may increase the speed of the reaction until a reasonable yield of ammonia may be obtained in a reasonable time. The exact conditions for commercial exploitation of this process were worked out by a German chemist, Fritz Haber (1868-1934). Large-scale production began in Germany in 1913. Prior to this discovery Germany was dependent chiefly on nitrate from Chile for her explosive and fertilizer raw materials. With the development of the Haber process, Germany was able to use the inexhaustible source of nitrogen in the atmosphere. It is obvious that with Allied control of the seas, Germany could not have continued to wage World War I for more than a very few months. But the Haber process made Germany completely independent of all external sources of nitrogen.*

Fig. 15-4. Part of a plant used in the synthesis of ammonia.

The Haber process consists of compressing a mixture of hydrogen and nitrogen to several hundred times atmospheric pressure, in the presence of a catalyst. The temperature may be raised to about 500° C. without reducing the ammonia yield too far. The catalyst is iron to which small amounts of potassium and aluminum oxides have been added. These added substances greatly increase the activity of the iron catalyst. They are referred to as **promoters.** The equilibrium mixture of nitrogen, hydrogen, and ammonia is removed from the catalyst, the ammonia taken out of the mixture, and the remaining gases are recirculated back to the catalyst chamber. The process requires a large supply of pure nitrogen and pure hydrogen. The former is

---

* A somewhat similar state of affairs existed at the beginning of World War II. Methods for making synthetic gasoline were developed just a short time before war began. These methods, which will be discussed in a later chapter, made Germany independent of external petroleum resources.

obtained through the liquid air process, the latter either by the water-gas reaction, the steam-hydrocarbon reaction, or by electrolysis. Purification of these gases is often a major expense in the process.

There are several other methods for the industrial production of ammonia. One of these is the utilization of by-product ammonia given off during the manufacture of coal gas and coke from coal.

Fig. 15-5. The great solubility of ammonia in water may be demonstrated by the apparatus shown. The flask is filled with ammonia. A few drops of water are forced into the flask from the medicine dropper. The water dissolves ammonia to such a degree that a partial vacuum is created. Water is then forced in by atmospheric pressure until the flask is almost full.

A method sometimes used for small-scale production is the treatment of magnesium nitride with water.

$$Mg_3N_2 + 6H_2O \rightarrow 3Mg(OH)_2 + 2NH_3$$

Ammonia is a colorless gas. It has a powerful pungent odor. The gas is easily liquefied at atmospheric pressure and moderately low temperature. Liquid ammonia has a number of interesting and valuable properties as a solvent and as a chemical agent. Gaseous ammonia is extremely soluble in water. One liter of water will dissolve over a thousand liters of ammonia gas. (See Fig. 15.5.)

The gas does not burn in air, but in oxygen it burns with a rather feeble flame. The products are water and nitrogen.

$$4NH_3 + 3O_2 \rightarrow 6H_2O + 2N_2$$

In the presence of a catalyst such as platinum, the reaction of ammonia and oxygen yields oxides of nitrogen plus water.

$$4NH_3 + 5O_2 \xrightarrow{\text{Pt catalyst}} 6H_2O + 4NO$$

One of the most characteristic properties of ammonia is its ability to combine with positive ions. For instance, ammonia will combine with the silver ion, Ag^+, to form the so-called silver ammonia complex ion,

$$Ag^+ + 2NH_3 \rightarrow Ag(NH_3)_2{}^+$$

or with cupric ion, Cu^{++}, to form the dark-blue copper ammonia ion.

$$Cu^{++} + 4NH_3 \rightarrow Cu(NH_3)_4{}^{++}$$

This peculiar property of ammonia seems to arise from the electronic configuration of the molecule. Nitrogen has five electrons in its highest normal energy level; to these are added three electrons from the three hydrogen atoms, giving three electron pair bonds and one electron pair left over.

$$\overset{..}{\underset{..}{N}}\cdot + 3H\cdot \rightarrow H:\overset{..}{\underset{H}{N}}:$$

This extra electron pair seems to be responsible for the ability of ammonia to combine with positive ions. This electron pair can act to form a covalent bond between the nitrogen and some other atom or ion. In the case of silver ion there are formed two covalent bonds through the otherwise unused electron pairs of two ammonia molecules.

$$Ag^+ + 2:\overset{..}{\underset{H}{N}}:H \rightarrow \left[H:\overset{..}{\underset{H}{N}}:Ag:\overset{..}{\underset{H}{N}}:H \right]^+$$

The commonest example of this property of ammonia is found in the combination with hydrogen ion. The product is called the **ammonium** ion. It is an ammonia molecule to which an extra proton (hydrogen ion) has been added.

$$H:\overset{..}{\underset{H}{N}}: + H^+ \rightarrow \left[H:\overset{..}{\underset{H}{N}}:H \right]^+$$

Ammonium ions are found in many important compounds such as ammonium chloride, NH_4Cl, ammonium nitrate, NH_4NO_3, and ammonium sulfate, $(NH_4)_2SO_4$. Ammonium ions are formed by the reaction of ammonia with any substance which can act as an acid—that is, any substance which can give up protons. Such substances are the common acids such as HCl, and other substances which can act like acids in the sense that they give up protons. Of these, water is the most familiar example. Ammonia combines with hydrogen chloride gas, giving a white cloud of ammonium chlo-

$$NH_3 + HCl \rightarrow NH_4Cl$$

ride, or with a solution of hydrochloric acid, giving ammonium ions and chloride ions.

$$NH_3 + HCl \rightarrow NH_4^+ + Cl^-$$

Ammonia, either as a gas or in solution, is able to take up protons and is, therefore, strictly speaking a base.

When ammonia is dissolved in water, some of the ammonia accepts a proton from the water, the products being the ammonium ion and the hydroxide ion. This solution is often called ammonium hydroxide. It is a weak base which smells very strongly of ammonia. Ammonium hydroxide is one of the commonest and most useful of laboratory reagents.

$$NH_3 + H_2O \rightleftarrows NH_4^+ + OH^-$$

The principal uses of ammonia are (1) for the preparation of ammonium salts, which are used mainly for fertilizers, explosives, and plastics, and (2) in the manufacture of nitric acid. Ammonium sulfate is a good example of an ammonium salt which is used directly as a fertilizer. This compound is made by passing ammonia into sulfuric acid.

$$2NH_3 + H_2SO_4 \rightarrow (NH_4)_2SO_4$$

The solution of ammonium sulfate in water is then evaporated to obtain the pure salt. Liquid ammonia (not to be confused with the solution in water) is extensively used in refrigeration units, especially fairly large-scale installations. Aqueous solutions of ammonia are commonly used for water softening and for other household purposes.

103. NITRIC ACID

This important compound, the formula for which is HNO_3, is manufactured industrially on a large scale. An early method, now almost obsolete, involves the treatment of Chile saltpeter, sodium nitrate, with concentrated sulfuric acid.

$$NaNO_3 + H_2SO_4 \rightleftarrows NaHSO_4 + HNO_3$$

This reaction is reversible, and little nitric acid could be made this way were it not for the fact that the boiling point of nitric acid is much lower than that of sulfuric. Nitric acid boils at 86° C., sulfuric acid at 338° C. Consequently, if the reaction mixture is heated, the nitric acid boils off and so is removed from the equilibrium mixture. The equilibrium tends then to shift toward the right, yielding more nitric acid, which is, in turn, boiled off. Ultimately all the sodium nitrate or the sulfuric acid, or both, will be used up. This reaction is a good illustration of how a reversible reaction may be carried to effective completion by removal of one of the products. It parallels

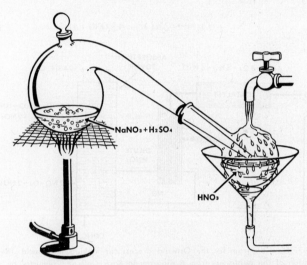

NaNO₃ + H₂SO₄

HNO₃

Fig. 15-6. Apparatus for the preparation of nitric acid on a laboratory scale.

the production of hydrogen chloride from sodium chloride and sulfuric acid.

The important industrial process for making nitric acid is known as the **Ostwald process.** When ammonia combines with oxygen, the products are normally nitrogen and water. But under the influence of a catalyst the products are nitric oxide, NO, and water.

$$4NH_3 + 5O_2 \rightarrow 4NO + 6H_2O + 215,000 \text{ cals.}$$

Ammonia mixed with an excess of air is heated and then passed over platinum gauze. The reaction is quite strongly exothermic, and as a result, the platinum becomes red or even white-hot. The nitric oxide formed in this reaction is now oxidized by air to nitrogen dioxide,

$$2NO + O_2 \rightarrow 2NO_2 + 27,800 \text{ cals.}$$

and the nitrogen dioxide is absorbed in water to form a mixture of nitric acid and nitric oxide.

$$3NO_2 + H_2O \rightarrow 2HNO_3 + NO$$

The nitric oxide so formed is treated again with air to form more nitrogen dioxide which, in turn, is absorbed in more water.

There is another nitric acid process which, though now obsolete, illustrates some scientific and economic relationships. Nitrogen and oxygen do not combine at ordinary temperatures. Not only is the rate of combination immeasurably slow, but the equilibrium lies so far to the left in the equation as written,

$$N_2 + O_2 \rightleftarrows 2NO - 43,000 \text{ cals.}$$

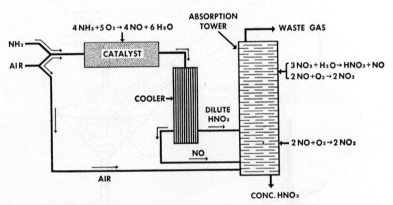

Fig. 15-7. Flow diagram for the Ostwald process for making nitric acid. (Redrawn by permission of the publishers from a diagram in *Basic College Chemistry* by Joseph A. Babor. Thomas Y. Crowell Co., 1946)

that no detectible amount of nitric oxide is formed. This conclusion is, of course, obvious from the fact that the atmosphere, which consists of nitrogen and oxygen, does not normally contain nitric oxide.

But it will be noticed that the reaction to form nitric oxide is endothermic. If, therefore, the temperature can be raised high enough, appreciable concentrations of nitric oxide will be formed. Sufficiently high temperatures are produced in the electric arc. If a stream of air is blown through an electric arc, the issuing gases contain a few per cent of nitric oxide. Once the nitric oxide is formed, the production of nitric acid proceeds in a manner similar to that of the Ostwald process. This method of making nitric acid has been used in Norway and elsewhere where electric power is very cheap. It is generally known as the **arc process** (Fig. 15-8), or the Birkeland-Eyde process. But the amount of electrical energy necessary is so large that this process has not been able to compete economically with the Ostwald method even though the latter requires that ammonia be produced first. For that reason no arc-process nitric acid is made at the present time.

Pure HNO_3 is a colorless liquid. It dissolves readily in water, forming the nitric acid of commerce. Nitric acid is a typical strong acid. In addition to its acidic properties, it possesses powerful oxidizing properties. With active metals such as magnesium, cold dilute nitric acid yields hydrogen.

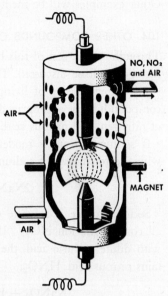

$$Mg + 2HNO_3 \text{ (cold, dilute)} \rightarrow$$
$$Mg(NO_3)_2 + H_2$$

But with more concentrated acid, the nitric acid itself is always reduced. The nitrogen in nitric acid has an oxidation state of $+5$. In the reduction products formed from nitric acid, the state may be lowered, for instance, to any of the values listed in the following compounds: $N^{+4}O_2$, $N^{+2}O$, N_2^0, or $N^{-3}H_3$. With concentrated nitric acid acting on metallic copper, the chief reduction product is nitrogen dioxide, NO_2.

$$Cu + 4HNO_3 \rightarrow$$
$$Cu(NO_3)_2 + 2NO_2 + 2H_2O$$

But with more dilute acid the chief reduction product is nitric oxide, NO.

Fig. 15-8. Diagrammatic representation of the arc process for making nitric acid. The magnet serves to spread the flame of the arc.

$$3Cu + 8HNO_3 \rightarrow 3Cu(NO_3)_2 + 2NO + 4H_2O$$

With zinc and *very* dilute nitric acid, the reduction product is ammonia, which, however, combines with more nitric acid to form ammonium nitrate.

$$4Zn + 10HNO_3 \text{ (very dilute)} \rightarrow 4Zn(NO_3)_2 + NH_4NO_3 + 3H_2O$$

A mixture of nitric acid and hydrochloric acid forms the interesting solution known as **aqua regia.** Aqua regia has the property of dissolving gold, although neither nitric nor hydrochloric acids can do this alone. Aqua regia contains chlorine and nitrosyl chloride, NOCl, formed through the mutual oxidizing and reducing action of the two acids.

$$HNO_3 + 3HCl \rightarrow Cl_2 + NOCl + 2H_2O$$

Nitric acid is produced industrially on a very large scale. It is used both as an acid and as an oxidizing agent, and also as a nitrating agent in the manufacture of explosives such as nitroglycerin and T.N.T. Many of its salts, the nitrates, are of great commercial importance. Some of these are saltpeter, KNO_3; Chile saltpeter, $NaNO_3$; and ammonium nitrate, NH_4NO_3. Other examples will be mentioned in due course.

104. OTHER COMPOUNDS OF NITROGEN

Throughout the rest of this book a large number of compounds containing nitrogen will be discussed. This will be particularly true when we come to study the chemistry of living matter. There are, however, a few nitrogen compounds most appropriately studied here. These are several of the oxides of nitrogen, and nitrous acid, and its salts, the nitrites.

If sodium nitrate is moderately heated, part of the oxygen is liberated, with the formation of sodium nitrite.

$$2NaNO_3 \rightarrow 2NaNO_2 + O_2$$

Sodium nitrite is a white solid, typical of the salts called nitrites. These all contain the ion NO_2^-. If a dilute solution of sodium nitrite is treated with dilute sulfuric acid, there is obtained a pale-blue solution which contains nitrous acid, HNO_2.

$$NaNO_2 + H_2SO_4 \rightarrow NaHSO_4 + \overset{+1 \,+3}{H}\overset{-}{NO_2}$$

This acid is unstable, and when efforts are made to concentrate it, or to isolate it from solution, the acid decomposes.

Nitrous acid is a weak acid: that is, it is not highly ionized. The oxidation state of the nitrogen in this compound is seen to be $+3$. Nitrous acid can, therefore, act either as an oxidizing agent or as a reducing agent.

We turn now to an interesting oxide of nitrogen. If ammonium nitrate is gently heated, the products are nitrous oxide and water.

$$\overset{+4}{N}{}^{-3}H_4N^{+5}\overset{-6}{O_3} \rightarrow N_2{}^{+1}O + 2H_2O$$

It will be noticed that in ammonium nitrate the nitrogen exists in two oxidation states, namely, -3 and $+5$. Heating this substance results in a sort of internal oxidation and reduction so that all the nitrogen appears with a state of $+1$, as in the nitrous oxide. The reaction is somewhat similar to that in which pure nitrogen is prepared by heating ammonium nitrite.

$$N^{-3}H_4N^{+3}O_2 \rightarrow N_2{}^0 + 2H_2O$$

Nitrous oxide is a colorless gas with a faint, not unpleasant odor. It was discovered in 1772 by Joseph Priestley, the famous discoverer of oxygen. Nitrous oxide is, like oxygen, able to support combustion. A glowing splinter of wood bursts into flame when it is placed in the gas.

When nitrous oxide is breathed, some peculiar symptoms result. The patient sometimes bursts into laughter: hence the name **laughing gas.** Nitrous oxide was investigated in 1800 by Sir Humphry Davy, who reported that after breathing the gas he danced around the laboratory like a madman. Further breathing of the gas produces insensibility and general anesthesia. Nitrous oxide is widely used for minor surgical operations and for the extraction of teeth. For such purposes it appears to be one of the best and least harmful of all anesthetics. It does not, however, give the degree of muscular relaxation necessary for major surgery, and the effects normally last only a few minutes. Prolonged breathing of pure nitrous oxide would result in death from suffocation. The gas is administered mixed with oxygen. Under such circumstances accidents with nitrous oxide are exceedingly rare.*

Another interesting use for nitrous oxide is found in the whipping of cream. If cream is treated with nitrous oxide under pressure, the gas dissolves to a considerable extent. This is simply an illustration of Henry's law to the effect that increase of pressure increases the solubility of a gas in a liquid. If now the pressure is released—as by allowing the cream to escape from the container—then the nitrous oxide comes out of solution, but is caught by innumerable bubbles which foam up to resemble whipped cream. This is the basis for the whipped-cream type of dispenser which is often seen at ice-cream counters in drug stores and elsewhere.

105. PHOSPHORUS

This element was discovered in the year 1669 by a German alchemist named Brand. The element was obtained through the distillation of urine. Phosphorus is very widely and plentifully distributed in nature in three great world areas: the United States, North Africa, and Russia. The principal minerals are *phosphorite,* $Ca_3(PO_4)_2$, and related substances. Phosphorus also occurs in vegetable and animal tissues. Urine contains appreciable amounts of phosphorus in the form of sodium ammonium phosphate. The chemical activity of phosphorus is so great that it is never found in nature as the free element.

The element phosphorus is prepared from phosphate rock by the reducing action of carbon in the presence of sand.

$$Ca_3(PO_4)_2 + 3SiO_2 + 5C \rightarrow 3CaSiO_3 + 2P + 5CO$$

* Other effects sometimes occur. The patient may experience extremely vivid dreams amounting in fact to hallucinations. Several famous medicolegal cases are based on this property of nitrous oxide. Doctors and dentists, therefore, generally insist on having an assistant, preferably a female nurse, present when using the gas on women. L. Goodman and A. Gilman, *The Pharmacological Basis of Therapeutics* (New York: Macmillan, 1941).

A high temperature is required, and this is produced by passing a strong alternating current between carbon electrodes. The phosphorus distils and is collected under water. The calcium silicate remains in the furnace as a slag. The demand for phosphorus is such that a considerable number of large-scale furnaces are in continuous operation.

Phosphorus exhibits an outstanding example of allotropy. There are at least three modifications. **White,** or yellow, **phosphorus** is a translucent solid

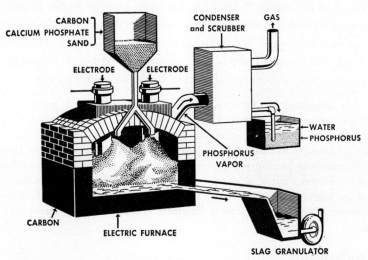

Fig. 15-9. Electric furnace for the production of phosphorus. The carbon, calcium phosphate, and sand are strongly heated by an electric furnace. The products are phosphorus vapor and slag.

resembling wax. It is soluble in organic solvents, especially in carbon disulfide, from which octahedral crystals of white phosphorus may be obtained. This substance is extremely poisonous. Breathing the vapors causes necrosis and decay of the bones, particularly those of the jaws and nose. This form of phosphorus ignites spontaneously in air. It should always be handled under water. Burns obtained through the action of white phosphorus are very painful and slow to heal.

If white phosphorus is heated to about 250° C. in the absence of air, it changes into **red phosphorus.** This action is catalyzed by iodine. Red phosphorus is insoluble in those organic solvents which dissolve the white modification. The red form is not poisonous and does not catch fire in air unless heated. Commercial red phosphorus often contains enough of the white form to make it dangerous.

A third, black, form of phosphorus is obtained by heating white phosphorus under high pressure.

All forms of phosphorus unite with atmospheric oxygen to form dense white clouds of phosphorus pentoxide.

$$4\overset{\circ}{P} + 5\overset{\circ}{O_2} \rightarrow 2\overset{+5}{P_2}\overset{-2}{O_5}$$

This reaction is the basis of phosphorus bombs as incendiary agents and for producing smoke screens. The more active white allotropic modification of phosphorus glows in moist air, owing to slow oxidation on the surface. This curious glow, or phosphorescence, is the source of the name of the element.

Most phosphorus produced commercially is converted into compounds of phosphorus. Large quantities of the element itself are used in making matches, in rat poisons, and in the production of phosphor-bronze.

Ordinary "strike-anywhere" matches were introduced in 1827. The head formerly contained white phosphorus, lead dioxide or potassium chlorate, some inert material such as clay, and some glue. The white phosphorus is so poisonous, however, that nearly all countries have laws preventing its use. It has been replaced by a sulfide of phosphorus, P_4S_3. "Safety" matches have a head generally composed of potassium chlorate and antimony trisulfide, Sb_2S_3. The active surface of the match box is coated with a layer of red phosphorus, antimony trisulfide, powdered glass, and glue.

It will be recalled that ammonia is one of the most important compounds of nitrogen. It might, therefore, be expected that an analogous compound would be formed by phosphorus. This is the case; **phosphine,** PH_3, is a gas with a strong disagreeable, garlic-like odor. Phosphine is formed by the action of water on calcium phosphide, a reaction which resembles the formation of ammonia by the action of water on magnesium nitride.

$$Ca_3P_2 + 6H_2O \rightarrow 2PH_3 + 3Ca(OH)_2$$

But phosphine is a relatively unimportant substance compared with ammonia. It burns in air, and impure samples often catch fire spontaneously. Sometimes a curious unearthly light is seen over marshy places. This light, known as the will-o'-the-wisp, is said to be caused by phosphine and other hydrides of phosphorus liberated in the decay of organic matter.

With the halogens, phosphorus forms halides, of which phosphorus trichloride and phosphorus pentachloride are examples. They are formed by the action of phosphorus with a restricted amount, or with excess, chlorine, as the case may be.

$$2P + 3Cl_2 \rightarrow 2PCl_3$$

$$PCl_3 + Cl_2 \rightleftarrows PCl_5$$

The formation of the pentachloride is a typical reversible reaction. Both these substances are useful reagents. With water they undergo hydrolysis to form hydrochloric acid, and phosphorous acid and phosphoric acid respectively.

$$PCl_3 + 3H_2O \rightarrow H_3PO_3 + 3HCl$$

$$PCl_5 + 4H_2O \rightarrow H_3PO_4 + 5HCl$$

With oxygen, phosphorus forms two important oxides, the trioxide and the pentoxide, in which the oxidation state of the phosphorus is respectively $+3$ and $+5$.

$$4P + 3O_2 \rightarrow 2P_2O_3$$

$$P_2O_3 + O_2 \rightarrow P_2O_5$$

Phosphorus pentoxide is a white powder. It is a very useful laboratory reagent, chiefly because of its very great dehydrating action. It is able to take up water from gases and from compounds to a very remarkable degree. As a dehydrating agent it is considerably more effective than concentrated sulfuric acid.

When water is added to phosphorus pentoxide, the product is metaphosphoric acid, although the existence of this acid has been disputed.

$$P_2O_5 + H_2O \rightarrow 2HPO_3$$

If the solution is boiled and the water is in excess, the metaphosphoric acid is converted to orthophosphoric acid.

$$HPO_3 + H_2O \rightarrow H_3PO_4$$

In both these acids it will be noted that the oxidation state of the phosphorus is $+5$, as it is in the phosphorus pentoxide.

If phosphorus *trioxide* is treated with water, the product is phosphorous acid (note the spelling).

$$P_2^{+3}O_3 + 3H_2O \rightarrow 2H_3P^{+3}O_3$$

Unlike the case of nitrogen, phosphorus in the $+5$ valence state forms several different acids. These are: HPO_3, metaphosphoric acid; H_3PO_4, orthophosphoric acid; and $H_4P_2O_7$, pyrophosphoric acid. These acids differ only in the number of moles of water per mole of phosphorus pentoxide. Of these acids, orthophosphoric is the most important, although the others are also useful. Orthophosphoric acid in solution forms an acid rather weaker than sulfuric but nevertheless still fairly strong. It does not have the powerful oxidizing properties of sulfuric acid, and it is less volatile than sulfuric acid, which is itself a relatively nonvolatile acid.

Phosphorus compounds are produced in large quantities and have important uses. The salts are often used as water softeners and as fertilizers. Some of these substances are used in medicines; others find application as yeast foods, in dyeing, as fireproofing agents, in baking powders, and in a wide variety of food products.

106. FERTILIZERS

In order to maintain the fertility of soil under cultivation, it is necessary to use fertilizers which replenish essential substances removed in the form of crops. The

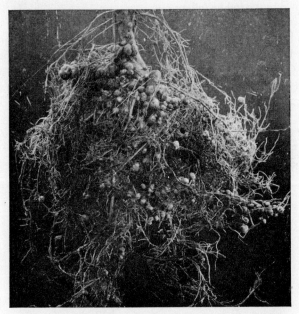

Fig. 15-10. Nitrogen-fixing growths on the root of a soybean plant. The development of these growths is aided by artificial inoculation. (U. S. Department of Agriculture)

importance of nitrogen to animal and plant life arises from the fact that all living matter consists, in part, of compounds known as proteins which contain carbon, hydrogen, oxygen, and nitrogen, as well as small amounts of other elements. All living matter therefore requires nitrogen for its growth. Nitrogen is present in abundance in the air, but most plants and all animals are so constituted that they cannot use nitrogen directly as they can oxygen. It is necessary for most plants to get nitrogen from nitrogenous compounds present in the soil, and for all animals

proteins = chon

to get nitrogen from plants taken as food, or from other animals which, in turn, have eaten plants. Human beings enjoying a normal diet are sure of an ample supply of nitrogen for body growth and repair. But plants continually take nitrogen-bearing compounds from the soil which, if not replenished, will soon become exhausted. In forests and other uncultivated land, the nitrogen is continually being returned to the soil by fall and decay of leaves and branches. But on farms the nitrogen is continually carted away in the form of crops. Farms, therefore, soon become worn out unless the nitrogen supply is maintained.

There are certain plants, notably clover, which have the power, through growths on the roots, of taking nitrogen directly from the air. Plowing under a crop of clover is a common method for enriching the soil. If soil is left idle for some years, the nitrogen supply is in part replenished because lightning storms create conditions favorable for the union of oxygen and nitrogen, forming oxides of nitrogen, which are carried down by rain in the form of very dilute nitrous and nitric acids. Ammonia is also given off by decaying animal and vegetable matter and is returned to the soil by falling rain.

But, in general, it is necessary to use artificial methods to restore the nitrogen to farm lands if crop production is to be maintained year after year. Fertilizers are of many forms; one of the commonest is the nitrogen-rich animal waste known as manure. Great quantities of ammonium sulfate, sodium nitrate, and calcium cyanamide ($CaCN_2$) are used as fertilizers. Ammonium phosphate is especially valuable because it supplies both nitrogen and phosphorus in a form available for plant use.

It will be observed that nitrogen undergoes a cyclic process. From the air it

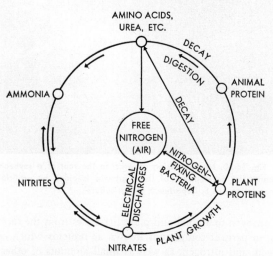

Fig. 15-11. The nitrogen cycle. Nitrogen in air is converted by electric storms and by bacteria to nitrates and plant proteins respectively. These are used to form animal protein which, in turn, decays to other nitrogen compounds or to nitrogen, which may be used again.

slowly deposited in soil as nitrates and nitrites; it goes then to the protein of plant tissues, then possibly to animals such as steers, finally perhaps to man in the form of beef. But from this point the nitrogen is given off in the form of waste products, and ultimately is all returned either to the air or to soil through the natural processes of animal decay. The individual nitrogen atoms in our bodies have certainly seen service in the tissues of plants or animals in the past, and may possibly again see such service in the future. (See Fig. 15-11.)

Nitrogen is, of course, by no means the only element required for plant growth. Other necessary substances include phosphorus, potassium, calcium, magnesium, and iron, together with carbon dioxide and water. It is probable that very small amounts of several other elements are essential for vigorous growth.

107. ARSENIC

The compounds of this element were well known to the ancients. The free element was first obtained by Albertus Magnus, about the year 1250. The name is derived from the Greek *arsenicon* applied by Theophrastus to arsenic sulfide. The word means "potent," possibly in reference to the highly poisonous character of this compound, a property which is shared by the element and most of its compounds.

In nature, arsenic occurs as the free element and in a number of compounds such as *realgar,* As_2S_3; *orpiment,* As_2S_2 (the modern mineral name orpiment is derived from the Latin "auripigmentum," meaning gold-colored); *mispickel* or *arsenical pyrites,* FeAsS; and *kupfernickel,* NiAs. Arsenic is a common impurity in iron pyrites, in some types of coal, and in zinc, copper, and lead ores. The supply of the element greatly exceeds the demand.

Arsenic is conveniently prepared from the oxide by reduction with carbon. The oxide As_2O_3 is mixed with powdered charcoal and heated. Carbon monoxide escapes and the arsenic sublimes on to a cooler part of the container.

$$As_2O_3 + 3C \rightarrow 3CO + 2As$$

The element, like phosphorus, has several allotropic forms. It is commonly obtained as a gray, brittle, metallic-looking substance. Physically it resembles metals much more than nonmetals. But chemically it is closely related to phosphorus. From the fact that arsenic sometimes occurs free in nature it may be inferred that the element is less active than phosphorus. Nevertheless it burns in air if heated to about 180° C. It also unites with chlorine, with other halogens, and with sulfur.

$$4As + 3O_2 \rightarrow 2As_2O_3$$

The chief popular interest in arsenic derives from its very poisonous character, although the element and its compounds have several important uses. Arsenic, generally in the form of the oxide, As_2O_3, was the favorite tool of the professional poisoners of the Middle Ages, and it remained in favor with criminals until fairly recently. Several reasons combined to give arsenic its popularity. The substance was easy to obtain, the onset of symptoms could be gradual and made to resemble disease, and the compounds used have little taste. Furthermore, embalming fluid formerly contained arsenic, and after its use the evidence for arsenic poisoning was obscured. In recent times the homicidal use of arsenic has greatly declined. This is due to laws prohibiting arsenic in embalming fluids, to general alertness for poisoning symptoms on the part of the medical profession, and to the development of sensitive tests for arsenic.

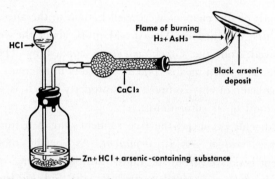

Fig. 15-12. Production of arsine, and Marsh test for arsenic.

Some of these tests have frequently been used as evidence in poisoning trials. One of these, the **Marsh test** for arsenic, will be described: * If a substance containing arsenic is added to a mixture of zinc and dilute sulfuric acid, the arsenic is converted to arsine, AsH_3, which is the arsenic analog of ammonia and of phosphine. The arsine is a gas and is swept out of the reaction mixture by hydrogen generated simultaneously by the action of the zinc and sulfuric acid. If the gas mixture is burned at a jet and if a porcelain dish is held in the flame, there will appear on the dish a black spot owing to decomposition of the arsine. The shiny, mirror-like black spot is metallic arsenic. In practice, a portion of the vital organs or of suspected material is placed in the flask with zinc and sulfuric acid. The test may be made very sensitive, and upon its evidence many murder convictions have been obtained.

We shall now describe a few of the more important compounds of arsenic. Arsenic trichloride is formed by the direct action of chlorine and arsenic.

$$3Cl_2 + 2As \rightarrow 2AsCl_3$$

* Modern tests actually used by chemists in the routine detection of arsenic will be found described in M. B. Jacobs, *The Analytical Chemistry of Industrial Poisons, Hazards, and Solvents* (New York: Interscience, 1944).

It is a volatile liquid and is extremely poisonous. Death may result from breathing the compound or through its application to the skin. Like phosphorus trichloride, arsenic trichloride hydrolyzes in water, forming hydrochloric acid and arsenous acid, H_3AsO_3.

$$AsCl_3 + 3H_2O \rightleftharpoons 3HCl + H_3AsO_3$$

But arsenic trichloride is not so completely hydrolyzed as the corresponding phosphorus compound, and the reaction with arsenic trichloride is reversible while that with phosphorus trichloride is not. This behavior on the part of arsenic trichloride is an evidence of the somewhat more metallic nature of arsenic as compared with phosphorus. Phosphorus shows practically no metal characteristics, arsenic shows some. This tendency on the part of arsenic is further emphasized by the behavior of the oxide, As_2O_3.

Arsenic trioxide, As_2O_3, is formed by burning arsenic in air. It is often called **white arsenic,** or simply, though incorrectly, "arsenic." This white powder dissolves slightly in water to form arsenous acid.

$$As_2O_3 + 3H_2O \rightarrow 2H_3AsO_3$$

The oxide has the property of dissolving both in strong bases and in strong acids. It will be recalled that metals have been defined as substances the oxides of which in water form bases, and nonmetals as substances the oxides of which in water form acids. Arsenic trioxide can in a sense do both. With strong bases it acts as an acid, forming a salt; and with strong acids it acts as a base, forming a salt.

$$\underset{\substack{acid\\(arsenic\\trioxide)}}{As_2O_3} + 6NaOH \rightarrow \underset{\substack{salt\\ \text{sodium arsenite}}}{2Na_3AsO_3} + 3H_2O$$

$$\underset{base}{As_2O_3} + \underset{acid}{6HCl} \rightarrow \underset{\substack{salt\\ \text{arsenic trichloride}}}{2AsCl_3} + 3H_2O$$

A substance which can act either as an acid or a base is said to be **amphoteric** (or amphiprotic). This behavior on the part of arsenic oxide is further evidence of the increasing metal-like properties of arsenic as compared with phosphorus and nitrogen.

Arsenic trioxide is used in glassmaking and in insecticides. Scheele's green, $CuHAsO_3$, is a pigment formerly used for coloring wall paper but abandoned partly because of the danger of arsenic poisoning. **Paris green** is a double salt, $Cu_3(AsO_3)_2 \cdot Cu(C_2H_3O_2)_2$, used as an insecticide. In spite of stringent laws, occasional cases of arsenic poisoning arise from failure to remove toxic amounts of arsenic from fruit and vegetables.

If arsenic or arsenic trioxide is heated with concentrated nitric acid, the arsenic is oxidized to an oxidation state of +5 as in arsenic acid, H_3AsO_4.

$$3As + 5HNO_3 + 2H_2O \rightarrow 3H_3AsO_4 + 5NO^-$$

Heating this substance yields arsenic pentoxide.

$$2H_3AsO_4 \rightarrow As_2O_5 + 3H_2O$$

Arsenic acid is a rather weak acid, but, unlike phosphoric acid, it is a useful oxidizing agent and finds application in analytical chemistry. It forms salts called arsenates, of which lead hydrogen arsenate, $PbHAsO_4$, may be mentioned. This substance and several other arsenates are widely used as insecticides.

108. ANTIMONY AND BISMUTH

The last two elements in Group 5 show more than ordinary resemblances. Antimony was known to the ancients and enjoyed great popularity as a medicine during the fifteenth century. The Latin name *stibium,* from which the symbol Sb is derived, was applied by Pliny to the mineral Sb_2S_3.

Bismuth was first characterized in the early seventeenth century by a monk, Johann Tholde, who wrote under the pseudonym Basil Valentine. The name "bismuth" is said to be derived from the German *weissmuth* (white matter), from the product of a peculiar reaction of some bismuth compounds with water.

Both antimony and bismuth occur free in nature, and as the sulfides, *stibnite,* Sb_2S_3; and *bismuth glance,* Bi_2S_3, respectively. Considerable quantities of both elements are derived as by-products in the refining of other metals, particularly lead. The metals may be obtained by roasting the sulfides in air to form the oxides, and then reducing with carbon. The equations for antimony and bismuth are similar.

$$2Sb_2S_3 + 9O_2 \rightarrow 2Sb_2O_3 + 6SO_2$$
$$Sb_2O_3 + 3C \rightarrow 2Sb + 3CO$$

Both elements are fairly dense solids with a high metallic luster. Antimony often is formed with a pronounced leaf-like crystalline pattern running throughout the mass.

Both elements unite with oxygen when heated, to form respectively antimony trioxide, Sb_2O_3, and bismuth trioxide, Bi_2O_3. Oxides in which the oxidation state is +5 are also known. The oxides Sb_2O_3 and Bi_2O_3 both dissolve in strong acid to form chlorides, thus exhibiting the typical properties of a metallic (basic) oxide.

$$Sb_2O_3 + 6HCl \rightarrow 2SbCl_3 + 3H_2O$$

$$Bi_2O_3 + 6HCl \rightarrow 2BiCl_3 + 3H_2O$$

Like arsenic trioxide, antimony trioxide dissolves in strong bases to form salts, of which sodium antimonite, Na_3SbO_3, is an example.

$$Sb_2O_3 + 6NaOH \rightarrow 2Na_3SbO_3 + 3H_2O$$

Antimony trioxide is, therefore, like arsenic trioxide, amphoteric. Bismuth trioxide, on the other hand, is almost entirely basic in character, being soluble in only the most concentrated sodium hydroxide solution.

The trichlorides of these two elements have another property which illustrates their lessened basicity as compared with arsenic. Antimony trichloride is stable in solution only if considerable excess hydrochloric acid is present. If water is added a white precipitate of antimony oxychloride appears.

$$SbCl_3 + H_2O \rightleftarrows SbOCl + 2HCl$$

A similar, reversible reaction occurs with bismuth trichloride.

$$BiCl_3 + H_2O \rightleftarrows BiOCl + 2HCl$$

These elements are the only ones which show this interesting property of forming a precipitate when water is added to the solution. Other soluble salts of antimony and bismuth show the same effect.

A few other compounds of antimony and of bismuth will be described. Antimony trisulfide occurs in nature as the black crystalline solid stibnite. If precipitated from a solution of the chloride by hydrogen sulfide, the antimony trisulfide appears as an orange-red compound. This orange substance is converted to a black modification above 115° C.

$$2SbCl_3 + 3H_2S \rightarrow Sb_2S_3 + 6HCl$$

Antimony trisulfide is used in matches and as a pigment. Red rubber is colored with this compound.

Like arsenic, antimony forms a hydride, SbH_3, called stibine. It resembles arsine but is less stable. Antimony trifluoride, SbF_3, has uses in the preparation of organic compounds such as the refrigerant difluorodichloromethane, CF_2Cl_2.

Bismuth trisulfide is a brownish-black substance precipitated when hydrogen sulfide is added to a solution of bismuth chloride.*

$$2BiCl_3 + 3H_2S \rightarrow Bi_2S_3 + 6HCl$$

Various bismuth compounds are used in medicine in such conditions as gastritis and as antisyphilitics.

Both antimony and bismuth have important uses as metals and in alloys. Antimony is used in shrapnel, primers, lead shot, and tracer bullets. The United States was dependent upon importations for much antimony used during World War II. Bismuth alloys are particularly useful because of their low melting points. **Wood's metal** contains 50 per cent bismuth, 12.5 per cent tin, 25 per cent lead, and 12.5 per cent cadmium. This alloy melts at 60.5° C. Such alloys are used in automatic fire extinguishers and safety devices. Generally a plug of the fusible alloy is arranged so that when it is heated above a certain critical value, the plug melts, allowing the mechanism to operate.

The elements of Group 5 in the Periodic Table form an unusually coherent group. The gradation of properties is regular and agrees in general with predictions which may be made concerning the change of nonmetal to metal and of acidic to basic. Nitrogen and phosphorus are typical nonmetals in appearance and in all properties. Bismuth is a typical metal in appearance and exhibits only a trace of nonmetallic property. The oxides of nitrogen and of phosphorus are strictly acid-forming. That of bismuth is definitely base-forming. Arsenic and antimony exhibit properties intermediate between these extremes. They are both amphoteric; arsenic is somewhat on the acidic side, antimony perhaps as much basic as acidic. Furthermore, the halides of these elements show a corresponding gradation of properties. Phosphorus chloride is completely hydrolyzed in water (nitrogen trichloride is extremely explosive). Arsenic trichloride is reversibly hydrolyzed, while antimony and bismuth chlorides are only partially hydrolyzed with the formation of insoluble oxychloride salts. Similar gradations of properties are found in many other compounds of these elements. Gradations of a parallel type are also found in other groups of the Periodic Table. In fact, it is a general rule that in any group, the more metallic, base-forming elements are those of highest atomic number. The more nonmetallic, acid-forming elements are at the top of each group.

---

* At one time bismuth compounds were used in cosmetics. Coal fires often yield traces of hydrogen sulfide, and it occasionally happened that a lady seated before a fireplace suffered a rather startling change of appearance as the bismuth changed into black bismuth sulfide.

A somewhat similar rule applies to the horizontal series of the Periodic Table. The elements to the right in any series tend to be more nonmetallic, those to the left more metallic. These rules are not without exceptions, but they often serve as an aid to memory in the comparison of one element with another.

EXERCISES

A. *Define or explain the following:*

ammonium NH_4	phosphorite
amphoteric (amphiprotic)	phosphorous acid
aqua regia	promoter (in catalysis)
Chile saltpeter $Na NO_3$	pyrophosphoric acid
laughing gas N_2O	red phosphorus
Marsh test	saltpeter KNO_3
orthophosphoric acid	white arsenic
Paris green	white phosphorus
phosphine	Wood's metal

B. 1. Indicate procedures and all equations for the following:

a. decomposition of ammonium nitrite by heat $NH_4NO_2 \rightarrow N_2 + 2H_2O$

b. passage of air over hot copper $O_2 + 2Cu \rightarrow 2CuO$ $N_2 + Cu \rightarrow$ no rxn.

c. $3Mg + N_2 \rightarrow$ Mg_3N_2 (magnesium nitride)

d. reaction of an ammonium compound with a strong base $NH_4Cl + NaOH \rightarrow NH_3 + NaCl + H_2O$

e. Haber process $N_2 + 3H_2 \rightarrow 2NH_3 + 21,880$ cal.

f. $Mg_3N_2 + 6H_2O \rightarrow 3Mg(OH)_2 + 2NH_3$

g. burning of ammonia in oxygen $4NH_3 + O_2 \rightarrow 2N_2 + 6H_2O$

h. catalytic oxidation of ammonia $4NH_3 + 5O_2 \xrightarrow{cat.} 6H_2O + 4NO$

i. reaction of ammonia with (1) Cu^{++} ions, (2) Ag^+ ions, (3) H^+ $NH_3 + H^+ \rightarrow NH_4^+$
   ions $Cu + 4NH_3 \rightarrow Cu(NH_3)_4$ $Ag + 2NH_3 \rightarrow Ag(NH_3)_2$

j. $NH_3 + HCl \rightarrow NH_4Cl$

k. $NH_3 + H_2O \rightleftharpoons NH_4^+ + OH^-$

l. $2NH_3 + H_2SO_4 \rightarrow (NH_4)_2SO_4$

m. nitric acid from Chile saltpeter $NaNO_3 + H_2SO_4 \rightleftharpoons NaHSO_4 + HNO_3$

n. Ostwald process for production of nitric acid (three equations) $4NH_3 + 5O_2 \rightarrow 4NO + 6H_2O + cal$

aqua regia o. $HNO_3 + 3HCl \rightarrow Cl_2 + NOCl + 2H_2O$ $2NO + O_2 \rightarrow 2NO_2 + cal.$
   $3NO_2 + H_2O \rightarrow 2HNO_3 + NO$

p. production of sodium nitrite $2NaNO_3 \xrightarrow{\Delta} 2NaNO_2 + O_2$

q. preparation of nitrous oxide $NH_4NO_3 \xrightarrow{\Delta} N_2O + 2H_2O$

r. production of phosphorus from the mineral calcium phosphate $Ca_3(PO_4)_2 + SiO_3 + 5C \rightarrow$
   $3CaSiO_3 + 2P + 5CO$

s. oxidation of phosphorus by oxygen (two possible products) $4P + 5O_2 \rightarrow 2P_2O_5$
   $4P + 3O_2 \rightarrow 2P_2O_3$

t. $P + Cl_2 \rightarrow$ (two possible products) $2PCl_3$ or PCl_5

u. hydrolysis of (1) PCl_3, (2) PCl_5 $PCl_3 + 3H_2O \rightarrow H_3PO_3 + 3HCl$ $PCl_5 + 4H_2O \rightarrow H_3PO_4 + 5HCl$

v. production of arsenic from As_2O_3 $+ 3C \rightarrow 3CO + 2As$

w. hydrolysis of arsenic trichloride, antimony trichloride, and bismuth
   trichloride $AsCl_3 + 2H_2O \rightleftharpoons 3HCl + H_3AsO_3$ $SbCl_3 + H_2O \rightleftharpoons SbOCl + 2HCl$
   $BiCl_3 + H_2O \rightleftharpoons BiOCl + 2HCl$

x. As_2O_3 plus (1) a strong acid, (2) a strong base $As_2O_3 + 6HCl \rightarrow 2AsCl_3 + 3H_2O$
   $As_2O_3 + 6NaOH \rightarrow 2Na_3AsO_3 + 3H_2O$

y. reaction of Sb_2O_3 and of Bi_2O_3 with (1) strong acid, and (2) strong
   base $Sb_2O_3 + 6HCl \rightarrow 2SbCl_3 + 3H_2O$
   $Bi_2O_3 + 6HCl \rightarrow 2BiCl_3 + 3H_2O$
   $Sb_2O_3 + 6NaOH \rightarrow 2Na_3SbO_3 + 3H_2O$
   $Bi_2O_3 + 6NaOH \rightarrow 2Na_3BiO_3 + 3H_2O$

(handwritten in top margin: PV = K, P = TK)

   z. reaction of hydrogen sulfide with (1) $AsCl_3$, (2) $SbCl_3$, and (3) $BiCl_3$, all in solution

(handwritten:)
$$2AsCl_3 + 3H_2S \rightarrow As_2S_3 + 6HCl$$
$$2SbCl_3 + 3H_2S \rightarrow Sb_2S_3 + 6HCl$$
$$2BiCl_3 + 3H_2S \rightarrow Bi_2S_3 + 6HCl$$

2. Why must the synthesis of ammonia from nitrogen and hydrogen be carried out at high pressure and moderate temperature? What is the function of the catalyst? *(handwritten: too high temp- will reduce yield / pressure increase yield / catalyst speeds reaction)*

3. Silver chloride, $AgCl$, is insoluble in water, but it readily dissolves in ammonium hydroxide. Suggest a reason. *(handwritten: ammonia combines with Ag to form / silver ammonia complex ion)*

4. List examples of nitrogen in each of its different oxidation states. *(handwritten: NH_4^+, NO_3^-, NH_3, HNO_2, NO, N_2O, NO_2, N_2)*

C. 1. When ammonium chloride is heated, it dissociates into ammonia *(hw: NH3)* and hydrogen chloride *(hw: HCl)*. If this is done in a tube closed at one end, and a piece of moist litmus paper is placed at the open end of the tube, the litmus first turns blue *(hw: base)*, then red *(hw: acid)*. Explain.

2. Nitric *(hw: NO)* oxide is more stable at high temperatures than at low temperatures. How is it, then, that if nitric oxide is heated it decomposes to nitrogen and oxygen? *(hw: reac. to form " " endothermic + if temp. / raised high enough, NO is formed)*

3. Would the use of a catalyst be useful or not in the preparation of nitric oxide from nitrogen and oxygen?

4. Write formulas for each of the following: ammonium sulfite *(hw: $(NH_4)_2SO_3$)*, antimony sulfate *(hw: $Sb_2(SO_4)_3$)*, ferric (ortho)phosphate *(hw: $Fe_2(PO_4)_2$?)*, ammonium chromate *(hw: $(NH_4)_2CrO_4$)*, cupric ammonia chloride *(hw: $Cu(NH_3)_4Cl_2$)*, manganous (meta)phosphate *(hw: $Mn(PO_3)_2$)*, sodium arsenate *(hw: Na_3AsO_3)*, aluminum nitrite *(hw: $Al NO_2$)*.

5. Write balanced equations for the following:

  a. calcium nitride plus water *(hw: $Ca_3N_2 + 3H_2O \rightarrow 3Ca(OH)_2 + N_2$)*

  b. ammonium sulfate plus calcium hydroxide (a strong base) *(hw: $(NH_4)_2SO_4 + Ca(OH)_2 \rightarrow 2NH_4OH + CaSO_4$)*

  c. $2KOH + 2NO_2 \rightarrow KNO_3 + KNO_2 + ?$ *(hw: H_2O)*

  d. $2HI + 2HNO_2 \rightarrow 2NO + 2H_2O + ?$ *(hw: I_2)*

  e. $Br_2 + HNO_2 + H_2O \rightarrow HNO_3 + ?$ *(hw: $2HBr$)*

  f. $2NaI + 2H_3PO_4 \rightarrow 2NaH_2PO_4 + ?$ *(hw: $I_2 + H_2O$)*

  g. $As_2O_3 + 6Zn + 6H_2SO_4 \rightarrow 2AsH_3 + 6ZnSO_4 + 3H_2O$

  h. $4AsH_3 + 3O_2 \rightarrow 4As + 6H_2O$

  i. $2Bi(NO_3)_3$ (in solution) $+ 3H_2S \rightarrow$ *(hw: $Bi_2S_3 + 6HNO_3$)*

  j. $As_2O_3 + HNO_3$ (conc.) $+ H_2O \rightarrow NO + ?$

6. Draw electron diagrams for $Cu(NH_3)_4^{++}$, NO, and PH_3.

7. Nitrogen dioxide has the property of *associating* reversibly to form dinitrogen tetroxide, according to the equation: $2NO_2 \rightleftarrows N_2O_4 + heat$. What will be the effect of (a) increased pressure, and (b) increased temperature on the above system at equilibrium?

8. Referring to p. 38, it was stated that single electrons act like little compass needles and are attracted to a magnet, whereas paired electrons are not. Which of the following substances might be expected to be attracted to a magnet: N_2O, NO, NO_2, N_2O_4? *(hw: $4 \times 6 = 24 + (2 \times 5) = 34$)*

9. Carbon monoxide, CO, and nitrogen, N_2, have many *physical* properties in common. What similarity of *electronic* structure may be responsible for this?

(handwritten electron dot diagrams at bottom:)
$$:O:C \qquad :N:N:$$
(hw: 10 e)

10. By consideration of the various reduction products obtained when a metal is treated with nitric acid, indicate in the blanks of the following chart the most probable reduction product or products when each of the three metals is treated in turn with dilute nitric acid and then with concentrated nitric acid. An example is given for the reaction of copper with dilute acid.

	Copper	Silver	Gold	Tin	Calcium
Dilute nitric acid	NO	H_2			
Concentrated nitric acid	NO_2				

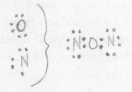

16 THE ATMOSPHERE

We live immersed at the bottom of a sea of elemental air . . . —
Evangelista Torricelli

109. COMPOSITION OF THE ATMOSPHERE *

Dry air contains approximately the following percentages by volume of the
gases indicated; it also contains traces and variable amounts of several other
substances.

Element	Volume, Per Cent
Nitrogen	78.09
Oxygen	20.95
Argon	0.93
Carbon dioxide	0.03
Neon	0.0018
Helium	0.00053
Krypton	0.0001

The actual composition of air appears to vary slightly from place to place,
and different experimenters obtain slightly different results. In addition to
the substances indicated, air contains water vapor which varies widely in
amount but which averages about 2 per cent. Air also contains traces of hydrogen, xenon, and radon; it often contains traces of nitrogen oxides, ammonia, and ozone; and it frequently contains dust, bacteria, and many other
substances. *Air is a mixture;* the percentages of the major constituents of air
are generally present in a definite proportion, but the proportion actually
varies slightly under certain conditions. Furthermore, the elements present in
air exhibit their own characteristic properties rather than those of a compound. And finally, air is readily separable into its constituents without recourse to chemical change. Air cannot be considered a chemical compound.

The several constituents of air may all be separated by mechanical processes
such as liquefaction. We shall indicate, however, methods by which the separation may be achieved by using the different chemical properties of the
various gases present.

* W. J. Humphries, *Physics of the Air* (New York: McGraw-Hill, 1940).

If air is passed through a drying agent, the moisture will be removed. Such drying agents include concentrated sulfuric acid and anhydrous calcium chloride. If a measured quantity of air is passed over a weighed amount of calcium chloride, the increase in weight of the calcium chloride owing to absorption of water will give the amount of water originally present in the air.

The atmospheric content of water vapor is generally reported as **relative humidity** rather than as actual weight or volume per cent. Relative humidity may be defined as the ratio of the actual pressure of water vapor in the air to the saturation pressure of water vapor at the same temperature. The saturation pressure of water vapor at various temperatures may be obtained from vapor pressure tables. This represents the maximum pressure of water vapor which could be maintained in air. Any excess pressure of water vapor would result in the formation of fog droplets or other form of condensation. Air normally contains less than this maximum pressure of water vapor. Relative humidity is the ratio of actual to theoretically highest possible pressures. At 25° C. the saturation vapor pressure of water is 23.5 mm. Suppose the actual pressure of the water vapor on a certain day when the temperature is 25° C. is 14.0 mm. Then the relative humidity is 14.0/23.5 = 59.5 per cent. Comfort depends in large part on relative humidity. If the air is too dry (as it often is in buildings in winter), then we feel chilly and the mucous membrane of the nostrils dries out. In summer the high relative humidity often produces far more discomfort than the high temperature.

Relative humidity is found by determining the **dew point.** This is the temperature at which moisture will condense from the air. It may be found by cooling a surface, such as the outside of a beaker, until a mist forms. Suppose the dew point is 10° C. and the room or atmosphere temperature is 23° C. The vapor pressures of water at 10° C. and at 23° C. are determined from tables to be respectively 9.1 mm. and 20.9 mm. The relative humidity is then 9.1/20.9 = 43.5 per cent. For meteorological purposes more complicated hygrometers and psychrometers are used. Inexpensive humidity indicators often depend on the expansion and contraction of a hair or strip which increases in length when the humidity increases. Electrical hygrometers are also in use.

Carbon dioxide in air may be found by passing the air over a strong base such as sodium hydroxide.

$$CO_2 + 2NaOH \rightarrow Na_2CO_3 + H_2O$$

Moisture must first be removed because that too is partially taken up by sodium hydroxide. An alternative method is to shake a quantity of air with a measured amount of standard base solution. The carbon dioxide acts as an acid and neutralizes part of the base. The remaining base may be found by titration.

Oxygen may be removed from air by the use of any substance which readily combines with oxygen but not with nitrogen. White phosphorus

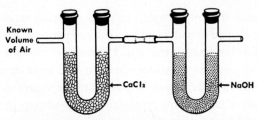

Fig. 16-1. Apparatus for the determination of water vapor and of carbon dioxide in air. A known volume of air is passed consecutively over anhydrous calcium chloride and sodium hydroxide. The former takes up water, the latter carbon dioxide. Each U-tube is weighed separately before and after the experiment. It is generally necessary to protect the tube openings from air during the weighing.

could be used for this purpose. Hot metallic copper is convenient. The product is chiefly cupric oxide. Nitrogen passes on unchanged.

$$2Cu + O_2 \rightarrow 2CuO$$

The oxygen in a weighed quantity of air may be estimated by finding the increase in weight of the heated copper. Magnesium metal could not be used for this purpose because of its tendency to form magnesium nitride.

$$3Mg + N_2 \rightarrow Mg_3N_2$$

There are several types of solutions which have the property of absorbing oxygen. Some of these are often used for routine gas analysis involving oxygen determination. There is also a method based on the principle that oxygen is slightly attracted by a magnet.

The gas remaining after removal of water vapor, carbon dioxide, and oxygen from air is substantially nitrogen except for the approximately 1 per cent of argon and other inert gases. These gases are generally separated by fractional distillation of the liquid. It would, however, be feasible to combine the nitrogen with hot magnesium, leaving the inert gases. Another way, used by Cavendish in the year 1785, was to pass a spark through a mixture of nitrogen and oxygen to form nitrogen dioxide and then to absorb this gas in potassium hydroxide (KOH). Cavendish actually observed when he did this that a small residue of gas always remained, but he did not recognize this as being due to a new element. It remained for Rayleigh and Ramsay in 1894 to identify the gas argon.

Separation of the inert gases is a tedious and expensive operation. It will be described later.

110. DISCOVERY OF THE INERT GASES *

																	H	He
Li	Be	B												C	N	O	F	Ne
Na	Mg	Al												Si	P	S	Cl	A
K	Ca	Sc	Ti	V	Cr	Mn	Fe	Co	Ni	Cu	Zn	Ga	Ge	As	Se	Br	Kr
Rb	Sr	Y	Zr	Nb	Mo	Tc	Ru	Rh	Pd	Ag	Cd	In	Sn	Sb	Te	I	Xe
Cs	Ba	La-Lu	Hf	Ta	W	Re	Os	Ir	Pt	Au	Hg	Tl	Pb	Bi	Po	At	Rn
Fr	Ra	Ac	Th	Pa	U-												

Until the year 1895 it was believed that air contained no appreciable amounts of any substances other than nitrogen, oxygen, water vapor, and carbon dioxide. This view was held in spite of the fact that Cavendish in 1785 had found a slight residue of air which appeared to be neither oxygen nor nitrogen. Cavendish apparently gave the matter no further consideration. In the year 1882 the famous English scientist, Lord Rayleigh, observed that "nitrogen" derived from air had a density slightly greater than that of nitrogen derived from the decomposition of ammonia. The figures were as follows:

Atmospheric nitrogen   1.2572 grams per liter

Nitrogen from ammonia   1.2505 grams per liter

This difference, while not great, was much greater than the largest probable error in the measurements. Rayleigh and Sir William Ramsay investigated this discrepancy by passing large quantities of atmospheric nitrogen over hot magnesium, which formed magnesium nitride. A small residue of gas was left. This residue they identified with the aid of the spectroscope as a new chemical element. They named the element argon, from the Greek word meaning "idle" or "inactive," because of the failure of the element to combine with other elements. The announcement of this discovery was made at

* Sir Wm. Ramsay, *The Gases of the Atmosphere* (London: Macmillan, 1915).

a meeting at Oxford in August, 1895. Chemists and others were astonished and somewhat incredulous that anything new should be discovered in a substance studied so thoroughly as air. Someone sarcastically inquired if the name of the new element had also been discovered. The newspapers hailed the discovery as a "triumph of the fourth decimal." The reason that "atmospheric" nitrogen has a higher density than "pure" nitrogen is that it contains about 1 per cent of argon. The density of argon is considerably greater than that of nitrogen.

The element helium has the unique distinction of having been discovered in the atmosphere, or rather photosphere, of the sun before it was discovered on earth. In 1868 the spectroscope was used for the first time to study a solar eclipse, which happened to be visible in India. The French astronomer P. J. C. Janssen observed some strong lines in the yellow part of the spectrum. At first it was thought that the lines might be due to sodium, but Janssen showed that this could not be true. E. Frankland and J. N. Lockyer suggested that the lines were caused by a new element to which they gave the name helium, from a Greek word meaning "the sun."

Helium was not discovered on the earth until 1895. In 1891 an American chemist, Hillebrand, observed that certain minerals contained small quantities of an inert gas which he mistakenly thought might be nitrogen. Hillebrand remarked to his assistant that they might possibly be dealing with a new element, but they let the matter drop and so missed a very important discovery. In 1895 Sir William Ramsay reinvestigated this gas, which he obtained by heating the mineral *cleveite* with acids. The gas proved to be helium. In this way the second of the inert gases was added to the Periodic Table.

The existence of these two elements, helium and argon, required the opening of a new group in the Periodic Table. It became evident at once that several more inert gases remained to be found. Three of these elements, neon, krypton, and xenon, were all found by Ramsay and Travers in the year 1898. The names mean respectively "new," "hidden," and "stranger." These elements were obtained from air by a process of fractional distillation. They were identified spectroscopically and by other tests.

Soon after these discoveries, it was found that the radioactive disintegration of radium gives off a gas similar in its chemical properties to the inert gases. This gas was discovered by Dorn, and its properties were established by Ramsay and Gray. Formerly the gas was called niton but it is now known as radon. Radon differs from the other natural inert gases in being not only formed by a radioactive process but in itself disintegrating by a similar

Fig. 16-2. William Ramsay

Ramsay was born in Scotland in 1852. He was educated at the University of Glasgow and in Germany. His discovery of the inert gases was made while he was a professor at University College in London. His work in the field of radioactivity was no less important than his discovery of the inert gases.

Ramsay was knighted in 1902, and in 1904 he received the Nobel Prize in chemistry. As a professor he is said to have given lectures unequaled for lucidity and interest.

He died in 1916. Few men have had the ability and privilege to open up such a substantial new area for scientific investigation. (*Journal of Chemical Education*)

process. Some of the interesting radiochemical properties of radon will be described more fully in a later chapter.

With these six elements, the zero group of the Periodic Table is complete. Sir William Ramsay had the honor of discovering, or of being closely associated with the discovery, of all six. He is regarded as one of the most able experimentalists in the history of chemistry. His determination of the density of radon is a classic of accurate scientific measurement.

111. PROPERTIES OF THE INERT GASES

Although these elements have no chemical properties, they have several interesting physical properties, and numerous important uses.

Helium is not abundant in air, but it occurs to the extent of several per cent in natural gases found in Kansas, Arkansas, Texas, and Utah. The presence of helium in these gases was discovered in 1907 by Professors Cady and McFarland, of the University of Kansas. The United States appears to have a world monopoly on large-scale helium production. The stimulus for this development came in World War I. Up to that time the gas used for balloons and dirigibles was hydrogen, and at the outbreak of World War I the use of helium for such purposes seemed to be completely fantastic. But helium has almost as much lifting power as does hydrogen, and it possesses the invaluable advantage of being noncombustible. Under the impetus of wartime necessity, large-scale plants were built and enough helium was extracted to fill several airships by the end of the war. The helium is extracted by liquefaction and fractional distillation. The United States Government controls all important domestic helium deposits and production facilities; so far as is known this amounts to a world monopoly. Shortly after the burning of the hydrogen-filled Hindenburg at Lakehurst, New Jersey, in 1937, the United States was asked to sell a fairly large amount of helium to Germany. This request was refused—a decision which proved to be only too well founded on the fear that Nazi Germany intended the helium for war use.

Helium has the second lowest density of all known substances, being exceeded in this respect only by hydrogen. It has the lowest boiling and freezing points of any substance. The freezing point under 26 atmospheres of pressure is $-272.2°$ C., or less than one degree from the absolute zero. Helium was first liquefied in 1908 by a Dutch physicist, Kamerlingh Onnes. The gas is colorless and odorless. It does not enter into chemical combination, but as will be described later, it is one of the products of radioactive disintegration.

Until fairly recently the principal use for helium was in lighter-than-air craft. The lifting power of a balloon depends on the difference between the weight of the balloon and the weight of air which is displaced. A liter of air (S.C.) weighs 1.29 grams. A liter of hydrogen weighs 0.09 grams, and a liter of helium weighs 0.18 grams. The lifting power of helium to that of hydrogen stands, therefore, in the ratio $(1.29 - 0.18)$ to $(1.29 - 0.09)$, or of $1.11/1.20 = 92.5$ per cent. We have the seeming paradox that although helium is twice as dense as hydrogen, yet its lifting power in a balloon is nearly as great as that of hydrogen.

In recent years other uses for helium have become of major importance, since, partly owing to a long series of disasters, the Zeppelin type of aircraft has been largely displaced by heavier-than-air craft. Among newly developed industrial uses for helium, one of the most important is in the welding of magnesium and its alloys in aircraft plants. The welding operation is shielded by an atmosphere of helium gas which cools the metal, controls its inflammability, and improves the strength and quality of the weld.

Helium has some uses in medicine. It owes these actions exclusively to its physical properties. When divers or others work under high atmospheric pressure, the nitrogen of the air dissolves in the blood and other body fluids. When the individual returns to normal pressure, the nitrogen is released from solution. Owing to its high solubility and relatively low rate of diffusion, the nitrogen takes a long time to escape from the body. The nitrogen may appear as bubbles of gas which give rise to serious symptoms, including excruciating pain. The effects are often fatal. This condition is popularly known as the *bends*. It is avoided by having the individual stay in a decompression chamber while the pressure is slowly reduced to normal. This slow decompression allows time for the nitrogen to escape, through the lungs, without forming gas bubbles in the body. The application of helium greatly reduces the time necessary for decompression and the attendant dangers.

Instead of breathing air, the person undergoing high pressures breathes a mixture of oxygen and helium. The helium is less soluble than nitrogen and its high rate of diffusion reduces the time necessary for its escape from the body.

Another medical use for helium is in the treatment of respiratory obstruction such as asthma. It fairly frequently happens that insufficient oxygen reaches the lungs because of some obstruction to free passage of air. The density of helium is much less than that of air, and it will be recalled that according to Graham's law, the rate of diffusion of a gas varies inversely as the square root of the density. Hence helium is able to move in and out of the lungs much more freely than is nitrogen. In the case of obstructed breathing the use of mixtures of oxygen and helium often gives great relief. Attacks of asthma are often completely relieved in a few hours. Owing to the expense involved, it may be necessary to devise some means of rebreathing the helium and of replenishing the oxygen, and removing carbon dioxide and water vapor.

Neon is obtained by the fractional distillation of air. Its principal use is in the familiar neon signs. Such signs, however, contain argon and other gases more frequently than neon. The signs operate by the passage of an electric discharge through the gas which is at a few millimeters of pressure. Neon alone gives a red glow in clear glass. Deep blue is obtained by a mixture of argon and mercury. Green is produced by argon in a yellow tube; white, by argon, neon, and mercury.

Argon, being by far the most abundant of the inert gases, is also by far the cheapest. It is produced on a large scale by fractional distillation of air. Its principal use is based on its inertness and availability. Argon is used to fill tungsten-filament electric light bulbs. Air cannot be present in such bulbs because the hot tungsten would combine with oxygen. A vacuum is not entirely satisfactory because the tungsten then slowly sublimes on to the walls of the bulb, darkening the glass. Filling the bulbs with argon solves the problem by reducing the volatilization of the tungsten yet not entering into chemical combination. Argon is more efficient than nitrogen for this purpose. Argon is also used at low pressure in fluorescent lamps. Some application of argon is made in welding operations, similar to the corresponding use of helium.

Krypton and xenon have, so far, only minor uses. If they were available at lower cost there is no doubt that they would find application in electric light bulbs, and elsewhere.

Radon, although a member of the inert gas group, is of interest mainly for its radioactive properties.

The outstanding characteristic of the zero group gases is their chemical inertness. A few scientists have claimed to have evidence for the transitory existence of compounds, particularly of argon. But these, if they exist at all, are stable enough for identification only at low temperatures and under special circumstances. In the ordinary sense, compounds of these gases do not exist.

Reasons for this behavior lie in the electronic configuration of the atoms. Helium has, in its highest normal energy level, two electrons. All the other inert gases have eight. In each case this is the maximum number of electrons which can be accommodated in the several energy levels. We might say that the respective energy levels are saturated with electrons. This condition obviously leads to stability and to lack of chemical reactivity. Completed, or saturated, energy levels cannot accept another electron to change the atom into a negative ion. They apparently cannot readily lose an electron to form a positive ion.

This stability associated with a completed energy level is shown in other ways. Chlorine, for instance, has seven electrons in the third energy level.

$$:\overset{..}{\underset{..}{Cl}}\cdot + \epsilon \rightarrow :\overset{..}{\underset{..}{Cl}}:$$

Chlorine easily gains an electron to become a negatively charged chloride ion. The highly reactive chlorine atom becomes a rather moderately active ion. Notice that in doing so, the chlorine has gained the same electron configuration as the inert gas of next highest atomic number, namely, argon. Similarly, the highly reactive sodium atom easily loses an electron to become the relatively stable sodium ion.

$$:\overset{..}{\underset{..}{Na}}:\cdot \rightarrow :\overset{..}{\underset{..}{Na}}: + \epsilon$$

In so doing the sodium atom reverts to the electronic configuration possessed by argon, namely, eight electrons in the highest level. In the same way magnesium easily loses two electrons to become magnesium ion. Similar relationships are found throughout the Periodic Table among the elements adjacent to or near the inert gases. This applies to elements of slightly higher atomic number than the inert gases and also to those of slightly lower atomic number.

112. LIQUID AIR

When a gas is highly compressed it generally tends to become warmer. This effect is not related to Charles's Law but is rather related to the fact that to compress a gas, work must be done on the molecules. This added energy content of the molecules appears as a somewhat elevated temperature. Conversely, when a gas under pressure is allowed to escape through a small orifice, the temperature of the gas drops. This fact, known as the **Joule-Thomson effect,** is used in the liquefaction of gases, including air.

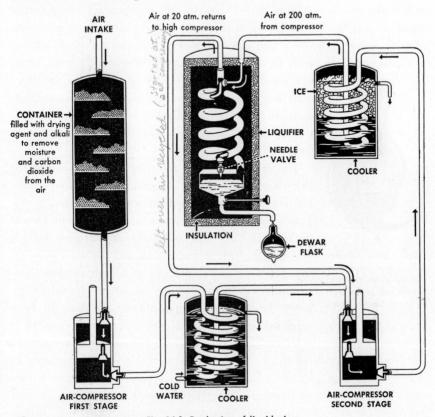

Fig. 16-3. Production of liquid air.

Liquid air is produced on a large scale by a process developed independently by Hampson and by Linde. Air is freed of carbon dioxide and moisture. It is then compressed to about 200 atmospheres and the heat so generated is absorbed by letting the gas flow through pipes cooled by running water. The compressed air is now passed through a spiral pipe and allowed to escape through a small orifice. In escaping, the gas is somewhat cooled. This cool air now flows over the outside of the spiral pipe, thereby cooling the air which is still coming through the pipe. The decompressed air is returned to the compressor. The air escaping from the orifice is now already somewhat cooled even before it expands, so that expansion lowers its temperature still further. This procedure goes on until the air escaping from the orifice is cold enough to liquefy. Liquid air collects below the orifice and is withdrawn from time to time.

Liquid air consists essentially of a mixture, as does the atmosphere. Separation of the various constituents is possible by fractional distillation. Oxygen boils under normal pressure at $-182.96°$ C. and nitrogen at $-195.8°$. It is therefore possible, by the use of appropriate, properly insulated distillation columns, to separate these two gases. Similarly, if liquid air is allowed to stand, the nitrogen tends to boil off first, leaving substantially pure liquid

oxygen. This is the method which is used for the large-scale industrial production of oxygen. The same principle, of fractional distillation, is used in the production of argon, and to a lesser extent the other inert gases.

The very low boiling points of all these gases means that they would rapidly evaporate unless placed in special containers. Such containers were invented by Sir James Dewar. These containers are known as **Dewar flasks** (Fig. 16-4), or popularly as Thermos bottles.

Fig. 16-4. Dewar flask. Liquid oxygen is shipped great distances in tank cars in the form of giant Dewar flasks.

These flasks have a double wall and the space between the two walls is pumped out to a high vacuum. The surfaces next to the vacuum are often silvered to improve the heat-insulating quality of the flask. In these flasks liquid air may often be kept for days or even for weeks. Liquid air is a familiar substance in scientific laboratories. Its use permits the inexpensive and convenient study of matter at low temperatures. It is also often used to freeze vapors such as water or mercury out of apparatus. At $-190°$ C. the vapor pressure of most substances is negligibly small. The most important industrial use of liquid air is in the production of oxygen. Other uses include the shrinkage of parts of machinery so as to make tight-fitting joints, as in the exhaust valves of automobiles.

Liquid air is so cold that it can be used for a number of amusing demonstrations. A kettle partly filled with liquid air will boil vigorously if placed on a block of ice. Rubber becomes brittle at these low temperatures; a rubber ball first immersed for a few moments in liquid air, then bounced on the floor, will shatter into fragments. Soft plumber's solder becomes strong and springy at these low temperatures. Mercury becomes solid and may be frozen into the shape of a hammer for driving nails. Combustible material dipped for a few moments into liquid oxygen will burn with great vigor. For instance, a cigar will flare up like a torch. Substances which will burn in air often form dangerously explosive mixtures with liquid oxygen. Such substances are alcohol, kerosene, and powdered aluminum.

$K - 273 = C$
$20.4 - 273 = C$
$252.6 = C$

113. VERY LOW TEMPERATURES

It will be recalled that the absolute zero is $-273°$ C. (more precisely $-273.15°$ C.). Liquid air, boiling at about $-190°$ C., is therefore still about $83°$ above absolute zero. Certain other gases liquefy at temperatures well below the boiling point of air. These are hydrogen, the normal boiling point of which is $20.4°$ K., and helium, which boils at about $4°$ K. Both of these gases are liquefied by a process of compression and expansion similar to that used for air, except that the gases are first precooled, generally through the use of liquid air.

If liquids are very vigorously boiled under reduced pressure, the temperature drops because the latent heat of vaporization is taken up from the liquid and its surroundings. It will be recalled that it is possible to freeze water simply by placing it in a vessel which is connected to a good vacuum pump. If the various liquefied gases are similarly subjected to high vacuum, they boil vigorously and finally freeze. In this way it is possible to make solid oxygen, nitrogen, hydrogen, and helium. Hydrogen melts at $14°$ K., helium melts at about $1°$ K. These very low temperatures are measured in terms of the vapor pressure exerted by these substances. At such low temperatures, matter exhibits several interesting properties. One of these is the almost complete disappearance of electrical resistance in certain metals. The metal is said to become **superconducting;** an electric current started in a wire ring under these circumstances may continue to flow for days.

Until about 1926 no lower temperatures than that of melting helium seemed possible. Two scientists, Professor Giauque of the University of California and Professor Debye, then in Germany but later at Cornell University, independently proposed a method known as *adiabatic demagnetization*. This method operates on an entirely new principle.

If a substance is cooled with liquid helium, then placed in a strong magnetic field, it may tend to warm up. This effect takes place with certain substances which have the property of being very feebly attracted to a magnet. Such substances are said to be paramagnetic. Examples are gadolinium sulfate, $Gd_2(SO_4)_3 \cdot 8H_2O$; and iron ammonium alum, $FeNH_4(SO_4)_2 \cdot 12H_2O$.

The heat so liberated is readily dissipated in the liquid helium so that the substance soon returns to the temperature of the helium, but it does so in the magnetized condition. If now the magnetic field is reduced or removed, the substance tends to cool off. By this means temperatures have been achieved down to within a few thousandths of a degree from the absolute zero. At this writing the lowest temperature attained seems to be about $0.004°$ K. Temperatures such as these may be measured by the change of magnetic properties shown by the magnetic substance.

At temperatures below about $2°$ K. helium shows properties not shown by any other substance. The liquid, known as helium II, has a heat conductivity about three million times greater than ordinary liquid helium and several hundred times greater than copper at room temperature. Helium II seems, under certain conditions, to have virtually no viscosity. A small flask full of helium II will empty itself by the liquid flowing up over the surface of the glass and dripping off the outside bottom of the flask. The helium II forms an extremely thin layer all over the glass surface, and this layer is able to flow without friction in any direction.

114. OZONE

When oxygen is exposed to ultraviolet light, or to certain forms of electric discharge, it tends to absorb energy and change to an allotropic modification. Three molecules of oxygen become two molecules of ozone.

$$3O_2 \rightleftarrows 2O_3$$

The sun's rays are rich in ultraviolet light of the proper wave length to bring about this change. Oxygen in the upper atmosphere is thereby converted in part to ozone. Occasionally minute traces of ozone are brought down to near the earth by descending currents of air, but the concentration of ozone found near sea level is always extremely small. Even at great heights the ozone concentration is never very large.

This ozone in the upper atmosphere has the property of absorbing part of the ultraviolet light from the sun. Consequently that light never reaches the earth. The ultraviolet light from the sun is strong enough to destroy all life on earth in a very short time. The ozone formed by rays from the sun thus acts as a filter to protect the earth from harmful radiations. The concentration of ozone in the atmosphere varies from time to time, and these changes have a considerable effect on the climate. The changes that occur have been studied with the aid of appropriate photoelectric cells mounted in small balloons.

Not infrequently persons at the seashore or at mountain resorts may be heard to remark, "Oh! Smell the ozone!" Ozone has a pronounced odor, but it is very doubtful if it ever reaches a high enough concentration for detection by the nose under normal conditions. Near electrical machinery and near ultraviolet lamps the odor is quite pronounced, but the popular conception of ozone is more likely the smell of the sea or of the pine forests.

Ozone is generally made by what is called a **silent electric discharge.** The object is to introduce energy to the oxygen without raising the temperature so high that the rather unstable ozone is decomposed as fast as it is formed. Two concentric glass tubes lined with tin foil are arranged so that air or, better, oxygen may pass through the space between them. (See Fig. 16-5.) The two terminals of an induction coil are connected to the tin foil on the two tubes respectively. If air is used, the issuing gas contains about half of 1 per cent of ozone. With oxygen the ozone rises to about 2 per cent. Higher yields are obtained by using dried gases at low temperatures and under elevated pressures. Nearly pure ozone may be prepared by liquefying the mixed gases, then allowing the oxygen to boil off. The boiling point of ozone is $-112.3°$ C. as compared with $-182.97°$ C. for oxygen.

Commercial ozonizers, or ozone generators, are built with a capacity running up to about one kilogram of ozone per hour. These all operate on the same principle of the silent electric discharge but often with elaborate controls for increasing the yield. The cost of electricity is the largest item of expense in ozone production.

Ozone is a pale blue gas; the liquid is deep blue. The pure substance has been obtained, but it is highly reactive and dangerous. Almost all work with ozone is done on dilute solutions in air or in oxygen. At low concentrations the odor of ozone is pleasing, but higher concentrations are strong and unpleasant. Ozone produces headache, and is poisonous. The gas is a strong

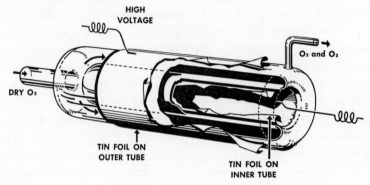

Fig. 16-5. Ozonizer.

oxidizing agent. An example of its oxidizing action is shown with a water solution of potassium iodide. The iodine is liberated and the ozone reverts to oxygen.

$$2KI + H_2O + O_3 \rightarrow I_2 + 2KOH + O_2$$

The fact that ozone consists of oxygen and that it is not a compound of oxygen and some other element is shown by decomposing a sample of ozone. The product is always oxygen and nothing but oxygen. The correct formula for ozone troubled chemists for many years, and the difficulty was enhanced by the trouble involved in obtaining ozone free from oxygen. Finally, however, it was shown that three volumes of oxygen produce two of ozone, and vice versa. Now, suppose the formula for ozone to be O_n—that is, that there are n atoms in the ozone molecule. Then two molecules of O_n must yield n molecules of O_2, or

$$2O_n \rightarrow nO_2$$

there being $2n$ atoms in each case.

According to experiment, two volumes of ozone yield three volumes of oxygen. Hence three molecules of oxygen must contain the same number of atoms as two molecules of ozone. As the formula for oxygen is O_2, we have $n = 3$, and the formula for ozone is O_3. This view has been amply confirmed in recent years by spectroscopic and other lines of evidence.

Ozone has a considerable number of uses. In the treatment of air, ozone is used to eliminate bad odors by oxidizing the substances which cause the smells. A concentration of 0.01 parts per million is sufficient to deodorize the air in public buildings. A concentration of one part per million is noticeable and may be dangerous to health. There is still, however, some uncertainty regarding the toxic properties of ozone at low concentrations.

Another use of ozone is in the treatment of water. It removes undesirable odors and tastes, and it kills harmful bacteria. The action is one of oxidation, and ozone has the advantage that the only by-product of its action is ordinary oxygen. Ozonizers are used by beverage makers and by bottlers of drinking water. They are also used for treating the water in swimming pools. The high cost has prevented widespread use of ozone for the treatment of municipal water supplies in the United States. But installations are in operation in such European cities as Paris, London, and Leningrad. Philadelphia has an ozone water-treatment plant.

Ozone also finds use in the bleaching of fabrics, starch, ivory, and certain oils. Several industrial chemical operations involve the use of ozone. Examples of these are the manufacture of artificial camphor and of vanillin (vanilla-extract). It has been proposed as a rocket fuel.

EXERCISES

A. *Define or explain the following:*

adiabatic demagnetization	liquid air
Dewar flask	ozone
dew point	ozonizer
helium II	relative humidity
inert gas	silent electric discharge
Joule-Thomson effect	superconductivity

B. 1. Considering air to be a mixture of nitrogen, oxygen, water vapor, carbon dioxide, and argon, show how each of these could be separated by use of their different chemical properties. (Give equations.)
2. How was argon discovered?
3. Describe the uses of the inert gases.
4. Describe the production of temperatures near the absolute zero.
5. How is ozone made?
6. Illustrate the oxidizing action of ozone (equation).
7. What uses has ozone?
8. What is the history of the discovery of helium?
9. How is a Dewar flask able to keep liquid air for a considerable period?

10. Prove that the formula for ozone is O_3.
11. What explanation has been offered for the chemical inertness of the group 0 gases?

C. 1. If air is a mixture, how does it happen that the composition is so nearly uniform throughout the world?
2. Find the relative humidity on a day when the dew point is 10° C. and the atmospheric temperature is 29° C. (Refer to a vapor pressure table.)
3. Calculate the weight of 22.4 l. of dry air (S.C.) neglecting the inert gases.
4. Write equations for the process used by Cavendish which almost led to the discovery of argon in the year 1785. (Reference may be made to Exercise C5 at the end of the previous chapter.)
5. How could pure nitrogen be obtained from ammonia?
6. The density of helium is twice as great as that of hydrogen, yet helium has about 92.5 per cent of the lifting power of hydrogen in a balloon. Explain this.
7. Why could Mendeleev not have predicted the existence of the inert gases?
8. Calculate the difference in velocity of diffusion of helium as compared with (a) hydrogen, and (b) nitrogen.
9. Design an apparatus for the rebreathing of helium so that a patient can get adequate oxygen, but so that no helium is lost. Recall that the exhaled breath normally contains air, carbon dioxide, and water vapor.
10. If ozone is constantly being generated by the action of ultraviolet light in the upper atmosphere, why does not all the oxygen ultimately become converted to ozone?
11. Calculate the density of pure ozone gas at S.C.

17 SILICON AND RELATED ELEMENTS

																H	He
Li	Be											**B**	C			N	O	F	Ne
Na	Mg											Al	**Si**			P	S	Cl	A
K	Ca	Sc	**Ti**	V	Cr	Mn	Fe	Co	Ni	Cu	Zn	Ga	Ge	As	Se	Br	Kr
Rb	Sr	Y	**Zr**	Nb	Mo	Tc	Ru	Rh	Pd	Ag	Cd	In	Sn	Sb	Te	I	Xe
Cs	Ba	La-Lu	**Hf**	Ta	W	Re	Os	Ir	Pt	Au	Hg	Tl	Pb	Bi	Po	At	Rn
Fr	Ra	Ac	Th	Pa	U-												

115. SILICON

This element is the second most widely distributed in the earth's crust, yet it is an element with which the average person is not familiar. It never occurs free in nature. Silicon occurs as the oxide, SiO_2, and in a great variety of silicates. The rocks of the earth's crust are usually aggregates of silicates, mechanically mixed together.

The element silicon is prepared by reducing the oxide with carbon or with an active metal such as magnesium. Neither reaction is particularly easy to perform.

$$SiO_2 + 2C \rightarrow Si + 2CO$$

$$SiO_2 + 2Mg \rightarrow Si + 2MgO$$

The product is generally contaminated with silicon carbide, SiC, or magnesium silicide, Mg_2Si, as the case may be. The difficulty in preparing the element lies in the great stability of silicon dioxide and of many other silicon compounds. Very powerful reducing conditions are necessary to break up these silicon compounds. Fairly pure silicon is now, however, a readily available article of commerce.

Silicon is a brittle, gray solid, with a decidedly metallic appearance. The element is not generally considered to be a metal, because its oxide is definitely acidic in character rather than basic. Silicon is hard enough to scratch glass, and its melting point is 1420° C.

Silicon is not very active at ordinary temperatures. Its chemical properties resemble those of carbon. The oxidation state of silicon in its compounds is always, or nearly always, four. Silicon burns in air at high temperatures to form the dioxide.

$$Si + O_2 \rightarrow SiO_2$$

It also combines with the halogens, and with several other elements. With chlorine, for instance, it forms silicon tetrachloride; with magnesium, magnesium silicide.

$$Si + 2Cl_2 \rightarrow SiCl_4$$

$$2Mg + Si \rightarrow Mg_2Si$$

The carbide, SiC, is used as an abrasive, and in lightning arresters.

Silicon is used in the casting of steel, copper, and bronze. It acts as a deoxidizer, or remover of oxygen. In steel-making, silicon is used in the form of the alloy **ferrosilicon,** which contains silicon and iron. The silicon combines with dissolved oxygen in the steel, thereby improving the quality. Steel containing an excess of silicon amounting to several per cent is used in magnet and transformer cores. Corrosion resistance of steel is increased by the presence of silicon. Silicon is also used for making plastics of a certain type, and in electronic devices.

The compound **silica,** or silicon dioxide, SiO_2, exists widely distributed in nature. It furnishes an outstanding example of polymorphism (different crystal forms). There are seven distinct forms known at different temperatures and under different conditions. The most familiar form is **quartz.** From a study of the different polymorphic forms of silica, the geologists are able to tell to what temperatures a given mineral may have been subjected in the past. Silica acts, therefore, in a sense as a geological thermometer.

Silica has several physical properties which make it valuable for laboratory equipment. It has a high melting point, about 1600° C. This is hundreds of degrees above the melting point of ordinary glass. Silica is, therefore, used for apparatus which is to be subjected to high temperatures. Furthermore, this substance has a very low thermal expansion coefficient; that is, it expands or contracts very slightly on change of temperature. A quartz vessel may be heated to redness, then plunged into ice water without cracking.

Clear silica is transparent to ultraviolet light. It is used in optical instruments (such as spectrographs) for examining the ultraviolet part of the spectrum, and for windows for the transmission of ultraviolet waves from sunlight or from artificial sources. Transparent silica is an article of commerce, and although it is rather expensive, it finds many applications. This material is made by fusing natural quartz (clean white sand). If the fusion is done under vacuum, the trapped air bubbles have a chance to escape, leaving the silica transparent. Otherwise the silica becomes milky when it is cooled.

Silica is deposited as an extremely fine powder from the skeletons of organisms living in the sea. These deposits, known as **kieselguhr** or **diatomaceous**

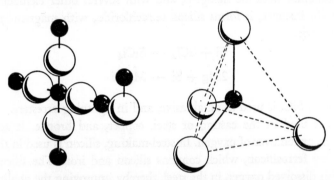

Fig. 17-1. Structure of silica, SiO₂. The diagram on the *left* shows each silicon atom, ●, surrounded by four oxygens, ○, and each oxygen by two silicons. This arrangement extends on indefinitely in space; the atoms being held together by electron pair bonds, or covalence. The valence bonds are represented by short lines between the atoms. This diagram fails, however, to show that the structure is three-dimensional. At the *right* there is shown how four oxygens are actually arranged at the four corners of a tetrahedron, at the center of which a silicon atom is situated. The diagram could be still further improved by having the atoms in effective mutual contact with each other, but this is somewhat difficult to show in a drawing.

earth, have uses as polishing agents and as adsorbents. They are also used as supports for catalytically active substances.

An added virtue of silica for laboratory apparatus is its resistance to chemical action. As mentioned in an earlier chapter, silica is attacked by hydrofluoric acid, with the formation of the gaseous compound, silicon tetrafluoride.

$$SiO_2 + 4HF \rightarrow SiF_4 + 2H_2O$$

Silica is also attacked by hot alkalis, such as sodium hydroxide, but it is not attacked by most acids, other than hydrofluoric.

$$SiO_2 + 4NaOH \rightarrow Na_4SiO_4 + 2H_2O$$

When silicon dioxide is mixed with water, no action takes place. The silica is insoluble. But it is, nevertheless, an acidic oxide as is shown by its reaction with bases to form salts such as the sodium silicate, Na_4SiO_4, shown above.

The inertness and high melting point of silica are probably related to the arrangement of atoms in this substance. There is no particle which may properly be thought of as a molecule of silica. SiO_2 does not represent a molecular formula. It appears that each silicon atom in the crystal is attached by electron sharing to four oxygen atoms, and that each oxygen atom is attached by electron sharing to two silicon atoms. The crystal of silica consists of a tightly bound covalent structure where the valence bonds extend, in a sense, throughout the whole crystalline mass. (See Fig. 17-1.) This ex-

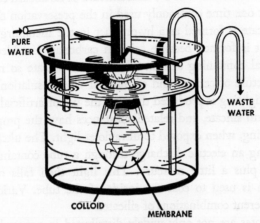

PURE WATER

WASTE WATER

COLLOID

MEMBRANE

Fig. 17-2. Dialysis.

planation is in agreement with the observed properties of silica, namely, its resistance to decomposition, its high melting point, and its low solubility.

If sodium silicate is treated with hydrochloric acid, **orthosilicic acid** is liberated.

$$Na_4SiO_4 + 4HCl \rightarrow H_4SiO_4 + 4NaCl$$

sodium silicate   orthosilicic acid

This substance may precipitate as a gelatinous mass, or it may remain as a colloid. The chloride may be removed by a process of **dialysis:** that is, the colloid is placed in a membrane such as is used for osmotic pressure experiments. (See Fig. 17-2.) The outside of the membrane is then washed with pure water. Salts, such as sodium chloride, diffuse through the membrane while the colloid remains behind. But silicic acid has a strong tendency to adsorb ions, and sometimes these are removed only with difficulty.

If orthosilicic acid is heated it loses water to form pure silica. This fact shows the relationship of silicon dioxide to silicic acid, even though the process cannot be reversed by adding water to silica.

Dehydration of silicic acid so that only 5 to 7 per cent of water remains yields a porous material known as **silica gel.** This is widely used for adsorbing gases and has many industrial applications.

Although the salts of silicic acid are among the commonest of all minerals, a few artificial silicates will be discussed first. Sodium silicate is prepared by heating silica with sodium hydroxide, or by fusing sand with sodium carbonate. Sodium silicate is known as **waterglass.** A solution of this substance in water is widely used in fireproofing and waterproofing textiles and wood. It is also used as an adhesive in the manufacture of cardboard containers. The solution was at one time commonly used in the preservation of eggs.

Calcium silicate is formed as a by-product in the metallurgy of iron and other metals. It is formed because calcium carbonate is added as a flux to remove material containing silicon. The calcium silicate so made has uses in the manufacture of cement and of mineral wool insulation.

Fluorescent lighting is produced through the use of artificial silicates. Zinc silicate, cadmium silicate, and related substances have the property of glowing, or fluorescing, when exposed to ultraviolet light. The ultraviolet light is made by passing an electric discharge through a tube containing argon (at low pressure) plus a little mercury. This light then falls on the silicate material which is used to coat the inside of the tube. Various colors are emitted by different combinations of silicates.

Natural silicates are not only widely distributed in nature but they often are of great industrial importance. Most natural silicates are very complex. **Granite** is a mixture of quartz, feldspar, and mica. There are many types of **feldspar,** of which orthoclase, $(K, Na)AlSi_3O_8$, will serve as an example. The weathering of feldspar yields clays from which bricks and porcelainware are made. This weathering to form **kaolin,** $Al_2Si_2O_5(OH)_4$, under the influence of water and carbon dioxide is also a primary reaction in the formation of soil from rocks.

$$2KAlSi_3O_8 + 2H_2O + CO_2 \rightarrow Al_2Si_2O_5(OH)_4 + 4SiO_2 + K_2CO_3$$

Mica also exists in several forms, of which one is $KAl_2(AlSi_3O_{10})(OH, F)_2$. This substance occurs in thin transparent sheets and is prized for electrical insulation purposes. A related substance is talc, used in face powders and in polishing agents. A formula for talc is $Mg_3(Si_2O_5)_2(OH)_2$.

Asbestos is a valuable fibrous material used for insulating purposes. It has the formula $H_4Mg_3Si_2O_9$. Other important natural silicates are garnet, $Ca_3Al_2(SiO_4)_3$; zircon, $ZrSiO_4$; olivine, $(Mg, Fe)_2SiO_4$; topaz, $(AlF_2)SiO_4$; and beryl, $Be_3Al_2Si_6O_{18}$. The gem stone, amethyst, is an impure form of silicon dioxide.

In the past few years there have been some amazing developments in the chemistry of silicon. These advances have been in connection with synthetic plastics; their presentation will be deferred until a later chapter.

116. GLASS

Glassy substances not infrequently occur in nature. Of these the commonest is obsidian, from which many primitive peoples made weapons and ornaments. The earliest artificial production of glass is lost in antiquity; Pliny ascribes the discovery of glassmaking to accident, thus:

The story is, that a ship, laden with nitre, being moored upon this spot [near the mouth of the river Belus in Syria], the merchants, while preparing their repast upon the seashore, finding no stones at hand for supporting their cauldrons, employed for the purpose some lumps of nitre which they had taken from the vessel. Upon its being subjected to the action of the fire, in combination with the sand of the seashore, they beheld transparent streams flowing forth of a liquid hitherto unknown; this, it is said, was the origin of glass.*

The earliest known glaze is that found on stone beads from Egypt, dating about 12,000 B.C. By the year 1000 B.C. very beautiful and fairly complicated glass objects were being made in several parts of the world. Glassmaking is thus one of the oldest of civilized arts. Clear, transparent glass was so highly prized among the very wealthy in ancient Rome that to quote Pliny again, "For drinking vessels glass has quite superseded the use of silver and gold."

Beginning about the eleventh century the city of Venice became a center for glass manufacture, and "Venetian glass" is still prized. The beauty of its design has never been surpassed. From Venice the art of glassmaking spread throughout the world, and it is now a major industry.

Many substances may be obtained in the "glassy" condition. Pure silica, for instance, may occur as a glass or as a crystalline material. We shall limit our discussion to commercial glasses, particularly the ordinary "window-pane" variety. Commercial glass is always a mixture rather than a pure chemical compound. The composition varies within considerable limits, depending on the kind of glass desired and the formula used by the glass manufacturer. Silicon dioxide is a constituent of practically all glasses, and, in window-glass amounts to about 70 per cent of the whole. The other constituents are alkali oxides and alkaline earths such as sodium oxide, calcium oxide, and magnesium oxide. A typical analysis of glass might be as follows: SiO_2, 70%; CaO, 10%; MgO, 2.5%; Na_2O, 15%; other oxides such as Fe_2O_3, Al_2O_3, etc.,

* The Natural History of Pliny, translated by J. Bostock and H. T. Riley (London: Bohn, 1857), Vol. 6, p. 379.

2.5%. These substances can scarcely be thought of as existing in the form of oxides in the glass. They are rather combined to form a mixture of, say, calcium silicate, magnesium silicate, and so forth. These several silicates are mutually dissolved in each other and in the excess of silicon dioxide. Glass

Fig. 17-3. The Portland Vase. This vase, which is now in the British Museum, was made in Rome about the year 69 B.C. It consists of dark glass with bas-reliefs in opaque white glass. The vase ranks with the great artistic treasures of all time. (*British Information Services*)

is, therefore, a complicated product, the composition and character of which has not been understood until quite recent years, although the actual manufacture of glass is one of the oldest of chemical industries.

Thanks to studies by X-ray diffraction methods, the essential difference between a glassy substance and the same substance in the crystalline state is now clear. In crystals, it will be recalled, the atoms are regularly arranged throughout the whole mass. In glasses the atoms may be combined to each other in the same fashion as in crystals, but the arrangement of the atoms in space is much more nearly random. The regular rows and planes which characterize atomic arrangement in crystals is absent in glasses.

Glasses are very like liquids in respect to the arrangement of atoms. Glasses may be thought of as solutions which have been subjected to a very great degree of supercooling so that the solution can no longer flow like a liquid. We might define a glass as a substance or mixture of substances which has been supercooled from the fused condition until it is for all practical purposes rigid. Glass which is very old, or which has been subjected to certain heat conditions, tends to crystallize, or **devitrify**, which is exactly what would be expected of a substance in a metastable, supercooled condition.

Commercial production of glass consists of mixing together clear white sand with the appropriate amounts of alkali and alkaline earth compounds. These latter may be added in the form of the oxides, but carbonates and sulfates and other compounds are often used because these are converted to oxide at the high temperature of the furnace. As the temperature is raised, the various ingredients begin to interact and to dissolve in each other. Finally, at temperatures ranging up to about 1500° C., the mixture becomes a clear, free-flowing liquid, which may be poured out and allowed to solidify to glass. There are, of course, innumerable technical details in the production of a glass with the desired properties, free from undesirable colors or air bubbles, and free from excessive internal strains. These details and many other interesting properties of glass will be found in works on the subject.*

The most outstanding properties of glass are probably its resistance to corrosion and its transparency. No substance may, strictly speaking, be considered insoluble in water, but glass possesses this property to a high degree; hence its almost universal use for containers for such diverse substances as milk, medicine, and acids. Comparatively few substances attack glass. Of these, hydrofluoric acid has already been mentioned. Fused alkali, such as sodium hydroxide, is another example. But glass resists the ordinary action of the air and of water for indefinitely long periods, as is witnessed by the good condition of stained-glass windows in ancient cathedrals. Indeed, the hazards of modern warfare have proved vastly more destructive to such works of art than has the age-long action of the weather.

The transparency of glass is, of course, the basis of its use for windows, lamp bulbs, and optical apparatus. What condition leads to transparency in a chemical substance is not completely known, but glass certainly possesses to a remarkable degree the two desirable properties of transparency and corrosion resistance.

* C. J. Phillips, *Glass: The Miracle Maker* (New York: Pitman, 1941).
  G. W. Morey, *The Properties of Glass* (New York: Reinhold, 1938).

Glass is subject to a condition known as "strain." If the sample is heated or cooled irregularly, there is set up a tendency for the glass to shatter. This is probably due to unequal expansion or contraction of the glass under changing temperature. In all large glass objects it is necessary to **anneal** the sample. Annealing consists of heating the glass to a temperature somewhat below its softening point, and then gradually lowering the temperature. Annealing is generally accomplished in a few hours, but in special cases may extend over months. Freedom from strain is indicated by the use of polarized light, and special glass apparatus is often so tested before being sold.

One other property of glass will be mentioned, and that is its low electrical conductivity. Glass has a measurable electrical conductivity, but this is so exceedingly small that for all practical purposes glass may be considered an excellent electrical insulator.

A large variety of glasses are made for special purposes. A few of these will be described. So-called **lead glasses** are made by melting lead oxide or lead silicate with alkalis and silica. The lead content may average about 15 per cent, although much higher concentrations are known and glasses containing up to 92 per cent lead oxide have been made. Such glass is as dense as cast iron. The lead glasses have a high refractive index and are important for optical lenses and prisms. The finest cut-glass tableware is made of lead glass.

The name **"Pyrex"** is well known as a brand of glass. This word is a trade mark of the Corning Glass Works, covering various glasses having valuable electrical, thermal, and corrosion-resistant properties. A common Pyrex glass has the percentage composition: SiO_2, 80.5; B_2O_3, 12.9; Na_2O, 3.8; K_2O, 0.4; Al_2O_3, 2.2. Borosilicate glasses, of which the above is an example, have unusual resistance to rapidly changing temperature, and they are specially valuable and prized for laboratory apparatus.

In 1934 a type of Pyrex glass was cast into a huge mirror for the Mount Palomar Observatory of the California Institute of Technology (Fig. 17-4). This disc is 200 inches in diameter, and its production by the Corning Glass Works is unquestionably the most ambitious undertaking in the history of glass manufacture. The disc was successfully cast on the second try, and, after literally years of careful fabrication and grinding, the mirror is now in operation at the observatory. The telescope, of which the mirror is part, extends to a fantastic distance the observable part of the universe.

An interesting glass approaching pure silica in its properties has been developed by the Corning Glass Works. This product, known as Vycor, is made by treating a special borosilicate glass with acid. The acid leaches out most of the boron oxide and other substances, leaving a sort of skeleton of

almost pure silica. When this material is heated, it fuses into a product almost
as resistant to heat and corrosion as pure silica, but, of course, very much
easier to fabricate. Vycor products are especially valuable for laboratory
equipment which must stand high temperatures.

One other special glass will be mentioned. All the glasses described above

Fig. 17-4. The underside of the great 200-inch glass disk which
is now installed as the mirror in the Mount Palomar telescope.
This disk, made by the Corning Glass Works, is by far the most
ambitious achievement in glass technology.

contain large proportions of silica. A glass has been devised which contains
the oxide of the rare earth element lanthanum, together with small amounts
of other oxides, but no silica. Such glass has an exceptionally high refractive
index and is valuable for lens systems in optical instruments.

Glass is often colored. The various colors are produced by added colored
compounds, or by the use of colloidal material. For instance, chromic oxide,
Cr_2O_3, can be used to give a green color; cobalt oxide gives a blue. The exact
color often depends upon the way in which the coloring material is added
and how the glass is later heated. Beautiful ruby glass is made by adding
gold to the glass melt. The gold is dispersed in the colloidal condition. Red
glass may also be made with copper, or more frequently with selenium.

Most red glass is made by adding selenium and cadmium sulfide. Translucent, or opal, glasses are made by adding powdered substances which do not dissolve in the glass melt. Fluorspar and cryolite are often used for this purpose.

117. CERAMICS

The manufacture of porcelain was discovered in China in the seventh or ninth century A.D. Chinaware was introduced to Europe in 1498, but the secret of its manufacture did not become generally known until 1709, when a factory was established in Saxony. The French factory at Sèvres, still famous for its porcelainware, was established in 1769. The production of pottery, as distinct from porcelain, goes back to prehistoric times.

The manufacture of these substances depends upon changes which take place in kaolin, or clay, when this substance is strongly heated. The formula for kaolin may be written $Al_2O_3 \cdot 2SiO_2 \cdot 2H_2O$. On strong heat treatment this substance loses water, and turns to a hard mixture of SiO_2 and $3Al_2O_3 \cdot 2SiO_2$. Bricks are made from impure kaolin mixed with iron oxide. The iron oxide imparts the characteristic red color to ordinary bricks. Pottery is made from a somewhat purer grade of kaolin, together with small amounts of other substances to give the desired color. **Porcelain** is made from the purest kaolin, called chinaclay, together with feldspar and silica. This material is fired at a high temperature and undergoes a partial melting. The finished, translucent product is not unlike a glass in being in part a solid solution. English bone china is so-called because it contains 30-50 per cent of calcium phosphate, or bone-ash, derived from heating old bones.

The glaze on pottery or on porcelain is essentially a glass surface put on by heating the ware after coating the surface with a mixture which will fuse at a somewhat lower temperature than the body of the ceramic.

The colors on ceramicware are generally oxides of metals, such as cobalt oxide, put on either before or after the glaze, and heated to fix the color. The manufacture of coloring agents for such purposes is an old and well-developed industry. These agents are known as **ceramic pigments.**

118. CEMENT AND CONCRETE *

Portland cement dates from the year 1824, but somewhat similar substances have been used as structural materials for thousands of years. The ancient Romans made cement by burning impure clay, then mixing the product with volcanic ash and water. This is the material of which the Emperor Augustus had an aqueduct built into the old French city of Nîmes. In 1824 an English

* R. H. Bogue, *Journal of Chemical Education,* 19:36 (1942).

bricklayer named Joseph Aspdin obtained a patent on the discovery that the clinker produced by burning certain types of impure limestone ($CaCO_3$), would, when mixed with sand and water, set to an exceptionally hard, strong building-material. The cement so produced closely resembled in appearance a natural limestone found near Portland, in England, from which is derived the name "portland cement." Like many other industries, the production of cement has grown to astonishing proportions. Annual world production is in the hundreds of millions of barrels.

The raw material for cement is usually limestone, chalk, oyster shells, or slag (from blast furnaces). This material is heated, generally with the addition of clay or other substances, until the percentage composition, after heating, is approximately as follows: calcium oxide, 64.6; silica, 21.8; aluminum oxide, 5.6; iron oxide, 3.3; magnesium oxide, 2.9; other substances, 1.6. The clinker obtained after heating consists in considerable part of several calcium silicates, some of them in a glassy condition.

Most portland cement is used in the form of concrete which consists of cement plus sand and gravel or crushed rock. These solid aggregates take no part in the setting process but are simply enclosed and held in place by the paste of cement and water. The setting of cement is an action of hydration somewhat resembling that occurring with plaster of Paris. Several reactions take place. The various calcium silicates present in the clinker take up water to form hydrated calcium silicate and, in some cases, calcium hydroxide. These substances constitute the tough binder which holds the mass of concrete as a rocklike solid. The aluminum oxide present also forms hydrated calcium aluminate, and other compounds.

For special purposes the composition of cement may be modified, and very extensive research has been done in producing cements for such diverse purposes as road-building, the Hoover Dam, and for sites in which the soil has a corrosive action on ordinary cement.

119. TITANIUM

This element is not generally known to the layman, and it is often passed over briefly or ignored entirely in courses on elementary chemistry. Yet it warrants attention on two counts. First, titanium is a fairly abundant element in nature, being more than a hundred times as abundant as such common elements as copper, lead, and zinc. And second, titanium compounds form a major article of commerce. The annual world production of titanium pigments is over 100,000 tons and has grown very rapidly in recent years.

Titanium often occurs associated with silicon in silicates. The element so closely resembles silicon that its presence in silicates is not infrequently overlooked. The commonest titanium mineral is ilmenite, $FeTiO_3$. It also occurs as the dioxide, TiO_2, in the form of the mineral **rutile,** or of other allotropic modifications.

Until 1948 the free metal titanium was little more than a laboratory curiosity. But the postwar development of efficient reduction methods promises to make titanium metal an important article of commerce. A method now used in commercial developments is reduction of titanium tetrachloride by magnesium, in an inert atmosphere such as helium gas.

$$TiCl_4 + 2Mg \rightarrow Ti + 2MgCl_2$$

Titanium metal is remarkably strong, light, and able to stand high temperatures without corrosion or loss of strength. Certain steels subject to shock and extreme stress, such as railway rails, are made with the aid of titanium. The mineral ilmenite is reduced with carbon to form an alloy ferrotitanium. This alloy, added to steel, aids in the removal of undesirable impurities such as nitrogen. Some metallic titanium also finds application in forming titanium hydride which is used for special metallurgical purposes.

The most important compound of titanium is the dioxide. This occurs in nature but it must generally be purified before use. Titanium dioxide is also prepared from ilmenite by the action of hydrogen chloride and chlorine.

The pure titanium dioxide is a white powder, insoluble in water and very resistant to corroding influences. It is used on a very large scale as a white pigment. This substance combines a high degree of chemical stability with excellent covering power. Titanium pigments do not darken under the influence of hydrogen sulfide, as is the case for pigments containing white lead. The titanium dioxide is used alone as a pigment, and also combined with barium or calcium sulfates. Titanium is used not only as a white pigment in high-grade paints, but large quantities are used as opacifiers in the paper used in "slick-paper" magazines. The titanium dioxide renders the paper opaque so that printing on one side does not show through to the other. Rutile is also on the market in the form of gems which rival diamond in brilliance.

Like silicon, titanium forms many salts such as potassium titanate, K_2TiO_3. The mineral ilmenite is, of course, an iron titanate.

Titanium tetrachloride, $TiCl_4$, is a fuming liquid, prepared by passing chlorine over a heated mixture of titanium dioxide and carbon.

$$TiO_2 + C + 2Cl_2 \rightarrow TiCl_4 + CO_2$$

Titanium tetrachloride hydrolyzes readily, like silicon tetrachloride.

$$TiCl_4 + 2H_2O \rightarrow TiO_2 + 4HCl$$

It formerly found some application for making smoke screens.

Below titanium in the Periodic Table there are three elements: zirconium, hafnium, and thorium. Zirconium and hafnium are very similar to titanium in their properties. Hafnium was not discovered until 1922. Thorium is used in gas mantles and as a catalyst. Thorium is radioactive.

120. BORON

The element boron is in Group 3 of the Periodic Table. Its principal oxidation state is 3. Apart from these differences, the element closely resembles silicon in its properties. Boron is a nonmetal, but it exhibits a few properties suggestive of a metal. The element is fairly widely distributed in nature, and it makes up a little less than one thousandth of 1 per cent of the earth's crust. The element never occurs free. The chief minerals are **borax,** $Na_2B_4O_7 \cdot$ $10H_2O$; *kernite,* $Na_2B_4O_7 \cdot 4H_2O$; and *colemanite,* $Ca_2B_6O_{11} \cdot 5H_2O$. These substances are found in large quantities in the dry lakes of southern California. The deposits of kernite in the Mojave Desert now furnish the major source.

The element boron may be prepared by reducing boric oxide with magnesium.

$$B_2O_3 + 3Mg \rightarrow 3MgO + 2B$$

The element may be prepared as transparent crystals, not unlike diamonds in hardness and brilliancy. At room temperature boron is stable, but it reacts with many elements and compounds when heated.

Boric oxide, B_2O_3, is formed by heating the element in air, or by heating boric acid.

$$\underset{boric\ acid}{2H_3BO_3} \rightarrow \underset{boric\ oxide}{B_2O_3} + 3H_2O$$

The oxide is used in making borosilicate glasses, of the Pyrex type.

Boric acid is prepared by treating borax with sulfuric acid. This substance is not very soluble in water and so precipitates.

$$\underset{borax}{Na_2B_4O_7} + H_2SO_4 + 5H_2O \rightarrow \underset{boric\ acid}{4H_3BO_3} + Na_2SO_4$$

Boric acid is such a weak acid that it scarcely affects litmus. It is a very weak germicide and some organisms are not killed by long exposure. However, a solution of the acid in water is often used as an eyewash because the solution does not irritate delicate membranes. Boric acid is also used as dusting powder in certain skin conditions. The ingestion of boric acid is harmful and its use as a preservative in foods is dangerous and, in most countries, prohibited by law.

The common salts of boric acid are, for the most part, more complex than would be expected from the formula for boric acid. For instance, sodium orthoborate, Na_3BO_3, is unstable. The most familiar borates seem to be derived from more complicated acids. Thus borax, $Na_2B_4O_7 \cdot 10H_2O$, is the decahydrate of sodium tetraborate. Other even more complex salts are much more common than are the simple derivatives of boric acid.

Borax is an important article of commerce. It is used for softening water, for making washing compounds and for glassmaking. It is also widely used as a flux in welding and soldering operations, in making glazes and enamels, in making paper and cardboard, and in the textile and leather industries.

The electrolysis of a solution of borax and sodium hydroxide or carbonate yields so-called **sodium peroxyborate,** $NaBO_2 \cdot 3H_2O \cdot H_2O_2$. This compound is a useful oxidizing and bleaching agent. It is widely used as an antiseptic and in the manufacture of washing powders. Boron carbide, B_4C, is the hardest known synthetic substance, although less hard than diamond.

EXERCISES

A. *Define or explain the following:*

annealing (of glass)	kaolin
asbestos	kieselguhr
borax	lead glass
boric acid	mica
cement	orthosilicic acid
ceramic pigment	porcelain
ceramics	Pyrex glass
concrete	quartz
devitrification	rutile
dialysis	silica
diatomaceous earth	silica gel
feldspar	(a) silicate
ferrosilicon	sodium "peroxyborate"
glass	water glass
granite	

B. 1. Indicate procedures and all equations for the following:

    a. production of silicon from silica
    b. burning of silicon in air
    c. reaction of silicon with chlorine
    d. $SiO_2 + HF \rightarrow$
    e. $SiO_2 + NaOH \rightarrow$

    f.   formation of orthosilicic acid

    g. dehydration of orthosilicic acid

    h. manufacture of glass

    i.   production of (a) bricks, (b) pottery, (c) chinaware

    j.   production of cement

    k. production of titanium from rutile

    l.   manufacture of titanium tetrachloride

    m. boric acid from borax

2. Describe the differences between a crystalline substance, a liquid, and a glass, from the standpoints of (a) physical properties, and (b) molecular structure.

3. In what respects does silicon play a predominant part in the chemistry of nonliving matter?

4. Draw a diagram showing a possible arrangement of the atoms, including electrons, in silicon dioxide.

5. List useful properties possessed by (a) silica, and (b) glass.

6. Describe different kinds of glass.

7. May a glass be considered a pure chemical substance?

C. 1. Boron trifluoride, BF_3, combines with ammonia by what is probably a covalent bond. The configuration of boron trifluoride consists of three fluorines around the boron. With the aid of an electron diagram show the probable structure of the compound BF_3NH_3.

   2. Boron forms a gaseous hydride, B_2H_6. Write possible electronic diagrams for this substance and point out any peculiarity which occurs to you. (There is no complete agreement on the actual structure.)

   3. Which oxide in each of the following pairs would probably be the more acidic: TiO_2 and SiO_2; CO_2 and SiO_2; Al_2O_3 and B_2O_3; ThO_2 and ZrO_2?

   4. If dialysis is used to remove ions from a colloid then it should be possible to assist the process by using an electric current. Design an apparatus for doing this, considering, first, removal of positive ions like Na^+, then of negative ions like Cl^-, then of both positive and negative ions. The process is known as electrodialysis.

   5. Design experiments to test whether silicon can form a hydride, such as SiH_4. Consider methods used for hydrides of elements studied earlier.

   6. Would you expect silicon tetrafluoride to react with ammonia in a manner analogous to the reaction of boron trifluoride with ammonia? (See Exercise C. 1. above.)

ACTIVE METALS

18

																	H	He
Li	Be	B												C	N	O	F	Ne
Na	Mg	Al												Si	P	S	Cl	A
K	**Ca**	Sc	Ti	V	Cr	Mn	Fe	Co	Ni	Cu	Zn	Ga	Ge	As	Se	Br	Kr
Rb	**Sr**	Y	Zr	Nb	Mo	Tc	Ru	Rh	Pd	Ag	Cd	In	Sn	Sb	Te	I	Xe
Cs	**Ba**	La-Lu	Hf	Ta	W	Re	Os	Ir	Pt	Au	Hg	Tl	Pb	Bi	Po	At	Rn
Fr	**Ra**	Ac	Th	Pa	U-												

In the past few chapters we have been concerned primarily with some of the more important **nonmetals.** In the next few chapters our attention will be directed toward some of the more important **metals.** It will be recalled that one distinction between metals and nonmetals has already been pointed out. This distinction is that the oxide of a nonmetal, such as that of sulfur, when dissolved in water, forms an acid. The oxide of a metal, when dissolved in water, forms a base. These definitions are serviceable; there are, however, other ways in which metals and nonmetals differ.

Metals, in general, have a quite different appearance from typical nonmetals. Sulfur looks quite different from gold, although both are yellow. This difference lies in what is called the "luster," or the way in which light is reflected from the surface of the element. Sulfur certainly reflects light, but it does not have the glistening quality of gold. We say that gold has a metallic luster, sulfur does not. This distinction seems to result from the fact that light penetrates somewhat into the sulfur before being reflected, but light is not able to penetrate past the surface of gold.

Another way in which metals differ from nonmetals is in electrical conductivity. Metals are good conductors of electricity. Nonmetals are generally nonconductors. Sulfur, for instance, is a good insulator. This distinction between metals and nonmetals seems to result from a certain freedom of motion possessed by the electrons in a metal. The electrons in a nonmetal are, by contrast, held more rigidly in place.

Still another distinction between metals and nonmetals is in the thermal conductivity. Metals are generally good conductors of heat. Nonmetals are frequently poor conductors.

Exceptions will be found to all these criteria between metals and nonmetals. The situation is, of course, further complicated by the amphoteric elements which show the properties both of metals and of nonmetals. But, so far as is generally necessary, the acidic or basic quality of the oxide, the luster, and the conductivity, should be ample to distinguish between the two groups of elements. To these criteria we may add one other. Metals always form positive ions, although they often enter into complex negative ions as well. Nonmetals generally form negative ions.

121. SODIUM, PRODUCTION

The compounds of sodium and of potassium have been known for a long time, but isolation of the elements themselves was not achieved until 1807.

Fig. 18-1. Humphry Davy

Davy was born in England in 1778. Among his achievements are the preparation of metallic sodium and potassium, and the proof that chlorine is an element.

Davy enjoyed a great reputation for brilliance and personal qualities. In later years his reputation was somewhat overshadowed by that of his distinguished pupil, Michael Faraday. Sometimes it is said that "Faraday was Davy's greatest discovery." But rereading of Davy's original papers shows that his contemporary reputation was richly deserved, and that modern chemistry owes as much to him as to anyone. This is both for his own experimental discoveries, for the stimulation he gave to research in the physical sciences, and for the aid he gave in directing Faraday's attention to fertile fields for research.

Davy was knighted for his achievements and for many years was director of the Royal Institution in London. He died in 1829. (Fisher Collection of Alchemical and Historical Portraits)

Prior to that time the hydroxides of these metals were considered to be the elements. In 1807 Humphry Davy * prepared metallic sodium by passing an electric current through melted sodium hydroxide. He heated a small sample of the hydroxide in a platinum spoon, then passed an electric current through

---

* Humphry Davy, *The Decomposition of the Fixed Alkalies and Alkaline Earths* (Alembic Club Reprints, No. 6).

the melted substance. Shiny droplets of metal were formed at the negative pole, and these ignited with a bright flame as they reached the air.

At the present time sodium metal is produced on a very large scale by the electrolysis of fused (melted) sodium chloride. Sodium chloride is an abundant raw material for the production of both sodium and chlorine.

It will be recalled that one of the methods for producing chlorine is the electrolysis of fused sodium chloride. The same procedure is used for the

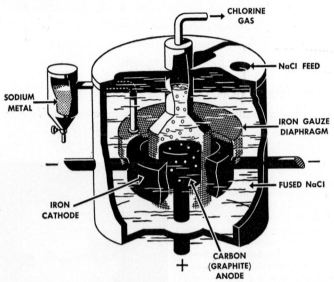

Fig. 18-2. Downs cell for producing sodium and chlorine by the electrolysis of fused sodium chloride.

production of sodium, and the two products are formed simultaneously. The equipment commonly used for sodium production is known as the Downs electrolytic cell. (See Fig. 18-2.) This consists of an iron box lined with firebrick. The anode (positive) is graphite and projects up through the bottom of the cell. The cathode is iron or copper and is circular, surrounding the anode. A partition of wire gauze keeps the products, sodium metal and chlorine gas, apart. Appropriate outlets are supplied for the products, and provision is made for adding more sodium chloride as required.

The reactions taking place in the Downs cell have already been described in connection with the production of chlorine. At the cathode the sodium ions gain an electron to become sodium metal.

$$Na^+ + \epsilon \rightarrow Na^0$$

At the anode, each chloride ion loses an electron to become a chlorine atom. Chlorine atoms then combine to form chlorine molecules.

$$2Cl^- \rightarrow 2\epsilon + Cl_2^0$$

Sodium is not a metal familiar to the layman, and owing to its great activity there are some difficulties in handling it. Yet in recent years it has become so useful that now it ranks among the most important of all metals produced. Most metals such as iron and aluminum are produced for structural uses such as in building bridges, railways, automobiles, and so forth. Sodium is quite worthless as a structural material, but it has other unique properties which make it a very useful metal indeed.

122. SODIUM, PROPERTIES AND USES

Sodium is a soft, silvery metal. Its melting point is only 97.5° C., and the density of the metal is 0.97 g. per cc.

Sodium is very active chemically. In air it tarnishes quickly, and it burns vigorously when heated. The flame of sodium is intensely yellow, owing to the two characteristic lines it shows in the yellow part of the spectrum. Sodium reacts strongly with water, forming hydrogen and sodium hydroxide.

$$2Na + 2H_2O \rightarrow H_2 + 2NaOH$$

Not infrequently the sodium catches fire, igniting the hydrogen and leading to an explosion. For obvious reasons water is not only useless but very dangerous to use on a sodium fire. Sodium also reacts with many other elements such as sulfur and chlorine and the other halogens. It also forms alloys with many other metals such as mercury, lead, and potassium. Some of these alloys are definite, so-called **intermetallic compounds,** that is, compounds between metals. Other alloys are more in the nature of solutions.

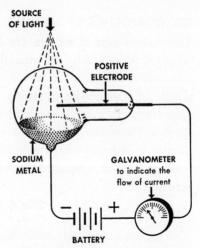

Fig. 18-3. Photoelectric cell. The space inside the bulb normally acts as an insulator, but when the sodium metal is exposed to light, it emits electrons which serve to complete the electrical circuit. Several metals other than sodium may be used.

Sodium, like other metals, possesses to a considerable degree the property of photoemissivity, or emission of electrons under the influence of light. This property is used in **photoelectric cells** (Fig. 18-3).

Because of its activity, sodium must be handled with caution. Under appropriate safeguards it is a common article of commerce and is shipped in large containers. In the laboratory it is kept under kerosene to prevent the action of air.

Sodium has many uses in the laboratory. It is a very effective drying agent for use with organic liquids such as ether and benzene. It enters into or promotes many diverse types of reactions, some of which will be described later. But the large tonnages of sodium metal find their way into the production of such materials as tetraethyllead, through the use of the substance NaPb; and into the manufacture of dyestuffs, organic chemicals, sodium peroxide, sodium cyanide, and plastics. Additional quantities are used in sodium vapor lamps, in photoelectric cells, and in certain types of heat transmission problems in engineering. The valves of most airplane engines are made hollow, to be filled with sodium metal. At operating temperature the engine heat melts the sodium which effectively aids in conducting excess heat away from the cylinders.

123. COMPOUNDS OF SODIUM

The various salts of sodium are among the commonest of all laboratory reagents. Sodium salts are generally cheap, at least cheaper than the corresponding salts of other metals, and they also have the virtue of being soluble in water. With extremely few exceptions all sodium salts dissolve quite readily in water. The common naturally occurring sodium salts are the chloride, the nitrate, and the borates. Most sodium compounds are derived, directly or indirectly, from sodium chloride.

When sodium is heated in excess of air the principal product is sodium peroxide.

$$2Na + O_2 \rightarrow Na_2O_2$$

This substance is a yellowish-white powder, and it is manufactured on a large scale as a powerful oxidizing agent. When water is added to sodium peroxide, at or above room temperature, oxygen is liberated.

$$2Na_2O_2 + 2H_2O \rightarrow 4NaOH + O_2$$

This reaction is sometimes used as a convenient method for making relatively small amounts of oxygen.

When sodium is heated in a restricted amount of air, there is formed some of the oxide, Na_2O. This is a typical oxide of an active metal; it dissolves in water to form sodium hydroxide, but otherwise this oxide is not of very much importance.

$$Na_2O + H_2O \rightarrow 2NaOH$$

Sodium hydroxide, or **caustic soda,** is an industrial chemical of prime importance. With sulfuric acid and a few other substances it is often spoken of as one of the *heavy chemicals.* This name refers not so much to the density of these substances, which is not particularly high, as to the very large tonnages produced. Annual world production of sodium hydroxide is several millions of tons.

There are two chief processes for the manufacture of sodium hydroxide. The electrolytic process has already been discussed in connection with chlorine production. It will be recalled that electrolysis of a water solution of sodium chloride yields, at the anode, chlorine, and, at the cathode, hydrogen and sodium hydroxide. The hydrogen is liberated from the water by the addition of an electron. The sodium ions are left in solution and, together with hydroxide ions left after the hydrogen ions are removed, forms a solution of sodium hydroxide. There are several types of electrolytic cells in operation in addition to those previously described. In one type the cathode is a pool of mercury. Under such conditions sodium rather than hydrogen is liberated at the cathode. The sodium metal dissolves in the mercury, forming an amalgam. This amalgam may be reacted with water to form sodium hydroxide, leaving the mercury free for reuse.

The other method for sodium hydroxide production uses the reaction between sodium carbonate and calcium hydroxide. The sodium carbonate is dissolved in water and is treated with the calcium hydroxide. Calcium carbonate precipitates, leaving sodium hydroxide in solution.

$$Na_2CO_3 + Ca(OH)_2 \rightarrow CaCO_3 + 2NaOH$$

Sodium carbonate for use in this process may be obtained from sodium chloride, and water, and carbon dioxide, by the Solvay process, which will be described later.

Sodium hydroxide is a white solid, readily soluble in water. Popularly it is called **lye,** although that name is also sometimes applied to potassium hydroxide. Sodium hydroxide solutions have a soapy feel, and the solid and its solutions have a very corrosive action on many substances, including human skin. The solutions are bitter to the taste. Sodium hydroxide is a typical alkali, or base, able to neutralize all acids and to undergo other types of reactions characteristic of strong bases. Because of its cheapness and general utility it is comparable to sulfuric acid for general industrial usefulness.

The principal uses of sodium hydroxide are in the manufacture of other chemicals, in rayon and cellulose film production, in soaps, pulp and paper, petroleum refining, and a host of others. There are few industrial chemical products which do not involve the use of a strong base, and sodium hydroxide is often the choice.

Out of a large number of other useful sodium compounds some, such as the chloride and other halides, have already been described. Sodium sulfide, Na_2S, is used in the preparation and use of certain dyes, and for removing hair from hides. The nitrate and nitrite of sodium have already been described in connection with the chemistry of nitrogen. The various phosphates, sulfites, and sulfates of sodium were mentioned under the elements phosphorus and sulfur. The very important carbonate and bicarbonate of sodium will be discussed in connection with the element carbon, as will the cyanide and related substances. It should not be overlooked that sodium enters into many organic compounds such as sodium acetate, $NaC_2H_3O_2$, and sodium oxalate, $Na_2C_2O_4$. These, and many others, will be described in due course.

Sodium compounds are practically all colorless, unless the negative ion combined with the sodium happens to be colored. Sodium chromate, Na_2CrO_4, is yellow, but this is not due to the sodium ion but rather to the chromate ion, $CrO_4^=$, which is yellow in most of its compounds.

Sodium ion is present in large amounts in the body. It is the principal positive ion in, for instance, blood serum. Its function in the body seems to be purely a matter of regulating the movement of fluids through cell walls by osmotic pressure. Sodium ion seems to have no specific effect on tissues. Nevertheless, the role of sodium ion in the body is very important, and any change of concentration leads to serious disturbances. Some of the distressing symptoms of severe diarrhea are related to loss of sodium ion from the body.

124. FAMILY RELATIONSHIPS AMONG THE ALKALI METALS

The **alkali metals** are commonly considered to be lithium, sodium, potassium, rubidium, and cesium. Lithium is, in some ways, rather less active than the others and shows rather less general resemblance to the group. Until recently there was a blank space corresponding to element 87 in the Periodic Table. This element has been made artificially and is properly considered as one of the alkali metals. It has been named *francium* (Fr).

All these elements are active in the sense that they tarnish in air, they react with water, and they combine vigorously with many other elements. All the alkali metals have an oxidation state of one, although compounds corresponding to peroxides and dioxides are also known. This strong similarity between these elements is attributable to the arrangement of electrons in their atoms. It will be recalled that sodium has in its several electron energy levels, respectively, two, eight, and one electrons. All the alkali metals have in common that they have one electron in the highest normal energy level. Thus the arrangement in the various levels is as follows:

	Energy Level					
	1	2	3	4	5	6
Lithium............	2	1				
Sodium............	2	8	1			
Potassium.........	2	8	8	1		
Rubidium.........	2	8	18	8	1	
Cesium............	2	8	18	18	8	1

When these elements enter into chemical changes, in the great majority of cases one electron is lost. The atom then becomes a positive ion with a charge of plus one; and, except for lithium, the highest energy level of the ion contains eight electrons, no matter which alkali metal is concerned. This similarity in electron configuration is responsible for the similarity in properties shown by these elements. Such differences as do occur are attributable chiefly to the difference in sizes of the ions in going from lithium to cesium (see Fig. 18-4).

The elements lithium, rubidium, and cesium are much less abundant than sodium or potassium. Lithium occurs chiefly in the mineral *spodumene*, $LiAl(SiO_3)_2$. Deposits are found in the Black Hills of South Dakota. The metal may be prepared by electrolysis of the fused chloride. It is the lightest metal known, the density, 0.534 g. per cc., being only slightly more than half that of water. Lithium is used in the heat treatment of steel parts such as propellers, and so forth. The lithium prevents oxidation of the steel surface. The element also has miscellaneous applications in making organic compounds, in the manufacture of special glasses and optical crystals, and in medicine.

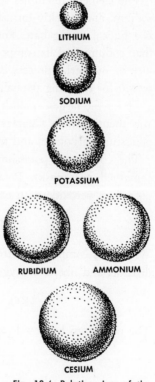

Fig. 18-4. Relative sizes of the ions Li^+, Na^+, K^+, Rb^+, Cs^+ and NH_4^+.

Lithium hydride is used to provide a very light, transportable source of hydrogen. Aviators forced down at sea can use this substance to inflate small balloons carrying aerials with which to send more powerful radio distress signals.

$$LiH + H_2O \rightarrow LiOH + H_2$$

Potassium occurs widely distributed in nature, but, because of its activity, always in compound form. Potassium is a constituent of rocks, of sea water, and of soil. Extensive deposits of the chloride and the sulfate, often associated with other elements, occur near Carlsbad, New Mexico, at Searles Lake in California, and at Stassfurt, Germany.

Potassium was first prepared as the metal by Davy, who electrolyzed potassium hydroxide. The name of the element is derived from **potash,** an old name for potassium carbonate, which, for centuries, was obtained from wood ashes. Potassium metal is now produced by an electrolytic process not unlike that used for metallic sodium. But the annual production of potassium metal is small.

The element resembles sodium in many ways. It is soft and silvery, like sodium, and quickly tarnishes in air. The hydroxide of potassium, KOH, is a typical strong base. Potassium and its compounds are more expensive than sodium and its compounds. Hence the choice of reagent for a laboratory or industrial process is generally sodium unless there is some specific reason for choosing potassium.

By far the largest quantity of potassium compounds goes to fertilizers, as was mentioned in Chapter 15. Compounds used for this purpose include potassium carbonate, and more important, potassium chloride, KCl.

The compound potassium superoxide, KO_2, has an application in self-contained gas masks. Potassium superoxide is made by the reaction of potassium peroxide with oxygen.

$$K_2O_2 + O_2 \rightarrow 2KO_2$$

When this compound is treated with water, it changes into potassium hydroxide, and liberates oxygen.

$$4KO_2 + 2H_2O \rightarrow 4KOH + 3O_2$$

The potassium hydroxide takes up carbon dioxide from exhaled breath.

$$KOH + CO_2 \rightarrow KHCO_3$$

The potassium superoxide in the gas mask thus serves the triple purpose of taking up exhaled water vapor and carbon dioxide, and of liberating fresh oxygen.

The only other potassium compound which need be mentioned is the nitrate, KNO_3, or **saltpeter.** This substance is found in small deposits in various parts of the world, and it is a product of the decay of animal matter. Potassium nitrate has long been used in making gunpowder, the two other ingredients being sulfur and charcoal. This is one instance in which the corresponding sodium salt will not serve as well as the potassium. Sodium nitrate tends to take up moisture from the air and this would, of course, ruin the gunpowder.

Potassium has some important biochemical functions. Just as sodium is the principal cation of the body fluids, potassium is the principal cation of the cells. The concentration of potassium ions in the fluids such as serum is not only low, but potassium salts injected into the body act in a definitely poisonous manner. On the other hand, if the potassium concentration of the body falls too low, various symptoms, including paralysis and finally death, may result. The body in health maintains very efficient control over the potassium concentration, and all normal diets contain adequate potassium. In certain diseases potassium salts are administered orally or intravenously. The oral administration is not nearly so dangerous as the intravenous. Many common drugs taken by mouth contain moderately large amounts of potassium ions. These are efficiently eliminated by healthy kidneys.

Rubidium and cesium were discovered by Bunsen shortly after the invention of the spectroscope. The names of the elements are derived from the red and the blue lines which, respectively, are found in the spectrum of the two elements. The melting point of cesium is only $28.5°$ C. Both these elements, as well as the other alkali metals, find application in radio tubes and in photoelectric cells.

It is a curious fact that discussions of the alkali metals almost always mention another substance which cannot be considered a metal in any sense of the word. The **ammonium ion,** $NH_4{}^+$, behaves chemically very much like the alkali metal ions, especially like potassium ion, except in its low stability to heat. Thus we have such compounds as ammonium hydroxide, NH_4OH, which is a base, although a rather weak one. We also have ammonium chloride, ammonium sulfate, ammonium nitrate, and many other compounds which resemble the corresponding compounds of the alkali metals.

The reason for this resemblance lies in the fact that the ammonium ion has the same electric charge as the alkali metal ions, namely, plus one. The ammonium ion has also just about the same size as the rubidium ion, and is only slightly larger than the potassium ion. These two properties, the charge and the diameter, largely determine the chemical behavior of an ion. The fact that the ammonium ion has these properties is, of course, accidental. It does not actually contain a metal, and it consists solely of a nitrogen atom plus four hydrogen atoms less one electron.

125. CALCIUM

The chemical elements of Group 2, subgroup A, in the Periodic Table, are calcium, strontium, barium, and radium. These are known as the **alkaline earth** metals.* Calcium is an element of considerable importance; barium is also important. Strontium is of minor importance, and radium is important because of its radioactivity. These elements are all rather reactive. They never occur naturally as the element. In this sense they resemble the alkali metals. On the other hand the only oxidation state shown by these elements is that of plus two. They also differ from the alkali metals in the solubilities of their compounds, and in other ways. The valence of plus two for all the alkaline earth elements is related to the two electrons which are present in the highest normal energy level for each element.

Calcium occurs in many minerals, widely distributed in various parts of the world. The most abundant sources are the carbonate, **limestone,** $CaCO_3$, and **dolomite,** $CaMg(CO_3)_2$. The sulfate, fluoride, and phosphate are also abundant. In the form of its compounds the element has been well known since ancient times.

Calcium metal was first prepared by Davy in 1808. The commercial method is to electrolyze fused calcium chloride. The metal deposits on an iron rod which is made the cathode. Chlorine is liberated at the anode, which is often in the form of a graphite crucible which serves to hold the melt. The annual production of calcium metal is not particularly large.

Calcium is a silvery-white metal, somewhat harder than the alkali metals. It is also considerably less subject to the action of air and water, although it burns when heated. With acids calcium reacts vigorously, liberating hydrogen. It has the property of combining with nitrogen to form calcium nitride.

$$3Ca + N_2 \rightarrow Ca_3N_2$$

The metal has various uses in the manufacture of steel and of other metallurgical products. The element is, however, chiefly of importance in the form of its compounds.

When calcium metal is heated in oxygen it forms the oxide. Heating the metal in air yields a mixture of the oxide and the nitride.

$$2Ca + O_2 \rightarrow 2CaO$$

On a commercial scale calcium oxide is prepared in very large amounts by heating limestone. The calcium oxide product is generally known as **quicklime,** or simply, as **lime.**

---

* The term "alkaline earth" refers, strictly speaking, to the oxides of these elements.

$$CaCO_3 \rightleftarrows CaO + CO_2$$

This important industrial operation is carried out in a kiln. A kiln is a tower in which the calcium carbonate may be heated to nearly 1200° C. Because the reaction is reversible, it is necessary to remove the carbon dioxide as it is formed, so that the equilibrium is continually displaced toward the right. The carbon dioxide may be blown out with a stream of air.

Calcium oxide, or quicklime, is a white solid with the very high melting point of 2572° C. When this substance is heated to incandescence, it gives off a brilliant white light called the "limelight." The limelight was once widely used, especially for spotlights in theaters. Electric lights have long since completely displaced this method of illumination, but the expression "to be in the limelight," has lingered in our speech to the present time.

Lime is a very important industrial chemical. The principal use is in mortars, cements, and plasters. Large quantities are also used in agriculture as a soil conditioner, in chemical industry as a cheap base (calcium oxide plus water yields calcium hydroxide), and in such operations as metallurgy, paper mills, sugar refineries, and water purification. Considerable amounts are also used as a refractory: that is, a substance which is resistant to high temperatures.

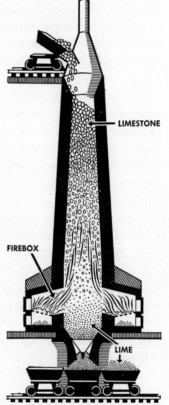

Fig. 18-5. A lime kiln: $CaCO_3 \rightleftarrows$ $CaO + CO_2$.

Quicklime combines with water with a hissing sound and the evolution of much heat. The product is calcium hydroxide, or **slaked lime.** A dilute solution of calcium hydroxide in water is called **limewater.**

$$CaO + H_2O \rightarrow Ca(OH)_2$$

Calcium hydroxide is a strong base, widely used because of its cheapness.

Mortar is made by mixing one part of quicklime with three or four parts of sand, then adding enough water to give a thick paste. When this material is exposed to air, the calcium hydroxide slowly takes up carbon dioxide from the air, and simultaneously it loses water.

$$Ca(OH)_2 + CO_2 \rightarrow CaCO_3 + H_2O$$

The mortar soon sets to a hard mass, but many years are necessary for the calcium hydroxide to become completely converted to calcium carbonate. Mortar in ancient Roman walls still consists, in part, of calcium hydroxide.

Building plaster used for walls and ceilings consists of mortar to which is added some binding material such as fiber. This is not to be confused with the attractive white outer coating used for decorative effects. The outer coating consists of plaster of Paris, derived from calcium sulfate. Plaster of Paris has already been described.

Calcium carbonate, which is familiar to us in the form of chalk, limestone, marble, coral, and pearls, will be discussed in detail in a later chapter.

Other compounds of calcium of interest include calcium fluoride, calcium chloride, calcium sulfide, calcium phosphate, and calcium cyanamide. The fluoride, CaF_2, occurs in nature as the mineral *fluorite* or *fluorspar*. It is the chief source of fluorine. The mineral is also used as a flux in metallurgical operations. Calcium chloride, $CaCl_2$, is a by-product of certain industrial processes. It is used in solution as a refrigerant and as an antifreeze in firebarrels. The anhydrous salt takes up moisture readily and is used as a drying agent, and to lay dust on dirt roads. Calcium sulfide, CaS, is used as a depilatory to dissolve hair. Certain substances, of which calcium sulfide is one, have the property of phosphorescing in the dark after exposure to light. The pure sulfide does not possess this property, but various mixtures containing calcium sulfide or barium sulfide or both are used in luminous paints. **Calcium cyanamide**, $CaCN_2$, is formed by the action of hot calcium carbide with nitrogen.

$$CaC_2 + N_2 \rightarrow CaCN_2 + C$$

This substance is used directly as a fertilizer. It was formerly used in the manufacture of ammonia by its action with water.

$$CaCN_2 + 3H_2O \rightarrow CaCO_3 + 2NH_3$$

126. PHYSIOLOGICAL PROPERTIES OF CALCIUM

The human body contains about 2 per cent of calcium. The element is essential to life. Many pathological conditions are caused by inadequate supplies or inadequate metabolism of this element. About 99 per cent of the total calcium in the body is in the bones. The remainder is distributed in the plasma and elsewhere.

The normal calcium content of bone is about 36 per cent of the bone ash. The nature of the particular calcium compounds in bone is not known, but suggestions which have been made include various combinations of calcium phosphate and calcium carbonate. The composition of teeth is somewhat similar to bone. In serum the calcium is present partly as calcium ion, and partly in combined forms.

If the calcium concentration of the body falls below certain values, various symptoms arise. These include muscle spasms, general convulsions, general muscular weakness, and collapse. Calcium deficiency may result from too low a concentration of calcium in the diet, or from glandular disturbances. The disease rickets is associated with calcium deficiency. Aside from its obvious necessity in building bone and teeth, calcium is essential to proper functioning of the nervous system.

Health can only be maintained if the diet contains sufficient calcium. For adults this amount is between 0.5 to 1.0 grams per day. Normal diets should contain this amount of calcium, but for various reasons this is not always the case. Milk and cheese are examples of foods which are rich in calcium.

In certain diseases and in pregnancy, it is necessary to supplement the diet by administering calcium compounds. Among the compounds used for this purpose are calcium chloride, calcium gluconate, $[CH_2OH(CHOH)_4CO_2]_2$-$Ca \cdot H_2O$, calcium lactate, $Ca(C_3H_5O_3)_2 \cdot 5H_2O$, calcium carbonate, and calcium phosphate.

127. STRONTIUM AND BARIUM

Strontium occurs in the minerals *celestite*, $SrSO_4$, and *strontianite*, $SrCO_3$. The name of the element is derived from the Scottish village of Strontian, near which a mineral containing strontium was first found. The element closely resembles calcium in its properties, although it is somewhat more active. Its sulfate is definitely less soluble than that of calcium. There are not many uses of strontium. The bromide and iodide have some application in medicine. Strontium hydroxide may be used in sugar refining. Strontium nitrate gives a scarlet color to a flame; it is used for flares and fireworks.

Barium is more abundant than strontium and it has more uses. The chief minerals are *barite*, $BaSO_4$, and *witherite*, $BaCO_3$. The name of the element is derived from a Greek word meaning "heavy." This is in reference to the high density of some barium compounds.

Barium metal may be prepared by reduction of barium oxide with aluminum. Electrolysis is also used. The metal is silvery-white and quite active. It readily liberates hydrogen from water. There are, however, not many uses for the metal.

Barium forms two oxides, BaO and BaO_2; the latter is a peroxide. The peroxide was at one time used in the manufacture of oxygen from air. The normal oxide, BaO, dissolves in water to form a typical strong base, barium hydroxide, $Ba(OH)_2$.

$$BaO + H_2O \rightarrow Ba(OH)_2$$

A solution of the hydroxide is often used in analytical work, especially for the absorption of carbon dioxide. The insoluble compound barium carbonate is precipitated.

$$Ba(OH)_2 + CO_2 \rightarrow BaCO_3 + H_2O$$

The use of barium sulfate mixed with zinc sulfide in the paint body called "lithopone" has already been described (p. 232). Barium sulfate has several other important uses. The largest tonnage of crude barite is used to handle high gas pressures in deep oil wells drilled in mud. Barium sulfate is also used as a white pigment (blanc fixé) and as a filler to give weight to paper, rubber, oilcloth, and so forth. In medical diagnosis barium sulfate is used to render visible the gastrointestinal tract. The patient swallows a tumblerful of a cream containing the compound. Because of its high atomic number, barium is virtually opaque to X rays. The shadow of the stomach, intestines, and other organs stand out as sharply defined shadows under the X ray. It is then comparatively easy for the physician to detect any lesions such as stomach ulcer or cancer in these organs. Soluble barium compounds are highly poisonous, but barium sulfate is so insoluble that it passes through the body without harming the patient.

128. ION EXCHANGE

Water is said to be *hard* when it contains certain classes of dissolved impurities. If the water contains bicarbonates of calcium, magnesium, and iron it is said to have temporary hardness. The hardness is temporary because it may readily be corrected by boiling the water. If the impurities consist of the sulfates of calcium and magnesium, then the water has permanent hardness. Permanent hardness is somewhat more difficult to correct.

Hard water is objectionable because it leads to wastage of soap, owing to insoluble compounds being formed by the soap with magnesium or calcium ions. Another difficulty is in boiler pipes which develop scale, leading to waste of heat and possible explosion.

Temporary hardness in water may be corrected by boiling because the following reaction takes place.

$$Ca(HCO_3)_2 \rightarrow CaCO_3 + H_2O + CO_2$$

The calcium carbonate precipitates, and the pure water may be poured or filtered off. Permanent hardness may be corrected by the addition of an agent which leads to precipitation of the calcium or magnesium impurities. Boiling will not do this. An agent commonly used for this purpose is washing soda, or sodium carbonate, Na_2CO_3. The reaction is as follows:

$$CaSO_4 + Na_2CO_3 \rightarrow CaCO_3 + Na_2SO_4$$

As before, the calcium carbonate precipitates. The sodium sulfate remains in solution but is not generally objectionable.

These two procedures and others for correcting hard water will be discussed more fully later. There is, however, an entirely different method for treating hard water and this has many applications to industrial problems. The method is known as **ion-exchange,** and it will be discussed in some detail.

There are certain substances, of which sodium aluminosilicate, $NaAlSi_2O_6$, is an example, that have the property of giving up the sodium ions in exchange for calcium or magnesium ions.

$$2NaAlSi_2O_6 + Ca^{++} \rightleftarrows Ca(AlSi_2O_6)_2 + 2Na^+$$

This process takes place when the sodium aluminosilicate is in contact with a solution containing the calcium or magnesium ions in the form of calcium or magnesium sulfate. The process is, as indicated, reversible. It is known as ion-exchange, and is a sort of reversible replacement of one ion by another.

Substances such as sodium aluminosilicate occur as minerals, of which the *zeolites* are an example. These minerals are used as found, or may be made synthetically for water-softening equipment such as the Permutit process (Fig. 18-6). The procedure is to have a tank loosely filled with the ion-exchanger and to allow

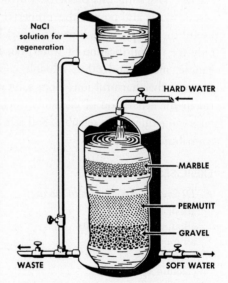

Fig. 18-6. The Permutit process for "softening" water by ion exchange.

the hard water to flow through it. The calcium and magnesium ions are replaced by sodium ions so that the water emerges soft rather than hard. In commercially available installations the exchange process takes place with great speed and completeness.

Of course, in time all the sodium ions in the exchanger will be replaced by calcium so that finally the apparatus will fail to operate. But when this happens the active material is easily regenerated. A strong sodium chloride solution is allowed to stand in contact with the zeolite for a short time. The calcium ions in the zeolite are replaced by sodium ions so that a solution of calcium chloride is drained off and discarded, while the zeolite is ready to function as a water softener again. The zeolites or other exchangers used in this process last for many years, and the only material necessary to keep them in working condition is common salt.

In recent years, ion exchange has been intensively studied. Exchangers are available for removing the negative ion as well as the positive ion of a salt from solution. By passing water first over an ion exchanger which will remove, say, negative ions, then over an exchanger which will remove positive ions, it is possible to produce water which rivals in purity the best distilled water. Mineral substances such as the zeolites are not the only ion-exchangers known. Peat, lignite, coal treated with sulfuric acid, dolomite, heavy-metal silicates, horn, wool, and alkali-treated asphalt are other substances possessing this property. Furthermore, synthetic resins or plastics of certain types also possess this property. Substances resembling "Bakelite" are useful for this purpose. Ion-exchangers have wide application in industry, not only for the purification of water, but also for the recovery of copper, manganese, nickel, and other valuable constituents from wastes, or to remove iron or other harmful ions from solutions. They have proved especially useful in the separation of elements, such as the rare earths, which are otherwise quite difficult to separate. Soil acts as an ion-exchanger, and this property contributes to its fertility.

EXERCISES

A. *Define or explain the following:*

alkali elements	limewater
alkaline earth elements	lithopone
ammonium ion	lye
barite	metal
calcium cyanamide	mortar
caustic soda	nonmetal
fluorspar	photoelectric cell
dolomite	plaster (building)
hard water	potash
intermetallic compound	quicklime (lime)
ion exchange	saltpeter
lime kiln	slaked lime
limestone	superoxide

B. 1. Indicate procedures and equations for the following:

    a. production of metallic sodium
    b. $Na + H_2O \rightarrow$
    c. $Na + air \rightarrow$
    d. $Na_2O + H_2O \rightarrow$
    e. manufacture of sodium hydroxide (two processes)
    f. heating calcium in air (two reactions)
    g. production of lime from limestone
    h. $CaO + H_2O \rightarrow$
    i. $Ca(OH)_2 + CO_2 \rightarrow$
    j. production of calcium cyanamide
    k. $BaO + H_2O \rightarrow$
    l. $Ba(OH)_2 + CO_2 \rightarrow$
    m. boiling a solution of calcium bicarbonate
    n. $CaSO_4 + Na_2CO_3 \rightarrow$
    o. action of a zeolite in softening water by ion exchange

2. Explain why sodium hydroxide, rather than sodium metal, is formed at the cathode, during electrolysis of sodium chloride in water solution.
3. How does "ammonium" ion resemble the alkali metal ions, and how does it differ?
4. Compare the alkali metals and the alkaline earth metals with respect to physical properties, electronic structure, abundance, occurrence, chemical properties, and valence.
5. Compare the alkali metal ions and the alkaline earth metal ions with respect to physical, chemical, and physiological properties.

C. 1. In general, are the alkali metals and the alkaline earth metals to be classified as oxidizing agents or as reducing agents? Explain fully.
2. When molten lithium hydride (LiH) is electrolyzed, lithium metal is formed at the cathode, hydrogen at the anode. Represent the electronic arrangement of this compound.
3. The following represent reactions by which hydrogen might be prepared for emergency use:

    a. $Na + H_2O \rightarrow$
    b. $Zn + HCl \rightarrow$
    c. $Al + NaOH + H_2O \rightarrow H_2 + NaAl(OH)_4$
    d. $LiH + H_2O \rightarrow$
    e. $NaH + H_2O \rightarrow$
    f. $CaH_2 + H_2O \rightarrow$

Assuming that ample water is available, but that *all* other reagents must be carried, find the reaction which will yield the most hydrogen per gram of reagent.

4. Standard steel tanks used for hydrogen weigh about 100 lbs., have a capacity of 2640 cu. in. (S.C.), and contain hydrogen under 2000 lbs.

pressure (normal atmospheric pressure is about 15 lbs.). How does this method of carrying hydrogen compare on a weight basis with the best of those in Question 3?

5. If ion exchange can remove both positive and negative ions (such as Na^+ and Cl^-) from water, leaving virtually pure water, what must be the equations for the two reversible exchange processes? (Use X for one exchanger; thus, X-Na when Na^+ ions have been taken up by the exchanger; and Y for the other exchanger.)

6. Suppose the two ion exchangers used for preparing pure water become unable to take up any more ionic impurities. How could they be regenerated?

CHAPTER 19

LIGHT METALS

																	H	He
Li	Be	B													C	N	O	F	Ne
Na	Mg	Al													Si	P	S	Cl	A
K	Ca	Sc	Ti	V	Cr	Mn	Fe	Co	Ni	Cu	Zn	Ga	Ge	As	Se	Br	Kr
Rb	Sr	Y	Zr	Nb	Mo	Tc	Ru	Rh	Pd	Ag	Cd	In	Sn	Sb	Te	I	Xe
Cs	Ba	La-Lu	Hf	Ta	W	Re	Os	Ir	Pt	Au	Hg	Tl	Pb	Bi	Po	At	Rn
Fr	Ra	Ac	Th	Pa	U-												

The paradoxes and interrelationships of chemical industry are endless. Not very many generations ago the King of France dined in state with aluminum table-service. He proudly told his guests that he had the only set of aluminum dishes in existence. Now anyone may have his dinner cooked in an aluminum saucepan. Light metals proved the key to mastery of the air; they made it possible to construct aircraft and aircraft engines strong enough and light enough to fly around the world.

A few years ago no one would have guessed that the demand for light metals would have made it economically feasible to mine the sea for magnesium; but every cubic mile of ocean contains ten billion pounds of magnesium.

The elements aluminum, magnesium, and beryllium are the useful light metals. These elements have, of course, many uses in connection with their compounds. But the primary use of each is in the form of the metal, or alloy, as a structural material. In this they are in sharp contrast to the alkali metals, some of which are light enough, but which because of their softness and chemical activity have no structural uses. Aluminum and magnesium are beginning to compare with steel as structural materials. In the domains of combined lightness and strength their only competitor is the growing field of plastics.

129. THE HALL-HÉROULT PROCESS FOR ALUMINUM

Aluminum is the third most abundant element in the earth's crust. It is the most abundant metal, and there exists an inexhaustible supply in the rocks and clays of all nations. Unfortunately the difficulty and expense of extracting the aluminum restrict the commercially useful ores to one, namely *bauxite,* which is an impure hydrated aluminum oxide, mixed with iron oxide. In the United States bauxite is found chiefly in Georgia, Alabama, Tennessee, and Arkansas. It is also found in France, and in British and Dutch Guiana.

The Hall-Héroult process for producing metallic aluminum consists of electrolyzing a solution of aluminum oxide. The solvent is fused *cryolite,* Na_3AlF_6. The first procedure is to purify the bauxite. This is done chiefly by the **Bayer process** as follows: Bauxite is pulverized, then heated with sodium hydroxide solution. The aluminum goes into solution in the form of **sodium aluminate.***

$$Al_2O_3 + 2NaOH + 3H_2O \rightarrow 2NaAl(OH)_4$$

Aluminum is a typical *amphoteric* element, the oxide of which may react as a base with acids to form salts, or which may react as an acid with bases to form salts. But, iron, the principal impurity in bauxite, is not amphoteric. The product of reaction between iron oxide and sodium hydroxide is insoluble iron oxide hydrate, or iron hydroxide. The iron is then readily filtered from the solution containing the aluminum. This simple procedure effectively separates nearly all impurities from the aluminum.

Next, the sodium aluminate solution is diluted with water and cooled. A reaction takes place, yielding a precipitate of pure aluminum hydroxide.

$$NaAl(OH)_4 \rightarrow Al(OH)_3 + NaOH$$

Several modifications of this second step are commonly used. The aluminum hydroxide may also be obtained in the form of the granular oxide hydrate, $Al_2O_3 \cdot 3H_2O$. If now the hydroxide or oxide hydrate is heated, the pure **alumina,** Al_2O_3, results.

Cryolite used as a solvent in the electrolysis of alumina is found in Greenland. It is also made synthetically, and a commonly used solvent consists of mixed sodium fluoride, calcium fluoride, and aluminum fluoride. The temperature of the electrolysis cell is maintained at about 1000° C., and under these conditions alumina readily dissolves and the solution is a good conductor of electricity. The cell consists of a rectangular iron box lined with carbon. (See Figs. 19-1 and 19-2.) This box is made the cathode ($-$) pole, and car-

* The name "sodium aluminate" is not very satisfactory for this substance. The formula is sometimes written $NaAlO_2 \cdot 2H_2O$.

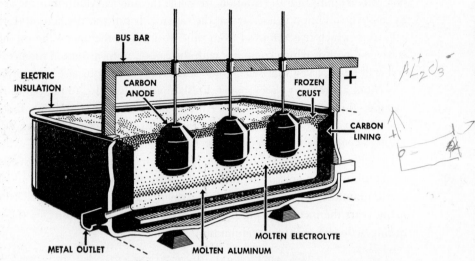

Fig. 19-1. Cell for electrolytic production of aluminum.

Fig. 19-2. A row of electrolytic cells in an aluminum-producing works. The objects running diagonally in front of each cell are bus-bars for carrying the very large current required.

bon rods dipping into the solution are made the anode. Aluminum metal in the molten condition is liberated at the cathode. It sinks to the bottom of the cell, from which it is removed from time to time. At the anode the product is oxygen, part of which combines with the carbon to form carbon monoxide.

It will be observed that the cryolite simply serves the purpose of a solvent and is not appreciably decomposed. Fresh alumina is added to the cell as the metallic aluminum is tapped off. Annual production of aluminum in the world is in the neighborhood of a million tons. Production facilities were greatly expanded during World War II.

Development of the Hall-Héroult process for the electrolytic production of aluminum is an epic in the history of chemical industry.

Aluminum was discovered by the German chemist Wöhler in 1827. For many years the metal was produced as a costly scientific curiosity by the reducing action of sodium on aluminum chloride.

$$AlCl_3 + 3Na \rightarrow Al + 3NaCl$$

The difficulty in the preparation of aluminum is that it takes a very large amount of energy to decompose aluminum compounds into their elements. Until fairly recently such large amounts of energy have not readily been available, and even now, aluminum reduction plants must be located adjacent to cheap sources of energy. In Paris the metal was produced commercially between the years 1855 and 1886, but the price was never less than $12 per pound.

In 1885 Charles Martin Hall was graduated from Oberlin College when he was twenty-one years old. A few months later he developed the process which goes by his name. Hall's interest in aluminum had been aroused when, as a student, he had learned that the element was very abundant in the earth's crust, and that an economical reduction process was the only thing necessary to make it available for a very large potential market. Financial support of the aluminum undertaking was difficult to obtain, but Hall succeeded in interesting a group of men in Pittsburgh, among them the Mellon interests. These men formed an organization which later became the Aluminum Company of America. Hall made a substantial fortune from his process, and his inventions made available cheap aluminum for a host of useful applications.

As not infrequently happens, the discovery of a cheap aluminum reduction process by Charles M. Hall was paralleled by a similar discovery by another scientist. Paul L. V. Héroult, working in France, discovered the same process independently. His work was made public at almost exactly the same time as that of Hall. The European development of aluminum is due in large part to Héroult, just as that in America is due to Hall.

No description of aluminum production is complete without some mention of the economic factors involved. One advantage possessed by the Hall-Héroult process is due to the use of aluminum oxide, instead of the chloride or fluoride as in earlier processes. Not only does the oxide contain nearly twice as much metal per pound as the chloride or fluoride, but it is much easier to prepare pure and at a low cost. This is important because nearly all impurities present in the raw material find their way into the final product. Another saving inherent in the Hall-Héroult process is the direct use of the electric current rather than the use of sodium, which itself has to be prepared by an electrical process.

In order to produce a ton of pure alumina there are required about two tons of crude bauxite, about two tons of coal or its equivalent in other fuels, and about 200 pounds of alkali, not to mention an ample supply of relatively pure water. The problem is greatly simplified where one can find a bauxite field, a coal mine, and ample power, all within the same general locality. This is actually the case in southern France. In the United States transportation charges are often a vital economic factor. For instance, bauxite is assembled from Arkansas and from British and Dutch Guiana at East St. Louis. Here they meet the necessary coal, and other fuels and materials, to produce pure aluminum oxide. This in turn is shipped to reduction plants in Tennessee, North Carolina, or New York, where adequate hydroelectric power is available.

The cost of electric power for the reduction process is another major factor. The average electrolytic cell for aluminum production takes up to 50,000 amperes. In most cases, the aluminum industry is driven to the wilderness to find locations at which power can be developed cheaply enough. There is a very large aluminum reduction plant situated in the heart of the province of Quebec, in Canada, and another in the wilds of British Columbia.

Still another major item of expense is the carbon electrodes used in the electrolytic cells. Until a few years ago about one pound of carbon was consumed for every pound of aluminum produced. The aluminum industry probably consumes as much tonnage of carbon electrodes as all other industries together.

130. PROPERTIES AND USES OF ALUMINUM

Aluminum is a fairly soft, silvery-white metal. Its melting point is 658.7° C. The density of the metal is 2.7 g. per cc. Aluminum may be drawn into wire and fashioned into various shapes. Between 100° and 150° C. it may be hammered into thin sheets, and at higher temperatures ground into powder. It is a good conductor of heat and of electricity. Its tensile strength and that of its alloys is such as to make it useful for many structural applications.

Aluminum is fairly high in the activity series of the metals, and when powdered it combines with oxygen with the utmost vigor. It may seem strange that such an active metal should be so safe to use for so many every-day purposes. While it is true that powdered aluminum may form an explosive mixture in air, yet aluminum metal in bulk only tarnishes slightly. This is due to a slight superficial oxidation.

$$4Al + 3O_2 \rightarrow 2Al_2O_3$$

The thin layer of oxide so formed protects the aluminum against further reaction.

Hydrochloric acid reacts vigorously with aluminum, as does dilute sulfuric acid, hydrogen being displaced in each case.

$$2Al + 6HCl \rightarrow 2AlCl_3 + 3H_2$$

$$2Al + 3H_2SO_4 \rightarrow Al_2(SO_4)_3 + 3H_2$$

But concentrated nitric acid has little effect on aluminum. It seems odd that such a powerful agent as boiling concentrated nitric acid has no action on aluminum unless a little mercury is added as a catalyst. On the other hand, alkalis such as sodium hydroxide react vigorously with aluminum. The products are hydrogen and sodium aluminate.

$$2Al + 2NaOH + 6H_2O \rightarrow 2NaAl(OH)_4 + 3H_2$$

Most of the uses of aluminum depend on its combined lightness and strength, on its electrical conductivity and resistance to corrosion, and on the readiness with which the metal and its alloys may be fabricated into useful objects. One important use of aluminum depends on the vigor with which it combines with oxygen.

As a structural material, aluminum has many well-known applications, ranging from kitchen pots and pans to streamlined trains and aircraft. A very large fraction of all metal objects in everyday use are made of aluminum or aluminum alloys. Aluminum competes in these fields with steel. The advantages possessed by aluminum are lightness and freedom from corrosion. The chief advantages possessed by steel are lower cost and increased strength. In automobile bodies the smaller cost is a deciding factor in favor of steel. In airplane bodies the lightness of aluminum tips the scales far in its favor.

In electrical equipment the chief advantages of aluminum are again its lightness and freedom from corrosion. Its electrical conductivity is not quite so high as that of copper, but for power-lines, aluminum wire, or steel coated with aluminum, finds much application.

Most persons are not aware that "tin foil" used for packaging candy, cigarettes, and so forth, generally contains no tin, but is made of aluminum or aluminum alloy. Tin is far too expensive to consider for the many uses of metal foil, although at one time it was so used. The aluminum foil is often used directly, or it may be glued to paper and painted with designs or advertising.

When aluminum is ground to powder it is used in the familiar aluminum paints.

Polished aluminum has an unusually high reflecting power for light, especially for ultraviolet light. For this reason it is used for coating the mirrors of special optical equipment, such as the great Mount Palomar telescope.

The alloys of aluminum are no less important than the metal itself. Some examples of aluminum alloys are **duralumin,** which contains aluminum, copper, manganese, and magnesium, and which is used for airplane parts; **alnico,** containing aluminum, nickel, and cobalt, and used for permanent magnets; and **aluminum bronze,** containing aluminum, copper, and other elements. The bronzes are used often for making crank cases and connecting rods for automobiles and airplanes.

We turn now to uses which are based on the chemical rather than the physical properties of aluminum. The reaction between aluminum and oxygen is highly exothermic, yielding about 399,000 calories for every mole of aluminum oxide formed. Aluminum, when finely powdered or when heated, combines with oxygen with the utmost vigor. Powdered aluminum mixed with ammonium nitrate may be used as a powerful explosive. Another use is as a scavenger or deoxidizer in making steel. It is often necessary to reduce the amount of oxygen in steel to very low proportions. This may be done by adding to the molten steel agents which will combine with the oxygen. Aluminum is very effective for this purpose. The resulting aluminum oxide floats to the top of the melt and may be skimmed off.

If aluminum powder is mixed with iron oxide and then ignited, a very vigorous reaction takes place, yielding aluminum oxide and metallic iron. The mixture of aluminum and iron oxide is known as **thermite.**

$$2Al + Fe_2O_3 \rightarrow Al_2O_3 + 2Fe$$

or

$$8Al + 3Fe_3O_4 \rightarrow 4Al_2O_3 + 9Fe$$

During the reaction the amount of heat liberated is so great that the iron is made white-hot and flows like water. Thermite is used for welding operations such as mending broken steel rails. The thermite is placed above a mold over the broken rail. Then the thermite charge is ignited with the aid of a magnesium ribbon and some barium peroxide. The mixture becomes white-hot, and the molten iron flows down around the broken rail, effectively fusing the ends and making a perfect mend.

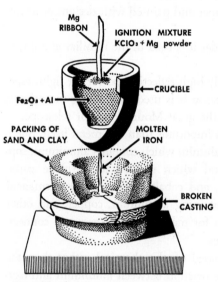

Fig. 19-3. Thermite welding: $Fe_2O_3 + 2Al \rightarrow Al_2O_3 + 2Fe$.

The thermite reaction has considerable application in industry. It was used for incendiary bombs during the early part of World War II. The bombs used on London frequently consisted of a magnesium cylinder into the core of which thermite was packed. A modification of the thermite reaction is sometimes used for the production of metals which are difficult to prepare otherwise. For instance, the element chromium was for a long time most efficiently prepared by igniting a mixture of aluminum powder and chromic oxide.

$$2Al + Cr_2O_3 \rightarrow Al_2O_3 + 2Cr$$

The process illustrated is known as **aluminothermy,** or sometimes by the name of the discoverer, a German chemist named Goldschmidt.

Aluminum in almost all its compounds has an oxidation state of +3. The oxide, Al_2O_3, may be prepared in at least two forms. The α-form is known as *corundum,* or in less pure varieties as *emery.* Next to diamond it is the hardest substance known, and is widely used as an abrasive and in polishing powders. The γ-alumina is used as an adsorbent and as a catalyst and catalyst support. Pure alumina is also used for the manufacture of synthetic rubies and sapphires.

Aluminum hydroxide is formed when a base is added to the solution of an aluminum salt.

$$AlCl_3 + 3NaOH \rightarrow Al(OH)_3 + 3NaCl$$

Aluminum hydroxide is a white gelatinous precipitate. On drying, it reverts to the oxide. The hydroxide is used in water purification, in waterproofing, and as a mordant in dyeing. Aluminum hydroxide is a typical amphoteric substance. With excess alkali it dissolves, forming a soluble aluminate.

$$Al(OH)_3 + NaOH \rightarrow NaAl(OH)_4$$

With excess acid, aluminum hydroxide also dissolves.

$$Al(OH)_3 + 3HCl \rightarrow AlCl_3 + 3H_2O$$

Various properties and uses have been described in earlier pages for such aluminum compounds as cryolite, aluminum sulfate (in water purification), the alums, and the aluminum silicate (in ceramics and cements). The only other aluminum compound which need be mentioned here is the chloride, $AlCl_3$, or Al_2Cl_6. This substance may be prepared by treating aluminum metal with chlorine,

$$2Al + 3Cl_2 \rightarrow 2AlCl_3$$

or by passing chlorine over a mixture of aluminum oxide and carbon.

$$Al_2O_3 + 3C + 3Cl_2 \rightarrow 2AlCl_3 + 3CO$$

Aluminum chloride is widely used in the syntheses of organic compounds.

131. MAGNESIUM

Magnesium is widely and abundantly distributed in nature, but always in compounds, never as the element. The chief minerals containing magnesium are *dolomite,* $CaCO_3 \cdot MgCO_3$, and *magnesite,* $MgCO_3$. The compounds of the element have been recognized for a long time, but the element was first prepared by Davy in 1807.

Magnesium metal has been produced commercially on a moderate scale for a number of years. During the years of World War II the demand for light metals for aircraft expanded at such a rate as to require a fabulous investment in new magnesium plants. In the United States the Dow Chemical Company, a pioneer in this field, was a major factor in the successful development of adequate production facilities.

The obvious source of magnesium is magnesite or dolomite, of which mountainous masses are available. But for various reasons other sources are equally or more important than these natural carbonates. These other sources are natural brine and sea water. It will be recalled that bromine is also obtained from these two sources.

Magnesium from sea water is prepared by electrolysis of fused magnesium chloride. The water is treated with a slurry (a thin watery mixture) of lime. The lime is obtained by burning oyster shells in the huge plant operated by the Dow Chemical Company at Freeport, Texas. The action of the calcium hydroxide is to precipitate magnesium hydroxide from the water. The magnesium hydroxide is freed from excess water, dissolved in hydrochloric acid, and dried. There are several differences in different plants concerning the details of drying and electrolysis.

$Ca(OH)_2$
(lime)

Anhydrous magnesium chloride is electrolyzed in steel pots which serve as the cathode. Graphite bars form the anode. The magnesium rises to the surface, as a liquid, and is removed from time to time for casting into bars. Metal prepared in this way is very pure. The product formed at the anode is, of course, chlorine. At the sea-water production plant, the chlorine is used for making hydrochloric acid, which, in turn, is used for dissolving the magnesium hydroxide. The chlorine undergoes a cyclic process from chlorine to hydrochloric acid to magnesium chloride and back to chlorine. No appreciable amount of chlorine is lost.

The outstanding property of magnesium is that it has the lowest density of any metal which can be used as a structural material. The density is 1.74 g. per cc. Magnesium is, therefore, much lighter than aluminum (d = 2.7 g./cc.). The density of, say, sodium is much less than that of magnesium, but because of its softness and great chemical activity sodium is useless for structural purposes.

Magnesium is a silvery-white metal, easily drawn or worked into desired shapes. It stands high in the activity series of the metals, but, like aluminum, it resists atmospheric corrosion to a great degree. This stability in air is apparently due to a thin film of oxycarbonate which forms on the surface.

Magnesium is not perceptibly attacked by cold water, but it liberates hydrogen from boiling water, and it reacts vigorously with steam.

$$Mg + 2H_2O \rightarrow Mg(OH)_2 + H_2$$

The element displaces hydrogen from strong or weak acids.

$$Mg + 2HCl \rightarrow MgCl_2 + H_2$$

When magnesium is heated in air or in oxygen, it burns with an intense white flame, forming magnesium oxide.

$$2Mg + O_2 \rightarrow 2MgO$$

This vigorous reaction of heated magnesium in air has led to some doubts concerning the widespread use of this metal. But the danger from massive pieces of magnesium is apparently considerably less than the use of, say, such an inflammable material as wood as a general structural material in building houses and furniture. On the other hand, finely powdered magnesium mixed with air is a dangerous explosive. But this is also true of any combustible material such as flour, dust, powdered aluminum, and similar material. The chief use of magnesium is based on its lightness, strength, and resistance to corrosion. During World War II magnesium was used on a tremendous scale for aircraft parts, and there is no doubt that it will become a very common material. But it is doubtful if magnesium will ever invade the kitchen in the way that aluminum has done in the past fifty years.

Certain alloys of magnesium with aluminum, zinc, and manganese have the highest ratio of strength to weight of any metallic structural material. They also have the desirable properties of corrosion resistance, machinability, and nontoxicity. Use of these alloys in a large airplane saves about one ton of weight.

Other uses of magnesium metal include flares and incendiary bombs. The metal is used as a deoxidizer in the production of nickel and nickel alloys. Magnesium is also used in the synthesis of organic compounds by what is known as the *Grignard reaction*.

132. MAGNESIUM COMPOUNDS

Magnesium has an oxidation state of two in practically all of its compounds. The oxide, MgO, is formed by burning the metal in oxygen. Magnesium has some tendency to unite with nitrogen at elevated temperature; hence, when the metal is burned in air, there is formed a mixture of oxide and nitride, Mg_3N_2. The oxide is a white powder, made commercially on a large scale by heating magnesite or magnesium carbonate.

$$MgCO_3 \rightarrow MgO + CO_2$$

Large quantities of magnesium oxide are used in lining furnaces and for crucibles. This use depends on the high melting point, about 2800° C., possessed by the oxide. Magnesium oxide is used as an insulator and, together with magnesium chloride, in the substance called Sorel cement or magnesia cement. The oxide is also used in toothpastes, powders, and toilet preparations.

Magnesium oxide slowly combines with water, yielding the hydroxide.

$$MgO + H_2O \rightarrow Mg(OH)_2$$

This substance is a typical weak base, only slightly soluble in water. It undergoes the characteristic reactions of weak bases. A suspension of magnesium hydroxide in water is known as **milk of magnesia.** Both the oxide and the hydroxide are used extensively in medicine to reduce gastric acidity.

The natural occurrence of magnesium carbonate has already been discussed. Artificial preparations containing the carbonate are known as **magnesia alba.** This substance is used in polishing powders and in toothpaste.

The silicates containing magnesium have also already been discussed. *Asbestos, talc,* and *soapstone* are important examples of naturally occurring magnesium silicates. Soapstone is often used as a desk top for benches in chemical laboratories. *Meerschaum* and *serpentine* are other magnesium silicates.

Magnesium sulfate occurs naturally in several parts of the world. The heptahydrate, $MgSO_4 \cdot 7H_2O$, is well known as **Epsom salts** after its occurrence at Epsom in England. This substance is used in medicine as a powerful cathartic. It has an uncommonly bitter, unpleasant taste. The physiological action is due, at least in part, to the magnesium ion. Other magnesium compounds also have a cathartic action. These compounds include the oxide and the citrate. Magnesium sulfate is also used in the manufacture of soaps, paints, and textiles.

Magnesium chloride, $MgCl_2$, has already been mentioned in connection with the electrometallurgy of magnesium. The hydrated salt finds use also as a dressing for cotton and woolen goods.

The only other magnesium compound which need be mentioned is the perchlorate, $Mg(ClO_4)_2$. This substance is used as a drying agent, chiefly for gases.

Magnesium is essential for animal and plant life, although in certain pathological conditions the element is toxic.

133. BERYLLIUM

This element is of much less importance than either of the others considered in this chapter. Nevertheless, beryllium has some interesting and valuable properties. The name of the element is derived from the name of the mineral *beryl*, $Be_3Al_2Si_6O_{18}$, a beryllium aluminum silicate. This mineral occurs in New England and elsewhere. Transparent samples colored green by small amounts of chromium compounds are known as *emerald*. The element is sometimes called *glucinum*, from a Greek word meaning "sweet," in reference to the taste of some beryllium compounds. Beryllium is not widely or abundantly distributed in nature. Its cost is fairly high, and seems likely to remain so.

The metal may be produced by electrolyzing a fused mixture of sodium chloride and beryllium chloride. The reduction is achieved with some difficulty, and this contributes to the expense. The metal is a light, silvery-white substance, very hard, and very strong. The density is 1.85 g. per cc., which makes the element slightly heavier than magnesium but considerably less so than aluminum. Beryllium resists corrosion in air. When heated it forms the oxide, BeO. The metal reacts with strong acids and with strong bases.

The combination of low density, great strength, and resistance to corrosion makes beryllium a remarkably attractive metal for many structural purposes. Unfortunately its high cost prevents its use on a large scale. Small amounts of the pure metal are used in X-ray tubes. Beryllium is almost transparent to X rays. The metal does, however, have a number of important applications in alloys. The most important of these is probably a copper-beryllium alloy used for springs. Most metals exhibit what is known as fatigue. On long use such metals tend to lose their strength. But copper-beryllium alloy springs have a very remarkable resiliency and resistance to fatigue.

In nearly all its compounds beryllium has an oxidation state of $+2$. The oxide, BeO, is useful as a refractory, its melting point being nearly 2600° C. Very pure grades of the oxide have been used in making the active powders for fluorescent lamps, for catalysts, special glasses, and for synthetic jewels.

A few years ago it was discovered that contact with beryllium or its compounds may lead to a serious chronic poisoning (called **berylliosis**) which is sometimes fatal.

EXERCISES

A. *Define or explain the following:*

alnico	emerald
alumina	Epsom salts
aluminothermy	magnesite
bauxite	milk of magnesia
beryl	refractory
berylliosis	scavenger (in metallurgical operations)
corundum	sodium aluminate
cryolite	thermite
duralumin	

B. *Indicate procedures and equations for the following:*

1. a. the Bayer process for purifying bauxite
   b. the Hall-Héroult process (include diagram)
   c. production of aluminum by the use of metallic sodium
   d. $Al + O_2 \rightarrow$
   e. $Al + HCl \rightarrow$; $Al + H_2SO_4$ (dil.) $\rightarrow$; $Al + HNO_3$ (conc.) $\rightarrow$
   f. $Al + NaOH + H_2O \rightarrow$
   g. $Al + Fe_2O_3 \rightarrow$; $Al + Fe_3O_4 \rightarrow$
   h. illustrate the amphoterism of aluminum hydroxide

    i.   synthesis of aluminum chloride

    j.   production of magnesium metal

    k. $Mg + O_2 \rightarrow$; $Mg + N_2 \rightarrow$

    l. $Mg + H_2O$ (hot) $\rightarrow$

    m. $Mg + HCl \rightarrow$

2. Why has such an abundant element as aluminum been used for only a relatively short time?

3. Why does aluminum not dissolve in hot concentrated nitric acid?

4. Compare the active metals and the light metals with respect to their properties, their compounds, and their uses.

C. 1. Addition of CO_2 to $NaAl(OH)_4$ solution causes the precipitation of $Al(OH)_3$. Write a possible equation for this reaction.

   2. If aluminum hydroxide can act both as an acid and a base, why does it not neutralize itself? (Consider the ionization of water in answering this question.)

   3. If magnesium is burned in air, then treated with water, it gives off a smell of ammonia. Why?

   4. Compare the volumes of hydrogen liberated (S.C.) when one gram-atom of sodium, magnesium, and aluminum are separately treated with excess hydrochloric acid. Explain the differences.

   5. What weight of magnesium will displace the same volume of hydrogen as 1 g. of aluminum, each metal being treated with excess dilute acid?

   6. Write probable formulas for scandium oxide, yttrium nitrate, lanthanum sulfate, actinium perchlorate.

   7. Write possible equations for the following:

     a. aluminum plus hot, concentrated sulfuric acid

     b. $Al + Mn_2O_3 \rightarrow$

     c. $MgO + Si \rightarrow Mg + ?$

     d. $Al(OH)_3 + OH^- \rightarrow ?$

     e. $Al(OH)_3 + H^+ \rightarrow ?$

CHAPTER 20 ELECTROCHEMISTRY

Repeatedly in the earlier pages of this book it has been pointed out that electrons are the fundamental particles of electricity. An electric current is a flow of electrons. It has also been emphasized that all chemical change involves a motion or a rearrangement of electrons. In one sense, therefore, all chemistry is electrochemistry. But for practical purposes the term *electrochemistry* is restricted to mean the application of electric currents and electric potentials to the solution of chemical problems. Electrochemistry is of major importance both to industry and to pure science. In the past pages we have frequently referred to electrochemical processes. The electrolysis of water, the production of hydrogen peroxide, chlorine, chlorates and perchlorates, sodium, sodium hydroxide, aluminum, and magnesium—all belong to electrochemistry. We shall now examine more fully the underlying principles of such processes. The reader will at once observe that a close relationship exists between electrochemistry and ionization.

134. ELECTRICAL UNITS

An understanding of a few electrical terms and units is essential to any study of electrochemistry.

The **volt** is the unit of electrical potential, or pressure. The ordinary household lighting circuit operates at 110 volts; a single dry cell yields about 1.5 volts.

The **coulomb** is the unit of electrical quantity; that is, it is the measure of the amount of electricity which may, for instance, flow in a wire during a given time.

The **ampere** is the unit of electrical current. A current of one ampere corresponds to the passage of one coulomb in one second. We have, therefore, the relationship

$$coulombs = amperes \times seconds$$

The **ohm** is the unit of electrical resistance. The ohm, the ampere, and volt are related by Ohm's Law, which may be stated:

$$amperes = \frac{volts}{ohms}$$

Or, in words, the current is equal to the potential divided by the resistance.

Electrical energy is generally sold by the kilowatt hour. The **watt** is the unit of power. It is related to the current and the potential as follows:

$$watts = amperes \times volts$$

A kilowatt hour is 1000 watts for one hour. One horsepower equals 746 watts.

The reader should distinguish between direct current (D.C.) and alternating current (A.C.). The former flows in one direction only, the latter reverses its direction periodically. In 60-cycle A.C., used for most cities, the direction of the current is reversed 120 times per second. Most of the electrochemical phenomena to be described in this chapter are related to direct currents.

135. ELECTROLYSIS

When an electric current flows through a copper wire, there is no movement of matter in the usual sense, and no observable chemical changes take place. The process is said to be one of **metallic conduction.** But when a current flows through acidified water, there are obvious chemical changes such as the evolution of hydrogen at the **cathode,** and oxygen at the **anode.** Such a process is known as **electrolytic conduction,** as opposed to metallic conduction. Conduction of electricity, with simultaneous chemical change, is referred to as **electrolysis.** The substance undergoing chemical change is said to be electrolyzed.

Let us examine again the mechanism by which a substance undergoes electrolysis. Fused sodium chloride will serve as an example. When sodium chloride is fused, or melted, it consists of sodium ions and chloride ions, each comparatively free to move independently. We place two electrodes into the liquid sodium chloride. These electrodes must, for our present purpose, be chemically inert: that is, they must undergo no chemical change themselves. Carbon rods would serve this purpose.

Now an electric potential is applied to the electrodes. A current will be found to flow. This current is carried in the fused sodium chloride, not by electrons as is the case in metals, but by the ions of sodium and of chlorine. The sodium ions, being positive, migrate to the negative electrode. The chloride ions, being negative, migrate to the positive electrode. This motion of charged particles constitutes a flow of electricity through the sodium chloride. The ions do not move very rapidly toward the electrodes. The ions are doubtless undergoing a very rapid random motion owing to the Brownian movement. But their directed rate of migration toward the electrodes may be quite slow.

At the electrodes certain chemical changes take place. As the sodium ions touch the negative electrode they each acquire an electron, thereby producing sodium metal.

$$Na^+ + \epsilon \rightarrow Na^0$$

This is, of course, the process by which sodium is made in the Downs, and other, electrolytic cells. At the anode, each ion of chlorine gives up an electron, thereby becoming a chlorine atom.

$$Cl^- \rightarrow Cl^0 + \epsilon$$

Two chlorine atoms then unite to form a chlorine molecule.

$$2Cl^0 \rightarrow Cl_2$$

Chlorine gas appears at the anode. If the electrolytic cell is connected to a generator or a battery for a source of direct current, then the generator or battery serves simply as an electron pump, pumping electrons around from the positive electrode to the negative. (Refer to Fig. 14-3.)

If, instead of fused sodium chloride, there is used a solution of sodium chloride in water, the conduction of electricity is exactly the same. That is, sodium ions migrate toward the negative pole and chloride ions toward the positive. But in this case the chemical process taking place at the cathode is different. Instead of sodium being formed there is an evolution of hydrogen gas, plus a formation of sodium hydroxide in the solution surrounding the negative electrode. This, as described in connection with the industrial production of chlorine, sodium hydroxide, and hydrogen, is because hydrogen ions take up electrons more easily than do sodium ions. But of this, and other complications, we shall have more to say later. Our next problem is the quantitative relationship which exists between the amount of electricity involved and the chemical changes which take place during electrolysis.

136. FARADAY'S LAW

The fundamental law of electrolysis was discovered by Michael Faraday.* Faraday stated his discovery in the form of two laws, which will be given first in Faraday's own words, then restated as one law in more modern

* *Philosophical Transactions of the Royal Society*, 124:77 (1834).

terminology. Faraday's first law is as follows: "the chemical power of a current of electricity is in direct proportion to the absolute quantity of electricity which passes." This means that if x coulombs of electricity liberate 10 g. of chlorine, then $2x$ coulombs will liberate 20 g. of chlorine. Faraday's second law was stated in this way: "several substances were placed in succession, and decomposed simultaneously by the same electric current . . . the results were comparable, the tin, lead, chlorine, oxygen and hydrogen

Fig. 20-1. Michael Faraday

Faraday was born in England in 1791. His family was poor and he was apprenticed to a book publisher. Someone took him to a lecture by Sir Humphry Davy at the Royal Institution in London and Faraday was so pleased by the lecture that he applied to Davy for a position. In 1813 he became Davy's assistant and a few years later was making discoveries of major importance.

Faraday discovered the laws of electrochemistry which bear his name; he discovered a fundamental relationship between electricity and magnetism upon which our electrical engineering is based; he studied the liquefaction of gases; he discovered magnetooptical rotation, the phenomenon of diamagnetism, and the important compound benzene. Many scientists regard Faraday as the most able experimentalist of all time. He was equally brilliant as a lecturer, and his diaries and lectures rank as great literature.

Faraday died in 1867. Almost his only rival is Marie Curie for the general esteem in which he was held by scientists and by the public. (*Ewing Galloway*)

evolved being definite in quantity and electrochemical equivalents to each other." This means that if the same quantity of electricity is allowed to pass through and decompose several different solutions, the quantities of each element evolved are proportional to their electrochemical equivalents, or to what we now call their equivalent weights.

We may restate **Faraday's laws** into one law as follows: **The number of equivalent weights of any substance deposited or evolved at an electrode is proportional to the quantity of electricity passing through the electrolyte (i.e., substance being electrolyzed).**

The term **equivalent weight,** sometimes called combining weight, has not been emphasized heretofore. It may be defined experimentally as *the weight of an element which will combine with or displace one gram of hydrogen* (more precisely 1.008 g.), *or 8 g. of oxygen.* This more exactly gives the gram-equivalent weight, or the equivalent weight expressed as grams. The equivalent weight is also defined as *the atomic weight divided by the oxidation state*.

Problem: What is the equivalent weight of a metal, 2.50 g. of which, on treatment with dilute hydrochloric acid yields 390 cc. of hydrogen (S.C.)?

Solution: 22,400 cc. (one mole) of H_2 weighs 2.0 g., so that 390 cc. of H_2 must weigh $2.0 \times 390/22,400 = 0.0349$ g. This weight of hydrogen is displaced by 2.50 g. of metal, then 1.0 g. of hydrogen would be displaced by $2.50 \times 1.0/0.0349 = 71.7$ g. metal. By definition, the equivalent weight of the metal is 71.7.

Problem: What is the equivalent weight of an element, 8.3 g. of which unite with 2.9 g. of oxygen?

Solution: If 2.9 g. of oxygen unite with 8.3 g. of the element, then 8.0 g. of oxygen would unite with $8.3 \times 8.0/2.9 = 23$ g. of the element.

Problem: What is the equivalent weight of copper in cupric sulfate, $\overset{+2}{Cu}\overset{=}{SO_4}$?

Solution: The atomic weight of copper is 63.57. The oxidation state of copper in cupric sulfate is +2. The equivalent weight is then $63.57/2 = 31.78$.

It is found by experiment that to deposit or evolve one gram equivalent weight of any element by electrolysis requires 96,500 coulombs of electricity. This quantity of electricity is called a **faraday.** Faraday's law will now be illustrated by several problems.

Problem: How many coulombs are required to deposit 100 g. of copper from a copper sulfate solution?

Solution: The equivalent weight of copper is 31.78. Then, 31.78 g. of copper would be deposited by 96,500 coulombs, and 100 g. of copper would be deposited by

$$\frac{100}{31.78} \times 96,500 \text{ coulombs} = 304,000 \text{ coulombs}$$

$$moles = \frac{gm}{eq.wt.}$$
$$eq.wt. \times moles = gm$$
$$eq.wt. = \frac{gm}{moles}$$

The problem might have been stated as follows: how long must a current of 100 amperes flow to deposit 100 g. of copper? It will be recalled that coulombs = amperes × seconds. The time would be

$$\frac{304,000 \text{ coulombs}}{100 \text{ amperes}} = 3040 \text{ seconds}$$

$$= 50.7 \text{ minutes}$$

Problem: What weight of silver could be deposited by a current of 15 amperes flowing through silver nitrate solution for one hour?

Solution: The number of coulombs is $15 \times 60 \times 60 = 54,000$ coulombs. The valence of silver in $AgNO_3$ is $+1$. Hence the equivalent weight of silver is the same as the atomic weight, or 107.880. Then 96,500 coulombs will deposit 107.880 g. of silver, so that 54,000 coulombs will deposit

$$\frac{54,000}{96,500} \times 107.880 = 60.4 \text{ g.}$$

Faraday's law is among the most important and exact laws of chemistry. As Faraday himself wrote:

I think I cannot deceive myself in considering the doctrine of definite electrochemical action as of the utmost importance. It touches by its facts more directly and closely than any former fact, or set of facts, have done, upon the beautiful idea, that ordinary chemical affinity is a mere consequence of the electrical attractions of the particles of different kinds of matter; and it will probably lead us to the means by which we may enlighten that which at present is so obscure, and either fully demonstrate the truth of the idea or develop that which ought to replace it.

Faraday's confidence in the importance of his discovery was fully justified. His work led to the conception of the electron and to its part in chemical change.

The reasons for this importance which we attach to Faraday's law are clear from a consideration of the changes which occur when a silver ion is converted at the cathode to a silver atom. This process consists of the gaining by the silver ion of one electron. Electrons are the fundamental particles of electricity. Hence it is clear why a definite weight of silver requires a definite

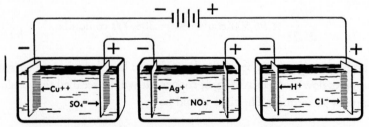

Fig. 20-2. A definite quantity of electricity is passed through each of several solutions. This may be done by connecting the cells in series as shown. It will be found that the actual weights of elements liberated at the electrodes vary greatly, but that the number of gram-equivalents of each is the same.

quantity of electricity for its deposition. But to deposit copper from copper sulfate requires two electrons per copper ion. Therefore a given quantity of electricity will deposit just half as many copper atoms as silver atoms. Analogous processes take place at the anode, where electrons are lost by the substance being liberated, instead of being gained as at the cathode.

137. TECHNICAL ELECTROLYSIS *

The principles developed in the preceding section will now be used in the description of some important technical applications of electrolysis. One of these, the production of aluminum, has already been mentioned.

It will be recalled that the Hall-Héroult process for aluminum is based on the electrolysis of aluminum oxide dissolved in fused cryolite. The only further detail of this process that we need describe is the large amount of electricity necessary to produce the metal. The atomic weight of aluminum is 27, and the valence, or charge on the ion, is 3. Hence the equivalent weight of aluminum is only 9. One faraday of electricity will produce only 9 g. of aluminum, whereas the same quantity of electricity will deposit 108 g. of silver. This is an important contributing factor in the requirement that aluminum production plants be located adjacent to sources of abundant and cheap electricity.

There is, however, an additional reason why the power consumption in this, and in other, electrometallurgical operations should be high. It is true that under ideal laboratory conditions, Faraday's law is one of the most accurately fulfilled laws of science. But under ordinary industrial conditions there are opportunities for electricity to be wasted. Sometimes this is due to faulty insulation or poor connections. More frequently it is due to redissolving of the metal after it has been liberated, or to the action of impurities in draining off fractional amounts of the current. Whatever the causes may be, electrochemical industries rarely approach 100 per cent efficiency in the utilization of electricity. In aluminum production the **current efficiency** varies between 75 and 90 per cent. This means that the weight of aluminum metal actually produced is only 75 to 90 per cent of that theoretically obtainable.

Problem: If the current is 20,000 amperes, what weight of aluminum may be produced in 24 hours, the current efficiency being 85 per cent?

Solution: The number of coulombs is $24 \times 60 \times 60 \times 20,000 = 1,730,000,000$ coulombs. One faraday or 96,500 coulombs will deposit $27/3 = 9.0$ g. of aluminum. Therefore 1,730,000,000 coulombs will deposit

---

* W. A. Koehler, *Principles and Applications of Electrochemistry*, Vol. II, *Applications*, 2nd Edition (New York: Wiley, 1944).

$$\frac{1,730,000,000}{96,500} \times 9 = 161,000 \text{ g.}$$

or 161 kilograms. But the current efficiency is only 85 per cent, so that the actual yield is $161 \times 0.85 = 137$ kg.

The other electrolysis process which will be described at this point is that known as **electroplating.** Many metals are successfully plated in thin adherent sheets. These include silver, chromium, cadmium, and several others. The purpose of electroplating is generally to improve the resistance

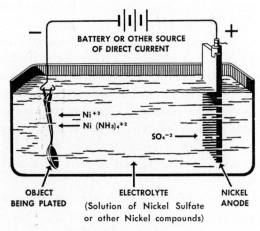

BATTERY OR OTHER SOURCE
OF DIRECT CURRENT

Ni^{+2}
Ni (NH$_3$)$_4$$^{+2}$

SO$_4$$^{-2}$

OBJECT
BEING PLATED

ELECTROLYTE
(Solution of Nickel Sulfate
or other Nickel compounds)

NICKEL
ANODE

Fig. 20-3. Electroplating nickel.

to corrosion, or the appearance, of a metal surface. The metal on which plating is performed is not infrequently iron. We shall, at this point, confine our discussion to nickel plating, which is one of the most important of the electroplating industries.

The object to be plated, such as a sheet of iron, is made the cathode; pure or nearly pure nickel bars are made the anode. The electrolyte may be a solution of nickel sulfate, $NiSO_4 \cdot 7H_2O$, or, more frequently, a mixture of salts such as nickel sulfate and ammonium sulfate.

The reaction at the cathode is a deposition of nickel metal. That at the anode is a dissolving of nickel.

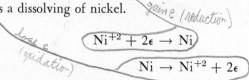

gain e (reduction)

$$Ni^{+2} + 2\epsilon \rightarrow Ni$$

lose e
(oxidation)

$$Ni \rightarrow Ni^{+2} + 2\epsilon$$

The electrolysis would, of course, proceed for a time even if the anode were made of some completely inert metal such as platinum. But then the nickel ions in solution would soon all be used up and the electroplating would stop. Use of nickel anodes maintains the nickel ion concentration in solution at the desired strength until the anodes are entirely dissolved, at which time they may conveniently be replaced by fresh anodes.

It should be mentioned that successful electroplating is almost as much an art as a science. It is often found expedient to add substances such as glue, which have been found to improve the deposit, yet for the action of which there is no very logical explanation. Details of such procedures will be found in standard works on the subject.*

138. VOLTAIC CELLS

In the preceding pages our concern has been with the chemical changes produced by electrical energy. But nearly all the chemical changes described are reversible. It is just as feasible to produce electrical energy by chemical change as to do the reverse. We may use the term *cell* to mean either a vessel in which substances are electrolyzed, or a vessel in which chemical reactions are used to produce electrical energy. The former is properly called an *electrolysis cell,* the latter a *voltaic cell,* after the Italian physicist Volta who, about 1800, constructed the first primary cell of which there is any record.

Any metal when placed in water has a tendency to dissolve with the formation of ions. This reaction is always reversible.

$$M \rightleftarrows M^+ + \epsilon$$

For active metals such as sodium the tendency is for the reaction to go completely to the right, as indicated. For inactive metals such as platinum the tendency is so slight that no perceptible formation of ions occurs.

If a strip of metallic zinc is placed in a solution of zinc sulfate, some of the zinc dissolves, forming Zn^{+2} ions. The electrons liberated in this process remain in the metallic zinc, imparting to the metal strip a negative charge. Normally, the process stops at this point, but arrangements may be made to have the reaction proceed until all the zinc is dissolved. We might indicate the reaction as follows:

$$Zn \rightleftharpoons Zn^{+2} + 2\epsilon$$

the long arrow being used to show that the reaction tends to go strongly toward complete solution of the zinc.

Now if a strip of metallic copper is placed in a solution of copper sulfate, the same type of reaction tends to occur. But copper is a much less active

* *Modern Electroplating,* The Electrochemical Society (New York: Columbia University, 1942).

metal than zinc. Its tendency to go into solution, or its **solution pressure** as it is called, is much less than for zinc. The reaction might be written:

$$Cu \rightleftharpoons Cu^{+2} + 2\epsilon$$

Notice that if copper comes out of solution, rather than going in, there will be a deficiency of electrons in the copper strip. The strip will thereby acquire a positive rather than a negative charge.

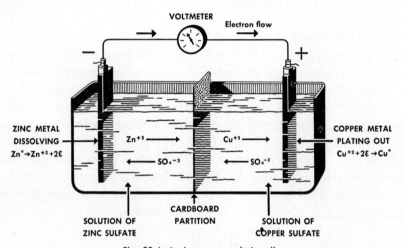

Fig. 20-4. A zinc-copper voltaic cell.

Now let the zinc, zinc sulfate, copper sulfate, copper system be combined in one cell. The zinc metal dips into the zinc sulfate; the copper metal dips into the copper sulfate; and the zinc sulfate and copper sulfate are separated by a sheet of cardboard or other porous partition. The cardboard prevents gross mixing of the solutions but permits diffusion of ions either way.

As a result of the different solution pressures exerted by the zinc and the copper, the zinc will acquire a negative charge with respect to the copper. This arrangement constitutes a cell for the generation of electricity. Current may be taken off by appropriate connections to the zinc and copper. The chemical reactions taking place are represented at the negative pole by

$$Zn \rightarrow Zn^{+2} + 2\epsilon$$

lose e (oxidation)

and at the positive pole by

$$Cu^{+2} + 2\epsilon \rightarrow Cu$$

gain e (reduction)

The electrons flow in the *external* circuit from the zinc to the copper. Within the cell the current is carried by a migration of the sulfate ions, which are able to diffuse through the cardboard partition.

Such an arrangement in which one or the other of the electrodes is actually used up is called a *primary cell*. The particular cell described is known as the Daniell cell.

It will be noted that many other metals could serve as the electrodes. The voltage given by the Daniell cell is normally a little over 1 volt. It will be seen that greater voltages could be obtained by using a more active metal on one side of the cell and a less active on the other. Magnesium and gold, for instance, would give a much higher voltage than, say, copper and silver, which are nearly alike in activity. Of course, a very active metal like sodium would not be practical in a cell because it would react too rapidly. Because of this relationship between activity of the metals and the voltage produced in electric cells, the activity series of the metals is often called the **electromotive series.**

139. SINGLE ELECTRODE POTENTIALS

Every electrochemical reaction may be thought of as the sum of two separate reactions, one an oxidation or loss of electrons taking place at one electrode (the anode), and the other a reduction or gain of electrons taking place at the other electrode (the cathode).* Similarly, the voltage or electromotive force **(EMF)** developed in a voltaic cell may be thought of as the sum of the **single electrode potentials** produced at the two individual electrodes. For a zinc-copper cell one may refer to the single electrode potential of the electrode, or **half cell,** consisting of zinc metal in contact with a solution containing zinc ions. Similarly, one may refer to the single electrode potential of the half cell consisting of copper metal in contact with a solution containing cupric ions. The overall reaction in this cell is the displacement $Zn^0 + Cu^{++}$ $\rightarrow Zn^{++} + Cu^0$, but the individual electrode reactions, or **half reactions** as they are

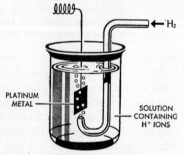

Fig. 20-5. Hydrogen electrode (half cell).

called, are $Zn^0 \rightleftarrows Zn^{++} + 2\epsilon$ and $Cu^{++} + 2\epsilon \rightleftarrows Cu^0$. The cell voltage that is measured is approximately the sum of the single electrode potentials for these two half reactions.

In a voltaic cell it is easy to measure the voltage with a voltmeter and to find which electrode is positive with respect to the other. It is also easy to compare

---

* The terms "anode" and "cathode" in an electrolysis cell are the positive and negative poles respectively; but in a voltaic cell these signs are reversed, the anode being negative and the cathode positive. A definition which will always serve is this: the **anode** is the electrode at which oxidation takes place, the **cathode** that at which reduction takes place.

one single electrode potential with another, but there is no known method of deciding the *sign* of a single electrode potential or of measuring its actual EMF. For this reason it has been necessary to adopt the quite arbitrary method of comparing single electrode potentials with that of a hydrogen electrode. A hydrogen electrode consists of a piece of roughened platinum foil surrounded by hydrogen gas and immersed in dilute acid. This arrangement behaves not unlike a half cell consisting of a metal in contact with a solution containing ions of the metal, the half reaction being $H_2 \rightleftarrows 2H^+ + 2\epsilon$. A **standard hydrogen electrode** is one in which the hydrogen gas surrounding the platinum is at one atmosphere pres-

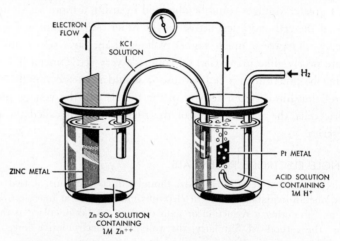

Fig. 20-6. Complete cell for measuring the EMF of the $Zn \rightleftarrows Zn^{++} + 2\epsilon$ half cell by coupling it with a standard hydrogen electrode. The inverted U-tube containing a conducting solution, such as KCl in water, serves the same purpose as the cardboard partition shown in Fig. 20-4.

sure and in which the effective concentration of hydrogen ions in the acid is one molar. *A standard hydrogen electrode is arbitrarily assumed to have an EMF of zero.* This serves as a standard for comparing other half cell potentials.

If now a complete cell is made up of, say, zinc metal in contact with $1M$ $ZnSO_4$ solution as one half cell, and a standard hydrogen electrode as the other half cell, then the voltage for the complete cell is the sum of the EMF for the half reaction at the zinc half cell plus that at the hydrogen half cell. If it has been assumed that the potential of the standard hydrogen electrode is zero, then the measured voltage of the complete cell must be the EMF of the zinc half cell. In this particular case the EMF happens to be 0.76 volts, and the hydrogen electrode is positive with respect to the zinc electrode.

In the manner described for the zinc half cell it is possible to find the single electrode potentials for any reactions involving oxidation and reduction. Table 11 gives a list of single electrode potentials as found for various half cell reactions.

The reader may have trouble with the sign of the single electrode potentials. When a metal such as zinc is placed in water some zinc ions tend to go into solution, leaving the remaining metal itself with a slight excess of electrons and consequently negative with respect to the solution. But the solution is now positive with respect to the metal, so that there is some ambiguity in deciding whether the half cell, consisting of metal and solution, is negative or positive. This ambiguity is resolved arbitrarily in Table 11.*

The electromotive series is useful in finding the voltage of a complete cell.

TABLE 11

THE ELECTROMOTIVE SERIES

Single electrode potentials and half cell reactions at room temperature for elements in contact with $1M$ * solutions of their ions †

Half Reaction	EMF (volts)	Half Reaction	EMF (volts)
$K \rightleftarrows K^+ + \epsilon$	2.92	$H_2 \rightleftarrows 2H^+ + 2\epsilon$	0.00
$Ca \rightleftarrows Ca^{++} + 2\epsilon$	2.87	$Sn^{++} \rightleftarrows Sn^{+4} + 2\epsilon$	$-.15$
$Na \rightleftarrows Na^+ + \epsilon$	2.71	$Cu \rightleftarrows Cu^{++} + 2\epsilon$	$-.34$
$Mg \rightleftarrows Mg^{++} + 2\epsilon$	2.34	$2I^- \rightleftarrows I_2 + 2\epsilon$	$-.53$
$Al \rightleftarrows Al^{+++} + 3\epsilon$	1.67	$2Hg \rightleftarrows Hg_2^{++} + 2\epsilon$	$-.80$
$Mn \rightleftarrows Mn^{++} + 2\epsilon$	1.05	$Ag \rightleftarrows Ag^+ + \epsilon$	$-.80$
$Zn \rightleftarrows Zn^{++} + 2\epsilon$	0.76	$Hg \rightleftarrows Hg^{++} + 2\epsilon$	$-.85$
$Cr \rightleftarrows Cr^{+++} + 3\epsilon$	0.71	$2Br^- \rightleftarrows Br_2 + 2\epsilon$	-1.09
$Fe \rightleftarrows Fe^{++} + 2\epsilon$	0.44	$Pt \rightleftarrows Pt^{++} + 2\epsilon$	$-1.2?$
$Ni \rightleftarrows Ni^{++} + 2\epsilon$	0.25	$2H_2O \rightleftarrows O_2 + 2H^+ + 4\epsilon$	-1.23
$Sn \rightleftarrows Sn^{++} + 2\epsilon$	0.14	$2Cl^- \rightleftarrows Cl_2 + 2\epsilon$	-1.36
$Pb \rightleftarrows Pb^{++} + 2\epsilon$	0.13	$Au \rightleftarrows Au^+ + \epsilon$	-1.68
		$2F^- \rightleftarrows F_2 + 2\epsilon$	-2.85

* The solutions are not exactly $1M$, a correction being necessary for a property known as the "activity" of the ions.

† More extensive tables will be found in W. M. Latimer, *The Oxidation States of the Elements and Their Potentials in Aqueous Solutions* (New York: Prentice-Hall, 1952).

Problem: Find the voltage of a zinc-copper cell, both metals being immersed in $1M$ solutions of their ion. (Such a cell is often designated $Zn \mid Zn^{++} \parallel Cu^{++} \mid Cu$).

Solution: The only difficulty here is with the signs of the half cell potentials. The half reaction at the zinc electrode is $Zn \rightarrow Zn^{++} + 2\epsilon$ for which the EMF is given in Table 11 as 0.76 volts. The half reaction at the copper electrode is *not* $Cu \rightarrow Cu^{++} + 2\epsilon$ as given in Table 11 with an EMF of -0.34 volts, but is actually the *reverse* of this, namely $Cu^{++} + 2\epsilon \rightarrow Cu$ with an EMF of $+0.34$ volts. Then the voltage of the complete cell is simply the sum $0.76 + 0.34 = 1.10$ volts. The zinc metal electrode becomes negative with respect to the copper, and electrons flow in the *external* circuit from zinc to copper.

The potentials in Table 11 refer to half cells containing $1M$ solutions. If the concentration of the solution is varied the electrode potential will vary in a manner

* Many workers use the opposite convention, namely, those half reactions placed above hydrogen in Table 11 are considered to have a negative EMF, and those below hydrogen a positive EMF.

predictable from Le Chatelier's principle. For the half reaction $Cu \rightleftharpoons Cu^{++} + 2\epsilon$, making the solution more concentrated, that is, raising the concentration of the Cu^{++} ions, will force the equilibrium toward the left. This has the effect of moving the copper half cell to a lower position in the electromotive series. Consequently, if there is set up a voltaic cell of which one half cell consists of copper metal in contact with concentrated copper sulfate solution, and the other half cell of copper metal in contact with dilute copper sulfate, then the complete cell will yield a small but definite voltage. The copper metal in contact with the more concentrated copper sulfate will be the more positive of the two electrodes.

This effect of changing EMF with changing ion concentration applies to all half cells. For a hydrogen electrode it is common to use the effect to measure

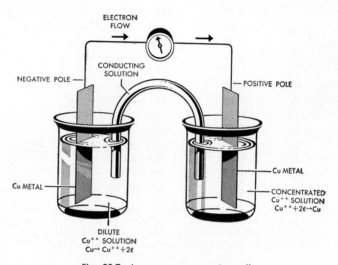

Fig. 20-7. A copper concentration cell.

hydrogen ion concentration. Instruments for doing this are widely used in scientific laboratories and for control of industrial processes. They are called **pH meters**.

140. DRY CELLS AND STORAGE BATTERIES

In this section we shall describe two familiar voltaic cells—the dry cell, used in flashlights and portable radios, and the lead storage battery, used in automobiles. The dry cell is an example of a primary cell, the lead storage cell an example of a secondary cell. Primary cells are voltaic cells in which the chemical changes occurring are for practical purposes irreversible. In the Daniell cell, for instance, once all the zinc is dissolved the cell is useless. Secondary cells are those which may be recharged an indefinite number of times.

A battery is, strictly speaking, several voltaic cells connected together.

The dry cell is dry only by comparison. It would not operate if it were free from moisture. The active material consists of a moist paste rather than of a liquid. The cell consists of a carbon rod which serves as the positive electrode; this is surrounded by a mixture of manganese dioxide and graphite, which is in turn surrounded by a wet paste of ammonium chloride often mixed with flour or starch. The whole is enclosed in a zinc container which serves as the negative electrode. Zinc chloride and mercuric chloride are added to the paste to improve the operation and life of the cell. The graphite serves to increase the electrical conductivity of the manganese dioxide mixture.

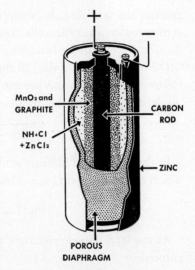

Fig. 20-8. Dry cell.

The chemical reactions taking place during operation of the dry cell are not perfectly understood but are believed to be approximately as follows: Zinc goes into solution, the liberated electrons imparting a negative charge to the zinc metal container.

$$Zn \rightarrow Zn^{+2} + 2\epsilon$$

The ammonium ions react with the manganese dioxide, yielding ammonia, and leaving the manganese with a valence of $+3$, perhaps in the form of $MnOOH$, or possibly as $ZnO \cdot Mn_2O_3$.

$$2NH_4^+ + 2MnO_2 + 2\epsilon \rightarrow 2NH_3 + 2MnOOH$$

The electrons necessary for this reaction come from the carbon rod, which thereby acquires a positive charge. The ammonia may combine with zinc ions, forming the complex ion, $Zn(NH_3)_4^{+2}$.

The voltage delivered by a dry cell of the above type is about 1.5 to 1.6 volts. Owing to an effect known as *polarization,* the voltage drops rapidly if large currents are withdrawn from the cell. But the cell recovers its voltage if allowed to stand. Dry cells are, therefore, most satisfactory for intermittent use.

In its simplest form the lead storage cell consists of a sheet of lead and a sheet of lead dioxide, PbO_2, placed in moderately dilute sulfuric acid. In practice the lead dioxide is supported on a sheet or grid of lead. In most commercially available cells there are several layers of lead and of lead dioxide, kept apart by insulating strips called separators.

During discharge of the cell the lead electrode tends to form lead ions, the electrons liberated in this process imparting a negative charge to the remaining lead. This forms the negative pole of the cell.

$$Pb \rightarrow Pb^{+2} + 2\epsilon$$

In the presence of sulfuric acid the lead ions form insoluble lead sulfate, which deposits, in part, as a white substance on the metallic lead.

$$Pb^{+2} + SO_4^= \rightarrow PbSO_4$$

At the lead dioxide electrode the lead with an oxidation state of $+4$ is reduced to $+2$.

$$PbO_2 + 2\epsilon + 4H^+ \rightarrow Pb^{+2} + 2H_2O$$

The hydrogen ions shown in this reaction come, of course, from the sulfuric acid. The electrons necessary to reduce Pb^{+4} to Pb^{+2} come from the lead

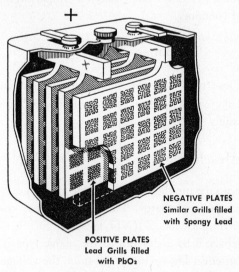

+

NEGATIVE PLATES
Similar Grills filled
with Spongy Lead

POSITIVE PLATES
Lead Grills filled
with PbO₂

Fig. 20-9. Storage cell.

dioxide electrode, imparting to it a positive charge. In the reaction at this electrode the lead ions formed combine with sulfate ions from the sulfuric acid.

$$Pb^{+2} + SO_4^{=} \rightarrow PbSO_4$$

Combining these equations we may write for the reaction taking place at the negative pole during discharge:

$$Pb + H_2SO_4 \rightarrow PbSO_4 + 2H^+ + 2\epsilon$$

and at the positive pole:

$$PbO_2 + 2\epsilon + H_2SO_4 + 2H^+ \rightarrow PbSO_4 + 2H_2O$$

the reaction at the negative pole gives up electrons, that at the positive pole takes up electrons.

We may now write one equation to represent the overall reaction in the lead storage cell during discharge. This equation is as follows:

$$Pb + PbO_2 + 2H_2SO_4 \rightarrow 2PbSO_4 + 2H_2O$$

Notice that this is a rather straightforward case of oxidation and reduction, with one surprising difference. The difference is that the reducing agent, Pb, and the oxidizing agent, PbO_2, are never in actual contact during the reaction. The transfer of electrons occurs, not by direct action from one substance to the other, but through the action of the electric current, which is, of course, itself a flow of electrons.

We turn now to the chemical reactions taking place during charging of the cell. To do this an external source of electricity is connected with negative pole to negative electrode and positive to positive. Electrons flow into the cell in the opposite direction from that during discharge. The chemical reactions taking place are exactly the opposite from those occurring during discharge. The lead ions at the negative pole are reduced to metallic lead. Those at the positive pole are oxidized to lead dioxide. The over-all equation for charging is exactly the reverse of that for discharge. We may, therefore, write

$$Pb + PbO_2 + 2H_2SO_4 \underset{\text{charge}}{\overset{\text{discharge}}{\rightleftarrows}} 2PbSO_4 + 2H_2O$$

One or two other points may be mentioned. The reactions taking place in the cell are not too well understood. This is especially true of the reactions of the lead dioxide. It may be that the equations given are oversimplified. Another point is that sulfuric acid is used up during discharge, and regenerated during charge. Sulfuric acid has a considerably higher density than water. Consequently, hydrometer (density) measurements are commonly made to determine how nearly charged a cell may be. At full charge the density is about 1.29 g. per cc. The cell, when fully charged, delivers a potential of slightly over 2 volts. The ordinary automobile battery delivers 6 volts but this is because three cells, each of several plates, are connected in series. The capacity in ampere-hours depends on the size of the battery, and may be quite large. Starting a car on a cold day may momentarily draw several hundred amperes.

The storage battery is a remarkably compact source of energy. It has numerous uses in addition to its use in automobiles. For instance, storage batteries are used in trucks for handling freight and material in warehouses and factories, in mining operations, submarines, switchboards, railway signaling, telephones, and for emergency lighting operations. The downtown sections of some large cities are supplied with great battery installations to take care of peak loads and emergencies. The annual production of batteries in the world runs into tens of millions.

EXERCISES

A. *Define or explain the following:*

ampere	half reaction
anode	kilowatt hour
cathode	metallic conduction
coulomb	pH meter
current efficiency (in electrolysis)	primary cell
electrolysis (electrolytic conduction)	secondary cell
electromotive series	single electrode potential
EMF	solution pressure
equivalent weight (combining weight)	standard hydrogen electrode
external circuit	volt
faraday (of electricity)	voltaic cell
half cell	watt

B. 1. State Faraday's law.
   2. Describe fully how electricity is carried through (a) fused sodium chloride, and (b) a water solution of sodium chloride. Show all reactions at each electrode.
   3. Show how nickel electroplating is done.
   4. With the aid of labeled diagrams show the construction of the following, and write equations for the reactions involved at each electrode: (a) Daniell cell, (b) dry cell, and (c) storage cell.
   5. What in general terms is the relationship between voltage produced in a cell and the activity of the elements? Illustrate the answer with a specific example and electrode reactions.

6. With the aid of a labeled diagram describe: (a) a zinc half cell, (b) a hydrogen half cell, (c) a complete zinc-hydrogen cell, showing direction of electrons in the external circuit.

C. 1. Find the equivalent weight of iron in the oxide, Fe_2O_3.
2. A current of 10 amperes is passed consecutively through the following: (a) a solution of $AgNO_3$, (b) a solution of $CuSO_4$, (c) a solution of H_2SO_4. What weight of silver and of copper will be deposited, and what volume of hydrogen and of oxygen (S.C.) will be liberated (in the H_2SO_4 cell)? The current flows for 1 hour.
3. Assuming 80 per cent efficiency (that is, that 20 per cent of the electricity is wasted), find the number of amperes necessary to produce 2.0 gram-atoms of aluminum from Al_2O_3 in 10 hours.
4. A current of electricity deposits 5.50 g. of copper in 20 minutes. What volume of chlorine (S.T.P.) will be produced simultaneously at the anode if the electrolyte is $CuCl_2$?
5. If a copper refinery produced 400 tons of metallic copper per day with a current efficiency of 95 per cent, what total amperage is required?
6. What weight of water could be decomposed by passing a current of 10.5 amperes through dilute sulfuric acid for 1 hour?
7. What general type of chemical reaction may be used for the production of electricity? Take an example, other than one of those described in the text, and show how it could be utilized.
8. What factor determines the total quantity of electricity obtainable from a voltaic cell?
9. In a zinc-copper cell the copper is positive, but in a copper-gold cell the copper is negative. Explain.
10. Does reduction take place at the positive or the negative pole (a) during electrolysis, (b) in a voltaic cell?
11. If a small dry cell costing 40 cents has a useful capacity of about 1 ampere for 1 hour of total use, and the voltage averages 1.4 volts, compare the cost of electrical energy per kilowatt hour with the cost of about 12 cents per kilowatt hour in a large city.
12. Of what two half reactions could each of the following reactions be considered to consist?
   a. $2H_2O + 2Cl_2 \rightleftarrows 4HCl + O_2$ (recall that HCl is virtually completely ionized).
   b. $2H_2O + 2Na \rightleftarrows H_2 + 2NaOH$ (NaOH is a strong base).
   c. $Zn + 2HCl \rightleftarrows ZnCl_2 + H_2$ (ZnCl₂ is completely ionized).
   d. $Cl_2 + 2KI \rightleftarrows I_2 + 2KCl$ (KI and KCl are completely ionized).
13. Find the voltage developed in each of the following voltaic cells ($1M$ solutions):
   a. $Mg \mid Mg^{++} \parallel Zn^{++} \mid Zn$
   b. $Cu \mid Cu^{++} \parallel Au^+ \mid Au$
   c. $Fe \mid Fe^{++} \parallel Ag^+ \mid Ag$
   d. $H_2 \mid H^+ \parallel Hg_2^{++} \mid Hg$

14. Write half reactions for each of the cells in Exercise No. 13. Write complete reaction equations, and state which electrode is positive.

15. Diagram the cell $Ni \mid Ni^{++} \parallel Hg^{++} \mid Hg$ and show which direction the electrons would flow in the external circuit between nickel and mercury.

16. For the cell of Exercise No. 15 find (a) the voltage (for $1M$ solutions of ions), (b) the effect on the cell voltage of raising the Ni^{++} concentration, and (c) the effect on the voltage of raising the Hg^{++} ion concentration.

17. A voltaic cell is made up of manganese metal in contact with Mn^{++} ions, and chlorine gas in contact with Cl^- ions.

   a. diagram the cell showing which direction the electrons flow in the external circuit, and write equations for the half reactions.
   b. write an equation for the complete reaction and show the cell voltage.
   c. indicate the effect on the cell voltage of lowering the Mn^{++} ion concentration.
   d. indicate the effect on the cell voltage of lowering the Cl^- ion concentration.
   e. indicate the effect of substituting the (I^-, I_2) half cell for the (Cl^-, Cl_2) half cell on the cell voltage.
   f. indicate the probable effect of raising the chlorine gas pressure.

18. It will be recalled that the formula weight of any substance expressed as grams is called a mole of that substance. Thus a mole of silver (Ag) weighs 107.880 g. The number of atoms of silver in a mole is extraordinarily large. This number is known as Avogadro's number.

   To deposit 107.880 g. of silver by electricity requires 96,500 coulombs. The electric charge on a single electron is known from experiments in physics to be about 1.6×10^{-19} coulombs. With this information calculate Avogadro's number.

HEAVY METALS I

Gold is for the mistress, silver for the maid,
Copper for the craftsman, cunning at his trade;
"Good!" said the Baron, sitting in his hall,
"But iron! Cold iron! is the master of them all."
                                        —Kipling

																H	He
Li	Be	B											C	N	O	F	Ne
Na	Mg	Al											Si	P	S	Cl	A
K	Ca	Sc	Ti	V	Cr	Mn	**Fe**	**Co**	**Ni**	**Cu**	Zn	Ga	Ge	As	Se	Br	Kr
Rb	Sr	Y	Zr	Nb	Mo	Tc	Ru	Rh	Pd	**Ag**	Cd	In	Sn	Sb	Te	I	Xe
Cs	Ba	La-Lu	Hf	Ta	W	Re	Os	Ir	Pt	**Au**	Hg	Tl	Pb	Bi	Po	At	Rn
Fr	Ra	Ac	Th	Pa	U-												

This chapter and the next will be devoted to certain elements of a class often known as **heavy metals.** The term "heavy" in this case refers partly to the comparatively high density of these elements, and partly to their moderate or low chemical activity as compared with the metals already discussed. About a dozen of the heavy metals will be described.

141. OCCURRENCE OF IRON

The ancient Egyptian, Assyrian, Sumerian, and Hebrew names for iron all signify "the metal from heaven," thus indicating an early knowledge of meteorites. The widespread distribution of iron in the earth's crust has been mentioned in an earlier chapter. Iron makes up about 5 per cent of the earth's crust. There is considerable evidence to show that the interior of the earth consists in large part of iron, and its occurrence in meteorites and, in fact, throughout the known universe has been amply demonstrated. Our discussion in this section will be limited to commercial deposits of iron ores.

Although iron is to be found in soil and rocks nearly everywhere, yet this does not mean that an iron mine may be located anywhere. On the contrary, many factors operate to decide whether a given deposit of iron is to be considered a practicable source of the metal. These factors include the chemical state of the iron, the physical state of the mineral, the accessibility, the cost of transportation, of labor, of coal and limestone, and of many others, many of them being economic factors rather than chemical or engineering problems.

The fact that minerals occur in workable deposits is, of course, due to geological influences. Chemical changes often result in the transport and deposition of valuable minerals. Furthermore, the action of waves, of the wind, and of heat and cold often produce great alterations in the extent to which specific minerals are deposited in certain places. However these forces operate, it must be said that their results have a profound effect on the economy of the nations. All the great industrial nations are those which have an abundant supply of iron ore and coal.

Iron forms three oxides, FeO, Fe_2O_3, and Fe_3O_4. The second and third occur in nature as iron ores. They are called, respectively, **hematite** and **magnetite.** Hematite forms dark gray or black crystals, but it readily adds water to form the hydrate known as *limonite,* the formula of which is often written $2Fe_2O_3 \cdot 3H_2O$. Limonite is a soft substance, reddish-brown in color. Magnetite is a fairly hard, black substance. It is strongly magnetic. Naturally magnetized samples have long been referred to as lodestones.*

Other minerals used as iron ores include **siderite,** $FeCO_3$, and **pyrite,** FeS_2. The latter is the substance known as "fool's gold." It burns in air, leaving a residue of iron oxide. Pyrite is used in the manufacture of sulfuric acid. The iron oxide by-product is used to a small extent in iron production.

By far the most important iron deposits in the world are situated in the **Mesabi Range** of northern Minnesota. This vast deposit has contributed in a vitally important degree to the unparalleled industrial position of the United States. The great steel centers stretching from Chicago to Buffalo could never have been established without the virtually inexhaustible ore reserves of the Mesabi. The transportation of this ore to the smelters has made the Duluth-Superior harbor one of the most active in the world. During the open season of about seven months on the Great Lakes, an ore-laden boat leaves every hour, day and night. Over a billion tons of ore have been taken from the Mesabi, about a billion tons of high grade ore remain, and the supply of lower grades of ore seems to be inexhaustible.

The minerals of the Mesabi were deposited in an ocean bed long geological ages ago. Since that time the ocean has disappeared and the mineral deposit

---

* In the Vedas, the most ancient book of the Hindus, lodestone is referred to as *Chumbuk,* or "kissing stone."

has been raised up at an angle and partly covered with slate. Successive ice ages have partly uncovered the minerals, then partly recovered them with sand and gravel. The minerals were apparently originally mixed with sand, but the action of water has removed most of the silica in certain regions. The best grade of ore is almost pure iron oxide. It is only a few feet below the surface. Mining is therefore done by open cuts, the largest of which is

Fig. 21-1. Mining iron ore by the open-pit method in the iron range at Hibbing, Minnesota. (*Ewing Galloway*)

at Hibbing. This, the Hull-Rust mine, reminds visitors of the Grand Canyon. The mine is 2½ miles long and ¾ mile wide. It ranks with Hoover Dam and the Panama Canal as one of the most spectacular engineering activities of all time.

Many iron ores are improved before smelting by a process known as **beneficiation.** This may consist of an alteration of physical or chemical properties in such a way that the ore is more efficiently and cheaply convertible to pig iron. Beneficiation may be simply a mechanical process of screening, crushing, or briquetting. On the other hand, the beneficiation may consist of a chemical process such as roasting in either an oxidizing or a reducing atmosphere. An example of how beneficiation may be used is in the concentration of iron oxide in ore not rich enough in iron for the usual procedures. The ore may be roasted under reducing conditions to convert the ferric oxide to magnetite.

$$6Fe_2O_3 + C \rightarrow 4Fe_3O_4 + CO_2$$

Moderate temperatures and comparatively little expenditure for coke are necessary to bring about this change. But when the iron has been converted to magnetite, it may very easily and inexpensively be concentrated by magnetic separators. The magnetite is, of course, strongly attracted to a magnet, while worthless residues such as silica and silicates are not attracted. The magnetic separators cannot be used on ferric oxide before it is converted to magnetite because ferric oxide is not appreciably attracted to a magnet.

142. PIG IRON

Iron is made by reducing iron oxide in large devices called **blast furnaces.** These are towers about 100 feet high and 25 feet wide. The furnace is charged from the top with alternate layers of iron ore, coke, and limestone. Preheated air is forced into the bottom of the furnace through tubes called tuyères. At the bottom of the furnace there is a space for the collection of molten iron, which is, from time to time, removed through an opening.

As soon as the heated air enters the blast furnace it combines with the coke, forming carbon monoxide. It is not improbable that this reaction goes through two steps, the initial product being carbon dioxide which is then reduced to the monoxide.

$$C + O_2 \rightarrow CO_2$$

$$CO_2 + C \rightarrow 2CO$$

Carbon monoxide is a good reducing agent and, being a gas, it very easily permeates through the lumps of iron oxide. The products of reaction between ferric oxide and carbon monoxide are iron and carbon dioxide.

$$Fe_2O_3 + 3CO \rightarrow 2Fe + 3CO_2$$

The carbon dioxide formed in this reaction may further be reduced by coming in contact with coke again, and in fact a considerable number of reactions take place, other than those for which equations have been given. Most of these reactions are reversible and various equilibria are established in various portions of the furnace. The temperature of the furnace ranges from 1400° C. near the bottom to about 200° C. at the top.

After the iron oxide is reduced to metallic iron, another reaction takes place, with a small part of the iron combining with carbon to form iron carbide, or **cementite,** the formula for which is Fe_3C. This substance dis-

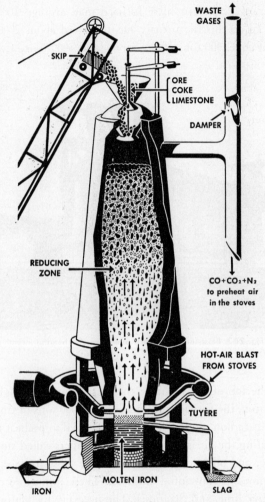

Fig. 21-2. Blast furnace.

solves in the iron to the extent of several per cent. The iron carbide is important because it lowers the melting point of the iron from about 1550° down to about 1150°. Near the bottom of the blast furnace the temperature is high enough to melt this dilute solution of iron carbide dissolved in iron. The molten material flows down to the bottom of the blast furnace and is removed from time to time. As the iron oxide is used up fresh charge is added from the top of the furnace. The molten iron is cast into bars and is known as "pig iron.". Pig iron contains about 92 to 94 per cent of iron. The other substances are carbon and traces of the various impurities present in the blast-furnace charge.

The capacity of a modern blast furnace may average 1000 tons of pig iron per day. To do this the furnace has to be fed about 2000 tons of iron ore, 900 tons of coke, 400 tons of limestone, and 3000 tons of air. The solids

Fig. 21-3. Blast furnace (right), and stoves for heating incoming air.

are added at the top of the furnace; the air is blown through the tuyères. In addition to iron, the furnace produces about 4000 tons of combustible gas, most of which is carbon monoxide. This gas is used to preheat the air for the tuyères. Preheating the air is done in large chambers called **stoves.**

The iron ore, and other materials, put in the blast furnace all bring impurities, sometimes in substantial amounts. These impurities consist largely of silica, alumina, lime, and magnesia. The necessity for getting rid of these substances is the reason for adding limestone. Taking silica as an example, the purpose of the limestone is to unite with the silica to form a fusible mass, or **slag,** which may be removed from the furnace without too much difficulty. The reaction is the familiar one of a basic substance reacting with an acidic substance.

$$CaCO_3 + SiO_2 \rightarrow CaSiO_3 + CO_2$$
$$\text{\small slag}$$

Calcium silicate and other substances formed during these reactions run down and float on the surface of the molten iron. As they accumulate they are allowed to flow out from time to time. The slag so obtained is not infrequently used for making cement.

Fig. 21-4. Aerial view of a blast-furnace assembly. Near the center of the picture there are two blast furnaces separated by a row of eight stoves (and a tall stack). Behind the furnaces there are large storage yards partly filled with iron ore (dark) and limestone (light). An ore ship is unloading in the canal.

143. STEEL

Iron which is nearly free from impurities such as sulfur, phosphorus, and silicon, but which contains small, definite percentages of carbon, is known as steel. The hardness and tensile strength of steel depend on the percentage of carbon present and on how the carbon is united with the iron. The distribution and mode of combination of the carbon may be altered by heating the steel, then cooling it rapidly or slowly, according to the particular properties desired. This operation is called *tempering*. If the carbon content of the steel is below 0.2 per cent, the product is mild steel, which is quite ductile. Rails and structural steel are made from medium steel, which contains between 0.2 and 0.6 per cent of carbon. Steels which contain up to 1.5 per cent of carbon may be made very hard by tempering and are used for razor blades and surgical instruments.

The chemical reactions involved in steel making are as follows: first, the pig iron is purified until it consists of little but pure iron; and second, proper amounts of carbon are added, generally in the form of iron-carbon alloys. Other substances are often added to aid in purifying the iron.

The **open-hearth process** consists of a furnace in which the pig iron charge is heated. The pig iron is placed in a shallow container holding 50 to 100 tons. Heat is supplied by burning gas or oil and the furnace is so designed that heat is directed down toward the charge from the top, or dome, of the

Fig. 21-5. Open hearth furnace.

furnace. The spent gases, containing oxidation products, are forced through a checkerwork of bricks which are thereby strongly heated. After an interval the direction of the gases is reversed, so that the hot bricks are used to heat the incoming air and other gases. In this manner, known as the Siemens regenerative process, a considerable saving of fuel is effected.

The chemical process occurring in the open-hearth furnace is an oxidation of impurities or a combination of impurities in such a way that they may be removed from the iron. Hematite is often added to the charge to give added oxygen for oxidizing impurities. Rusty iron serves the same purpose because iron rust is essentially iron oxide. This is the chief reason why iron scrap was so thoroughly collected during the World Wars.

Removal of impurities from the charge in the open-hearth process requires several hours. This allows ample time for testing of the iron. When practically all the carbon has been burned out, the proper amounts of carbon are introduced in the form of coke or as carbon-iron alloy. At the same time manganese or titanium may be added. These elements, and some others, have the effect of removing air bubbles which otherwise would make holes in the finished steel, thus weakening it. Sometimes alloys combining carbon and manganese are used for adding to the iron in the open hearth at the proper time. Examples of such alloys are ferromanganese and spiegeleisen. Substances used for removing air bubbles in steel are called scavengers or deoxidizers.

Open-hearth steel is used for a multitude of purposes, such as girders, armor plate, and rails. The fact that the process goes rather slowly is an advantage in that accurate control by analysis is possible throughout the whole operation. Another process widely used, especially in earlier steel-making days in the United States, is the Bessemer process in which the impurities are burned out by a blast of air. The Bessemer process is rapid, but it is not possible to control the quality of steel produced, at least as compared with the open-hearth. Other methods of steel production include the electric furnace and the crucible steel process. These methods are used for the production of steel for special purposes.

Ordinary steels contain only carbon in addition to iron. **Alloy steels,** which are of great importance, contain other elements in addition to iron and carbon. Among alloy steels the more important include manganese steel, chrome-vanadium steel, nickel steel, and chromium steel. These, as a rule, contain several per cent of the element indicated. They have special properties such as great resistance to wear, great toughness, or hardness, as the case may be. **Stainless steel,** which is very popular for its appearance and resistance to rusting, contains quite large percentages of chromium. For instance, "18-8"—or Allegheny metal—contains 18 per cent chromium and 8 per cent nickel, the remainder being low-carbon steel. But these examples are only a very few of the wide variety of special steels which are available for many different purposes.

144. IRON AND IRON COMPOUNDS

Pure metallic iron is a silvery-white metal, with a melting point of 1535° C. Iron is one of several metals which have the property of ferromagnetism; that is, it is strongly attracted by a magnet. Iron is a moderately active metal. It reacts vigorously with most acids, liberating hydrogen.

$$Fe + 2HCl \rightarrow FeCl_2 + H_2$$

Finely powdered iron burns in oxygen and sometimes spontaneously ignites in air. The product is magnetic oxide of iron, Fe_3O_4.

$$3Fe + 2O_2 \rightarrow Fe_3O_4$$

The same oxide is formed when iron is heated in steam.

$$3Fe + 4H_2O \rightarrow Fe_3O_4 + 4H_2$$

Very pure iron does not react very rapidly with air at ordinary temperatures, but ordinary iron or steel quickly corrodes in moist air. The product of corrosion, ordinary **rust,** is a hydrated form of ferric oxide, for which no definite formula can be given other, perhaps, than $Fe_2O_3 \cdot xH_2O$.

In our discussion of the important nonmetals such as sulfur, nitrogen, and chlorine it was pointed out that these elements show several different valences in different compounds. Thus sulfur has oxidation states of $+4$ and of $+6$ respectively in the oxides SO_2 and SO_3. Iron is the first metal we have discussed which shows a very pronounced tendency toward variable valence. Iron shows at least two oxidation states, $+2$ and $+3$, known as the *ferrous* and the *ferric* states respectively. The compound $FeCl_2$ is ferrous chloride; $FeCl_3$ is ferric chloride. These two valences are readily interconvertible by appropriate oxidizing or reducing agents.

As previously pointed out, when iron is dissolved in hydrochloric acid, the products are hydrogen and ferrous chloride. So long as excess iron is present, the ferrous chloride is stable, but if the iron is removed and the solution comes in contact with air, oxidation rapidly forms ferric chloride, or ferric hydroxide, depending on whether the solution contains excess acid or not.

Other ferrous compounds of interest include the sulfide, FeS, formed by direct union of iron and sulfur,

$$Fe + S \rightarrow FeS$$

or by precipitation from a basic solution, as follows:

$$Fe(OH)_2 + H_2S \rightarrow FeS + 2H_2O$$

Ferrous sulfide is a black solid from which hydrogen sulfide is obtained by action of a dilute acid.

$$FeS + 2HCl \rightarrow FeCl_2 + H_2S$$

This is a common laboratory preparation method for hydrogen sulfide.

Among the ferric series of compounds the oxide Fe_2O_3 is, of course, the well-known ore of iron. In the laboratory, ferric oxide may be prepared by precipitating ferric hydroxide, then heating the hydroxide to drive off water.

$$Fe_2(SO_4)_3 + 6NH_4OH \rightarrow 2Fe(OH)_3 + 3(NH_4)_2SO_4$$

$$2Fe(OH)_3 \rightarrow Fe_2O_3 + 3H_2O$$

Ferric oxide is a reddish-brown substance. The color depends on how finely powdered the compound is obtained. Some varieties are bright red. The pigment **Venetian red** is ferric oxide. It is used in painting bridges, barns, and similar outdoor structures. **Rouge** is a specially purified form of ferric oxide.

Ferric hydroxide is a brown gelatinous substance formed as indicated above. It seems to be responsible for the brown color found in many iron compounds. The ferric ion, Fe^{+3}, seems to be pale green or nearly colorless, but this is rarely observed because of the ever-present hydroxide formed through hydrolysis or other cause. Ferric hydroxide has a tendency to form a colloid. If a few drops of ferric chloride are placed in boiling water, an intense reddish-brown color is developed. This is due to ferric hydroxide colloid formed by hydrolysis.*

$$FeCl_3 + 3H_2O \rightarrow Fe(OH)_3 + 3HCl$$

Magnetite, Fe_3O_4, or magnetic oxide of iron, is a peculiar compound in which part of the iron has an oxidation state of $+2$ and part of $+3$. The formula of this compound ought perhaps to be written $FeO \cdot Fe_2O_3$. The FeO may be replaced by other oxides in which the metal atom has a valence of $+2$. Examples are $MgOFe_2O_3$, and $CuOFe_2O_3$. Furthermore, the Fe_2O_3 may be replaced by other oxides in which the metal atom has a valence of $+3$. Examples are $MgOAl_2O_3$ and $ZnOCr_2O_3$. Such substances are not infrequently written as $MgAl_2O_4$, and $ZnCr_2O_4$. These are often called magnesium aluminate and zinc chromite, respectively. All these substances crystallize in the same form; some of them are important minerals. This class of chemical compound is called a **spinel.**

Iron has important physiological functions. **Hemoglobin,** the red coloring matter of the blood, contains iron. The element, in various compounds, has medical applications in the treatment of some types of anemia.

145. COBALT AND NICKEL

These elements which are adjacent to iron in the eighth group of the Periodic Table are by no means unimportant, although very much less important than iron. The chief producer of cobalt is the Belgian Congo. Most nickel comes from Ontario, in Canada. Cobalt and nickel resemble iron, but are less subject to corrosion. Both share with iron the property of being strongly attracted to a magnet.

Cobalt is used in the production of special alloy steels. These, as a rule, have the properties of hardness and resistance to corrosion, and the ability

* While chemists often write the formula for ferric hydroxide as $Fe(OH)_3$, there is considerable evidence that it is actually an oxide hydrate, and perhaps should be written $Fe_2O_3 \cdot xH_2O$.

to maintain these properties at high temperatures. High-speed tools and surgical instruments are often made of cobalt alloys. Cobalt also is used in several types of magnets and magnet cores. Cobalt metal and its compounds have important applications in catalysis. This is especially true in connection with the production of synthetic gasoline. Cobaltous oxide, CoO, is used to give a deep blue color to glass.

Most metallic nickel is used in the manufacture of alloy steels. Large amounts are also used in nickel plating. Nickel may be electroplated from an ammoniacal solution which contains the complex ion $Ni(NH_3)_6^{+2}$, or possibly $Ni(NH_3)_4^{+2}$. Nickel plate takes a high polish and was at one time very popular, but chromium plate has displaced nickel for many purposes. However, chromium is often electroplated over a layer of nickel. This combination gives a more permanent finish than does chromuim plate alone.

Nickel is used extensively in catalysis. Finely divided nickel is very frequently used to catalyze a type of reaction known as **hydrogenation.** Hydrogenation is the chemical addition of hydrogen to a substance (such as cottonseed oil) so as to make an edible solid fat.

Many useful alloys contain nickel. These include Allegheny metal (a stainless steel), monel metal, permalloy, German silver, and nichrome. Nickel coins contain copper-nickel alloy.

The only common valence of nickel is the $+2$ state. Familiar compounds are the oxide, NiO, the sulfide, NiS, and the sulfates, $NiSO_4$ and $NiSO_4 \cdot 6H_2O$. Nickel salts are, in general, green in color. Like other elements nearby in the Periodic Table, nickel has to a considerable degree the ability to form complex ions, of which the nickel ammonia complexes indicated above are examples.

146. COPPER

The name "copper" is derived from the Latin word *cuprum,* which refers to its production by the Romans in the island of Cyprus. The metal has been known since prehistoric times. Copper is found abundantly as the metal in the Lake Superior region, and in Arizona and New Mexico. Extensive ore deposits occur in Utah, Montana, Nevada, and in Canada, Mexico, South America, Siberia, and other parts of the world. The principal ores are *chalcocite* (Cu_2S), *chalcopyrite* ($CuFeS_2$), and *cuprite* (Cu_2O).

We shall limit our discussion of the metallurgy of copper to treatment of a sulfide ore such as chalcocite. The raw ore is processed first to eliminate worthless material. This preliminary treatment may take the form of crushing and shaking, washing, or of oil flotation. **Oil flotation** is a process, widely used, in which the crushed ore is thoroughly mixed with a froth of air bubbles in water to which a small amount of an oil has been added. The process depends on the fact that some mineral surfaces are more "wettable" than others by such an oil-water mixture. Those particles which are wetted by the liquid fall to the bottom of the vessel, while those not wetted cling to the air bubbles and are thus buoyed up to the top of the container where they are easily removed. In this way an efficient separation of valuable mineral from worthless material is easily and cheaply achieved. It should be emphasized that the process does not depend on the relative density of valuable and worthless materials, but rather on how effectively each is wetted by the oil-water froth.

The second step in the treatment of copper sulfide ores is roasting. The ore is strongly heated in air. This converts part, but not all, of the copper sulfide to copper oxide. The reaction, and those that follow, are complex but are reasonably well represented by the following equations.

$$2Cu_2S + 3O_2 \rightarrow 2Cu_2O + 2SO_2$$

Part of the copper sulfide must remain unchanged for success of the following operations.

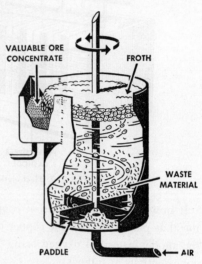

Fig. 21-6. Enrichment of ore by oil flotation.

The third step in copper production is smelting. The treated ore is heated with limestone, $CaCO_3$. This removes silica as a slag, which floats on top of the melted copper oxide-sulfide mixture.

$$SiO_2 + CaCO_3 \rightarrow CaSiO_3 + CO_2$$

The fourth step is the actual reduction of the copper sulfide-oxide mixture to metallic copper. The mixture is strongly heated in a converter not unlike the Bessemer converter used in steel production. The process is called *bessemerizing*. Air is blown into the molten mass and the reaction which takes place may be represented as follows:

$$Cu_2S + 2Cu_2O \rightarrow 6Cu + SO_2$$

The molten copper is generally poured out into slabs for cooling and solidification. The rather impure metal so obtained is called **blister copper** because gases escaping as the metal solidifies give the metal a blistered appearance.

Most copper is further subjected to electrolytic purification. If a solution of copper sulfate, $CuSO_4$, is electrolyzed with the use of platinum electrodes, copper will plate out on the cathode, and oxygen will be liberated at the anode. The reason that copper is deposited at the cathode rather than hydrogen is that copper, being less active, accepts electrons more readily than does hydrogen.

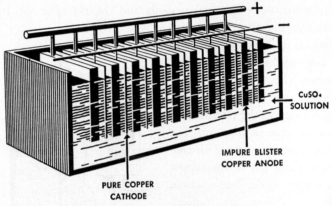

CuSO₄
SOLUTION

IMPURE BLISTER
COPPER ANODE

PURE COPPER
CATHODE

Fig. 21-7. Electrolytic purification of copper.

If now the anode is made of copper rather than of such a very inactive metal as platinum, then the copper metal will lose electrons and dissolve off the anode, instead of oxygen being liberated. The competing processes here are essentially as follows:

$$2O^= \rightarrow O_2 + 2\epsilon$$

and

$$Cu \rightarrow Cu^{++} + 2\epsilon$$

Notice that the anode process is one of oxidation, or loss of electrons, in either case. It is easier for copper to lose electrons than for oxide ions to do so.*

In the electrolytic purification of copper, impure "blister" copper is cast into slabs for use as anodes. Thin sheets of pure copper are used as cathodes. The electrolyte is copper sulfate solution acidified with sulfuric acid. Copper dissolves away from the anode in the form of copper ions. Copper deposits on the cathode according to the reaction, $Cu^{+2} + 2\epsilon \rightarrow Cu$. The electrolyte gains copper ions and loses copper ions at the same rate; hence it does not appreciably change. Elements present in the anode copper as impurities are of two classes. They are either more active or else less active than

---

* The oxygen in the electrolyte is not, strictly speaking, present as oxide ions but is rather combined in OH^- and $SO_4^=$ ions. This does not affect our argument.

copper. If they are more active they go into solution, forming ions. Zinc will serve as an example, $Zn \rightarrow Zn^{+2} + 2\epsilon$. But at the cathode zinc ions cannot compete with copper ions in the gaining of electrons; the zinc simply remains in the solution as zinc sulfate. From time to time the electrolyte may be removed for recovery of the accumulated zinc. Elements less active than copper do not form ions because they cannot compete with copper in the loss of electrons. As the anode is dissolved away, such less active impurities, of which silver is an example, simply fall to the bottom of the cell as a sludge. This sludge is recovered from time to time for the valuable substances which it may contain. In this way, pure copper, so-called *electrolytic* copper, is obtained.

Copper is a characteristic reddish-brown color. Copper and gold are the only common metals which have other than a silvery or gray appearance. The density of copper is 8.9 grams per cubic centimeter, and the melting point is 1083° C. The metal is a notably good conductor of electricity, and it resists atmospheric corrosion, except for superficial tarnishing, owing to formation of a surface layer of copper oxide. In its physical and chemical properties copper closely resembles nickel, which it follows in the Periodic Table.

Copper does not react with hydrochloric acid or other nonoxidizing acids. But with nitric acid or with hot concentrated sulfuric acid, it reacts to yield reduction products of the corresponding acid together with the appropriate copper salts.

$$3Cu + 8HNO_3 \text{ (mod. dil.)} \rightarrow 3Cu(NO_3)_2 + 2NO + 4H_2O$$

$$Cu + 4HNO_3 \text{ (conc.)} \rightarrow Cu(NO_3)_2 + 2NO_2 + 2H_2O$$

$$Cu + 2H_2SO_4 \text{ (hot conc.)} \rightarrow CuSO_4 + SO_2 + 2H_2O$$

Copper is very widely used in electrical apparatus, especially for wire. For this purpose it combines good electrical conductivity and freedom from extensive corrosion. Other uses include sheets for roofing and for covering ship hulls. Its use in small-value coins is well known. Common silver coins contain several per cent of copper for hardening the silver, which would otherwise be too soft for coinage purposes. Copper is used for making plates for printing text and illustrations in books.

Copper also finds extensive application in alloys besides the silver-copper alloy used in coins as mentioned above. Among the more important alloys are **bronze** (copper, tin, and a little zinc); **brass** (copper, zinc); aluminum bronze (copper, aluminum); and **German silver** (copper, zinc, and nickel).

Copper commonly exhibits two oxidation states, the +1 (cuprous, Cu^+)

state, and the $+2$ (cupric, Cu^{+2}) state. Of these the cupric compounds are by far the more important, and to these our attention will be confined.

Cupric oxide, CuO, is a black solid formed by heating copper in air or oxygen.

$$2Cu + O_2 \rightarrow 2CuO$$

If copper or copper oxide is dissolved in sulfuric acid, there results a solution of cupric sulfate.

$$CuO + H_2SO_4 \rightarrow CuSO_4 + H_2O$$

Crystals of cupric sulfate form with five molecules of water, $CuSO_4 \cdot 5H_2O$. This is a blue substance widely used industrially for a variety of purposes. It is often called blue vitriol. This substance contains the cupric (Cu^{+2}) ion, which in the presence of water is always blue or greenish-blue. However, if blue vitriol is gently heated it loses water, leaving a white powder of anhydrous cupric sulfate.

$$CuSO_4 \cdot 5H_2O \rightleftarrows CuSO_4 + 5H_2O$$

Small concentrations of copper sulfate are added to the water in reservoirs to prevent the growth of algae.

If a base is added to a solution of a cupric salt such as the sulfate or nitrate, there is precipitated a pale blue gelatinous substance called cupric hydroxide. The formula for this substance is $Cu(OH)_2$.

$$CuSO_4 + 2NH_4OH \rightarrow Cu(OH)_2 + (NH_4)_2SO_4$$

$$CuSO_4 + 2NaOH \rightarrow Cu(OH)_2 + Na_2SO_4$$

If now an excess of ammonium hydroxide is added (but not of sodium hydroxide), the pale blue precipitate dissolves and a beautiful dark blue solution appears. This dark blue solution is believed to contain the complex ion $[Cu(NH_3)_4]^{+2}$. Formation of this deep blue color on addition of excess ammonia is a characteristic test for the presence of copper in solution. The copper-ammonia complex is also used in one process for the manufacture of artificial silk.

147. SILVER

Silver has a long history. It was the *argentum* of the Romans, and from this name the symbol Ag is derived. To the alchemists silver was the "moon element" and was given the crescent moon symbol, $\mathbb{D}$.

The element occurs native and in veins of various minerals such as the sulfide, either alone or as double salts with other metals. Much silver is found with lead ores and is mined as a by-product. The principal silver-producing country is Mexico, followed by the United States and Canada. Silver production in Mexico has been little short of phenomenal.*

Of the several processes used for treating different silver ores, the one chosen for presentation is the important recovery of silver from lead. It will be recalled that the mud or slime which accumulates in the electrolytic refining of copper contains valuable elements, of which silver is one. A similar situation exists in the electrolytic refining of lead, which will be described in the following chapter. Silver may, however, be obtained directly from impure lead by the Parkes process.

The **Parkes process** makes use of partition of the silver between two immiscible solvents. It will be recalled that the general principles of partition have been described in connection with the properties of iodine. Iodine may be separated from water by the addition, with shaking, of a substance such as carbon tetrachloride. The carbon tetrachloride does not dissolve in the water, but it dissolves the iodine very effectively, thereby removing most of the iodine from the water.

Impure lead may contain several per cent of silver. It is important to recover the silver, both because of its intrinsic value and because the presence of silver gives undesirable properties to the lead, such as making it too hard for certain purposes. To the molten impure lead there is added a small amount of zinc. The zinc does not dissolve in the lead, but floats as a liquid on top. Silver dissolves preferentially in the zinc. Hence, after suitable agitation, the zinc may be ladled or poured off, taking with it practically all the silver. The zinc and silver are now easily separated by strong heating, which volatilizes the zinc, leaving nearly pure silver. Further purification may, if necessary, be achieved by electrolysis or various other procedures.

The appearance of metallic silver needs no description. The density of the metal is 10.5 g. per cc. and the melting point is 960.5° C. It is the best conductor of heat and electricity of all metals, and it is unparalleled as a reflector for visible light. The metal does not tarnish in pure air, but traces of hydrogen sulfide or other sulfur compounds darken the silver owing to formation of black silver sulfide. It is well known that yolk of egg and rubber bands, both of which contain sulfur, lead to rapid tarnishing of silver. The metal is not attacked by hydrochloric acid, but it rapidly dissolves in warm concentrated nitric acid, yielding silver nitrate, nitrogen dioxide, and water.

---

* Visitors to Taxco or Cuernavaca will have heard the story of how the wealthy Frenchman, de la Borda, offered to pave the streets with silver if the King of Spain would visit him. There is every reason to believe that de la Borda could have made good his offer.

$$Ag + 2HNO_3 \rightarrow AgNO_3 + NO_2 + H_2O$$

Silver metal is used, alloyed with a few per cent of copper, for coins, tableware, jewelry, and household ornaments. **Sterling silver** contains 7.5 per cent copper. Pure silver is too soft for general use, but it finds application in making mirrors.

Silver plate is made by electroplating a thin layer of silver on to a cheaper metal, such as nickel. For this purpose, the object to be plated is hung in a solution of a silver salt. Sodium argenticyanide, $NaAg(CN)_2$, is generally used for this purpose. This object being plated is made the negative pole, and bars or strips of pure silver are hung in the cell as the positive pole. Under proper conditions the silver plate is formed as a smooth adherent coating. This is the method used in the manufacture of large quantities of moderately priced tableware.

Mirrors are silvered by covering the well-cleaned glass surface with a solution from which metallic silver is deposited. A solution often used for silvering contains an ammoniacal solution of silver nitrate, to which is added some mild reducing agent such as formaldehyde or a reducing sugar. The ammoniacal silver nitrate solution is not added to the reducing solution until the mirror is ready to be silvered. When the solutions are mixed, metallic silver is slowly deposited and some of it adheres to the glass. Silver shows, in its compounds, only one important valence, namely that of $+1$. The valence of $+2$, similar to copper is, however, not unknown.

When sodium hydroxide is added to a solution of a silver salt, there is formed an amorphous substance approximating in composition to silver oxide, Ag_2O.

$$2AgNO_3 + 2NaOH \rightarrow Ag_2O + 2NaNO_3 + H_2O$$

This substance acts as a basic oxide and as a good oxidizing agent. It has applications in organic chemistry and as a catalyst.

The addition of hydrochloric acid, or of any soluble source of chloride ions, to a solution of a silver salt results in the immediate precipitation of silver chloride, $AgCl$.

$$AgNO_3 + HCl \rightarrow AgCl + HNO_3$$

Silver chloride is a white, insoluble substance. Similar precipitates are formed by the addition of bromide ions or of iodide ions to a soluble salt. The products in these cases are silver bromide, $AgBr$, and silver iodide, AgI.

$$AgNO_3 + HBr \rightarrow AgBr + HNO_3$$

$$AgNO_3 + HI \rightarrow AgI + HNO_3$$

These substances are even less soluble in water than is silver chloride. The bromide is ivory-colored, the iodide is yellow. These three compounds all have the remarkable property of being photosensitive; that is, they are partially altered and decomposed on being exposed to light. Silver chloride soon changes from white to lavender when it is exposed to bright electric light, or for a few moments to sunlight. This property is the basis of the art of photography, to be described in the next section.

Silver nitrate, the preparation of which has already been mentioned, can be obtained as colorless crystals, very soluble in water. This substance leaves a black stain on skin or clothing, owing to reduction of the silver to the free metal by organic matter. Silver nitrate can give severe burns. It is sometimes called lunar caustic. However, a drop or two of a *very dilute* solution is put into the eyes of newly born babies to prevent a certain type of infection which would, if unchecked, lead to blindness.

Like copper, silver ions have a marked tendency to form complex ions. Thus, if silver chloride is treated with ammonium hydroxide the white precipitate of silver chloride will disappear, owing to formation of silver ammonia complex ions, $Ag(NH_3)_2{}^{+1}$.

$$AgCl + 2NH_4OH \rightarrow Ag(NH_3)_2Cl + 2H_2O$$

The precipitate may be made to reappear if the solution is acidified.

$$Ag(NH_3)_2Cl + 2HNO_3 \rightarrow AgCl + 2NH_4NO_3$$

Under silver in the Periodic Table there will be found the element gold, known to the ancients as *rex metallorum,* king of metals. Gold is one of the least active of metals and it often occurs as the element. Much gold is obtained as a by-product from metallurgical plants producing copper and lead. The appearance of gold is known to all. It is characterized by a brilliant yellow color, high density (19.3 g. per cc.), and a remarkable ductility and malleability. Gold may be beaten into leaves so thin that they are transparent. The element has two oxidation states, $+2$ and $+3$. The compounds have few uses.

148. PHOTOGRAPHY

The art of photography is based upon the photochemical reaction of light on certain silver halides. A photographic film or plate is coated with a sensitive **emulsion** which consists principally of silver bromide mixed in gelatin. The individual grains of silver bromide are so small as to be almost colloidal. Photographic films of different sensitivities may contain varying proportions of silver chloride and silver iodide, together with small amounts of other substances, such as silver sulfide.

When a photographic emulsion is used in a camera, the exposure to light may be for a very small fraction of a second. No visible change takes place on the photographic plate, but some chemical change must take place because the exposed part of the emulsion reacts differently to mild reducing agents than does the unexposed part. What actually takes place during the exposure is not known with any certainty. But it is possible that the action of the light is to reduce a very few silver ions in each tiny silver bromide crystal. The atoms of silver so formed might then serve as nuclei to promote, or catalyze, the more general reduction of the silver which takes place in the developing process.

The exposed film or plate is now placed in a **developing bath.** This consists of a solution containing a mild reducing agent such as hydroquinone. The action is one of reduction, the exposed parts of the silver bromide emulsion being reduced to metallic silver. Indicating the developer simply as a supplier of electrons we might write:

$$Ag^+ + \epsilon \rightarrow Ag^0$$

During this developing process the "picture" becomes visible but in reversed tones: the parts normally being light are dark and vice versa. The reason for this is that the parts of the emulsion receiving most light during exposure are those most easily reduced to metallic silver by the developer. Very finely divided silver, such as is produced during development, is black rather than silvery in appearance.

After the film or plate has been exposed, developed, and washed, it consists in part of an unchanged emulsion of silver bromide plus some finely divided metallic silver. If accidentally exposed to light at this stage, the remaining silver bromide would be affected and the whole emulsion would turn dark, with destruction of the picture. The emulsion, after development, must be treated with a fixing solution which dissolves away the unreduced silver bromide but leaves the metallic silver unchanged. In doing this, use is made of the tendency of the silver ion to form complex ions. The **fixing solution** contains sodium thiosulfate, $Na_2S_2O_3$. This is the substance called **photographer's "hypo."** Sodium thiosulfate forms a soluble complex compound with silver bromide. This is owing to formation of a complex ion, the formula of which may be $[Ag(S_2O_3)_2]^{-3}$. The equation for the reaction is then:

$$AgBr + 2Na_2S_2O_3 \rightarrow Na_3Ag(S_2O_3)_2 + NaBr$$

In this process the unexposed (and undeveloped) silver bromide is washed away as a soluble compound, but the developed metallic silver remains to form the **negative** of the picture.

Formation of a **positive** print involves placing the negative over a piece of paper which has been coated with photographic emulsion. The paper is then briefly exposed to light. The parts of the negative which are covered with metallic silver protect the printing paper from exposure. Thus the tones of the negative are reversed in the print, or positive. After the exposure, the print is developed and fixed in the usual way. The endless ramifications of the art of photography lie beyond the scope of this book. There are innumerable texts on how to be a successful photographer, either amateur or professional. For the theory of the photographic process the reader is referred to more advanced works.*

The action of light on silver halides is an example of a **photochemical change.** Photochemistry is an important branch of chemistry. It might be defined as the study of light and its influence on chemical change. The most important of all photochemical reactions is the photosynthesis of carbohydrates in growing vegetation. This reaction will be described in a later chapter.

EXERCISES

A. *Define or explain the following:*

alloy steel	photographer's hypo
beneficiation (of an ore)	photographic developer
blast furnace	photographic emulsion
blister copper	photographic negative
brass	photographic positive
bronze	pig iron
cementite	pyrite
chalcocite	rouge
electrolytic copper	rust
hematite	stainless steel
hemoglobin	sterling silver
hydrogenation	spinel
oil flotation	steel
open hearth	

B. *Indicate procedures and all equations for the following:*

1. manufacture of pig iron
2. manufacture of steel

*C. E. K. Mees, *The Theory of the Photographic Process* (New York: Macmillan, 1942).

   3. reactions for the formation of ferrous chloride, magnetite, ferrous sulfide,
      ferric hydroxide, ferric oxide
   4. production of electrolytic copper from an ore
   5. use and theory of oil flotation
   6. reaction of copper with nitric acid; with sulfuric acid
   7. formation of ammonia complexes by Cu^{++}, Ni^{++}, and Ag^+
   8. separation of lead and silver by partition
   9. conversion of silver metal to each of the following: $AgNO_3$, Ag_2O, $AgCl$,
      $AgBr$, AgI
  10. reactions involved in developing and in fixing a photographic negative
  11. formation of a silver mirror (Indicate reduction simply by an addition of
      electrons.)

C. 1. Which of the three oxides of iron has the highest percentage of iron?
   2. When attempts are made to form ferric iodide, FeI_3, it immediately de-
      composes into ferrous iodide and iodine. Explain.
   3. Why is it that some rare metals have been known for a long time, while
      some common ones have been known for a much shorter time?
   4. If a copper wire is placed in a solution of silver nitrate there soon appear
      beautiful crystals of metallic silver. Explain.
   5. A water solution of ammonia is thought to contain ammonia, ammonium
      ions, and hydroxide ions. This solution will readily dissolve silver chloride.
      Suggest an experiment which will prove that the solvent action is due to
      ammonia and not due to the ammonium ion.
   6. Write probable equations for each of the following:

      a. $FeCl_2 + Cl_2 \rightarrow$
      b. $Fe_3O_4 + CO \rightarrow$
      c. $Cu(NO_3)_2 \rightarrow NO_2 + O_2 + ?$
      d. $CuO + CH_4 \rightarrow Cu + ? + ?$
      e. $Ag(NH_3)_2{}^+ + H^+ \rightarrow$

   7. Having available the four metals, iron, nickel, copper, and silver, con-
      struct the voltaic cell with the maximum EMF.
   8. There have been recent developments in the use of pure oxygen rather
      than air in the blast furnace. If the object is to *reduce* the iron oxide how
      could pure oxygen be of much help?
   9. In the equation $Cu_2S + 2Cu_2O \rightarrow 6Cu + SO_2$ the copper is reduced, but
      what is the reducing agent?

HEAVY METALS II

																H	He
Li	Be	B											C	N	O	F	Ne
Na	Mg	Al											Si	P	S	Cl	A
K	Ca	Sc	Ti	V	Cr	Mn	Fe	Co	Ni	Cu	Zn	Ga	Ge	As	Se	Br	Kr
Rb	Sr	Y	Zr	Nb	Mo	Tc	Ru	Rh	Pd	Ag	Cd	In	Sn	Sb	Te	I	Xe
Cs	Ba	La-Lu	Hf	Ta	W	Re	Os	Ir	Pt	Au	Hg	Tl	Pb	Bi	Po	At	Rn
Fr	Ra	Ac	Th	Pa	U-												

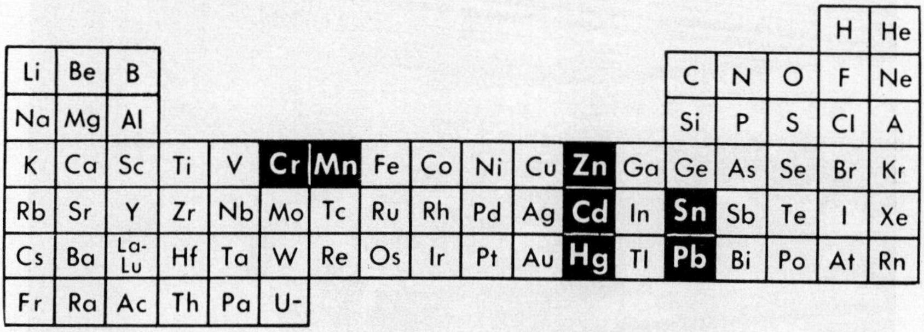

149. ZINC

Zinc probably never occurs in a native state, but is widely distributed in compounds, the chief mineral being the sulfide, ZnS, or *sphalerite*. The element has been found in alloys dating back to ancient times.

When zinc occurs as the sulfide it is first converted to the oxide by roasting in air.

$$2ZnS + 3O_2 \rightarrow 2ZnO + 2SO_2$$

Some zinc, however, occurs as the oxide, so that the roasting step may be eliminated. A considerable quantity of zinc is sold as zinc oxide, so that no other process may be necessary. When the metal itself is required, the zinc oxide must be reduced. There are two ways in which this reduction is achieved industrially. The reducing agent may be carbon, in which case a mixture of the oxide and coke is strongly heated.

$$ZnO + C \rightarrow Zn + CO$$

The escaping carbon monoxide is burned, and the zinc volatilizes into receivers where it is collected as a liquid.

The other process for zinc reduction utilizes electrolysis from a solution of zinc sulfate in water. It is rather surprising that an element standing fairly high in the activity series of the metals can be deposited by electrolysis from a water solution, and the process requires considerable care. The zinc oxide is dissolved in sulfuric acid. The solution is then fed to large tanks containing alternate rows of aluminum cathodes and lead anodes. During electrolysis the zinc deposits on the cathodes from which it is stripped off from time to

Fig. 22-1. Tank room for the electrolytic production of zinc.

time (Fig. 22-2). While the zinc is being deposited the concentration of sulfuric acid in the cells rises.

$$2ZnSO_4 + 2H_2O \text{ (electrolysis)} \rightarrow 2Zn + 2H_2SO_4 + O_2$$

The product at the anode is oxygen, which is allowed to escape. The sulfuric acid thus generated is used for dissolving more zinc oxide, so that little acid has to be added after the process is in operation.

Zinc is a moderately hard metal with a silvery appearance. It has a density of 7.14 g. per cc. and a melting point of only 419.4° C. Extensive use is made of metallic zinc. It is a component of dry cells, being used for the outer casing and negative pole. Large quantities of zinc are used in protecting sheet iron and steel from corrosion. Galvanized iron is iron which is coated with a thin layer of zinc.

Other important uses of zinc include many alloys, of which brass (Cu-Zn) is the most important. Many bronzes also contain zinc.

Zinc has only one oxidation state, that of +2, in its compounds. But the hydroxide of the element has to an unusual degree the property of amphoterism (amphiprotism), or the property of acting as either an acid or a base. The only other element discussed this far which shows a similar degree of amphoterism is aluminum. It will be recalled that aluminum hydroxide may dissolve in an acid as though the aluminum hydroxide were a base. It may also dissolve in bases as though it were an acid.

Zinc oxide, ZnO, is an important article of commerce. It is formed by roasting zinc ores in an excess of air, or by burning finely powdered zinc

Fig. 22-2. Stripping pure electrolytic zinc from the aluminum sheet cathode on which the zinc is deposited during electrolysis.

metal in air. The oxide is white when cold, yellow when hot. It is used as a white pigment, in white-walled automobile tires, in oilcloth, and in rubber goods. Zinc oxide also has some uses in medicine, chiefly in the form of ointments such as calamine lotion.

Zinc hydroxide, $Zn(OH)_2$, is a white substance formed by the addition of a base to a solution of a zinc salt.

$$ZnCl_2 + 2NaOH \rightarrow Zn(OH)_2 + 2NaCl$$

A slight excess of base redissolves the hydroxide owing to formation of a compound often stated to be sodium zincate, Na_2ZnO_2.

$$Zn(OH)_2 + 2NaOH \rightarrow Na_2ZnO_2 + 2H_2O$$

Of course, zinc hydroxide will also dissolve in an acid, such as hydrochloric.

$$Zn(OH)_2 + 2HCl \rightarrow ZnCl_2 + 2H_2O$$

In this case the zinc hydroxide is acting as a base, while in the reaction with sodium hydroxide it is acting as an acid.

Zinc hydroxide will also dissolve in an excess of ammonium hydroxide. The reaction here is not one of zinc hydroxide acting as an acid, but is rather due to formation of the zinc ammonia complex ion, $Zn(NH_3)_4{}^{+2}$. In this respect zinc resembles copper and nickel, among the metals so far studied.

$$Zn(OH)_2 + 4NH_4OH \rightarrow Zn(NH_3)_4(OH)_2 + 4H_2O$$

If hydrogen sulfide is added to an acidified solution of a zinc salt, no reaction occurs. But if the solution contains ammonium hydroxide there is formed a white precipitate of zinc sulfide, ZnS. Zinc sulfide finds extensive use in paints. If zinc sulfate is mixed with barium sulfide the products of reaction are zinc sulfide and barium sulfate, both of which are insoluble in water.

$$ZnSO_4 + BaS \rightarrow ZnS + BaSO_4$$

This mixture, of the two salts, is used as a white pigment under the name **lithopone.** Lithopone does not darken on exposure to hydrogen sulfide or to city air which often contains traces of that gas.

The element cadmium is immediately under zinc in the Periodic Table. In its occurrence, metallurgy, and properties it closely resembles zinc, although it is a little less active. The metal is used as a protective coating on steel, and in alloys. Cadmium hydroxide is not amphoteric, but it does dissolve to form an ammonia complex. Cadmium sulfide, CdS, is widely used as a yellow pigment.

150. MERCURY

This interesting element was known to Aristotle and for many centuries has been an object of prime fascination. It has the almost unique property among metals of being a liquid at ordinary temperatures; hence the ancient name quicksilver, and the Latin name *hydrargyrum* (silver water), from which the symbol Hg is derived. The reasons for the early discovery and use of mercury are not difficult to find. It stands low in the activity series of the metals and is easy to obtain from its ore. This, added to its peculiar properties, and to its fairly abundant occurrence in certain restricted localities, were more than enough to excite the interest of ancient natural philosophers.

Mercury occasionally occurs as the element. But the chief ore is the sulfide, *cinnabar,* HgS. In nature this compound is found as a bright red solid, although as ordinarily prepared in the laboratory the compound is black.

The principal source of mercury since ancient times has been the famous Almaden Mine, in Spain.

Most cinnabar deposits must be enriched by flotation or other processes. But the actual reduction to the metal is easy. The cinnabar is roasted in air. The sulfur combines with oxygen to form sulfur dioxide, and the mercury is set free.

$$HgS + O_2 \rightarrow Hg + SO_2$$

Purification of the mercury is achieved by filtering and by treating it with dilute nitric acid which dissolves more active metals which may be present as impurities. For special laboratory purposes mercury is often dis-

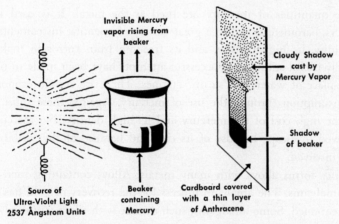

Fig. 22-3. Making the evaporation of mercury visible through the use of ultraviolet light and a fluorescent screen.

tilled to give a product of high purity. It is said that in the time of Pliny (A.D. 23-79) the mercury mines of Spain exported about ten thousand pounds a year. Most of this must have been used in gold mining. The amalgam process for extracting gold has been known for well over two thousand years.

The physical appearance of mercury scarcely needs any description. It is a silvery white liquid, quite stable in air. The melting point is −38.39° C. The element will, therefore, freeze at the lowest winter temperatures found in northern climates. The normal boiling point is 356.9° C. The density of mercury is 13.5 grams per cubic centimeter. This is a rather high density, but by no means as high as gold or platinum. The metal is an excellent conductor of electricity.

Mercury if left in an open dish has scarcely any perceptible tendency to evaporate. Yet its vapor pressure is measurable and amounts at 20° C. to the equivalent of 0.0013 mm. of mercury. The slow evaporation of mercury may be made visible by a very beautiful experiment using ultraviolet light. The vapor of mercury has the property of strongly absorbing light of a definite wave-length, namely, 2537 Ångström units. This light lies far in the ultraviolet and is not visible to the eye, although it can cause severe damage to the unprotected retina. If a source of this light is arranged so that the light falls on a sheet of cardboard coated with anthracene, the anthracene will glow with a greenish luminescence. If now an open beaker containing mercury is placed between the source and the anthracene, part of the ultraviolet light is absorbed by the mercury. This is registered on the anthracene as a shadow. The shadow generally has the appearance of smoke rising slowly from the beaker. By this means the otherwise imperceptible evaporation of mercury is made visible.

Large quantities of mercury are used as the metal. It is used in thermometers, barometers, and in a great variety of scientific instruments where its liquidity, its high density, and its freedom from corrosion make it an extremely useful substance. Successful attempts have been made to use mercury in place of water for "steam" engines. There are certain economies in fuel consumption through the use of mercury. Against these must be balanced the high cost of the mercury and its high density. No mercury may be allowed to escape because of its cost and because of the serious health hazard involved.

Mercury forms alloys with many metals. Alloys containing mercury are called **amalgams.** The amalgam process for the recovery of gold has already been mentioned. Some amalgams, such as that with silver, are used in dentistry.

While mercury is stable in air at ordinary temperatures, yet it combines with oxygen if heated. It will be recalled that the classical researches of Lavoisier, in which he established the nature of combustion, and the composition of air, involved converting mercury to mercuric oxide.

$$2Hg + O_2 \rightleftarrows 2HgO$$

The reaction is slow, and the product floats on the mercury as a red powder. If, as is well known, the mercuric oxide is more strongly heated, it decomposes. The reaction is, therefore, reversible.

Hydrochloric acid is without action on mercury, but nitric acid dissolves it with the formation of mercuric nitrate.

$$3Hg + 8HNO_3 \rightarrow 3Hg(NO_3)_2 + 2NO + 4H_2O$$

Mercury has two series of compounds. In one of these, the mercuric, it clearly has the oxidation state of $+2$, as shown above for mercuric nitrate. For the other series the mercury apparently has the oxidation state of $+1$. It might be expected that mercurous nitrate would have the formula $HgNO_3$. There is ample evidence, however, to show that the formula is more properly written $Hg_2(NO_3)_2$. This doubled formula is characteristic of all mercurous compounds. Another peculiarity of mercury compounds is that both mercuric and mercurous salts are poorly ionized in solution. The solutions are poor conductors of electricity. This is in sharp contrast to the behavior of the salts of almost all other metals.

Only one other mercurous salt will be mentioned, and that is the chloride. If chloride ion is added to the solution of mercurous salt, there is precipitated white mercurous chloride. For instance, if hydrochloric acid is added to mercurous nitrate solution, mercurous chloride precipitates.

$$Hg_2(NO_3)_2 + 2HCl \rightarrow Hg_2Cl_2 + 2HNO_3$$

It will be noted that mercurous chloride has the peculiar doubled formula. Mercurous chloride is also known as **calomel.** Its physiological properties and its uses in medicine will be described below.

Mercuric oxide and mercuric nitrate have already been mentioned. Mercuric chloride is a white substance, quite soluble in water. Mercuric chloride is also known as **corrosive sublimate.** It is a particularly violent poison.

Mercury and its compounds have some interesting physiological effects. Mercury poisoning not infrequently occurs among persons who work with the element or who breathe the fumes which it gives off at elevated temperatures. There is some danger from spilled mercury in laboratories even though the mercury is not warmed. The symptoms from such exposure generally come on slowly and include loss of appetite, anemia, and mental depression. The hair tends to fall out and the teeth become loose. The patient is often ill for years.

Severe mercury poisoning is more generally caused by swallowing mercuric chloride, either accidentally or with intention to commit suicide. Tablets of mercuric chloride are generally dyed blue, made in the shape of a coffin, and stamped POISON. Reaction to the poison is severe, and unless vomiting quickly and completely empties the stomach, the chance of survival is slight. Even if the patient seems to recover at first, the probability is that the kidneys have received fatal injury. The reader should note that mercurous chloride (calomel) was once widely used in medicine and is not particularly dangerous, but that mercuric chloride (corrosive sublimate) is a violent poison. More than one life has been lost by failure to distinguish between these two compounds.

Mercurous chloride (calomel) was at one time one of the most popular remedies prescribed by doctors. Its action is cathartic. *cleansing* It is rarely used now because of certain dangers, and because safer cathartics are available.

Mercuric chloride (corrosive sublimate) is used as a disinfectant. It is an extremely powerful germicide, even when used greatly diluted with water. However, it is very poisonous and irritating. It is sometimes used on the skin, where no cut or abrasion occurs. For instance, a surgeon may wash his hands with a very dilute solution.

In recent years many compounds have been developed in which the germicidal properties of mercury are present but the toxic and irritating properties are reduced. One of the most popular of these is mercurochrome, which has become a common household antiseptic. Unfortunately it does not possess the potency often claimed for it.

151. TIN

Articles made of tin date back to at least the year 1400 B.C. Reference to the metal occurs in Homer and in Pliny. The "Islands of Cassiterides" from which tin was brought to ancient Rome doubtless refer to the British Isles. For many centuries Cornwall, in the south of England, was the principal world source of the element. At the present time the major tin deposits are in the South Pacific, in the Malay States, and in the Netherlands Indies. Bolivia is also an important tin producer. Japanese occupation of the South Pacific contributed to a desperate shortage during the years of World War II.

The only important ore of tin is the mineral *cassiterite,* which is stannic oxide, SnO_2. As a general rule, the ores must first be concentrated by washing and oil flotation. Once the impurities have been removed, the actual reduction to the metal is an easy step. This, of course, accounts for the long history which the metal has enjoyed. If stannic oxide is heated with charcoal, metallic tin is readily produced.

$$SnO_2 + 2C \rightarrow Sn + 2CO$$

Tin has a low melting point and may be purified by letting it flow away from less easily melted impurities.

At ordinary temperatures, tin is a familiar silvery-white metal. The metal is fairly soft and has a density of 7.28 grams per cubic centimeter. The melting point is 231.9° C. In addition to this common form, tin also has allotropic modifications. In this respect tin resembles sulfur and phosphorus.

The most familiar allotropic form is that which is stable below 18° C. If the metal is held at a low temperature, or exposed to the cold in a reasonably severe climate, it gradually is converted to a gray powder. The growth of this powder often occurs in spots on the surface of the metal. Hence the transformation is sometimes called tin disease, or tin pest. Tin resists ordinary atmospheric corrosion. It also possesses the peculiar property of emit-

Fig. 22-4. Tin pest. (From W. Foster, *The Romance of Chemistry*, 1927 edition, opposite p. 177. By permission of Appleton-Century-Crofts, publishers)

ting a sound (called "tin cry") when a piece of the metal is struck or bent.

The chief use of tin is in **tin plate.** This consists of sheet iron or steel which is coated with a thin layer of tin. Tin cans are made from tin plate. For packaging foods such cans are very satisfactory, and tin plate has in this sense become a major part of our civilization. But tin plate is too expensive for general use in combating corrosion.

Tin plate is made by the comparatively simple process of cleaning the sheets of steel in acid, then dipping them in molten tin. The cleaning process is often called "pickling." After it has been coated with tin, the steel sheets may be rolled to any desired thickness. Some tin is used as the pure metal, and the distilled water supplies of many chemical laboratories are carried through block tin pipes. But the high cost of tin has led to the use of other metals such as aluminum for such purposes in recent years. Most of the remaining tin production goes into alloys. Some of the more important alloys include **solder** (50Sn-50Pb), **pewter** (80Sn-20Pb), **type metal** (26Sn-1Cu-58Pb-15Sb), **Babbitt metal** (89Sn-3.7Cu-7.3Sb), and **bronze** (33Sn-67Cu), and **tin foil** (88Sn-4Cu-8Pb-0.5Sb). Much of the material called tin foil is actually aluminum foil or is made of alloys containing small amounts of tin. The cost of tin for nonessential uses is generally prohibitive.

The resistance of tin to atmospheric corrosion has already been mentioned. At elevated temperatures tin burns, forming the dioxide, or stannic oxide, SnO_2.

$$Sn + O_2 \rightarrow SnO_2$$

Although tin is slightly above hydrogen in the activity series, it is not appreciably acted upon by water. Dilute acids, however, dissolve tin and liberate hydrogen.

$$Sn + 2HCl \rightarrow SnCl_2 + H_2$$

Concentrated nitric acid yields a substance sometimes called metastannic acid. On ignition this yields stannic oxide.

$$Sn + 4HNO_3 \rightarrow SnO_2 + 4NO_2 + 2H_2O$$

Tin, like mercury, forms two series of compounds, in which the tin has oxidation states of +2 (stannous) and +4 (stannic) respectively. Both valences give amphoteric compounds, the stannous series being somewhat basic and the stannic somewhat acidic. Stannous compounds are good reducing agents and are often so used.

Stannous chloride may be obtained as a crystalline hydrate, $SnCl_2 \cdot 2H_2O$. This is known as "tin salt." It is used as a reducing agent, as a mordant in dyeing, and in weighting silk. Silk, impregnated with stannous chloride, which then undergoes hydrolysis and oxidation, has a heavy, luxurious appearance. The reducing action of stannous chloride is illustrated by its action on mercuric chloride. With a small amount of stannous chloride the products are stannic chloride and mercurous chloride.

$$SnCl_2 + 2HgCl_2 \rightarrow SnCl_4 + Hg_2Cl_2$$

But with excess stannous chloride, free mercury is a product.

$$SnCl_2 + HgCl_2 \rightarrow SnCl_4 + Hg$$

It should be pointed out that stannic chloride does not exist as $SnCl_4$ in water solution, but undergoes hydrolysis.

Stannic oxide is a white substance which occurs, of course, as the mineral *cassiterite*. It combines with bases with the formation of *stannates* of which sodium stannate, Na_2SnO_3, is an example.

Stannic chloride, $SnCl_4$, is an important compound formed by the action of excess chlorine on metallic tin.

$$Sn + 2Cl_2 \rightarrow SnCl_4$$

It is a colorless, fuming liquid which boils at $114.1°$ C. This compound is used in one of the processes for recovering tin from tin cans. The cans are subjected to an atmosphere of chlorine. This forms stannic chloride which because of its relatively low boiling point is easily separated from impurities by a process of fractional distillation. Stannic chloride is also used for weighting silk, and as a mordant in dyeing.

152. LEAD

Like tin, lead has been known and used for a long time. Roman ruins in Europe contain many examples of lead used for water pipes. Lead is decidedly more abundant and cheaper than tin. Commercial deposits of lead are widely distributed. Many countries have substantial though by no means inexhaustible supplies.

The most important ore of lead is the sulfide *galena,* PbS. Our discussion of the metallurgy of lead will be confined to this ore. The metallurgical processes involved resemble in part those used for copper. The ore is often enriched by flotation. It is then roasted, during which operation most of the sulfide is converted to lead oxide.

$$2PbS + 3O_2 \rightarrow 2PbO + 2SO_2$$

The lead oxide is now mixed with coke and with fresh sulfide ore. Other agents may be added as circumstances require. Smelting of this mixture occurs in a blast furnace. The chief reactions are probably those indicated below.

$$PbS + 2PbO \rightarrow 3Pb + SO_2$$
$$2PbO + C \rightarrow 2Pb + CO_2$$

In any event the product is metallic lead, and the escaping gases contain sulfur dioxide and carbon dioxide.

The metal obtained in this way is rarely pure enough for commercial use. Furthermore, the impurities present, such as silver, may be valuable enough to make further purification economical. The Parkes process for the removal of silver from lead has already been described. It will be recalled that this process takes advantage of the partition of silver between molten lead and molten zinc. Another process widely used to purify lead is the *electrolytic method*. This process is very similar to that used for producing electrolytic copper, except that the solution has a different composition. The impure lead is cast into slabs which form the anodes in the electrolytic cells. Thin sheets of pure lead form the cathodes. The electrolyte is a solution of lead fluosilicate, $PbSiF_6$, to which is added a little fluosilicic acid, H_2SiF_6. Pure lead migrates in the form of the Pb^{+2} ion from the positive to the negative pole. Impurities higher than lead in the activity series remain in solution; those lower than lead are deposited as a mud in the bottom of the electrolytic cell, or adhere to the anode.

Lead is a dense gray metal. Freshly cut surfaces are bright and silvery, but the metal soon tarnishes superficially and becomes dull. A "lead-colored sky" is a common descriptive phrase. In spite of this superficial tarnishing, lead resists further corrosion to a remarkable degree. The density of the metal is 11.3 grams per cubic centimeter. This is a high density but does not approach that of gold. "As heavy as lead" is an expression which reveals that lead is one of the commonest of the very dense metals. The metal is unusually soft and may readily be scratched with the finger nail. The melting point of lead is 327.4° C.

Total consumption of lead in the United States in a normal year is well in excess of half a million tons. By far the most important use is in the manufacture of storage batteries. It will be recalled that these batteries contain alternate plates of lead and lead dioxide. Other important uses include covering for cable carrying electrical wires, ammunition, lead foil, solder, type metal, and bearing metal. Substantial amounts of lead are used in the form of the oxides and other compounds, as will be described below.

If lead is heated in air, it forms lead monoxide, PbO. Distilled water, or "soft" water, containing dissolved oxygen attacks lead fairly rapidly, but ordinary hard tapwater containing dissolved sulfates or carbonates is almost without effect on lead. Dangerous poisoning has resulted from the use of lead pipes to carry soft water.

Lead resembles tin in that it has two oxidation states, the plumbous (Pb^{+2}) and the plumbic (Pb^{+4}). Both of these states yield amphoteric compounds although the plumbic state tends to be almost entirely acidic.

Dilute acids have little effect on lead, but concentrated nitric acid dissolves it readily.

$$3Pb + 8HNO_3 \rightarrow 3Pb(NO_3)_2 + 2NO + 4H_2O$$

Lead forms several oxides, some of which are of great industrial importance. The formation of lead monoxide, PbO, by heating metallic lead in air has been indicated above. This compound is prepared as a yellow powder called massicot. Further heating yields a buff-colored powder known as **litharge.** This has essentially the same composition. Major uses of litharge include storage batteries, insecticide manufacture, paints, pigments, and oil refining.

An important compound called **red lead,** or minium, has the formula Pb_3O_4. Red lead is prepared by heating litharge in air to about 450° C. It is used for making storage batteries and for paints. The familiar red paint on bridges and ship hulls contains red lead because it is effective in preventing corrosion.

Lead dioxide, PbO_2, may be prepared by the oxidation of divalent lead with chlorine or sodium hypochlorite, in alkaline solution. For instance the action on lead monoxide might be represented as follows:

$$PbO + Cl_2 + 2NaOH \rightarrow PbO_2 + 2NaCl + H_2O$$

It will be recalled that lead dioxide is the substance formed on the anode of the lead storage battery during charging. Lead dioxide is a brown solid, useful as a strong oxidizing agent. Like many compounds rich in oxygen, it decomposes, liberating oxygen when heated.

$$2PbO_2 \xrightarrow{\Delta} 2PbO + O_2$$

There are numerous other lead compounds of scientific and industrial importance. Formation of the nitrate, $Pb(NO_3)_2$, has been indicated above. It is a colorless solid, very soluble in water. It is often used as a starting material for the preparation of other lead compounds.

Lead chloride, $PbCl_2$, is precipitated from a solution of lead nitrate on the addition of chloride ions.

$$Pb(NO_3)_2 + 2HCl \rightarrow PbCl_2 + 2HNO_3$$

It is a white solid, relatively insoluble in cold water, but readily soluble in hot water. Together with silver chloride and mercurous chloride, lead chloride completes the list of common metal chlorides which are insoluble in cold water. To this list we may add the rare thallous chloride, TlCl, which is also insoluble.

Treatment of litharge with acetic acid yields lead acetate, $Pb(C_2H_3O_2)_2$.

$$PbO + 2HC_2H_3O_2 \rightarrow Pb(C_2H_3O_2)_2 + H_2O$$

This useful compound is soluble in water and has a sweet taste. It is, however, a dangerous poison. Because of the sweet taste, lead acetate is sometimes called "sugar of lead."

Lead sulfide has already been mentioned as the important mineral *galena*. It forms as an insoluble black precipitate when hydrogen sulfide is added to a solution containing lead ions, such as lead acetate.

$$Pb(C_2H_3O_2)_2 + H_2S \rightarrow PbS + 2HC_2H_3O_2$$

Formation of lead sulfide is responsible for the darkening of old paintings which have been exposed to the air of cities where small amounts of hydrogen sulfide are present. This reaction is used as a sensitive test for the presence of hydrogen sulfide. If a strip of paper is moistened with lead acetate solution, then exposed to hydrogen sulfide, the paper will darken—owing, of course, to the formation of black lead sulfide.

Lead sulfate, $PbSO_4$, is a white solid nearly insoluble in water. It is formed by the addition of dilute sulfuric acid to a solution containing lead ions. Lead arsenate, $Pb_3(AsO_4)_2$, is a white insoluble compound used as an insecticide. Lead chromate is a yellow insoluble compound extensively used as a yellow pigment.

One of the most important compounds of lead is the substance known as **white lead.** This has the approximate composition $Pb(OH)_2 \cdot 2PbCO_3$. It is, therefore, a double compound of lead hydroxide and lead carbonate. White lead is used on a very large scale in paints. It gives the paint its covering power. There are several methods for making white lead. In the old Dutch process, pieces of metallic lead, called "buckles," are placed in an earthenware pot which contains a little acetic acid. Many of these pots are placed in a chamber which also contains spent tanbark placed over each layer of pots. The tanbark ferments, giving off carbon dioxide. The water and acetic acid convert the lead to a mixture or compound of lead hydroxide and lead acetate. The carbon dioxide in turn converts the mixture to lead hydroxycarbonate, or white lead. The whole process takes several months. Other methods have been developed for speeding up this process, but many professional painters seem to prefer white lead prepared in the old-fashioned way.

We glance now at compounds of lead in the $+4$ oxidation state. Lead dioxide is, of course, one of these. Two others will be mentioned.

Lead tetrachloride, $PbCl_4$, is a dense yellow liquid, which fumes strongly in air. It is formed through the action of chlorine on lead dichloride. It will be recalled that tin tetrachloride is also a liquid. This is a general characteristic of the tetrachlorides in Group 4 of the Periodic Table.

Tetraethyllead, $Pb(C_2H_5)_4$, is an important compound produced by the action of ethyl chloride, C_2H_5Cl, on an alloy of lead and sodium.

$$4PbNa + 4C_2H_5Cl \rightarrow Pb(C_2H_5)_4 + 4NaCl + 3Pb$$

This compound is a liquid which is added to gasoline to reduce the "knocking" of automobile and airplane engines. Technically, the tetraethyllead is said to raise the "octane number" of the gasoline. One gallon of good-grade gasoline normally contains about two cubic centimeters of tetraethyllead. The magnitude of the tetraethyllead industry will be obvious.

The physiological action of lead and its compounds is noteworthy. The element has no important applications in medicine, but its highly poisonous character has been known since the time of Hippocrates (460-359? B.C.). The widespread uses of lead and lead compounds in industry and in the home make it important that people should be aware of the dangers of lead poisoning. Acute, or sudden, poisoning from lead is rare. But slow chronic poisoning is all too common. Lead acts slowly, and often in ways difficult to recognize. But the element is a very powerful poison, and delay in treatment may result in severe or fatal illness.

The symptoms of lead poisoning, or **plumbism,** as it is sometimes called, may include changes in character such as moodiness and excitability. The face and lips may become ashen pale. Sometimes there is a dark line in the gums near the teeth. Other symptoms include nausea and vomiting, neuritis and paralysis, and pain in muscles and joints. Changes in the blood cells are often characteristic of lead poisoning. The condition is difficult to recognize in its early stages, and often beyond treatment in its more advanced stages. Health officers connected with industrial use of lead are constantly on the alert for symptoms of lead poisoning, and for hazards which might give rise to poisoning. But these safeguards are as a rule not operative in the home. The presence of lead in the feces is an indication of possible exposure to toxic amounts of lead. Healthy persons normally are exposed to and excrete appreciable quantities of lead. Men working in the paint and storage-battery industries may excrete ten or twenty times the normal amount of lead.

Lead poisoning in the home has arisen when children eat the paint on their cribs. Cases more frequently arise from the use of lead pipes to carry water. It will be recalled that hard water has little corrosive action on lead, but that soft water or distilled water has a marked corrosive action. The elusive nature of lead poisoning is illustrated by the case of an elderly man in New England who developed the symptoms. He lived in an old house, the water supply of which passed through lead pipes. Other members of the household were not affected. It developed that he was in the habit of being the first person in the house to arise in the morning, and that he took a drink of water at that time. The water which had been standing in the lead pipes all night contained enough lead to poison the man. As soon as this portion of water was removed, fresh water containing no lead flowed into the system.

153. CHROMIUM AND MANGANESE

It will have been noted that the elements to which we have been directing our attention in the last few chapters show actually more resemblances in the horizontal series of the periodic tables rather than in the vertical groups. Copper, silver, and gold bear definite resemblances to zinc, cadmium, and mercury. Similarly, chromium resembles manganese, while both bear some resemblances to iron, cobalt, and nickel. This likeness and unlikeness is apparently due in part to the arrangement of electrons in these elements. In the series of elements from scandium to zinc, from yttrium to cadmium, and from lanthanum to mercury the major differences in electronic structure lie, not in the highest normal energy level, but deeper in the interior of the atom. Reference to the table of electronic energy levels (page 30) will show how these differences occur. The elements mentioned show many curious effects because of their unusual structure. For instance, they show variable valences, their ions are nearly all strongly colored, their ions are nearly all attracted by a magnet, and nearly all the elements show pronounced catalytic effects. Such elements are called "transition-group" elements. Chromium and manganese are typical transition-group elements, and show all the unusual properties referred to above.

The principal mineral containing chromium is *chromite,* $FeCr_2O_4$, often called chrome iron ore. The chief producers are South Africa and Turkey.

Pure chromium metal may be obtained by the Goldschmidt reaction of heating chromic oxide with powdered aluminum.

$$\overset{+++}{Cr_2}\overset{=}{O_3} + 2\overset{\circ}{Al} \rightarrow 2\overset{\circ}{Cr} + \overset{+++}{Al_2}\overset{=}{O_3}$$

But most of the chromium used industrially is obtained either as an alloy with iron, or in the electroplating of chromium. The iron-chromium alloy, known as **ferrochrome,** is prepared by heating the mineral *chromite* with carbon. This alloy is used in the manufacture of stainless steel.

$$FeCr_2O_4 + 4C \rightarrow Fe + 2Cr + 4CO$$

Chromium is obtained by electrolysis of a solution which contains chromium in both the $+3$ and $+6$ oxidation states. Such a solution is sometimes called a chromic chromate. But although the composition of the solution is not well understood, the chromium-plating industry is very large.

In the past twenty years chromium finishes have become almost too common on automobile parts and many varieties of metal objects and fixtures.

Chromium is a hard metal with a brilliant silvery luster. It has a density of 6.9 grams per cubic centimeter and the high melting point of 1615° C. The metal is very resistant to atmospheric corrosion.

In addition to its uses for decorative purposes and for protective coatings on other metals such as steel, large amounts of chromium go into various kinds of alloy steels. Small percentages of chromium give steel increased hardness and tensile strength. Stainless steel contains 11 to 18 per cent of chromium and, as the name implies, is extremely resistant to corrosion.

We turn now to the compounds of chromium. Like other members of Group 6 in the Periodic Table, chromium shows a wide range of oxidation states including +2, +3, +4, and +6. Many chromium compounds are strongly colored, a fact from which the element derives its name.

The chromous (+2) compounds, of which chromous chloride, $CrCl_2$, is an example, are all strong reducing agents. They are not, in general, very important.

Chromic (+3) compounds are important. Many hydrated or dissolved chromic salts are an intense green color, others are violet. Chromic oxide, Cr_2O_3, is a green solid. It may be obtained by heating the metal in oxygen, or by heating chromic hydroxide, $Cr(OH)_3$, or ammonium dichromate, $(NH_4)_2Cr_2O_7$. Chromic oxide finds extensive use as a green pigment in paints and in ceramics. It is also an important catalyst.

Chromic sulfate, $Cr_2(SO_4)_3$, may be prepared by dissolving chromic oxide in sulfuric acid. It occurs in green and violet forms. It is useful as a convenient source of chromium for the preparation of other chromium compounds.

The addition of sodium hydroxide or ammonium hydroxide to a solution of a chromic salt yields a gelatinous pale green precipitate often referred to as chromic hydroxide, $Cr(OH)_3$.

If chromic oxide is strongly heated with sodium hydroxide or other strong base in the presence of air, the chromium is oxidized to the +6 state. The substance formed, Na_2CrO_4, is called sodium chromate.

$$2Cr_2O_3 + 8NaOH + 3O_2 \rightarrow 4Na_2CrO_4 + 4H_2O$$

This and related salts are important as oxidizing agents and pigments, and in tanning, dyeing, etching metals, and for a variety of other purposes. It will be noticed that the chromates are not unlike the sulfates such as Na_2SO_4 in which the sulfur has an oxidation state of +6. It will be recalled that chromium and sulfur are in the same group in the Periodic Table.

If concentrated sulfuric acid is added to a solution containing sodium or potassium chromate, there is formed a substance called chromium trioxide, CrO_3. This separates as red needles. This substance is analogous to sulfur trioxide, SO_3. Chromium trioxide dissolves in water to form chromic acid, H_2CrO_4. This is not a very strong acid, but it is a powerful oxidizing agent and is often used as such. A solution of sodium chromate in sulfuric acid is often used as a cleansing agent for laboratory glassware. Its use for this purpose is hazardous.

The strong oxidizing tendencies of the chromates may be illustrated by the reaction with sulfur dioxide. The chromium is reduced to the green $+3$ state.

$$2Na_2CrO_4 + 3SO_2 + 2H_2SO_4 \rightarrow 2Na_2SO_4 + Cr_2(SO_4)_3 + 2H_2O$$

Among interesting chromates the following may be mentioned: lead chromate, $PbCrO_4$, an important yellow pigment, as are barium and zinc chromates, $BaCrO_4$ and $ZnCrO_4$. Silver chromate, $AgCrO_4$, is an intensely colored red compound. All these are precipitated by the addition of the appropriate ion to a soluble chromate.

$$Na_2CrO_4 + 2AgNO_3 \rightarrow Ag_2CrO_4 + 2NaNO_3$$

If acid is added to the solution of a chromate, the solution turns from yellow to orange. This change results from the following ionic reaction:

$$2CrO_4^{-2} + 2H^+ \rightleftarrows Cr_2O_7^{-2} + H_2O$$

The ion $Cr_2O_7^{-2}$ is known as the dichromate ion, and it is in equilibrium with chromate ions. Addition of acid forms more dichromate; addition of water, or of a base, forms more chromate. Many dichromate compounds are known, such as potassium dichromate, $K_2Cr_2O_7$. Such compounds are, like the chromates, good oxidizing agents and they find many uses.

The chief ore of manganese is *pyrolusite*, which is manganese dioxide, MnO_2. The name pyrolusite means literally "fire-wash" and refers to the very old practice of decolorizing glass by the addition of the mineral. Manganese ores are found extensively in Russia, Africa, and elsewhere.

Manganese metal may be produced by reduction of the oxide with carbon, or with aluminum. Electrolytic reduction is also possible. But most metallic manganese is produced as the iron alloy, ferromanganese. This is obtained by the use of carbon to reduce a mixture of manganese and iron oxides.

Manganese is a gray-silver metal. The density is 7.2 grams per cubic centimeter and the melting point is 1260° C. The metal is rarely needed in the pure form. This is in sharp contrast to the case with manganese compounds, some of which are among the most familiar of chemical substances.

Manganese is important in the manufacture of steel. It is used both to free steel from oxygen and sulfur, and as an essential ingredient in valuable alloy steels. Steel rails and heavy machinery are often made of manganese alloy steel. Manganese also enters into important nonferrous alloys.

Manganese has as complete a range of oxidation states as any element. Well-known compounds contain the element in the $+2, +3, +4, +6$, and $+7$ states. Possibly other states exist also. The oxides MnO, Mn_2O_3, Mn_3O_4, and MnO_2 all occur in nature. Manganous sulfate, $MnSO_4$, is a familiar pink compound in solution or in hydrated crystals. The oxide and hydroxide, MnO and $Mn(OH)_2$, rapidly take up oxygen from the air, being oxidized to $MnOOH$, Mn_3O_4, etc. The hydroxide $Mn(OH)_2$ is definitely basic in its properties.

Among the higher oxides of manganese, by far the most important is manganese dioxide, MnO_2. It is used on a very large scale in making dry cells, where its function is generally spoken of as "depolarizing." Manganese dioxide is a good oxidizing agent. Its use in removing objectionable color from glass has been mentioned. It is also well known as a catalyst. It will be recalled that manganese dioxide catalyzes the decomposition of potassium chlorate in the laboratory preparation of oxygen. On an industrial scale, manganese dioxide together with other oxides is used to oxidize carbon monoxide in certain types of gas masks. As an example of the oxidizing action of manganese dioxide there may be recalled the preparation of chlorine.

$$MnO_2 + 4HCl \rightarrow MnCl_2 + Cl_2 + 2H_2O$$

When any lower oxide of manganese is fused with a strong base in the presence of air, the manganese is oxidized to the $+6$ state.

$$2MnO_2 + 4KOH + O_2 \rightarrow 2K_2MnO_4 + 2H_2O$$

The compound K_2MnO_4 is a green substance called potassium manganate. It is representative of a series of salts which may be considered to be derived from a hypothetical manganous acid, H_2MnO_4. If now the solution is acidified, even by such a weak acid as a solution of carbon dioxide, the potassium manganate is converted into a mixture of a purple solution and a precipitate of hydrated manganese dioxide. The purple solution contains the important compound potassium permanganate, $KMnO_4$. This reaction is best understood if it is written in the ionic form:

$$3MnO_4^{-2} + 2H_2O \rightleftarrows 2MnO_4^- + 4OH^- + MnO_2$$

The manganate ions react with water to form permanganate ions, hydroxide ions, and manganese dioxide. In the presence of an acid, the hydroxide ions would be neutralized, forming a salt and water. The function of the acid is to reduce the hydroxide ion concentration, thereby shifting the equilibrium to the right.

Potassium permanganate is a powerful oxidizing agent, frequently used in the laboratory. It also finds many applications in industry, although it is rather expensive. By treating a solution of potassium permanganate with dilute sulfuric acid, there is formed a solution of permanganic acid, $HMnO_4$. Concentrated sulfuric acid should not be added to potassium permanganate because an explosive oxide Mn_2O_7 may be formed.

The wide valence range shown by manganese illustrates a property of many elements. When the manganese has a low oxidation state as in $Mn(OH)_2$, it acts as a base-forming element. As the valence rises, the basic properties diminish. The oxides Mn_2O_3 and MnO_2 tend, for instance, to be amphoteric. At the highest oxidation states manganese is definitely an acid-forming element, as in permanganic acid. It is a general rule that when an element shows variable positive valence, the lower states tend to be basic, the higher acidic. This property is shown not only by manganese, but by chromium as in $Cr(OH)_2$ (basic), and in H_2CrO_4 (acidic), and in many other elements.

This completes our presentation of the important metals. It will be recognized that there are many other useful and interesting elements showing more or less metallic character. The platinum-palladium group comprising ruthenium, rhodium, palladium, osmium, iridium, and platinum are especially worthy of note. These elements are characterized by great resistance to corrosion and very high density. Osmium has the highest density of any known substance (d = 22.48 g. per cc.). Similarly, molybdenum, tungsten, and uranium are elements of great interest, the first two in steelmaking, uranium in connection with the atomic bomb. For further information on these and other elements the reader is referred to advanced texts on inorganic chemistry.*

154. CORROSION

Most metals have a tendency to react chemically with water, oxygen, carbon dioxide, or other substances found under normal atmospheric conditions. This

* T. Moeller, *Inorganic Chemistry* (New York: Wiley, 1952).
N. V. Sidgwick, *The Chemical Elements and Their Compounds* (Oxford: Clarendon Press, 1950).

process is called corrosion. Corrosion is, in a sense, the reverse of those metallurgical procedures described in the last few chapters. Corrosion destroys useful metal structures such as rails, pipelines, bridges, and ships, or would do so unless means were taken to slow down or stop the reactions involved. Iron, the commonest structural metal, is very subject to corrosion. Our discussion of corrosion will, therefore, be limited to this metal.

The products of iron corroding, or rusting, consist generally of oxides of iron, more or less hydrated. Thus a sheet of iron exposed to the atmosphere soon becomes covered with reddish-brown rust. The most popular theory as to why corrosion takes place assumes that electrochemical action may occur on the surface of the metal. Suppose that a sheet of iron has on its surface a speck of less active metal as impurity, and that a drop of water lies over this region. The water, being exposed to air, will contain dissolved oxygen, carbon dioxide, and other impurities, some of which will make the water electrically conducting. We have, then, all the essentials for a tiny voltaic cell, namely, a more active metal, a less active metal, and a conducting solution. The iron, being more active, will dissolve, owing to the reaction:

$$Fe \rightarrow Fe^{+2} + 2\epsilon$$

loss of e = oxidation

and will become the negative pole. The less active metal impurity will become positive by the reaction:

$$2H^+ + 2\epsilon \rightarrow H_2$$

gain of e = reduction

and hydrogen will be liberated. Finally, the ferrous ions, Fe^{+2}, will be oxidized to ferric, Fe^{+3}, by the oxygen, and will combine with oxygen to form ferric oxide,

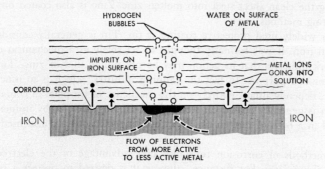

Fig. 22-5. Schematic diagram showing how the presence of speck of less active metal as an impurity can set up a voltaic cell on a moist iron surface. The reaction on the impurity is $2H^+ + 2\epsilon \rightarrow H_2$; that on the iron surface is $Fe \rightarrow Fe^{++} + 2\epsilon$. This latter reaction leads to corrosion.

Fe_2O_3, with more or less water, to make rust. Evidence that this view is correct is shown by the rapid corrosion of pure iron in contact with an inactive metal such as platinum, and, of course, exposed to the atmosphere.

It is not necessary that a less active metal be present as impurity before corrosion can start. The metal in different portions of a single piece of iron may have slightly different activity. This difference may be very small, yet large enough for one part of the metal to become positive and the other negative, so that corrosion may set in. Furthermore, if the oxygen concentration in different portions of the water is different there may be set up a slight electrochemical action. The same is true of other substances which may be present as impurities in the water. But, whatever the causes may be, corrosion is an extremely expensive problem. Much research and engineering development have been devoted to controlling this major factor in industrial waste.

Most efforts to control corrosion involve coating the metal with an inactive substance such as another metal, or with a paint. Metals which are used to coat steel include zinc, tin, cadmium, copper, lead, chromium, and silver. Occasionally the more expensive noble metals such as gold and platinum are used. It may seem surprising that iron can be protected by a more active metal such as zinc.

Certain metals, of which zinc is one, do not rapidly corrode although the metal happens to be fairly high in the activity series. This is true of zinc and of aluminum because these metals become coated with a carbonate or oxide layer which protects against further corrosion. If steel is coated with zinc, the zinc mechanically protects the iron from the atmosphere, while the zinc itself has its carbonate coat. However, a zinc coating acts in another way. Suppose a voltaic cell is set up between zinc and iron. Zinc is the more active of the two; it therefore becomes negative and tends to corrode rather than the iron. The zinc in a sense protects the iron both mechanically and electrochemically, a fact first reported by Michael Faraday in 1829. Until all the zinc coat is destroyed, the iron remains positive and so has little tendency to lose electrons and go into solution. Zinc is inexpensive and is widely used for the protection of steel against corrosion. **Galvanized iron** is sheet steel coated thinly with zinc. The zinc is put on by dipping the clean sheet steel into molten zinc. Zinc is also coated on steel by electroplating methods.

Another widely used protective coating is tin. Tin is generally considered less active than iron. It was formerly thought to act solely as a mechanical coat, but recent work indicates that its action may be not unlike that of zinc. Tin is very effective for this purpose. In fact the canning industry, which is so much a part of our life, depends almost entirely on the excellence of **tin plate** in containers for foods. Tin is generally coated on steel by hot-dipping, that is, by immersing the clean steel in a bath of molten tin. Electroplating methods are also used for this metal.

Other methods of corrosion resistance take advantage of the electrochemical nature of the process. For instance, suppose it is desired to protect a steel tank containing a water solution of salts or other electrolytes. Stainless steel bars are placed in the solution. A small electric current is made to flow from the bars, which are made positive, to the tank, which is made negative. This system is often used to protect boilers, tanks, and pipelines. Still another method often used to protect pipelines is to connect the pipe through wires to bars of more active metals such as magnesium. These active metal bars may be buried in the ground. The active metal corrodes fairly rapidly but during this process the pipeline is protected.

The use of paints and lacquers to protect metals is familiar to everyone. Steel bridges and ship hulls are constantly being painted against corrosion. The paints protect merely by mechanically preventing access of moisture and air to the metal surface.

One final method for protecting aluminum surfaces will be mentioned. With the growth in use of aluminum for naval construction, especially for naval aircraft, the corrosion of aluminum becomes a major problem. It is found that aluminum may be given a heavy coat of aluminum oxide by making it the anode in an electrolytic cell. So-called **anodized aluminum** has remarkable corrosion-resistant properties.

155. REVIEW OF METALLURGICAL PROCESSES

In the last five chapters, attention has been directed toward metallurgical processes by which the important metals may be obtained from their respective ores. It will be worth while now to review the general principles involved in these processes, and to attempt a somewhat more quantitative approach to the general problem.

Except for a few metals which occur in the free, or native, condition, all metals must be obtained by a process of reduction. This is true because the metals all form positive ions. The general process for producing a metal may, therefore, be indicated as an addition of electrons. The addition of electrons is reduction.

$$M^+ + \epsilon \rightarrow M^0$$

We may say then that metallurgical processes involve reduction of the metal ions to metal, through the action of a reducing agent.

Some metal ions are easy to reduce, that is, they require little energy. Another way of stating this is to say that weak reducing agents are effective. An example is mercury, which may be obtained from its principal ore, cinnabar, by moderate roasting.

$$HgS + O_2 \rightarrow Hg + SO_2$$

It will be noted that the mercury is reduced, while the sulfur is oxidized. In this case the sulfide ion, S^{-2}, may be considered as the reducing agent.

In other cases, of which iron is an example, more powerful reducing agents are required. Carbon monoxide is a fairly powerful reducing agent.

$$Fe_2O_3 + 3CO \rightarrow 2Fe + 3CO_2$$

It may be noted that mere heating of iron sulfide, or oxide, either in air or otherwise, would produce no metallic iron. We say, in general, that iron is a more active element than mercury; it stands higher in the activity series; it requires more energy to reduce it to the metal.

Still other metals, of which aluminum will serve as an example, require very powerful reducing agents. To reduce aluminum oxide to metal requires a substance such as metallic sodium, which has a very powerful tendency to give up electrons.

$$Al_2O_3 + 6Na \rightarrow 2Al + 3Na_2O$$

Fortunately there is an electrolytic method of adding electrons to an ion, and this is the method actually used in the Hall-Héroult process.

$$Al^{+3} + 3\epsilon \rightarrow Al^0$$

Not infrequently it is possible to predict whether a certain reducing agent will be effective in producing metal. This is done by considering the heats of reaction involved. If a reaction is strongly exothermic, it is likely to proceed easily. If it is strongly endothermic, the reaction is not likely to be successful.

We shall take the reduction of copper oxide by hydrogen as an example.

$$CuO + H_2 \rightarrow Cu + H_2O$$

The heat of reaction for the straight decomposition of copper oxide is as follows:

$$2CuO \rightarrow 2Cu + O_2 - 69,800 \text{ calories}$$

In other words, the reaction is highly endothermic. Now, the heat of reaction for the formation of water is highly exothermic, as follows:

$$2H_2 + O_2 \rightarrow 2H_2O + 116,400 \text{ calories}$$

It will be advisable to review what these equations mean. The first equation may be read to the effect that two moles (159.1 g.) of copper oxide may decompose to two moles of copper metal and one mole of oxygen gas, and that this process absorbs 69,800 calories. The second reaction means that two moles (4 g.) of hydrogen gas react with one mole of oxygen gas to yield two moles of water, and that simultaneously 116,400 calories of heat are liberated. These data for the heats of reactions have been obtained through careful thermochemical studies. The data are found in standard reference works.

Now, we may add the two equations to obtain a third equation, as follows:

$$2CuO \rightarrow 2Cu + O_2 - 69,800 \text{ calories}$$

$$2H_2 + O_2 \rightarrow 2H_2O + 116,400 \text{ calories}$$

$$2CuO + 2H_2 + O_2 \rightarrow 2Cu + O_2 + 2H_2O - 69,800 \text{ calories} + 116,400 \text{ calories}$$

It will be noticed that the O_2 may be canceled, leaving:

$$2CuO + 2H_2 \rightarrow 2Cu + 2H_2O + 46,600 \text{ calories}$$

Finally, dividing by two, we obtain:

$$CuO + H_2 \rightarrow Cu + H_2O + 23,300 \text{ calories}$$

This reaction is seen to be fairly strongly exothermic. We should, therefore, expect that copper oxide would be readily reduced by hydrogen. Such is actually the case.

We turn now to the possible reduction of aluminum oxide by hydrogen. If such a reaction took place it could be represented as follows:

$$Al_2O_3 + 3H_2 \rightarrow 2Al + 3H_2O$$

The heat of formation of aluminum oxide is 399,000 calories per mole of Al_2O_3. We may then write:

$$2Al_2O_3 \rightarrow 4Al + 3O_2 - 798,000 \text{ calories}$$

The heat of reaction involved in the formation of six moles of water would be

$$6H_2 + 3O_2 \rightarrow 6H_2O + 349,200 \text{ calories}$$

Adding these equations as before, we obtain:

$$2Al_2O_3 \rightarrow 4Al + 3O_2 - 798,000 \text{ calories}$$
$$6H_2 + 3O_2 \rightarrow 6H_2O + 349,200 \text{ calories}$$

$$\overline{2Al_2O_3 + 6H_2 \rightarrow 4Al + 6H_2O - 448,800 \text{ calories}}$$

This equation reduces to:

$$Al_2O_3 + 3H_2 \rightarrow 2Al + 3H_2O - 224,400 \text{ calories}$$

This reaction is evidently strongly endothermic, and in consequence it would not be expected to proceed. Actually it is impossible to reduce aluminum oxide with hydrogen.

These examples will serve to show how comparatively simple thermochemical calculations may save much experimental labor. It should be pointed out that the sign of the heat of reaction gives only a rough estimate as to whether the reaction will proceed or not. In more advanced calculations a thermodynamic quantity called the "free energy" is used. Also, the calculations do not tell whether the reaction is likely to be fast or slow. Nevertheless, such examples as those given are among the most useful types of computations made by chemists and chemical engineers. A few hours spent calculating heats of reaction may save very large sums in the design and construction of large-scale industrial chemical equipment.

EXERCISES

A. *Define or explain the following:*

amalgam	galena	red lead (minium)
anodization	galvanized iron	solder
calomel	litharge	sphalerite
cassiterite	lithopone	tetraethyllead
cinnabar	plumbism	tin plate
corrosive sublimate	pyrolusite	white lead

B. 1. *Indicate procedures and all equations for the following:*

a. reactions involved in the metallurgy of zinc: (1) reduction with carbon and (2) reduction by electrolysis

b. (illustrate) amphoteric properties of zinc hydroxide

c. $Zn(NO_3)_2 + NH_4OH(\text{excess}) \rightarrow$

d. $ZnSO_4 + BaS \rightarrow$

e. $HgS + O_2 \text{ (heat)} \rightarrow$

f. $Hg + O_2 \text{ (heat)} \rightarrow$

g. $Hg + HNO_3 \rightarrow$

h. formation of $HgCl_2$, and of Hg_2Cl_2

i. metallurgy of tin

j. $Sn + HCl \rightarrow$

k. $Sn + HNO_3 \text{ (conc.)} \rightarrow$

l. $SnCl_2 + HgCl_2 \text{ (excess)} \rightarrow$

m. $HgCl_2 + SnCl_2 \text{ (excess)} \rightarrow$

n. $Sn + Cl_2 \rightarrow$

o. metallurgy of lead

p. electrolytic purification of lead

q. $Pb + HNO_3 \text{ (conc.)} \rightarrow$

r. $PbO_2 \text{ (heat)} \rightarrow$

s. $Pb(NO_3)_2 + H_2S \rightarrow$

t. $Pb(C_2H_3O_2)_2 + H_2S \rightarrow$

   u. manufacture of tetraethyllead
   v. production of a chromate from chromic oxide
   w. (illustrate) the oxidizing action of a chromate
   x. (explain) the conversion of a chromate to a dichromate
   y. $MnO_2 + HCl \rightarrow$
   z. formation of (1) a manganate, (2) a permanganate

2. Describe the electrochemical theory of corrosion.
3. Describe the prevention of corrosion by (a) paints, (b) galvanizing, (c) tinning, (d) electrochemical means, and (e) anodization.
4. In general terms, how can one tell in advance whether the oxide of a metal will be easy to reduce or very difficult to reduce to the free metal?
5. In what respects do the transition elements resemble each other? Why is this so, in terms of atomic structure?
6. How can the evaporation of mercury at room temperature be made visible?

C. 1. Devise a method for large-scale production of pure oxygen through the use of mercury. Comment on the feasibility of the process.
   2. A sample of impure lead contains silver and zinc. Trace these elements through the electrolytic purification of lead.
   3. An element has three oxidation states, $+2, +3, +5$. Write possible formulas for (a) a basic oxide, (b) an acidic oxide, (c) a possible amphoteric oxide of this element.
   4. Write probable equations for the following:
      a. $CdO + C \rightarrow$
      b. $Zn(OH)_2 + OH^- \rightarrow$
      c. $Zn(OH)_2 + H^+ \rightarrow$
      d. $Cd(OH)_2 + NaOH \rightarrow$
      e. $Cd(OH)_2 + NH_3 \rightarrow$
      f. $Hg_2^{++} + HCl \rightarrow$
      g. $Na_2CrO_4 + H_2S + H_2SO_4 \rightarrow S + ? + ? + ?$
      h. $Mn(OH)_2 + HCl \rightarrow$
      i. $HMnO_4 + NaOH \rightarrow$
      j. $HMnO_4 + Mn(OH)_2 \rightarrow$

   5. With the aid of a labeled diagram show the half reactions and electron flow when a steel pipeline is protected against corrosion by connecting it through wires to magnesium bars buried in (moist) ground.
   6. Determine the feasibility of the following reaction

$$Mn_3O_4 + 4H_2 \rightarrow 3Mn + 4H_2O$$

given that

$$3Mn + 2O_2 \rightarrow Mn_3O_4 + 325,000 \text{ cals.}$$

and the heat of formation of water as given in Section 155.

   7. A smelter uses 100,000 amperes of electricity in the production of zinc. Assuming 70 per cent current efficiency, what is the daily output of zinc?

IONIC EQUILIBRIA

In Chapter 13, Section 91, there were summarized some of the conditions under which a chemical reaction may be expected to go to completion, or nearly so. These conditions include (a) those reactions in which a precipitate may be formed, (b) those in which one of the products is a gas, (c) those in which one of the products is only slightly ionized, and (d) certain reactions between oxidizing agents and reducing agents. It was further shown, in Chapter 22, that reactions in which quite large amounts of heat are evolved may be expected to go effectively to completion.

In the present chapter we shall consider some of these topics again, but will be concerned with placing the subject on a quantitative, numerical basis, instead of the general terms in which it was presented before. The examples chosen for presentation will be some ionic reactions involving substances which are only slightly ionized, some reactions in which a precipitate is formed, and some in which oxidation and reduction takes place.

156. WEAK ACIDS, WEAK BASES

Strong acids are substantially completely ionized in water and their behavior is not readily predictable by the law of mass action. Weak acids— those in which ionization is slight—dissociate reversibly as follows:

$$HA \rightleftarrows H^+ + A^-$$ anion

where A^- stands for the anion. For such a system in equilibrium it is found that

$$\frac{[H^+] \times [A^-]}{[HA]} = K_i$$

where K_i is called the **ionization constant.** In words, the above expression states that, for the weak acid HA, the product of the molar concentration of hydrogen ions, H^+, multiplied by the concentration of A^- ions, and divided by the concentration of HA molecules, is a constant at any given temperature. In all the following discussion the square brackets [ ] represents the concentration in moles per liter of solution. Thus $[H^+]$ means moles of H^+ per liter. It is understood that the equation defining K_i should perhaps contain an expression for the water involved in the reaction, but as the concentration of water remains practically constant it may be ignored.

Use of ionization constants will be illustrated by some problems.

Problem: Given that the ionization constant for acetic acid (abbreviated to HAc) is 1.8×10^{-5} in water solution at room temperature, find the molar concentration of hydrogen ions in a 0.10M acetic acid solution.

Solution: The equation is

$$HAc \rightleftarrows H^+ + Ac^-$$

so that the ionization constant expression is

$$\frac{[H^+] \times [Ac^-]}{[HAc]} = 1.8 \times 10^{-5}$$

It is clear that $[H^+] = [Ac^-]$, because the ionization of acetic acid produces one, and only one, hydrogen ion for every acetate ion. It is also clear that $[HAc] = 0.10 - [H^+]$ because the total concentration of acetic acid (both molecular and ionized) is 0.10M, and ionization has reduced this by an amount equal to $[H^+]$. However, $[H^+]$ will be quite small because acetic acid is a weak acid and hence, by definition, only slightly ionized. Without introducing too much error it may be said that $0.10 - [H^+] = 0.10$. Then, let $[H^+] = [Ac^-] = x$, so that

$$\frac{x^2}{0.10} = 1.8 \times 10^{-5}$$

whence $x^2 = 1.8 \times 10^{-6}$, and $x = 1.3 \times 10^{-3}$ moles per liter. The concentration of hydrogen ions in this solution is 1.3×10^{-3} M.

Problem: What is the percentage ionization of the acetic acid solution referred to in the previous problem?

Solution: If 0.10 moles of acetic acid per liter were originally present and if 1.3×10^{-3} moles of this acid ionized, then the degree of ionization is

$$\frac{1.3 \times 10^{-3}}{0.10} = 1.3 \times 10^{-2}$$

that is to say, the acid is 1.3 per cent ionized.

TABLE 12

IONIZATION CONSTANTS FOR SOME WEAK ACIDS AND BASES

Acid	Reaction	K_i
Acetic...............	$HAc \rightleftarrows H^+ + Ac^-$	1.8×10^{-5}
Bicarbonate ion.......	$HCO_3^- \rightleftarrows H^+ + CO_3^=$	4.7×10^{-11}
Bisulfate ion.........	$HSO_4^- \rightleftarrows H^+ + SO_4^=$	1.2×10^{-2}
Boric...............	$H_3BO_3 \rightleftarrows H^+ + H_2BO_3^-$	5.8×10^{-10}
Carbonic............	$H_2CO_3 \rightleftarrows H^+ + HCO_3^-$	4.3×10^{-7}
Hydrocyanic..........	$HCN \rightleftarrows H^+ + CN^-$	4×10^{-10}
Hydrosulfide ion.......	$HS^- \rightleftarrows H^+ + S^=$	1.2×10^{-15}
Hydrosulfuric........	$H_2S \rightleftarrows H^+ + HS^-$	9.1×10^{-8}
Hypochlorous........	$HClO \rightleftarrows H^+ + ClO^-$	9.6×10^{-7}
Silicic (ortho).........	$H_4SiO_4 \rightleftarrows H^+ + H_2SiO_4^-$	1×10^{-10}
Sulfurous............	$H_2SO_3 \rightleftarrows H^+ + HSO_3^-$	1.2×10^{-2}
Ammonium hydroxide..	$NH_4OH \rightleftarrows NH_4^+ + OH^-$	1.8×10^{-5}

Problem: What is the pH of the above solution?

Solution: The hydrogen ion concentration is 1.3×10^{-3} moles per liter, and pH is defined as the negative logarithm of the hydrogen ion concentration. Then, from logarithm tables or slide rule,

$$pH = -(\log 1.3 \times 10^{-3})$$
$$= -(\log 1.3 + \log 10^{-3})$$
$$= -(0.11 - 3.0)$$
$$= 2.89$$

The pH of a solution is rarely meaningful beyond the first decimal, hence the answer to the problem may be written pH = 2.9.

One further problem of this type will show, given the degree of ionization, how to calculate the ionization constant.

Problem: Hydrocyanic acid ionizes according to the equation

$$HCN \rightleftarrows H^+ + CN^-$$

A $0.050M$ HCN solution is found to be 0.009 per cent ionized. Find the ionization constant for this acid.

Solution: The ionization constant is given by

$$\frac{[H^+] \times [CN^-]}{[HCN]} = K_i$$

The concentration of HCN molecules is substantially $0.050M$. The concentration of hydrogen ions is the same as the concentration of cyanide, CN^-, ions and is equal to 0.050×0.009 per cent. This is more conveniently expressed exponentially as $5 \times 10^{-2} \times 0.9 \times 10^{-4} = 4.5 \times 10^{-6}$. Hence,

$$K_i = \frac{(4.5 \times 10^{-6})^2}{5 \times 10^{-2}} = 4 \times 10^{-10}$$

Similar problems may be encountered for weak bases such as ammonium hydroxide, the ionization constant for which is

$$\frac{[NH_4] \times [OH^-]}{[NH_4OH]} = 1.8 \times 10^{-5}$$

It should be remembered that sodium hydroxide, calcium hydroxide, and the like, are strong bases and do not lend themselves to calculations such as those given above.

From the above discussion it will be clear that if to an acetic acid solution there is added some sodium acetate, the result will be to repress the ionization of the acid. The equilibrium involved is, as above

$$HAc \rightleftarrows H^+ + Ac^-$$

sodium acetate, like almost all salts, may be considered to be completely ionized.

$$NaAc \rightarrow Na^+ + Ac^-$$

The increase of acetate ion concentration caused by the addition of sodium acetate will force acetate ions to combine with hydrogen ions to form more molecules of acetic acid. This statement follows from a consideration of the expression for the ionization constant

$$\frac{[H^+] \times [Ac^-]}{[HAc]} = 1.8 \times 10^{-5} = K_i$$

where it is clear that an increase of $[Ac^-]$ must be matched by a decrease of $[H^+]$ or an increase of $[HAc]$, or both, if K_i is to remain constant at 1.8×10^{-5}.

The effect described is known as the **common ion effect**. In the example given the acetate ion is the ion which is common to both acetic acid and sodium acetate. The common ion effect will be illustrated by the following problem:

Problem: What is the molar concentration of hydrogen ions in a 0.10*M* acetic acid solution which also contains 0.05*M* sodium acetate?

Solution: As was done in one of the problems above, the concentration of acetic acid molecules, [HAc], may be taken as substantially 0.10*M*. The concentration of acetate ions [Ac⁻] is only negligibly greater than that of the added sodium acetate, namely 0.05*M*. Hence we write

$$\frac{[H^+] \times 0.05}{0.10} = 1.8 \times 10^{-5}$$

and

$$[H^+] = \frac{1.8 \times 10^{-5} \times 10^{-1}}{5 \times 10^{-2}} = 3.6 \times 10^{-5}$$

The effect of adding a small quantity (0.05*M*) of sodium acetate to a 0.10*M* acetic acid solution is, therefore, to reduce the hydrogen ion concentration from 1.3×10^{-3} to 3.6×10^{-5}, nearly a fortyfold reduction.

The acetic acid–sodium acetate mixture will serve to illustrate another related effect. Suppose to such a mixture there is added a drop of a strong acid such as hydrochloric. The hydrogen ions so introduced will combine with the acetate ions from the sodium acetate to form acetic acid molecules. The solution will not become nearly so strongly acid, that is [H⁺] will remain much lower, than if the same quantity of hydrochloric acid had been added to pure water. On the other hand suppose a drop of strong base such as sodium hydroxide is added to the acetic acid–sodium acetate mixture. Then the hydroxide ions from the base will merely combine with the hydrogen ions from the acetic acid, a little more acetic acid will ionize, and the final result will be little change in the hydrogen ion concentration. A solution such as acetic acid–sodium acetate to which moderate amounts of acid or of base may be added without greatly changing the pH of the solution is said to be a **buffered solution.** The acid-salt mixture is called a buffer. There are many substances and mixtures which can serve as buffers. They are important in the chemistry of living matter. For instance, human blood is normally buffered at about pH 7.4 by the various salts and organic compounds present.

157. SOLUBILITY PRODUCT

A saturated solution of silver chloride in water contains a very small amount of dissolved silver chloride—this compound being commonly, though not quite accurately, referred to as being insoluble. This dissolved silver chloride must, owing to its great dilution, all be present as ions. We may then write

$$AgCl \ (solid) \rightleftarrows Ag^+ + Cl^-$$

For such a solution of a very slightly soluble salt it is found that the product of the two ion concentrations is a constant, that is,

$$[Ag^+] \times [Cl^-] = K_{sp}$$

where $[Ag^+]$ and $[Cl^-]$ represent the molar concentrations of silver ions and chloride ions respectively, and K_{sp} is called the **solubility product.**

For the more general case of any slightly soluble salt A_mB_n yielding m positive and n negative ions according to the equation

$$A_mB_n \ (solid) \rightleftarrows mA^{pos} + nB^{neg}$$

the expression for the solubility product is:

$$[A^{pos}]^m \times [B^{neg}]^n = K_{sp}$$

the concentration of each ion being raised to the power represented by the subscript following it in the formula. For instance, for arsenic sesquisulfide, the reaction is

$$As_2S_3 \rightleftarrows 2As^{+3} + 3S^=$$

and the solubility product is given by

$$[As^{+3}]^2 \times [S^=]^3 = K_{sp}$$

The use of solubility products makes it possible to predict whether or not a given system will produce a precipitate. In the case of silver chloride, referred to above, if in the solution the product of the silver ion concentration multiplied by the chloride ion concentration exceeds the solubility product for silver chloride, then a precipitate may form.

Table 13 gives solubility products for some commonly encountered salts. Use of these data will be illustrated by the following problem:

Problem: To a liter of water are added 2.3 mg. of silver ion and 8.5 mg. of chloride ion. Will a precipitate of silver chloride be formed?

Solution: The ion concentrations must first be expressed as moles per liter. $[Ag^+] = 0.0023/107.9 = 0.0000213 = 2.13 \times 10^{-5}$ moles per liter, and

TABLE 13

SOLUBILITY PRODUCTS AT ROOM TEMPERATURE

Compound	Reaction	K_{sp}
Silver chloride........	$AgCl \rightleftarrows Ag^+ + Cl^-$	1.7×10^{-10}
Silver bromide.........	$AgBr \rightleftarrows Ag^+ + Br^-$	3.3×10^{-13}
Silver iodide..........	$AgI \rightleftarrows Ag^+ + I^-$	8.5×10^{-17}
Lead chloride........	$PbCl_2 \rightleftarrows Pb^{++} + 2Cl^-$	1.7×10^{-5}
Lead chromate........	$PbCrO_4 \rightleftarrows Pb^{++} + CrO_4^=$	1.8×10^{-14}
Aluminum hydroxide...	$Al(OH)_3 \rightleftarrows Al^{+++} + 3OH^-$	1×10^{-33}
Calcium hydroxide.....	$Ca(OH)_2 \rightleftarrows Ca^{++} + 2OH^-$	7.9×10^{-6}
Cupric hydroxide......	$Cu(OH)_2 \rightleftarrows Cu^{++} + 2OH^-$	6×10^{-20}
Ferrous hydroxide.....	$Fe(OH)_2 \rightleftarrows Fe^{++} + 2OH^-$	1.6×10^{-15}
Silver sulfide.........	$Ag_2S \rightleftarrows 2Ag^+ + S^=$	1.0×10^{-51}
Cupric sulfide.........	$CuS \rightleftarrows Cu^{++} + S^=$	4×10^{-38}
Ferrous sulfide........	$FeS \rightleftarrows Fe^{++} + S^=$	1×10^{-19}
Mercuric sulfide.......	$HgS \rightleftarrows Hg^{++} + S^=$	3×10^{-53}
Lead sulfide...........	$PbS \rightleftarrows Pb^{++} + S^=$	1.0×10^{-29}
Zinc sulfide...........	$ZnS \rightleftarrows Zn^{++} + S^=$	4.5×10^{-24}
Barium sulfate........	$BaSO_4 \rightleftarrows Ba^{++} + SO_4^=$	1×10^{-10}
Calcium carbonate.....	$CaCO_3 \rightleftarrows Ca^{++} + CO_3^=$	4.8×10^{-9}
Calcium fluoride.......	$CaF_2 \rightleftarrows Ca^{++} + 2F^-$	3.4×10^{-11}

$[Cl^-] = 0.0085/35.5 = 0.000240 = 2.4 \times 10^{-4}$ moles per liter. The product of these two is

$$[Ag^+] \times [Cl^-] = 2.13 \times 10^{-5} \times 2.4 \times 10^{-4} = 5.1 \times 10^{-9}$$

The solubility product for silver chloride is 1.7×10^{-10} which is smaller than 5.1×10^{-9}. A precipitate will, therefore, be formed.
precip. formed when sol. prod. exceeded

Several other points will now be illustrated by further problems.

Problem: The solubility product of lead chloride, $PbCl_2$, being 1.7×10^{-5} at room temperature, find the solubility of lead chloride in grams of lead ion per liter of solution.

Solution: Since
$$PbCl_2 \ (solid) \rightleftarrows Pb^{++} + 2Cl^-$$
we have, by definition

$$[Pb^{++}] \times [Cl^-]^2 = 1.7 \times 10^{-5}$$

Let x be the concentration of lead ions in a saturated solution of lead chloride, or,

$$[Pb^{++}] = x$$

then

$$[Cl^-] = 2x$$

this last statement being true because according to the equation there are two chloride ions for every lead ion. Hence

$$x \times (2x)^2 = 1.7 \times 10^{-5}$$

$$4x^3 = 1.7 \times 10^{-5}$$

$$x = 1.6 \times 10^{-2} \text{ moles per liter}$$

To convert to grams per liter multiply by the atomic weight of lead, which is 207. Then a saturated solution of lead chloride in water at room temperature contains $1.6 \times 10^{-2} \times 207 = 3.3$ g. of lead ion per liter.

The common ion effect may be applied to slightly soluble salts to alter their apparent solubility. This is illustrated by the following problem:

Problem: What is the solubility of lead chloride, at room temperature, expressed as grams of lead ion per liter of solution containing 2.0M hydrochloric acid?

Solution: As in the previous problem

$$[Pb^{++}] \times [Cl^-]^2 = 1.7 \times 10^{-5}$$

but now virtually all the chloride ion concentration is supplied by the hydrochloric acid. With only negligible error it may be assumed that $[Cl^-] = 2.0$ moles per liter. Then

$$[Pb^{++}] \times (2.0)^2 = 1.7 \times 10^{-5}$$

whence

$$[Pb^{++}] = \frac{1.7 \times 10^{-5}}{4}$$

$$= 4.2 \times 10^{-6}$$

Expressed as grams this $4.2 \times 10^{-6} \times 207 = 8.7 \times 10^{-4}$ grams per liter. The addition of a moderate amount of hydrochloric acid has, therefore, reduced the concentration of lead ions in solution by five thousandfold.

One of the applications of the solubility product principle is to so-called insoluble sulfides such as CuS, As_2S_3, and ZnS. This application calls for use both of the solubility product principle and the ionization constant. It will be illustrated by two problems.

Problem: A solution contains 0.15M Cu^{++} ion and 0.30M H^+. The solution is now saturated with hydrogen sulfide gas. Will a precipitate form and if so, what concentration of cupric ions will remain in solution after equilibrium has been reached?

Solution: We must first calculate the concentration of sulfide ions, $S^=$, in a saturated solution of hydrogen sulfide in water. Reference to Table 12 will show that hydrogen sulfide ionizes in two steps represented by

$$H_2S \rightleftarrows H^+ + HS^-$$

and

$$HS^- \rightleftarrows H^+ + S^=$$

for which

$$\frac{[H^+] \times [HS^-]}{[H_2S]} = K_i = 9.1 \times 10^{-8}$$

and

$$\frac{[H^+] \times [S^=]}{[HS^-]} = K_i = 1.2 \times 10^{-15}$$

Multiplying the first ionization constant by the second we obtain

$$\frac{[H^+] \times [HS^-]}{[H_2S]} \times \frac{[H^+] \times [S^=]}{[HS^-]} = 9.1 \times 10^{-8} \times 1.2 \times 10^{-15}$$

hence

$$\frac{[H^+]^2 \times [S^=]}{[H_2S]} = 1.1 \times 10^{-22}$$

A saturated solution of hydrogen sulfide in water at one atmosphere pressure contains a constant concentration of H_2S amounting to about $0.1M$. We may write, for a saturated H_2S solution,

$$[H^+]^2 \times [S^=] = 1.1 \times 10^{-23}$$

If the solution under investigation contains $0.3M$ H^+, then the sulfide ion concentration must be

$$[S^=] = \frac{1.1 \times 10^{-23}}{(0.3)^2} = 1.2 \times 10^{-22} \text{ moles per liter}$$

Having found the sulfide ion concentration we may now turn to the cupric ion. The solubility product for CuS is 4×10^{-38}, so that

$$[Cu^{++}] \times [S^=] = 4 \times 10^{-38}$$

substituting for the value of $[S^=]$ found above,

$$[Cu^{++}] = \frac{4 \times 10^{-38}}{1.2 \times 10^{-22}} = 3 \times 10^{-16} \text{ moles per liter}$$

This is to say that at equilibrium in this solution the concentration of cupric ions remaining in solution will be only about 10^{-16} moles per liter. As the solution originally contained $0.15M$ Cu^{++} ions it is clear that not only will a precipitate form, but that all but an infinitesimal portion of the copper will precipitate as cupric sulfide.

Hydrogen sulfide was formerly, and still is, used to precipitate metal ions in qualitative analysis. The use of this reagent depends on the very different solubility products of the different metal sulfides. For instance, ferrous ion, Fe^{++}, in solution is readily separated in this way from cupric ion even though both cupric sulfide and ferrous sulfide are commonly classed as "insoluble" substances. The way in which this separation is possible should be clear from the following problem:

Problem: A solution is identical with that in the problem immediately above except that $0.15M$ Fe^{++} is substituted for $0.15M$ Cu^{++} ion. Find, as before, if any precipitate will form, and what concentration of ferrous ions remains in solution at equilibrium.

Solution: The hydrogen ion concentration is $0.30M$ as before, hence the sulfide ion concentration remains at 1.2×10^{-22} moles per liter.

We have

$$[Fe^{++}] \times [S^=] = 1 \times 10^{-19}$$

so that, substituting for $[S^=]$

$$[Fe^{++}] = \frac{10^{-19}}{1.2 \times 10^{-22}}$$

$$= 10^3 \text{ moles per liter}$$

This is to say that at equilibrium this system could theoretically hold in solution the absurdly high total of 1000 moles ferrous ions per liter. But the solution originally contained only $0.15M$ Fe^{++}. It is clear that no precipitate would form. *(Sol. prod. not exceeded)*

158. OXIDATION-REDUCTION REACTIONS

Table 11 (p. 375) gave single electrode potentials and half reactions for a number of half cells. There will now be reviewed how these data may be used to predict the course of a chemical reaction and how the data are related to the equilibrium constant, although no actual calculations of equilibrium constants from electrode potentials will be attempted.

Distinguish clearly between the reduced form of the half reaction and the oxidized form. In the half reaction

$$K \rightleftarrows K^+ + \epsilon$$

the reduced form is K and the oxidized form is K^+.

In the half reaction:

$$2H_2O \rightleftarrows O_2 + 2H^+ + 4\epsilon$$

The reduced form is H_2O, the oxidized form $O_2 + 2H^+$. In all the half reactions given in Table 11 the reduced form is at the left.

Now in general it may be said that at standard concentration *the reduced form in any half reaction will reduce the oxidized form in any half reaction for which the electrode potential is less.* Thus, potassium metal, K, will reduce aurous ion, Au^+, the complete reaction being

$$K + Au^+ \rightleftarrows K^+ + Au$$

and the voltage of the complete cell being $2.92 + 1.68 = 4.60$ volts. This is, of course, a typical displacement reaction and we have simply stated in more explicit terms what was said much earlier about the displacement of one metal by another.

In Table 11 potassium metal is the most powerful reducing agent, fluoride ion, F^-, the weakest. (Those reduced forms lower than about silver are seldom, if ever, referred to as reducing agents.) Similarly, fluorine, F_2, is the most powerful oxidizing agent, potassium ion, K^+, the weakest. (Those oxidized forms higher than about cupric ion, Cu^{++}, are not often referred to as oxidizing agents.)

The expectation of a reaction going to completion, or nearly so, is greater the larger the voltage for the complete reaction. Thus, the reaction of potassium and aurous ion will go effectively to completion, but that between tin and plumbous ion,

$$Sn + Pb^{++} \rightleftarrows Sn^{++} + Pb$$

with an EMF of $0.14 - 0.13 = 0.01$ volts, will by no means go to completion. A supposed displacement reaction of aluminum ion by nickel

$$3Ni + 2Al^{+++} \rightleftarrows 3Ni^{++} + 2Al$$

yields a negative EMF of $0.25 - 1.69 = -1.44$ volts and hence cannot proceed to the right as written, but can proceed to the left, aluminum displacing nickel ion.

The mathematical relationship between electrode potential and the equilibrium constant is

$$RT \ln K = E^0 F$$

where R is a constant known as the gas constant, T is the absolute temperature, $\ln K$ is the *natural* logarithm of the equilibrium constant K, E^0 is the cell voltage, and F is the faraday of electricity. Although application of this equation may seem a trifle formidable it will be clear that the existence of such a formula makes it possible to calculate equilibrium constants for many reactions under varied conditions if the single electrode potentials are known. Reference texts containing this information are of great value for predicting the possible course of a reaction.

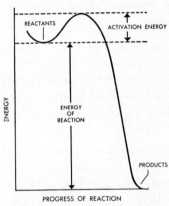

Fig. 23-1. This diagram illustrates the difference between activation energy and energy of reaction. Reactants often behave as if they lie in a trough of energy from which they must be lifted before reaction starts.

159. ACTIVATION ENERGIES

Calculations such as those given earlier in this chapter tell us when reactions are theoretically possible, but they tell nothing about the speed of a reaction. A reaction may be theoretically possible but its speed may be so slow that for all practical purposes the reaction is useless.

The reason for this is that chemical reactions behave somewhat like a billiard ball placed in a shallow trough. If the ball is given a gentle shove over the edge of the trough, then it falls readily to the floor. Many a chemical reaction needs a little energy to get it started over the hump, so to speak, then, if the electrode potentials are appropriate, the reaction may proceed virtually to completion. The energy which must be put into a reacting system, by heating it for instance, is called the **activation energy** of the system, and should not be confused with the heat of reaction, previously discussed. The activation energy is defined by an equation due to Arrhenius

$$k = k'e^{-A/RT}$$

where k is a quantity which expresses the velocity of the reaction, k' is a constant, e is the base of the natural system of logarithms, A is the activation energy, and T the absolute temperature.

We shall not attempt any calculations with the Arrhenius equation. If the activation energy is low the reaction may proceed with high velocity. If the activation energy is high, then the reaction may be quite slow even though calculations based on electrode potentials tell us that the reaction is theoretically possible. In such a case, if the reaction is one of possible value, it would be justifiable to spend time and money searching for a catalyst for the reaction.

160. CATALYSIS

Catalysts occupy a strategic position in many fields of chemistry. Use of the proper catalysts often causes a chemical reaction to proceed to equilibrium in a period of seconds rather than of hours or days. In industry this speeding up by catalysis may make all the difference between financial success and failure. Among the more important industrial applications of catalysis the following come to mind: the synthesis of ammonia, the contact sulfuric acid process, wood alcohol, synthetic gasoline, the hydrogenation of coal, tars, oils, and fats, polymerizations to produce plastics and synthetic rubber, aviation gasoline, and many others.

Although catalysis is so important and has been the subject of many thousands of scientific studies, there is at present no generally satisfactory theory to explain it. Many theories have been advanced and some of these apply in a satisfactory manner to some types of reactions, but not to all. A general theory of catalysis would be very helpful in explaining how and why catalysts work, and especially in making possible the prediction of what catalysts would be most effective for definite reactions.

For a long time the definition of a catalyst was the classical definition of Ostwald: "A catalyst is any substance which changes the velocity of a chemical reaction without being changed itself." But now there is a tendency to broaden this definition. Many authorities in the field are inclined to define a catalyst simply as *a substance which changes the velocity of a chemical reaction.* Thus, the catalyst may or may not be itself changed, it may or may not actually change the course of a chemical reaction, as well as change the velocity.

Discussion of catalysis is often divided into **homogeneous catalysis** and **heterogeneous catalysis.** The former implies that the catalyst and the reacting substance are all in the same phase, that is, there is no readily observable boundary between them. A drop of acid added to a water solution of two reacting substances would be an example of homogeneous catalysis. The contact process, in which the platinum or other catalyst is physically distinguishable from the reacting gases, is an example of heterogeneous catalysis.

Some of the various ways in which catalysts are supposed to operate will be described briefly. One of these is the "intermediate compound" theory. Suppose that a certain reaction, $A + B \rightarrow AB$, proceeds quite slowly, but that $A + C \rightarrow AC$ proceeds rapidly and that $AC + B \rightarrow AB + C$ also proceeds rapidly. Then if we mix $A + B + C$ the final products are $AB + C$. The substance C is restored in its original form so that it simply acts as a catalyst to speed the combination of $A + B$. There is a good probability that many catalytic actions proceed in some such fashion as this. Unfortunately, it is generally very difficult indeed to prove the existence of these intermediate compounds (such as AC), but in some cases, at least, there is definite evidence concerning their existence. When smooth platinum acts as a catalyst in the oxidation of ammonia, the surface of the platinum gradually becomes rough.

$$4NH_3 + 5O_2 \rightarrow 4NO + 6H_2O$$

This apparently is the result of some kind of intermediate compound formed by the platinum. Similarly, when manganese dioxide or ferric oxide act to catalyze the decomposition of potassium chlorate, there is fairly good evidence that the catalyst temporarily assumes a form in which the valence of the manganese, or iron, rises to a higher value.

$$2KClO_3 \rightarrow 2KCl + 3O_2$$

Another way in which some catalysts may operate is through the phenomenon of adsorption. Many substances have the ability to hold others by a loose physical or chemical process, the precise nature of which is not known. For instance, charcoal can thus hold large volumes of various gases, particularly at low temperatures. The military gas mask works on this principle. When gases or other substances are adsorbed in this way, their concentrations must be very greatly increased along the surface of the adsorbing substance. It is well known that increase of concentration speeds up a chemical reaction. The velocity of chemical change must, therefore, be much higher in the layer of adsorbed material.

Still another possible mode of action of catalysts lies in the effect of an adsorbing substance on the valence forces acting in an adsorbed molecule. For instance, when hydrogen is adsorbed on nickel, the distance between the two hydrogen atoms in each molecule is probably greatly increased. The hydrogen may almost be thought of as being adsorbed in the condition of single atoms rather than of molecules. Atomic hydrogen is certainly much more active and able to react chemically much more vigorously than is ordinary molecular hydrogen.

EXERCISES

A. *Define or explain the following:*

activation energy	ionic equilibria
buffered solution	ionization constant
catalyst	solubility product
common ion effect	weak acid
heterogeneous catalysis	weak base
homogeneous catalysis	

C. 1. Write expressions for the ionization constants of the following:
   a. ionization of bicarbonate ion, HCO_3^-.
   b. ionization of silicic acid, H_4SiO_4 (first ionization stage only).
   c. ionization of silver hydroxide, AgOH (a fairly soluble weak base).

   2. a. Calculate the hydrogen ion concentration in a $0.01M$ H_3BO_3 (boric acid) solution.

b. What is the percentage ionization of the boric acid in this solution?

c. What is the pH of the solution? $pH = -\log [H^+]$

3. Calculate the ionization constant for nitrous acid, HNO_2, which in a $0.05M$ solution has a hydrogen ion concentration of 4.7×10^{-3} moles per liter.

4. a. Find the hydrogen ion concentration in a solution which contains $1M$ HCN plus $0.5M$ NaCN.

   b. Find the hydroxide ion concentration in a solution which contains $0.5M$ NH_4OH plus $1M$ NH_4Cl.

5. A drop (0.01 cc.) of concentrated, $18N$, hydrochloric acid added to a liter of buffered solution may change the hydrogen ion concentration by less than 1 per cent. What change of hydrogen ion concentration is produced by adding 0.01 cc. of $18N$ HCl to a liter of pure water?

6. In venous blood the following equilibrium is set up by the carbon dioxide

$$H_2CO_3 \rightleftarrows H^+ + HCO_3^- \quad \frac{[H^+][HCO_3^-]}{[H_2CO_3]} = K = 4.3 \times 10^{-7}$$

If the pH of blood is 7.4, what percentage of the total carbon dioxide is actually present as bicarbonate ions? as pH goes up, acid goes down "down" "up"

7. Write solubility product expressions for the following:

   a. $Ni(OH)_2$.

   b. Ag_2SO_4.

   c. Hg_2I_2 (contains the ion Hg_2^{++}).

8. a. To 500 cc. of water containing 7.2 mg. of barium nitrate, $Ba(NO_3)_2$, there are added 500 cc. of water containing 3.3 mg. of sulfuric acid. Will a precipitate of barium sulfate be formed? (Note that the total volume becomes virtually 1000 cc.)

   b. Find the solubility of calcium fluoride in milligrams per liter of solution.

9. The solubility of silver chromate, Ag_2CrO_4, is about 0.030 g. per l. Find the solubility product.

10. Find the weight, in milligrams per liter, of silver ion which will remain in solution if to $0.0025M$ silver nitrate solution there is added sodium bromide to make the solution $0.30M$ in bromide ion.

11. a. Find the weight of Pb^{++} ion which would remain in 100 cc. of solution, $0.5N$ in strong acid, after saturation with hydrogen sulfide.

    b. Find the same for Zn^{++} ions.

12. From the solubility product of mercuric sulfide, and Avogadro's number (6.03×10^{23}) calculate the number of mercury ions present in a liter of saturated mercuric sulfide solution.

13. a. Between which of the following pairs of substances may an oxidation-reduction reaction be expected to take place?

Mn and Hg^{++}	I^- and Br_2
Mn and Mg^{++}	K^+ and H^+
Ca and Zn	Fe and I_2
Ni and F^-	Pt and Ni^{++}
Cl_2 and H_2O	H_2 and Cu^{++}

    b. Write balanced ionic equations for those pairs which react, and show the EMF produced in cells containing $1M$ solutions of the ions.

14. Under what conditions might the following reaction go to the right?

$$H_2 + Pb^{++} \rightleftarrows Pb^0 + 2H^+$$

15. a. Use of a catalyst often, though not always, results in a decrease of activation energy. Represent this statement by a suitable diagram.

    b. The reaction between permanganate ion and oxalic acid

$$2MnO_4^- + 5H_2C_2O_4 + 6H \rightleftarrows 2Mn^{++} + 10CO_2 + 8H_2O$$

is said to be "autocatalytic" because it is catalyzed by one of the products, manganous ion (Mn^{++}). This reaction, although having a favorable EMF, is often quite sluggish about starting. Suggest a method for getting the reaction to go.

NUCLEAR CHEMISTRY

> *. . . such interchange of state,*
> *Or state itself confounded to decay.*
> —William Shakespeare

161. NATURAL RADIOACTIVITY *

In Chapter 2 we briefly mentioned the discovery of radioactivity, and of the elements polonium and radium. We shall first review those discoveries and amplify our previous remarks.

X rays were discovered in 1895, and the stimulus thereby given to scientific research was shown by many studies in related fields. A French scientist, Henri Becquerel, undertook to investigate possible radiations, like X rays, which he thought might be emitted by the fluorescent salts of uranium. Potassium uranyl sulfate was one of these substances. Becquerel found that this compound, and other compounds containing uranium, emit rays which are able to darken a photographic plate even though the plate is completely covered with black paper. His discovery was reported to the French Academy of Sciences in 1896.

The following year, the study of Becquerel rays, as they were called, was undertaken by Pierre and Marie Curie. The Curies observed that certain minerals containing uranium emit stronger Becquerel rays than does pure uranium metal. They suggested that the minerals might contain a new element and that this element might show the property of radioactivity to a greater degree than does uranium.

A careful study of the mineral *pitchblende* led, in 1898, to discovery of the element polonium, so named after Mme. Curie's native country. This element emits Becquerel rays with an intensity several hundred times that of uranium.

Further study of *pitchblende* led the Curies, in the same year, to the discovery of radium. The separation and identification of radium proved to be

* G. Hevesy and F. A. Paneth, *A Manual of Radioactivity* (London: Oxford University Press, 1938).

a tedious job. The first pure sample was not obtained until 1902. It showed about *three million times* as great radioactivity as uranium.

Since the initial discovery of radioactivity by Becquerel, there have been

Fig. 24-1. Marie Curie

Marie Sklodowska was born in Poland in 1867. She studied at the Sorbonne in Paris and married her professor, Pierre Curie. Together they discovered polonium and radium, opening a new world for scientific research. Her husband died in 1906, but she continued her scientific studies and was twice awarded the Nobel Prize, once in physics and once in chemistry. She raised two daughters: one, Eve, a well-known author; the other, Irene, to become the distinguished codiscoverer of artificial radioactivity.

The life of Marie Curie was one of extraordinary selfless devotion to her work and to her family. She died in 1934 beloved by her country and by scientists everywhere. Of her Albert Einstein once said: "She is the only one whom fame has not corrupted." (*Culver Service*)

found about fifteen naturally occurring elements showing this property. But a very much larger number of radioactive elements has been made synthetically.

The radiations emitted by radioactive substances are of several different kinds. Considering only the naturally occurring radioactive elements, there appear to be three different kinds of radiations. The identity of these radiations was established largely by Sir Ernest Rutherford. The radiations are called **α-**, **β-**, and **γ-rays.** They differ in several respects, as follows:

The α-rays have a low penetrating power and are greatly reduced in intensity by a single sheet of paper. They are also deflected by a magnetic or electric field in such direction as to show that they are positively charged. Measurements on the mass and charge of these rays show that they are helium ions, namely helium atoms which have lost two electrons. An α-particle is, therefore, the nucleus of a helium atom. The velocity with which α-rays are ejected during radioactive disintegration is of the order of 20,000 kilometers per second.

The β-rays have higher penetrating power, and the direction of deflection in a magnetic field shows that they are negatively charged. β-rays are electrons traveling with speeds above 100,000 kilometers per second, and often approaching the velocity of light.

The γ-rays, on the other hand, are not particles. They have no weight and show no deflection in a magnetic field. They have high penetrating power. These rays are similar to X rays but have somewhat shorter wave lengths. Their velocity is the same as that of light, namely 300,000 kilometers per second.

Table 14 summarizes these facts concerning the three types of radiations emitted by various radioactive elements. It should be pointed out that the various radioactive elements emit either α- or β-rays, rarely both. The γ-rays are emitted immediately after the emission of either an α- or a β-ray.

TABLE 14

PROPERTIES OF α-, β-, AND γ-RAYS

Ray	Mass	Charge	Penetrating Power	Velocity	Identity
α	4	$+2$	Poor	20,000 km/sec.	He^{+2}
β	$\frac{1}{1837}$	-1	Fair	100,000	$-\epsilon$
γ	0	0	Large	300,000	Electromagnetic wave

The several rays from radioactive substances are not necessarily now detected by their effect on a photographic plate. The most useful instruments for the study of these radiations are the electroscope, and the Geiger counter. The latter will be described more fully in a later section.

The phenomena associated with radioactivity are believed to be a consequence of the disintegration, or natural decay, of the atoms. The nuclei of these atoms are regarded as having a certain degree of instability. Out of every large group of atoms of radium, some atoms will explode soon, others later. For a single atom of radium it would be impossible to predict the moment of disintegration. But for the very large numbers of atoms present in weighable amounts of radium, the number of atoms which will disintegrate in any time interval is readily predictable. This situation is not unlike that faced by life insurance companies. The life span of one man is not predictable. But for a large group of men it is possible to predict the number who will survive to any given age.

The weight of a radioactive element which will disintegrate in a given time depends solely on the weight taken at the start of the measurements. The time necessary for half the weight of any sample to decay, or disintegrate, is called the **half-life** of the element. If we started with one gram of radium, then at the end of one half-life there would be half a gram of radium left. At the end of the second half-life there would be one quarter gram left, and at the end of the third half-life one eighth gram left.

The rate of decay of an element, and consequently its half-life, do not depend upon temperature, pressure, chemical combination, or any other ascertainable condition.* Some elements such as uranium have very long half-lives. Others such as radium C' have half-lives of the order of a few millionths of a second. The half-life of radium is 1600 years.

The emission of an α-ray or a β-ray has a definite predictable effect on the atom undergoing this process. It will be recalled that the atoms of the various elements are characterized by the nuclear charge, or atomic number.

Suppose a radioactive atom has an atomic number Z and an atomic weight A. The emission of an α-particle reduces the atomic number to $Z - 2$, and reduces the atomic weight to $A - 4$. These changes are a consequence of the facts that α-particles have a charge of $+2$ and a mass of 4. If the atomic number is reduced by two units, the element will be changed to an element situated two places to the left in the Periodic Table. To take a specific example, radium has the atomic number 88 and the atomic weight 226. It emits an α-particle, thus losing two charge units and four mass units. It will then become an element with the atomic number 86 and the atomic weight 222. The element with atomic number 86 is called *radon* and belongs in the inert gas series of elements in Group 0. It differs in almost every respect from radium, which chemically and physically resembles barium.

The emission of a β-particle produces a different kind of change. β-particles

See notes Fall qtr. [handwritten marginal note]

---

* A very slight dependence of decay rate on mode of chemical combination has recently been reported for some elements.

have a charge of -1, but the mass is negligible by comparison with that of the heavier atoms. Emission of a β-particle will raise the atomic number to $Z + 1$, but the atomic weight will remain substantially unchanged. For instance, an element with atomic number 82 (lead) would be converted to 83 (bismuth), but the atomic weight would remain unchanged. Do not confuse the electron coming from the nucleus with those in the various energy levels surrounding the nucleus. Some authorities think that the beta particle results from a neutron in the nucleus splitting into a proton plus an electron. Thus the emission of a beta particle would have the effect of raising by one unit the positive charge on the nucleus.

Problem: A.: element with atomic number 86 and atomic weight 222 emits in succession two α-particles and one β-particle. What is the atomic number and atomic weight of the final product?

Solution: Loss of two α-particles would lower the atomic number by four units, while loss of a β-particle would raise it by one unit. The final atomic number would be 83. Loss of two α-particles would lower the atomic weight by eight units, while loss of a β-particle would not change the atomic weight. The final atomic weight would be 214.

We shall now start with uranium and trace the sequence of radioactive changes which occur. Ordinary uranium may be represented as $_{92}U^{238}$, meaning * the isotope with atomic number 92 and atomic weight 238. This emits α-particles, becoming an element sometimes called uranium X_1, but of the same atomic number as thorium. We shall designate it $_{90}Th^{234}$. The decay of $_{92}U^{238}$ has a half-life of 4.5×10^9 years. The element $_{90}Th^{234}$ in turn emits a β-particle, yielding uranium X_2, or $_{91}Pa^{234}$. This change has a half-life of 24.1 days. These changes, and the subsequent ones, are shown in the chart below. This chart shows the sequence of radioactive changes from uranium to the final product, which is lead. The chart shows not only the various elements formed, but also the kind of radiation accompanying each change, and the half-life of each element. For convenience, the chart is arranged in the same fashion as the short form of the Periodic Table. It will be noted that no *gamma* radiation is indicated. The γ-rays are emitted by a secondary process following either α- or β-ray emission. Emission of γ-rays does not in itself produce any change in the element. The chart does not indicate some minor complications caused by some of the elements disintegrating in more

* An international committee has recommended that the atomic weight be placed at the upper left corner of the symbol, thus: $_{92}^{238}U$. The designation $_{92}U^{238}$ is current American practice.

TABLE 15

RADIOACTIVE DISINTEGRATION OF URANIUM TO LEAD

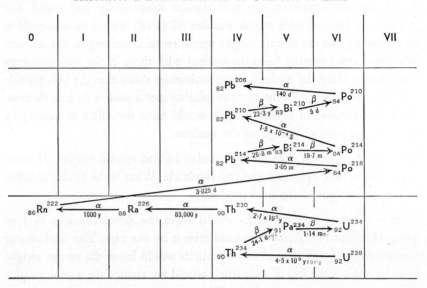

than one way. This chart shows what is commonly called the *uranium dis-integration series*. There are three other series known among the naturally occurring elements, and many such series among the synthetic radioelements.

It will be noted that several of the radioactive elements exist with more than one atomic weight. For instance, there are shown in the chart three kinds of lead, namely $_{82}Pb^{206}$, $_{82}Pb^{210}$, and $_{82}Pb^{214}$. The atomic number in each case is, of course, the same; otherwise the element could not be lead. But the existence of several atomic weights shows that several isotopes of lead are present. This observation was actually one of the first in which isotopes were noted. It was not until later that isotopes were found to be common among nearly all the elements, whether radioactive or not.

The different isotopes of an element may show very different radiochemical properties. For instance, $_{82}Pb^{214}$ is strongly radioactive with a half-life of only 26.8 minutes. But $_{82}Pb^{206}$ is stable (nonradioactive); one might say that the half-life of this isotope is infinity. It is clear from these observations that radioactivity is a property of the individual isotopes of the elements, and not of the mixture of isotopes often found in nature. It may be worth recalling at this point that the atomic weights of the elements as commonly given in tables refer to the natural mixture of isotopes, rather than to any specific isotope.

162. AGE OF THE EARTH

And God said, "Let the waters under the heaven be gathered together unto one place, and let the dry land appear": and it was so.—Genesis 1

Most astronomers think that the planets were torn from the sun, possibly by a passing star. Creation of the earth occurred so long ago, and was attended by such titanic disturbances, that we can only conjecture when in the dim past that event may have taken place. But the moment that the rocks began to solidify into their present patterns, they began to leave signs which we can now interpret. The principles of radioactivity may be used to estimate the ages of rocks and minerals, including those of meteorites. These methods constitute a major tool in the science of geology.

There are several methods for the radiochemical estimation of the age of a mineral. We shall describe one method in some detail.

Reference to Table 15 will show that a uranium atom undergoes the emission of eight α-particles (plus several β-particles) before it is finally converted to a stable isotope of lead. Each α-particle is a helium ion. From the rate at which uranium decays, it may be shown that 1 gram of uranium, in its various stages of disintegration, would produce helium at the rate of 1.18×10^{-7} cubic centimeters (S.C.) of helium per year. Then the age of the mineral is given by the formula:

$$\text{Years} = \frac{\text{cc. of Helium}}{\text{g. of Uranium} \times 1.18 \times 10^{-7}}$$

$$= \frac{\text{cc. He}}{\text{g. U}} \times 8.5 \text{ million years}$$

This method for determining the age of minerals and rocks is subject to certain corrections. For instance, the uranium is slowly used up during disintegration, so that what may be a gram of uranium now will have actually been considerably over a gram a billion years ago. Furthermore, thorium is often associated with uranium in rocks, and the disintegration of thorium also yields helium. Finally, the helium formed in rocks and minerals tends to leak out, so that the amount found is smaller than that actually generated. In this way the ages of rocks as found by this method tend to be too short. Nevertheless, when care is taken in the analytical work and in the selection of specimens, this method can give surprisingly concordant results. Several corrections are commonly applied because of the several difficulties mentioned above. The method is applicable to rocks which contain as little as 10^{-5} cubic centimeters of helium per gram, and correspondingly minute amounts of uranium.

The ages run from a few million to a maximum of about two billion years. Meteorites give similar results, ranging from about 100 million to 2,800 million years. It appears that the oldest geological specimens to which we have access have ages not much in excess of two billion years. We can only conclude that this was the time at which the earth first began to solidify, and also that the history of the meteorites has not been greatly different from that of minerals on the earth. It seems certain from these studies that the meteorites actually belong to our planetary system, and are not visitors from interstellar space.

163. THE SUN

Nuclear chemistry has an answer to the old problem concerning the source of energy in the sun. How is the sun able to pour energy into space in such prodigious amounts for such long periods? The solar energy theory most popular at the present time is that hydrogen is being converted into helium.

The over-all equation for this process may be written

$$4_1H^1 \rightarrow {}_2He^4 + 2\beta^+ + \gamma$$

or, in words: four hydrogen atoms are converted into one helium atom and at the same time there are liberated two positrons * and a large amount of energy in the form of γ-rays.†

It may be wondered why such a process yields such large quantities of energy. We can answer this question by reference to a very celebrated relationship developed on theoretical grounds by Albert Einstein. Einstein showed that mass and energy are related to each other by the expression

$$E = mc^2$$

where E is the energy, m is the mass, and c is the velocity of light. From this relationship one may calculate that a mass of one gram is equivalent to the very large energy of about 2×10^{13} calories. This means that the conversion of one gram of mass into energy would be equivalent to the burning of roughly three thousand tons of coal. The true significance of Einstein's relationship will, however, become apparent in a later section when we consider the process of nuclear fission.

Now let us go back to our equation for the conversion of hydrogen into helium and write down the exact atomic weights. Four moles of hydrogen atoms weigh $4 \times 1.008 = 4.032$ g. One mole of helium atoms weighs 1×4.003 g. The mass lost is then 0.029 g. for four moles of hydrogen atoms, or roughly 0.007 g. per gram of hydrogen. This weight may be reduced a trifle by the two positrons emitted. From this we see that the conversion of one gram of hydrogen to helium would be an exothermic process and that

---

* We use the symbol β^+ for the **positron**, or positive electron. This particle has the mass of an electron but has a positive charge. It was first discovered by Anderson at California Institute of Technology in 1932. The positron is a common product of artificially induced radioactivity.

† The transmutation of hydrogen to helium probably takes place through a sequence of steps. The equation shows only the initial reactant and the final products.

the energy released would be about 140 billion calories. Fortunately hydrogen is present in the sun in abundance, or at least enough at the present rate of consumption to last another billion years.

164. ARTIFICIAL RADIOACTIVITY *

The problem of atomic **transmutation,** the conversion of one element into another, has interested natural philosophers since the earliest times. The long history of alchemy, the forerunner of modern chemistry, is an endless description of efforts to transmute base elements, such as lead, to more precious elements, such as gold. But all these efforts were unsuccessful.

The modern theories of atomic structure indicate how atomic transmutation must be achieved. No superficial change involving the electron cloud will suffice to change one element into another. The basic differences between elements lie in the charge in the nucleus. Transmutation must occur by addition or subtraction of protons from the nucleus, but this is a difficult operation. The nucleus of an atom is like an inaccessible valley surrounded by high mountains. The addition of a negative charge to the nucleus is hindered by the repulsion of the negative electron cloud. The addition of a positive charge is hindered by the positive nucleus itself. Of course, it will be clear that the natural radioactive changes described in the preceding section are examples of atomic transmutation. But these occur spontaneously. We are not able to control the process, and it occurs with only a relatively few kinds of atoms.

The first artificial atomic transmutation was announced by Lord Rutherford in 1919. It was clear that the electrical barrier surrounding a nucleus could only be penetrated by very powerful atomic projectiles. The α-particles emitted by some of the decay products from radon are given off at very high velocities. Rutherford bombarded nitrogen gas with these high-energy α-particles. In a small fraction of atomic collisions between α-particles and nitrogen atoms there were produced atoms of hydrogen.

For such a change it is possible to write an equation, just as the more familiar chemical reactions are represented by equations. The equation for the transmutation of nitrogen under the influence of α-particles is as follows:

$$_7N^{14} + {}_2He^4 \rightarrow {}_1H^1 + {}_8O^{17}$$

This equation states that nitrogen atoms with a mass of 14 react with helium atoms to yield hydrogen atoms plus an isotope of oxygen with a mass of 17. (The reader may wonder what has happened to the two positive

* E. Pollard and W. L. Davidson, Jr., *Applied Nuclear Physics* (New York: Wiley, 1951).

charges on the α-particle. Such charged particles quickly pick up electrons from external sources and become neutral. For instance, radium emits α-particles, but if radium is placed in an enclosed tube, the tube soon contains neutral helium atoms.)

The equation written above is a typical equation for a nuclear reaction. It will be noted that both mass and nuclear charge are balanced, and that in this respect the nuclear equation differs from a chemical equation. The mass

Fig. 24-2. Ernest Rutherford

Rutherford was born in New Zealand, in 1871. He was educated at the University of New Zealand and at the University of Cambridge.

He taught at McGill University, Montreal, and later at the University of Manchester. In 1919 he became director of the celebrated Cavendish laboratory at Cambridge. In 1908 he received the Nobel Prize in Chemistry, and in 1931 he became Baron Rutherford of Nelson.

Rutherford made many of the basic discoveries in the field of radioactivity. With Bohr, and others, he elaborated a theory of atomic structure. In 1919 he produced the first artificial transmutation of an element (that of nitrogen into oxygen). For many years he was a vigorous leader in laying the foundations of the great developments in atomic science, which he did not live to see. He died in 1937. (*Wide World Photo*)

numbers (atomic weights) add up to 18 on each side, and the charge numbers (atomic numbers) add up to 9 on each side. The fact that hydrogen and an isotope of oxygen are produced in this reaction is amply proved by several lines of evidence, including studies in the Wilson cloud chamber.

This method for producing atomic transmutations is effective in a few cases other than that described. But even the most energetic α-particles from natural sources have insufficient energy to penetrate any but the lighter nuclei. In recent years, however, electrical devices have been constructed for imparting extremely high energies to particles such as α-rays, β-rays, protons, etc. One of such instruments, namely the cyclotron, will be described below. With the aid of high energy (high velocity) particles produced in this way, a great variety of atomic transmutations has become possible. Some of the more important of these nuclear reactions will be described now.

The bombardment of aluminum-27 with α-particles yields in part silicon-30 and hydrogen.*

$$_{13}Al^{27} + {}_2He^4 \rightarrow {}_1H^1 + {}_{14}Si^{30}$$

This reaction is, of course, very similar to that described above for the transmutation of nitrogen-14.

Nuclear transmutations may be induced by particles other than α-particles. For instance, high velocity protons can bring about such changes as that shown below.

$$_8O^{18} + {}_1H^1 \rightarrow {}_9F^{18} + {}_0n^1 \quad \text{or} \quad O^{18}(p, n)F^{18}$$

The ions of heavy hydrogen, or deuterium, are very effective in bringing about nuclear changes. It will be recalled that deuterium is the isotope of hydrogen which has a mass of two. The ions of this isotope are called **deuterons**. A deuteron bears the same relationship to an atom of deuterium $(_1H^2)$ as the proton bears to ordinary hydrogen $(_1H^1)$. Examples of nuclear changes induced by deuterons include the following:

$$_{11}Na^{23} + {}_1H^2 \rightarrow {}_{11}Na^{24} + {}_1H^1$$

Notice that in the above reaction the product is an isotope of the original atom of sodium.

The neutron, as a subatomic particle, was not discovered until 1932. It was identified by Chadwick at Cambridge University as a product of a nuclear reaction similar to some of those mentioned above. Chadwick bombarded beryllium with α-particles obtained from a naturally radioactive source. The reaction which takes place is as follows:

$$_4Be^9 + {}_2He^4 \rightarrow {}_6C^{12} + {}_0n^1$$

This discovery not only marked a major advance in nuclear structure, but added a particularly valuable projectile for nuclear bombardment. Neutrons have a great advantage over protons, α-particles, and deuterons. The neutrons, having no charge, are not repelled by either the electron cloud surrounding

---

* Nuclear reactions such as that shown above are not infrequently represented by a simplified equation, as follows:

$$Al^{27}(\alpha, p)Si^{30}$$

This shows that aluminum-27, bombarded by alpha particles yields silicon-30 plus protons. This method is simpler and gives just as much information as the more conventional type of equation.

the nucleus or by the nucleus itself. They are able to penetrate the nucleus with great ease. Thus the efficiency of nuclear bombardment is greatly increased by the use of these particles. Furthermore, the neutrons are easily produced by the comparatively simple method of mixing beryllium with a little radium. The radium acts as a source of high energy α-particles, which in turn liberate neutrons during the $Be^9(\alpha, n)C^{12}$ reaction. The spectacular advances leading to perfection of the atomic bomb have yielded an even more abundant source of neutrons. This is the uranium pile, which will be described in the following chapter.

Examples of nuclear reactions induced by neutrons include the following:

$$_{47}Ag^{107} + {}_0n^1 \rightarrow {}_{47}Ag^{108}$$
$$_{15}P^{31} + {}_0n^1 \rightarrow {}_{15}P^{30} + 2{}_0n^1$$

It should be pointed out that prior to the atomic bomb development, the actual amounts of elements involved in nuclear changes was exceedingly small. No one had actually seen the products of nuclear bombardment. The products were always identified by indirect evidence. But the large-scale transmutation of elements is now well established. At the time of writing, not only are elements being manufactured in pound lots, but at least traces have been made of every chemical element of atomic numbers 1 to 98, including all the elements not yet discovered to occur in nature!

In 1933 the bombardment of certain light elements by α-particles was being conducted in France by Irene Curie and her husband Frederic Joliot.*

One of the elements under investigation was boron, and the nuclear reaction is as follows:

$$_5B^{10} + \overset{\alpha}{{}_2He^4} \rightarrow {}_7N^{13} + {}_0n^1$$

It was found that when the source of α-particles was removed, the boron mixture continued to emit radiations and that this peculiar radioactivity behaved as though there were present a radioactive element with a half-life of about ten minutes.

This observation was the first discovery of **artificial radioactivity.** It opened a new world for scientific research. The explanation is that the nitrogen isotope with a mass of 13 is itself radioactive. It disintegrates with the emission of a positron, leaving the isotope of carbon with a mass of 13. The reaction is:

$$_7N^{13} \rightarrow {}_6C^{13} + \beta^+$$

It will be noted that the isotope $_7N^{13}$ is not found in nature. Ordinary atmospheric nitrogen is not radioactive. The radioactive isotope must be

* These people are respectively the daughter and son-in-law of Pierre and Marie Curie.

regarded as a product of artificial synthesis. Perhaps when the world was made this radioactive isotope of nitrogen was also made. But owing to its high activity, and corresponding short half-life, the isotope has long since disappeared. The same is true of many artificial radioactive isotopes. In fact, only those with tremendously long half-lives have managed to survive to the present time. Radium has, of course, a half-life of only 1600 years, but it is continually being formed through the decay of uranium, which has a half-life of over a billion years.

Immediately after the initial discovery of artificial radioactivity, attempts were made to find other examples of the effect. These attempts were brilliantly successful. Neutron-induced reactions were found to be particularly valuable in producing radioactive isotopes. At the present time several hundred radioactive isotopes are known. Some of these have proved to be of the very greatest importance in chemistry, physics, biology, and medicine. We shall describe some of these substances and their uses in the next section.

We now review briefly, in Table 16, the several principal types of nuclear transmutations of which examples have been given above. It should be understood that while Table 16 will serve as an aid to the memory, it by no means exhausts the various types of nuclear reactions known. As an example of the use of Table 16 one might give the following: suppose it is desired

TABLE 16

PRINCIPAL TYPES OF NUCLEAR REACTIONS

Bombardment with	Often Produces
Protons............	p, n
Deuterons..........	d, p; and d, n
Alphas.............	α, p; and α, n
Neutrons...........	n, − (simple capture)

to make some tritium (hydrogen isotope with mass of three). Two reactions worth trying would be (1) bombardment of deuterium, $_1H^2$, with neutrons, and (2) bombardment of deuterium with deuterons. The first does not work very well, but the second is satisfactory.

$$_1H^2 \text{ (or } _1D^2) + _1H^2 \rightarrow _1H^3 + _1H^1$$

We shall conclude this section with a brief discussion of the **cyclotron** (Fig. 24-3). This is an instrument devised by Professor Ernest O. Lawrence of the University of California. The first model was built in 1932. The cyclotron is designed to give high velocities, and as a consequence high energies, to the various subatomic particles which have been found useful in producing nuclear transformations. These particles include electrons, α-rays, protons, and deuterons.

The particles in question all bear electric charges. The acceleration of such particles becomes a problem of subjecting them to such electric fields that they will move more and more rapidly until they reach the velocity required for nuclear bombardment. The chief difficulty in doing this directly is the inconveniently high electric fields required. Professor Lawrence invented

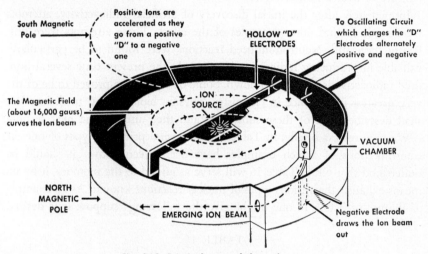

Fig. 24-3. Principal parts of the cyclotron.

a method for accelerating the particles with the use of only moderate electric fields.

If a particle carrying an electric charge is caused to move in a magnetic field, the particle will be forced into a curved path. A proton moving in a magnetic field will go around in a circle. This is simply the result of the action of the magnetic field on a moving electrical charge.

In the cyclotron the charged protons, or other particles, are placed near the center of a strong magnetic field produced by a very large electromagnet. The magnetic field is divided into two compartments shaped like the two halves of a pie cut across a diameter. The protons are placed at the center of the pie. The whole pie is in the magnetic field. The upper and lower crusts of the pie consist of metal plates to which strong electric charges may be brought. The protons are free to move in an evacuated space between upper and lower pie crusts. These two halves of the pie are more commonly referred to as the "D's" (dees) of the cyclotron, from their obvious resemblance in shape to the capital letter D.

One D is now made positive, the other negative. The proton moves in a curved path toward the negative side and thereby acquires some velocity. Just as the proton has completed a semicircle, the charges on the dees are reversed so that the proton receives a new impulse and hastens toward completion of a circular path. Each time the proton completes a semicircle, the charge on

Fig. 24-4. Cyclotron at the University of Rochester. The large cylindrical objects are magnet coils and poles. They are surrounded by a yoke of iron. The men are looking in toward the "Dees." (Acme Photo)

the dees is reversed so that the proton goes faster and faster. As the proton's circular velocity increases, it tends also to fly away from the center of the magnetic field; hence it actually spirals away toward the outer circumference of the dees. All the while the velocity keeps increasing until it is fast enough to produce the desired nuclear changes. Then the proton is allowed to strike whatever element is under study.

This instrument has been remarkably successful in the production of new isotopes, and it was a major factor in research leading to the separation of plutonium for use in the atomic bomb. The cyclotron and related instruments, such as the betatron and the synchrotron, are very important devices in the study of nuclear transmutations.

165. TRACER RESEARCH

In Chapter 8 reference was made to the use of heavy hydrogen as a tracer element for the solution of a variety of chemical problems. For instance, the progress of the individual atoms in a drink of water may be followed through the animal body by using heavy water. The discovery of artificial radio-activity has extended this technique to include nearly all the chemical elements in a great variety of chemical reactions and processes. The method

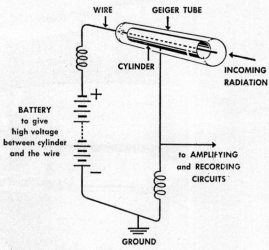

Fig. 24-5. Geiger-Müller tube and electrical circuit for counting ionizing radiations as from radioactive substances.

will be illustrated by a few examples chosen from several different branches of chemistry.

We shall first describe one of the instruments used in tracer research. This is the **Geiger-Müller counter.** Suppose we have a small metal cylinder through the center of which there is a thin metal wire. The wire is insulated from the cylinder and a very high voltage difference is applied across the cylinder and wire. The whole apparatus is enclosed in a glass tube from which all air is removed, but which contains a small amount of vapor such as a mixture of alcohol and argon.

If now any ionizing radiation, as from a radioactive substance, enters the counter tube, it sets up a slight electrical discharge from cylinder to wire. This discharge may be amplified and recorded in a number of ways. Thus, we can measure the intensity of the radiation from any radioactive source by placing it near a Geiger tube. The intensity of radiation may be recorded as a dial reading, as a number of clicks, or recorded graphically on a sheet of paper. Such instruments of many varieties are commercially available and find applications in all types of nuclear research. They are especially valuable in tracer research.

Application of tracer methods may be illustrated by the following: Air contains a very minute, though measurable, amount of carbon-14 which is radioactive with a half-life of 5580 years. The C^{14} is present as carbon dioxide. When living organisms, such as trees, grow they take in carbon dioxide, including the trace of radioactive material. This then proceeds to disintegrate slowly, giving up beta rays. After the tree is dead no further uptake of carbon dioxide occurs, hence it is possible, by measuring the radioactivity of the carbon in the wood, to estimate how long it is since the tree stopped growing. In this way quite accurate dates have been found for prehistoric buildings going back 10,000 years and more.*

It would be difficult to overemphasize the advantages which have come to biology and medicine through these tracer techniques. Radioactive iron has brought new knowledge concerning the red blood cells, concerning the manufacture and use of hemoglobin in the body, and what happens to red blood cells during a transfusion. Radioiron, along with sodium, hydrogen, and other tracer elements, has been used in studies of the placental barrier between mother and fetus. Radiosodium has been used in studies of the blood circulation and in many other biochemical problems. In fact, many ideas in biology and physiology have been radically altered by these new experimental tools. One of the most useful tracers has proved to be the third isotope of hydrogen, $_1H^3$, which has a half-life of about 20 years, and which is produced by a $D(d, p)$ reaction—in other words, by the bombardment of deuterium with deuterons. Much of the early work on plutonium in producing the atomic bomb was done on a tracer scale.

166. MEDICAL USES OF ARTIFICIAL RADIOACTIVITY

Tracer experiments of the types described in the preceding section will ultimately provide great advances in medicine, through better understanding of biochemical processes. The large quantities of artificial radioelements now available from the uranium piles are also stimulating the medical uses of these substances. But in this section we will consider only two radioelements and their status in the treatment of certain diseases at the present time. These elements are phosphorus and iodine, P^{32} (14.3 day half-life), and I^{131} (8 day

* W. F. Libby, *Radiocarbon Dating* (Chicago: Univ. of Chicago Press, 1950).

half-life). The first application is of radioiodine to a pathological condition of the thyroid gland.

The thyroid gland is located in the neck. It has the important function of taking iodine from the blood stream and converting it to the organic compound thyroxin, $C_{15}H_{11}O_4NI_4$, which controls the rate of oxidation of living tissues. When the thyroid is overactive, too much thyroxin is generated. The patient exhibits severe poisoning symptoms, and death may result. The disease is often treated by removing part of the gland by surgery, but this operation is always unpleasant and often dangerous.

Radioiodine is exactly similar to ordinary iodine in all its chemical properties. It differs only in being radioactive. Up until the instant that the active atom disintegrates, it is scarcely possible to distinguish between active iodine and inactive, ordinary, iodine. The thyroid gland certainly can make no such distinction. If radioiodine is given to an animal, this iodine quickly collects in the thyroid gland. This may be proved very easily by placing a Geiger counter near the neck of the animal. However, the radioactivity of such iodine tends to destroy tissue in which it is imbedded. A proper dose of radioiodine will effectively reduce the amount of thyroxin generated, and so relieve the patient of his symptoms.

At the present time it seems well established that overactivity of the thyroid gland may be controlled in about 80 per cent of the patients by giving radioactive iodine. This is a very important advance in the treatment of this disease. There is, however, some danger in the use of this treatment. Overexposure to radiations of any kind has a tendency in the living tissue to produce cancer. There remains some uncertainty regarding the exact dosage to cure the hyperthyroidism, but not to induce an even more serious disease.

There are also conditions in which radiophosphorus has proved useful. The disease *polycythemia* is a condition in which the formation of red blood cells is abnormally rapid. It is not a form of cancer and the disease in itself is not fatal, but the symptoms are severe and the complications may lead to death. It is found that proper doses of radioactive phosphorus result in disappearance of the symptoms, and that this improvement lasts several years without further treatment. The patient is enormously relieved. The use of radiophosphorus appears now to be the method of choice in the treatment of this disease.

Very extensive experimentation is under way in the possible treatment of cancer by radioelements. In a few isolated cases there appear to have been cures. The situation at the time of writing, however, is that while these experiments give some hope of leading to eventual cures, no great optimism is as yet justifiable.

EXERCISES

A. *Define or explain the following:*

α-, β-, and γ-rays   neutron
cyclotron (diagram)   nuclear reaction
deuteron   positron
$E = mc^2$ tracer (in radioactivity)
Geiger (Geiger-Müller) counter   transmutation
half-life (as applied to radioactive substances)

B. 1. Describe the discovery of natural radioactivity.
    2. Compare the radiations from radioactive substances. (This is conveniently done in a table.)
    3. How may the age of rocks and minerals be determined?
    4. Describe a current theory for the sun's energy.
    5. What was the reaction in Rutherford's first nuclear transmutation?
    6. Write nuclear equations for the production of the following: Si^{30}, F^{18}, Na^{24}, Ag^{108}, P^{30}.
    7. What reaction was used in the discovery of neutrons?
    8. Describe the discovery of artificial radioactivity.
    9. What, in general, are the nuclear reactions to be expected on bombardment with (a) protons, (b) deuterons, (c) alphas, and (d) neutrons?
    10. Give an example of the use of radioactive tracers.
    11. How may radioisotopes be used in medicine?

C. 1. Define the term "chemical element," and defend your definition.
    2. Discuss the Law of Conservation of Mass in the light of modern knowledge.
    3. Uranium-235, $_{92}U^{235}$, loses successively an α-particle, a β-particle, an α-particle, and a β-particle. What is the name, atomic number, and mass number (atomic weight) of the element formed?
    4. Starting with any nucleus of atomic number (charge) Z, and atomic mass A, show the effect of each of the following changes. (The effect of a beta particle coming out and of a neutron going in to the nucleus, are shown as examples.)

	Change	Effect on Z *(at. no.)*	Effect on A *(at. wt.)*
$_{1}\beta^{0}$	Beta out	+1 ?	None
$_{0}n^{1}$	Neutron in	None	$A+1$
	Neutron out	*none*	$A-1$
$_{1}H^{1}$	Proton in	$Z+1$	$A+1$
	Proton out	$Z-1$	$A-1$
$_{1}H^{2}$	Deuteron in	$Z+1$	$A+2$
	Deuteron out	$Z-1$	$A-2$
$_{2}He^{4}$	Alpha in	$Z+2$	$A+4$
	Alpha out	$Z-2$	$A-4$
	Positron out		
	H^3 in		

5. a. It is found that a sample of radioactive material is half disintegrated in 18 hours. How much will remain at the end of 36 hours?

b. The half-life of a radioactive element is 5 days. Starting with 1 g., what weight will remain in 30 days? Starting with 2 g., what weight will remain in 30 days?

6. An ordinary chemical reaction such as the burning of hydrogen yields about 29,000 calories per gram. How sensitive a balance would be necessary to detect the conversion of mass to energy in this reaction?

7. Complete, and balance, the following nuclear equations:

a. $_1H^2 + \gamma \rightarrow n + ?$

b. $_7N^{14} + n \rightarrow _7N^{13} + ?$

c. $? + _1H^1 \rightarrow _{10}Ne^{20}$

d. $_9F^{19} + ? \rightarrow _8O^{16} + _2He^4$

e. $_7N^{14} + _2He^4 \rightarrow ? + _1H^1$

f. $_{15}P^{31} + _1H^2 \rightarrow _{15}P^{32} + _1H^1$

g. $_{83}Bi^{209} + _2He^4 \rightarrow _{85}At^{211} + ?$

8. Indicate possible equations for nuclear reactions which might properly be attempted for production of the following:

a. N^{13} from C^{12}

b. Br^{80} from Br^{79}

c. C^{14} from C^{12}

d. S^{35} from S^{34}

e. Au^{198} from Au^{197}

9. There have recently been discovered some bombardment reactions involving fairly heavy particles. The preparation of californium-244, $_{98}Cf^{244}$, by bombardment of U^{238} with carbon-12 is an example of such a reaction. Write the nuclear equation for this reaction.

10. a. Two blocks of iron are pressed tightly together. Design an experiment to test if the atoms in one block ever diffuse into the other block.

b. Design an experiment involving a tracer element to measure the total volume of blood in an animal without removing more than a drop of the blood.

CHAPTER

25 ATOMIC POWER

Know ye that no man can split an atom . . .

These words, spoken by John Dalton in the year 1803, are no longer true.

The appalling implications of nuclear energy burst upon the world a short time before this book was written. We shall try in this chapter to trace something of the general principles and historical background of the subject. We do so confident that many new developments will have been discovered, and perhaps made public, before the gentle reader turns this page.

167. NUCLEAR FISSION

Discovery of the neutron, and of its potentialities in the induction of nuclear transmutations, opens up an old problem which has interested generations of scientists. This is the problem as to whether elements of higher atomic number than uranium can exist in nature, or can be made artificially. Bombardment of uranium with neutrons might be expected to yield products such as U^{239} by neutron capture.

$$_{92}U^{238} + _{0}n^{1} \rightarrow _{92}U^{239}$$

This reaction might be followed by emission of a β-particle, with consequent formation of element 93.

$$_{92}U^{239} \rightarrow 93^{239} + \beta^{-}$$

Neutron bombardment of uranium was conducted in 1934 by an Italian physicist, Enrico Fermi.* The products obtained through this bombardment were difficult to identify, but for some years they were actually accepted as new elements of atomic numbers greater than that of uranium. We know now that this identification was wrong, but these initial experiments eventually led to one of the most important scientific discoveries of all time.

This general problem, the neutron-bombardment of uranium, was undertaken by two German scientists, both of whom had had a long and distin-

---

* Fermi later in the United States became a very distinguished leader in research leading to the atomic bomb.

467

guished experience in nuclear chemistry and physics. Their names were Otto Hahn, and his coworker, Strassmann. In January of 1939 they announced their discovery that the bombardment of uranium with neutrons yields not **trans-uranium** elements (elements of higher atomic number than uranium), but common elements of which barium was the first identified. The appearance of barium, with an atomic number of 56 and a mass of about 138, from $_{92}U^{238}$ could only take place by a splitting of the uranium nucleus into fragments. This was the discovery of a hitherto unsuspected type of nuclear reaction, and of a process which was to have a profound effect on the history of the world. This process by which uranium atoms split into two roughly equal parts is called nuclear *fission*. The extraordinary importance attached to fission is due not to the elements formed in this way, but to the prodigious amount of energy released at each nuclear explosion, and to the possibility of the reaction becoming self-perpetuating, or chain-reacting.

We shall examine the fission process in more detail. Uranium is subjected to bombardment with neutrons. Uranium has several isotopes of which that with the mass of 235 most readily undergoes fission. For the moment, we shall confine our attention to the most abundant isotope with mass 238.

The nucleus of $_{92}U^{238}$ must consist of 92 protons plus 146 neutrons. Suppose that this nucleus is broken exactly in half. Then each fragment would consist of 46 protons and 73 neutrons. The element produced by such a process would be palladium and the atomic weight would be $46 + 73 = 119$. But the heaviest known isotope of palladium has an atomic weight of only 111, and the heaviest stable isotope has an atomic weight of only 110. It is clear that there are too many neutrons. We might tentatively describe the process as follows:

$$_{92}U^{238} + _0n^1 \rightarrow _{46}Pd^{110} + _{46}Pd^{110} + 19 \text{ excess neutrons}$$

Actually, the split of uranium occurs in such a way that two unequal fragments are formed, one with the approximate mass of 140 and the other with mass of 90. Furthermore, these primary products are themselves highly radioactive and emit neutrons or electrons, or both, until stable isotopes are formed. In this way a large number of products (called **fission products**) may actually be identified as resulting from uranium fission. Many of these are extremely radioactive and contribute greatly to the difficulties and hazards associated with nuclear energy. However, for the primary process we may write, as an example:

$$_{92}U^{238} + _0n^1 \rightarrow _{56}Ba^{140} + _{36}Kr^{94} + 5 \text{ excess neutrons}$$

But even this equation is subject to correction, as we shall see.

For the moment, let us focus our attention on the excess neutrons. Suppose that for every uranium atom undergoing fission only two excess neutrons were ejected. These two neutrons could induce fission in two more uranium atoms. The four neutrons ejected could cause fission in four more uranium atoms. The number of neutrons will double at each "generation," so that their number will multiply extremely rapidly. Recall that at each fission a very large amount of energy is also liberated. It is clear, therefore, how once the fission process is started it can quickly reach extreme violence. This sudden release of great energy constitutes the atomic explosion.

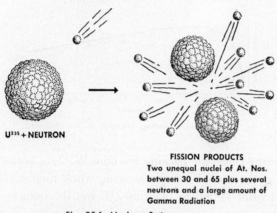

U²³⁵ + NEUTRON

FISSION PRODUCTS
Two unequal nuclei of At. Nos.
between 30 and 65 plus several
neutrons and a large amount of
Gamma Radiation

Fig. 25-1. Nuclear fission process.

Shortly after the discovery of nuclear fission it was found that the most abundant isotope of uranium, $_{92}U^{238}$, was not responsible for the effect. Another isotope, $_{92}U^{235}$, was shown to be the source of all this energy. Uranium-235 is present in ordinary uranium as found in nature to the extent of only seven-tenths of one per cent. The reason why atomic explosions do not occur in every sample of uranium is clear. The bulk of the uranium is $_{92}U^{238}$, which is not ordinarily subject to fission. It acts as a diluting agent for the $_{92}U^{235}$ just as the nitrogen in air dilutes the more active oxygen.

The final question to be discussed in this section is the obvious one: "Where does all the energy come from?" The answer to this question goes back to a point already discussed, namely the conversion of matter into energy. It was pointed out in a previous section that the sun's energy probably comes from the transmutation of hydrogen into helium and that this process involves a loss of mass because four hydrogen atoms weigh more than one helium atom.

A similar state of affairs is found in the fission of uranium-235. The fission

products and excess neutrons together weigh slightly less than the original
U^{235}. This excess mass amounts to only about $\frac{1}{1000}$ of the original weight
of the U^{235}. But in accordance with Einstein's law this mass is converted into
a very large amount of energy. Over Hiroshima about one gram of mass was
actually converted to energy, but the energy produced was enough to destroy
the city.

This possibility of nuclear reactions taking place with liberation of great
amounts of energy can occur only with certain chemical elements. These
elements are those of quite low atomic weight and also those of quite large
atomic weight. In order to describe this effect we shall find it necessary to

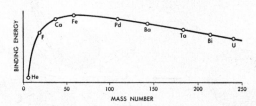

Fig. 25-2. Nuclear binding energies of the elements.

explain a quantity called the **packing fraction.** We have heretofore referred
to the masses of the various isotopes as being whole numbers. For instance,
we refer to chlorine-35 and to uranium-238. But the isotopes do not have
weights which are accurately expressible as whole numbers, even though we
take oxygen-16 as our standard. Thus the hydrogen atom actually weighs
1.008, calcium-40 weighs 39.999, uranium-238 weighs about 238.001. These
slight deviations from whole numbers are called packing fractions. The
elements from hydrogen to fluorine have positive packing fractions (i.e., the
masses are larger than whole numbers); the elements from fluorine to platinum have negative packing fractions; and those heavier than platinum have
positive packing fractions.

The packing fraction of an element is a measure of its nuclear binding
energy. **Binding energy** is the energy required to break a nucleus into the
protons and neutrons of which it is made. Those elements with the largest
positive packing fraction are said to have the smallest binding energy, while
those with the lowest packing fraction (Fig. 25-2) are said to have the
highest binding energy. Those elements with the lowest binding energy are
considered to be unstable with respect to conversion into those of higher
binding energy.

If an element is transmuted to one of larger binding energy, energy will
be released. Thus hydrogen converted to helium releases energy, but cal-

cium converted to fluorine would require the absorption of energy. Bismuth converted to tantalum would release energy, but iron could scarcely be converted to any other element without the absorption of energy. These relations are not unlike those existing between exothermic and endothermic chemical reactions. It should now be clear that atomic energy might, in theory at least, be produced by breaking down (by **fission**) the heaviest known elements, or by building up (by **fusion**) from the lightest elements, but not by transmutations involving the elements of intermediate atomic weight. Of course, just as in the case of ordinary chemical reactions, the energy relations may be favorable for a nuclear reaction but the speed of the reaction may or may not be such as to make it useful. For the fission of U^{235} the speed is favorable, but for the fission of U^{238} it is not.

We may now summarize the fission process as shown by uranium-235. A neutron enters the nucleus of $_{92}U^{235}$. The nucleus becomes unstable as a result of this intrusion. The nucleus splits into two fragments, one a little larger than the other. These fission fragments are together a little lighter than the uranium-235, and the excess mass is converted to energy. Simultaneously excess neutrons are liberated and, under favorable conditions, these neutrons produce a chain reaction leading to a terrific explosion.

168. URANIUM-235

Realization that only a less abundant isotope of uranium undergoes fission presents a new problem in the development of nuclear energy. If uranium-235 can be obtained relatively free from uranium-238, then the production of an atomic explosion is comparatively easy. But this poses a major difficulty. Isotopes are so nearly alike in chemical and physical properties that their separation was for a long time regarded as virtually impossible.

Until about the year 1922 no positive separation of isotopes had been obtained, and not until 1932 was any appreciable separation possible. In 1931 the heavy isotope of hydrogen was discovered. Heavy hydrogen, or deuterium, differs from ordinary hydrogen to a greater degree than do the isotopes of any other element. This is because the deuterium atom is 100 per cent heavier than the hydrogen atom. Consequently, all the properties which depend upon mass, such as diffusion, are appreciably different in these two isotopes. The methods for separating and preparing pure deuterium have already been discussed in Chapter 8.

But the separation of U^{235} from U^{238} is a very different problem. The difference in mass is only slightly over 1 per cent. At first glance the problem seems to be insoluble. But under the lash of wartime necessity the problem was not only solved, but solved in several different ways. We shall first say something about the occurrence and properties of uranium.

The element uranium was discovered by Klaproth in 1789. The element was named uranium because the planet Uranus had been discovered by the astronomer Herschel in 1781. Uranium was the first element in which the phenomenon of radioactivity was discovered.

Uranium occurs chiefly as *pitchblende,* a complex mineral containing about 80 per cent of the oxide U_3O_8; and as *carnotite,* a complex mineral containing chiefly oxides of uranium, potassium, and vanadium. Uranium is a fairly rare element. The principal known world deposits are in northern Canada and the Belgian Congo. There are also well-known deposits in Czechoslovakia, Colorado, and Utah, and in several other parts of the world. If any major unknown deposits exist anywhere in the world, they will probably be discovered soon in view of the extraordinary importance which this element has assumed. Before World War II not much metallic uranium had ever been prepared. It is a silvery metal, almost as dense as tungsten, but with a somewhat lower melting point. It is considerably more active chemically than either molybdenum or tungsten. Small amounts of uranium are used in alloy steels, in ceramics, and in various other ways. But all these are of quite negligible importance in comparison with the atomic bomb. A few compounds which will be mentioned are as follows: uranyl nitrate, $UO_2(NO_3)_2$; sodium zinc uranyl acetate, $NaZn(UO_2)_3(C_2H_3O_2)_9 \cdot 9H_2O$; sodium diuranate, $Na_2U_2O_7 \cdot 6H_2O$; "green" oxide, U_3O_8; uranium hexafluoride, UF_6; uranium peroxide, $UO_4 \cdot 4H_2O$; and uranium dioxide, UO_2.

One of the methods successfully used to separate U^{235} was through the use of diffusion. It will be recalled that according to Graham's law the rate of diffusion of a gas varies inversely as the square root of the density. If we have a gaseous compound of uranium, the molecules containing the lighter isotope will diffuse slightly faster than those containing the heavier isotope. The difference is very slight. But uranium forms a gaseous compound, uranium hexafluoride, (UF_6), and by repeating the process thousands of times it is possible, as all the world now knows, to prepare pure U^{235}. The engineering difficulties in this operation were staggering and the cost has been stated to have been well over half a billion dollars. But the plant at Oak Ridge, Tennessee, was successful.

Another method which was successful in separating U^{235} was based on the same principle on which the mass spectrograph operates. A stream of uranium ions is passed through a strong magnetic field. The field causes the ions to move in a curved path. The radius of curvature depends on the mass of the ions. Thus, if we have ions of different masses they will travel along different paths and thereby become separated. This method, called the electromagnetic method, is fantastically expensive, yet it yielded good results.

Methods for fabricating an atomic bomb from the purified isotope have not been made public at this writing. The general principle involved is, however, understandable. Any atom of uranium-235 tends to undergo fission with attendant expulsion of neutrons. These neutrons can cause fission in more atoms. If each uranium atom undergoing fission gives off enough neutrons to cause *more* than one other atom to explode, then the process will spread rapidly and a large-scale explosion will result. But in normal circumstances some neutrons are lost and some react with impurities. A small lump of uranium-235 does not explode because the **reproduction factor** is not over one. That is, each atomic fission results in no more than one more fission. The explosion process never builds up to a dangerous degree. But in a large lump of uranium-235, fewer neutrons are lost by escape to the surroundings, hence more are available for producing more fission. The reproduction factor is greater than one, and a great explosion results.

The mass of uranium which is just large enough to explode is called the **critical mass.** Anything larger will explode; anything smaller than the critical mass will not explode. A method of making an atomic bomb should now be clear. Two lumps of U^{235} of a little less than the critical mass are assembled. These are kept apart until the moment for explosion arrives. Then the two lumps are quickly brought together, as by shooting one lump at the other from a gun. As the two lumps come together their combined mass exceeds the critical mass, and an atomic explosion results.

169. PLUTONIUM

The separation of uranium-235 is a monumental achievement. But surely the advances to be described in the present section constitute the most fantastic in all the long history of science. This advance is no less than the large-scale synthesis of an element with higher atomic number than uranium.

Throughout the preceding discussion it may have been implied that uranium-235 is the only substance which undergoes nuclear fission. This is not the case. Fission has been demonstrated for several other elements. It is possible to predict with reasonable accuracy what isotopes will be subject to fission and what elements will not. Possibly at sufficiently high temperatures all heavy elements undergo this process. An approximate theory developed by Bohr and others enables us to say in advance whether a given isotope is likely to be serviceable for the development of atomic energy or not. On the basis of this theory it was predicted in 1941 that an element of atomic number 94 and atomic weight 239 would readily undergo fission. The suggestion that such an element could be made synthetically and actually used to hasten the end of World War II must have seemed utterly irresponsible.

It has been shown how the common uranium isotope with a mass of 238 does not readily undergo fission. But this isotope takes part in another reaction. When $_{92}U^{238}$ is bombarded with neutrons, a nuclear reaction takes place leading to formation of another isotope of uranium.

$$_{92}U^{238} + {_0}n^1 \rightarrow {_{92}}U^{239}$$

This reaction takes place only under the special condition that the neutrons must not be traveling too fast. The neutrons ejected by uranium-235 during fission are traveling at speeds far too great for them to be absorbed and react with uranium-238. If, however, these neutrons can be slowed down, they may then react with the U^{238}. The U^{239} product is itself radioactive. It emits a β-ray leading to formation of element 93 with a mass of 239. Element 93 is called **neptunium** (Np).

$$_{92}U^{239} \rightarrow {_{93}}Np^{239} + \beta^-$$

The half-life of $_{92}U^{239}$ is only 23 minutes; consequently the product of bombarding uranium with slow neutrons is quickly converted to neptunium.

The isotope $_{93}Np^{239}$ itself emits a β-ray with the formation of element 94 with a mass of 239. This element is called **plutonium** (Pu). The half-life of $_{93}Np^{239}$ is 2.3 days.

$$_{93}Np^{239} \rightarrow {_{94}}Pu^{239} + \beta^-$$

Consequently neptunium is soon converted to plutonium. So far as further disintegration is concerned, plutonium is reasonably stable, but it is definitely subject to the fission process.

The synthesis of plutonium can, therefore, be achieved as follows: pure uranium contains 0.7 per cent U^{235}. This spontaneously undergoes fission and the process may be accelerated by preventing escape of the neutrons ejected in the fission process. No large-scale explosion takes place because of the diluting effect of the uranium-238, which is present in large amount. If now the neutrons can be slowed down, some of them will react with U^{238}, forming in turn U^{239}, Np^{239}, and finally Pu^{239}. Plutonium differs chemically from uranium. It may, therefore, be separated from the remaining uranium and the accumulated fission products by ordinary appropriate chemical reactions such as precipitation and filtration.

It is found that neutrons may be slowed down by any light element, of which the most efficient are deuterium, oxygen, carbon, and beryllium. Carbon in the form of graphite was the choice for the plants which actually produced plutonium during World War II. Heavy water has also been used.

The apparatus in which uranium is converted in part to plutonium is

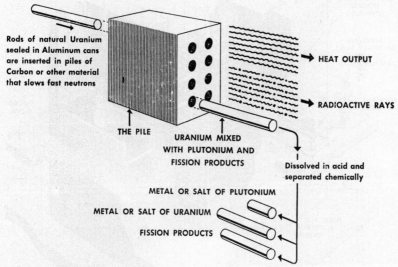

Fig. 25-3. Manufacture of plutonium. (After E. C. Weaver and L. S. Foster, *Chemistry for Our Times*, McGraw-Hill Company, 1947. By permission)

called a nuclear reactor (or uranium pile). It consists of a huge pile of graphite (which is referred to as the **moderator**) surrounded by massive concrete walls to prevent escape of the fearful and deadly radiation emitted during the process. The graphite pile has many holes through it. Into these holes there are inserted lumps of uranium metal encased in aluminum cans. These are called "slugs." The uranium stays in the pile for some time, after which it is removed and treated chemically for the extraction of the accumulated plutonium. Rigid control is necessary to prevent neutrons from accumulating so rapidly that a disastrous explosion would result. Control of the pile is effected by the insertion of some substance which will absorb neutrons. Such substances are cadmium, or boron steel. When the pile is not in operation several such cadmium strips may be inserted into slots in the pile. These will bring the reproduction factor to less than one. Then as the pile is set in operation, the control rods are slowly removed until the neutron intensity reaches a favorable value for production of plutonium, but not so high that an explosion might occur.

The first uranium pile was operated on December 2, 1942, at the Univer-

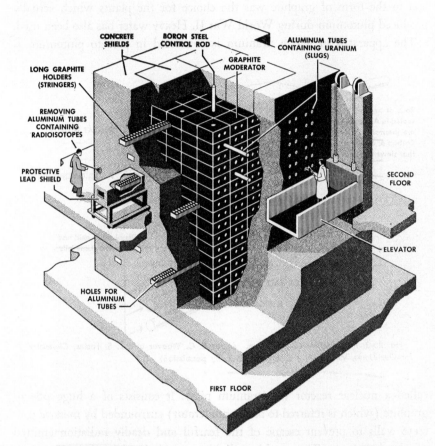

Fig. 25-4. A cutaway drawing showing the main features of a nuclear reactor. The method used for preparing radioisotopes is shown, as well as the inserting of the tubes containing uranium for producing the chain reaction. (*Brookhaven National Laboratory*)

sity of Chicago. It was first operated at an energy output of ½-watt, about the same as a flashlight bulb. But the great pile at Hanford, Washington, required the Columbia River to dissipate the tremendous energy liberated.

After the uranium slugs have been in the pile for some time, they are removed for extraction of the plutonium. The actual percentage of plutonium is still extremely small, and the situation is further complicated by the presence of the fission products. The fission products are highly radioactive and thus extremely dangerous. They are equivalent to tons of radium. For this reason all the chemical operations necessary to obtain pure plutonium must be carried on by remote control. The problem is to make a chemical

Fig. 25-5. One face of the nuclear reactor at Brookhaven National Laboratory. (*Brookhaven National Laboratory*)

separation of several grams of plutonium from several thousand grams of uranium in the presence of twenty or more dangerously radioactive fission products.

The exact method for doing this separation has not been made public. A possible method makes use of **coprecipitation,** a procedure commonly used in radioactive chemistry. This method involves the precipitation of small concentrations of an element along with a "carrier" precipitate of some other element. For instance, a trace of iron in solution may be precipitated by adding aluminum ions, then ammonium hydroxide. The aluminum hydroxide precipitate carries down the trace of iron, even though the solubility product of iron hydroxide is not exceeded.

Plutonium has several oxidation states. The separation process actually used at Hanford could take advantage of these oxidation states as follows: Plutonium in the +4 oxidation state could be precipitated with a carrier precipitate. Then the combined precipitate could be dissolved, the plutonium oxidized to the +6 state, and the carrier element reprecipitated while the plutonium remains in solution. Some fission products which are not precipitated with the carrier remain in solution when plutonium (+4) is precipitated. Other fission products are removed when the plutonium is in the +6 state. Successive cycles of oxidation and reduction are carried out until the plutonium is sufficiently pure.

After plutonium is extracted as indicated above, it may be fabricated into an atomic bomb in the same way that uranium-235 is used.

It should be pointed out that the uranium piles have an important use not connected with the production of plutonium. The high neutron intensities are valuable for irradiating many elements for producing radioactive isotopes. The general availability of these isotopes will have a great effect on tracer research, especially that of a biochemical and physiological nature.

The uranium piles also have possible applications as sources of power. Large energies are liberated, and the use of such sources for industrial and domestic purposes may in some circumstances prove to be economically feasible.

Uranium-235 is the only known naturally occurring fissionable nucleus, but one other, in addition to plutonium-239, may be made artificially. This is uranium-233 which may be made from thorium in accordance with the following sequence of reactions:

$$_{90}\text{Th}^{232}(\text{n}, \gamma)_{90}\text{Th}^{233} \xrightarrow[\text{23 min.}]{\beta^-} {}_{91}\text{Pa}^{233} \xrightarrow[\text{27 days}]{\beta^-} {}_{92}\text{U}^{233}$$

It will be seen that a nuclear reactor operating at high efficiency might be able to produce more fissionable material, Pu^{239} or U^{233}, than is used up in the process. This could occur when there are enough neutrons available to produce, say, two atoms of plutonium for every atom of uranium-235 undergoing fission in the reactor. A reactor in which this is done is known as a **breeder,** and offers the hope of regenerating the atomic fuel until all the uranium (238 as well as 235) has been used up. This would result in a great economy and an increase in our energy resources.

In this discussion nothing has been said about the hydrogen bomb. But the principle of fusion of light elements to heavier ones, and the attendant release of energy, should be clear. The impression at this writing is that the only way such a process could be brought about would be to raise the mixture to a temperature approaching that in the sun. The only known way to achieve such temperatures is in the atomic bomb explosion itself. Thus it would presumably be necessary to set off a uranium-235 or a plutonium-239 bomb in order to set off the hydrogen bomb.

170. THE TRANS-URANIUM ELEMENTS

In this section we shall make some general remarks concerning the elements, both natural and artificial, which lie near uranium in the Periodic Table. Before doing so it will be desirable to go a little more fully than heretofore into the electronic configuration of the elements known as the **rare earths.**

TABLE 17

THE RARE EARTHS (LANTHANIDES)

			La	Ce	Pr	Nd
Pm	Sm	Eu	Gd	Tb	Dy	Ho
Er	Tm	Yb	Lu			

The rare earth elements are those from lanthanum (57) to lutetium (71). These elements show great resemblances to each other in their chemical and physical properties. For instance, they all show the valence of +3, and the solubilities of their compounds differ only slightly. A reason for this curious similarity is found in the arrangement of electrons within this group. For most elements an increase of atomic number is attended with the addition of an electron to the highest normal energy level. For sodium the electron arrangement may be expressed as 2, 8, 1—that is, there are two electrons in the first energy level, eight in the second, and one in the third. For magnesium the arrangement is 2, 8, 2; and for aluminum 2, 8, 3. In each case the change occurs in the highest normal energy level. But for the rare earth group of elements the highest normal energy level has the same number of electrons throughout. The change occurs deep inside the atom. The only difference in electronic configuration between praseodymium (atomic number 59) and neodymium (60) is that the fourth energy level has one more electron in the latter. Actually, electrons are present in both these elements out to the sixth energy level.

The elements from thorium to californium resemble each other more than they do the elements hafnium to platinum. This state of affairs has suggested to several scientists that the elements near uranium might form a group similar to the rare earths. In this group the additional electrons would be built into the fifth energy level rather than the fourth. There is some evidence in favor of this view.

Fig. 25-6. Atomic bomb explosion at Bikini. The small dark objects are Navy ships. (*United States Air Force*)

The rare earth elements are sometimes called lanthanides after lanthanum, the first member of the group. The name "actinides" has been applied to those elements starting with actinium and including thorium, protactinium, uranium, neptunium, plutonium, americium, curium, berkelium, and californium. But at the present time opinions are divided concerning where in the Periodic Table this series actually begins. The weight of evidence at this writing is that the series which resembles the rare earths does not start with actinium, and may not start before neptunium or even plutonium, in which case the name "actinides" is not very appropriate.*

As of today, the periodic system consists of ninety-eight known, identified elements. There are positively known at least one isotope, stable or radioactive, for each element from atomic number 1 to 98 inclusive.

* J. K. Dawson, *Nucleonics*, Vol. 10, pp. 39-45 (1952).

Thus we conclude the most fantastic development in all science. We have purposely omitted most of the names of distinguished scientists who led the atomic bomb project. Our reasons for so doing are obvious. Compton, Fermi, Urey, Oppenheimer, Lawrence, Szilard, Seaborg, Bohr, Oliphant, Chadwick, and many others are household words, known wherever men can read.

For development of the atomic bomb everyone should be familiar with the famous Smyth report, *A General Account of the Development of Methods of Using Atomic Energy for Military Purposes under the Auspices of the United States Government* (Princeton University Press, 1945). Some other general references are given below.

S. Glasstone, *A Sourcebook on Atomic Energy* (New York: Van Nostrand, 1950).
R. R. Williams, *Principles of Nuclear Chemistry* (New York: Van Nostrand, 1950).

EXERCISES

A. *Define or explain the following:*

actinide	moderator
americium	neptunium
binding energy (nuclear)	nuclear fission
breeder reactor	nuclear fusion
carnotite	packing fraction
coprecipitation	pitchblende
critical mass	rare earth
curium	reproduction factor
fission products	transuranium elements

B. *Indicate procedures and all equations possible:*

1. Describe the discovery of nuclear fission.
2. Why was the production of U^{235} so expensive?
3. Where does the energy come from in nuclear fission?
4. Under what conditions can nuclear fission become a continuous, or chain-reacting, system?
5. What is the significance of the packing fraction with respect to nuclear energy?
6. What method might be feasible in the construction of an atomic bomb?
7. How is plutonium produced? Include nuclear equations.
8. Describe, so far as possible, the uranium pile.
9. How does the production of plutonium differ from that of uranium-235?
10. Why is the production of plutonium extremely dangerous?
11. Discuss the possible electronic structure and properties of the elements near uranium in the Periodic Table.
12. In the development of atomic power each of the following elements has an important use: carbon, boron or cadmium, aluminum, uranium, and fluorine. Describe in detail the particular use of each element, with due

reference to sources and possible substitutes. Do not, for instance, merely say that carbon is used as a neutron moderator. Explain how it works and why it is necessary.

13. Write nuclear equations for the production of uranium-233.

C. 1. The interior of the earth is believed to be largely metallic iron. Discuss the possibility that the earth could blow up in one vast nuclear fission explosion.

2. Why is the energy released in nuclear fission so much greater than that released in ordinary radioactivity, such as U^{238} emitting an alpha particle?

3. a. All the methods for separating uranium-235 depend on having the uranium as a gaseous compound. Why is this?

   b. Compare the diffusion rates of U^{235} and U^{238} in the compound uranium hexafluoride.

4. Suppose two lumps of U^{235} are obtained of slightly less than the critical mass. These are brought together quite slowly rather than rapidly. What might be expected to happen?

5. Why does not plutonium form in uranium ore deposits?

6. Before use, plutonium must be purified from fission products. Why is this not necessary for uranium-235?

7. Is there any obvious reason why all possible chemical elements should now be known?

8. In a breeder reactor the accumulating fission products might eventually act like a control rod in lowering the reproduction factor. How could this difficulty be surmounted?

9. Write a possible balanced nuclear equation for the fission of uranium-233.

CHAPTER 26 CARBON

																H	He
Li	Be	B												**C**	N	O	F	Ne
Na	Mg	Al												Si	P	S	Cl	A
K	Ca	Sc	Ti	V	Cr	Mn	Fe	Co	Ni	Cu	Zn	Ga	Ge	As	Se	Br	Kr
Rb	Sr	Y	Zr	Nb	Mo	Tc	Ru	Rh	Pd	Ag	Cd	In	Sn	Sb	Te	I	Xe
Cs	Ba	La-Lu	Hf	Ta	W	Re	Os	Ir	Pt	Au	Hg	Tl	Pb	Bi	Po	At	Rn
Fr	Ra	Ac	Th	Pa	U-												

Carbon occupies a position unique in the science of chemistry. We know far more compounds which contain carbon than those which do not contain carbon. Carbon is the central element in the structure of the **biosphere,** the layer of living matter which inhabits the earth's surface, and of which we are part. The compounds of carbon make up a large and important branch of chemistry—some would say the most important single branch. This is the science of foods, dyes, drugs, perfumes, hormones, plastics, and endless arrays of new substances in infinite variety.

It was once thought that most of the carbon compounds could only be prepared through the action of a mysterious vital force acting in living matter; hence the name "organic" was applied to this branch of chemistry, as compared with "inorganic" chemistry to which most of our attention has been devoted in the preceding chapters. But in 1828 a German chemist, Friedrich Wöhler, reported that he had synthesized an organic compound. He converted a typical inorganic substance, ammonium cyanate, NH_4OCN, into urea, $CO(NH_2)_2$. Urea is a common organic substance excreted in human urine. Since that time hundreds of thousands of organic compounds have been prepared.

Although "organic" chemistry has lost some of its original significance, yet the name remains. **Organic chemistry** is the chemistry of the carbon compounds, and to these the remaining chapters of this book will be devoted. Nevertheless a few carbon compounds belong more properly to inorganic than to organic chemistry. The more important of these will be described in this chapter.

Carbon is an element of contrasts: the foulest odors and the sweetest perfumes, the deadliest poisons and the miraculous life-giving drugs, the humble lump of coal and the glittering diamond.

171. ALLOTROPY OF CARBON

Carbon forms at least two crystalline allotropic modifications, graphite and diamond. If sugar, as an example, is heated excessively it is converted to a black substance called **charcoal.** Charcoal seems to consist of minute, imperfect crystals of graphite. The properties and uses of charcoal are sufficiently different from those of graphite that they will be discussed separately.

Charcoal is a soft, black substance without odor or taste. It melts at the very high temperature of over 3500° C. Charcoal conducts the electric current. It burns in air and unites vigorously with oxygen, but it is inert to a great many other chemical reagents.

Charcoal is obtained by heating, in a restricted amount of air, substances containing carbon. Such substances are wood, sugar, shells and pits of nuts, various petroleum products, animal matter, and coal. The name "charcoal" is generally restricted to that derived from wood, sugar, or nuts such as coconut shells. Its principal use, and that of bone-black derived from animal matter, is based on its ability to remove poisons, disagreeable odors, and colors from air, sewage, and edible products such as corn syrup. Lampblack or **carbon black** is made by burning oil in a reduced amount of air—that is, the oil is made to burn with a smoky flame. In this way a large part of the oil becomes converted to water and carbon instead of to water and carbon dioxide. This very soft black powder is used as a black pigment, in rubber tires, India ink, typewriter ribbons, and printer's ink. The charcoal derived from heating coal in a restricted amount of air is called "coke." This is of great importance in metallurgical operations such as the manufacture of iron.

Charcoal possesses to a remarkable degree the power to **adsorb** other substances. If a solution of indigo or of brown sugar is poured through a layer of charcoal, the liquid emerges quite colorless. This power is developed most strongly by first heating the charcoal in air or in steam. The charcoal is then said to be **activated.** This is the principle upon which military gas masks operate. Air is drawn through a layer of charcoal contained in the canister. Most poisonous gases are completely removed in the fraction of a second during which the air is in contact with the charcoal. The adsorptive property of properly activated charcoal is so great that many hours of exposure to poison gas is permissible before the mask begins to fail. Charcoal in gas masks does not protect against gases of low density such as carbon monoxide, or against toxic smokes. But comparatively simple devices such as a catalyst mixture and a paper filter render the mask effective against all known chemical warfare poisons.

Similar considerations apply to the decolorizing of sugar and the treatment of sewage wastes. The mixture is agitated with activated charcoal or boneblack and all disagreeable substances are removed. In some cases this process is so efficient that effluent water from sewage disposal plants is safe to drink.

Adsorption is not quite the same as chemical combination. In most cases the adsorbed substance is easily removed by heating the charcoal. Adsorption seems to be related to the surface area of the charcoal. Because of its exceedingly fine-grained and irregular character, the effective surface of a cubic inch of charcoal may measure several acres. This is like the coast of Norway which, because of its irregular shape with numerous fjords, is many times as long as it would otherwise be. Adsorption is a property of many substances besides charcoal; it plays an important part in many chemical reactions, particularly those involving catalysis.

The crystals of **graphite** that form charcoal are poorly formed and submicroscopic in size; they might almost be called "embryonic" crystals. In the substance known as graphite these crystals are large and well-formed. They impart unusual properties to the substance. Graphite is a dark gray substance with a characteristic greasy or unctuous feel. Generally it is found in the form of easily separated sheets like mica but much softer. Graphite burns when heated in air or oxygen, but on the whole it is less reactive than charcoal. It does not show the outstanding adsorptive properties of charcoal. Graphite was not completely understood to be an allotrope of carbon until as late as 1855. For a long time it was confused with molybdenum sulfide which it greatly resembles superficially. Further doubts concerning its composition are reflected in the names "plumbago" and "black lead," still occasionally used for graphite.

X-ray diffraction studies on graphite crystals have revealed the reason for the unique properties of this substance. The carbon atoms are arranged in layers, each atom closely bound to three others in the same plane so that the structure looks like a vast sheet of little hexagons. At considerable distances from each other, atomically speaking, other layers of carbon atoms are found, but the bonds between layers are weak. The structure is not unlike a honeycomb, without the honey. Graphite, like charcoal, conducts the electric current.

Natural graphite is found in Ceylon, Madagascar, Mexico, the United States, Canada, and various other parts of the world. Graphite is manufactured artificially by a process discovered in 1896 by an American chemist, Edward G. Acheson. In the Acheson process, coal, coke, or charcoal obtained from petroleum is heated in an electric furnace to about 3000° C. Silica or iron oxide, or both, are added to catalyze the reaction. It is thought that silicon carbide, SiC, is first formed. This decomposes at the very high temperature to yield silicon and graphite.

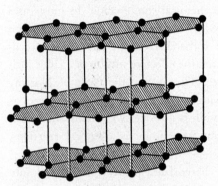

Fig. 26-1. Arrangement of carbon atoms in graphite.

Massive graphite is used in foundry operations, especially for making crucibles which will withstand very high temperatures. It is also used for electrodes for arc lights, electric furnaces, and in spectrographic analysis. One of the most spectacular uses is in the uranium pile for the production of atomic power.

Colloidal graphite has many applications. Because of its greasy feel, the suitability of graphite as a lubricant has been recognized for a long time. Where high temperatures are involved, graphite may be used as a "dry" lubricant under conditions which would destroy an oil or grease.

There are numerous uses of graphite in electrical equipment—such as in the lubrication of high-tension insulators, the manufacture of rectifiers, radio tubes, cathode-ray tubes, and of photoelectric cells. Lead pencils contain no lead: the substance called "lead" in pencils is a mixture of graphite, wax, silica, and clay, mixed in different proportions in different grades of pencils.

Diamond is the hardest substance known. When pure it is transparent and colorless. It is much less reactive chemically than other forms of carbon, although when heated strongly in air, diamond will burn. In sharp contrast to graphite, diamond does not conduct the electric current, but because it is an excellent conductor of heat, diamond feels cold to the touch. X rays readily penetrate diamond, but paste or glass imitations are opaque to X rays. This and the hardness make good tests for real diamonds. It is difficult to believe that a substance so different from graphite can, nevertheless, be the same chemical element. But the truth of this is easily proved. Diamond may be burned in oxygen to yield nothing but carbon dioxide and a trace of ash. Exactly the same result is obtained by burning graphite. Diamond is an allotrope of graphite, an allotrope with striking differences in properties and a fantastic difference in price. Diamonds cost, weight for weight, up to two hundred and fifty million times as much as graphite.

Examination of diamond crystals by X-ray diffraction methods shows that the structure of diamond is quite different from that of graphite. Instead of being arranged in parallel layers, each carbon atom is closely bound by electron sharing to four other carbon atoms. This tightly knit, interlocking arrangement is doubtless responsible for the extreme hardness and general lack of reactivity shown by diamond in comparison with other forms of carbon.

Diamonds are sparingly distributed in several parts of the earth. The principal sources are the Belgian Congo, Brazil, South Africa, the Urals, India, Borneo, and Australia. Africa is at present the chief source. The diamonds are found in the so-called "blue ground," or *kimberlite,* a curious type of rock believed to be the shafts or pipes of extinct volcanoes. The diamonds are believed to have been formed by slow crystallization of carbon from iron or molten rock under the combined action of high temperature and great pres-

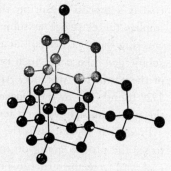

Fig. 26-2. Arrangement of carbon atoms in diamond.

sure. Diamonds, as found, rarely weigh more than an ounce. The largest known stone weighed 1¼ lbs. before being cut. This is the Cullinan diamond discovered in Pretoria in 1905 and presented in 1909 as an addition to the Crown jewels of England.

From time to time there have been efforts to make diamonds artificially. So far as is known at the present time, all these efforts have been unsuccessful.

In addition to diamonds used as gems, there is a large trade in "industrial" diamonds. From a practical standpoint these are of much greater value than the gem stones. **Bortz** (bort or boart) is poorly crystallized diamond of a dark color. **Carbonado** is opaque, black, and tough. These substances are used in diamond drills for cutting rock in drilling oil-wells and tunnels.

172. COAL

Coal is distributed throughout the world in, or adjacent to, all important industrial nations. It is found underground in seams, averaging from a few inches to several feet in thickness. Sometimes the coal is near enough to the surface so that strip-mining is possible; more frequently deep mines are necessary.

Coal is formed by the gradual decomposition of vegetation containing cellulose, $(C_6H_{10}O_5)_n$. On exposure to air such vegetation rapidly decays to water and to volatile compounds of carbon. But when the vegetation lies on the ground covered by earth or water, so that access of air is restricted, the decomposition process is different. Particularly under the influence of increased pressure and temperature, moisture and some gaseous substances are released and the carbon content rises through the stages of **peat, lignite, bituminous** or soft coal, and **anthracite** or hard coal. This process may be observed in all stages at the present time, although the formation of hard coal is a process requiring thousands of years. The presence of coal beds implies the existence at some time in the remote past of luxuriant forests covering the area, perhaps at a later date to be completely destroyed and even submerged by oceans. Such beds give information regarding the past history of the earth. For instance, Admiral Byrd's expedition to the South Pole in 1929 found coal in the Queen Maud mountains. At one time, that part of the world must have been temperate or even tropical.

Proof that vegetation is the source of coal is found, not only in our ability to see the process going on in all stages, but also from the fossil content of coal, and from the structures of wood sometimes actually found in soft coals.

The different kinds of coal differ in composition. It is not to be thought that these kinds of coal are sharply differentiated. Coals are found in all gradations from lignite to anthracite. A few representative data are shown in Table 18.

TABLE 18

Approximate Percentage Composition of Different Coals

	Anthracite	Bituminous	Lignite
Volatile matter	3-5	12-26	28
Carbon	90-93	75-90	60-75
Hydrogen	2-4	4-5	6
Oxygen and nitrogen	3-5	6-15	20-30
Moisture	2-7	2-12	6-20

All coals, of course, contain varying percentages and kinds of ash. The carbon in coal is not present as the element carbon. This is shown by the large amount of carbon which may be driven off in the form of volatile compounds, and by the appreciable solubility of coal in pyridine. Carbon is not soluble in pyridine or, for that matter, in any other ordinary solvent, although it does dissolve in molten iron.

The combustion of coal is, of course, an exothermic reaction. The heat which may be derived from coal is generally expressed in **British Thermal**

Units (B.T.U.). One B.T.U. is the heat necessary to raise the temperature of one pound of water one Fahrenheit degree. One B.T.U. equals 252 calories. Coal averages from 10,000 to 14,000 B.T.U. per pound. By comparison, wood averages 7000 B.T.U. per pound, and hydrogen gas 62,100 B.T.U. per pound. Of course, the user will be guided in his coal purchases in part by the quantity and kind of ash and other characteristics, but his primary consideration is for the number of B.T.U. per pound. Large users have tests made on representative samples to determine the heat value of the coal. They

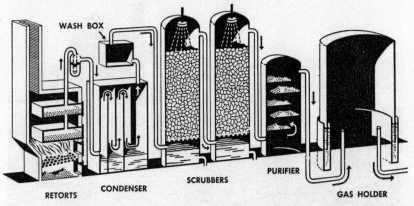

Fig. 26-3. Coal gas plant. The coal is heated in retorts; the valuable liquid products are removed in a series of operations; the coal gas product is purified and finally stored in huge gas-holders for sale or use on demand. (After H. T. Briscoe, *College Chemistry*, Houghton Mifflin Company, 1945. By permission)

are thus essentially paying for B.T.U. rather than for tons of coal. These tests are made by taking a weighed quantity of the coal and burning it in excess oxygen in a special type of calorimeter.

If coal is heated to between 700° and 1000° C. in the absence of air, it decomposes to yield combustible gas, a mixture of liquids, and coke. This process is called **destructive distillation**; it forms a large and important branch of chemical industry. From a ton of soft coal there normally is obtained about 10,000 cubic feet of gas, over 100 pounds of liquids, and about 1500 pounds of coke. Each of these products is valuable.

The mixture of gases called **coal gas** consists chiefly of hydrogen, methane (CH_4), ethane (C_2H_6), and carbon monoxide (CO), together with various undesirable substances such as sulfur-containing compounds which give a bad smell to the gas. These impurities are removed by washing the gas before it is distributed for use. The gas so obtained is often used without further treatment; sometimes it is fortified with water gas, a mixture of hydrogen and carbon monoxide; and sometimes it is mixed with "natural" gas which consists in large part of methane. The domestic gas supplies of many cities in the United States consist almost entirely of natural gas, often piped hundreds or thousands of miles, but at one time coal gas was used almost exclusively.

There are at present well over one hundred marketable products derived from **coal tar,** the liquid residue recovered from coke ovens or gas-manufac-

Fig. 26-4. Large-scale coke oven operation.

turing plants. This residue constitutes an extraordinary source of valuable substances. These range from easily volatilized ammonia and benzene to pitch. The ammonia which is partly given off with the coal gas is absorbed in sulfuric acid to form ammonium sulfate. This is used in fertilizers. Other substances obtained by fractional distillation of coal tar are toluene, xylene, phenol (carbolic acid), naphthalene, anthracene, and other organic compounds of great importance. These substances are probably not present as such in the coal but are formed during the heating. Detailed discussion of these must wait for a later chapter. They are used in the manufacture of drugs, dyes, perfumes, and many other substances.

The residues remaining after removal of the more volatile substances from coal tar are thick, black liquids or solids used for weatherproofing and as imitation asphalt for road paving. Petroleum pitch is used for the same purpose. True asphalt is a complicated substance probably derived from petroleum. It is found naturally in Trinidad and elsewhere.

The **coke** finally remaining in the retorts from the destructive distillation of coal contains 80 to 90 per cent of carbon plus all the nonvolatile impurities originally present in the coal. In gas-manufacturing plants the coke is often heated with steam to form **water gas,** a mixture of carbon monoxide and hydrogen.

$$C + H_2O \rightarrow CO + H_2$$

This combustible mixture of gases is used to fortify the coal gas and also as a source of heat to bring about decomposition of the coal. In modern coke ovens, however, the coke is a major product and is sold for metallurgical operations, the chief of which is the manufacture of pig iron.

173. CARBON MONOXIDE

The first carbon compound we shall consider in detail is the deadly carbon monoxide. This substance, with the formula **CO,** is a colorless, odorless gas, and a very dangerous poison.

Pure carbon monoxide is prepared by treating formic acid, HCO_2H, with concentrated sulfuric acid.

$$\overset{O}{\underset{\parallel}{H-C-OH}} + H_2SO_4 \longrightarrow CO + H_2SO_4 \cdot H_2O$$

The sulfuric acid acts as a dehydrating agent. A similar reaction is obtained by putting sulfuric acid on oxalic acid, $H_2C_2O_4$, but in this case a mixture of carbon monoxide and carbon dioxide is evolved.

When carbon is burned in an ample supply of oxygen, carbon dioxide is formed,

$$C + O_2 \rightarrow CO_2$$

but if the supply of oxygen is limited, carbon monoxide is formed.

$$2C + O_2 \rightarrow 2CO$$

It is generally thought that this last reaction proceeds in two steps: first carbon dioxide is formed and then this is reduced by contact with fresh carbon.

$$CO_2 + C \rightarrow 2CO$$

Carbon monoxide generated in this way sometimes escapes from coal furnaces with disastrous results because of its highly poisonous nature. When fresh coal is added to a fire, the blue flame of carbon monoxide burning is often visible.

$$2CO + O_2 \rightarrow 2CO_2$$

Flue gases from coal furnaces always contain some carbon monoxide, but large quantities of this gas indicate faulty combustion and consequent loss of energy.

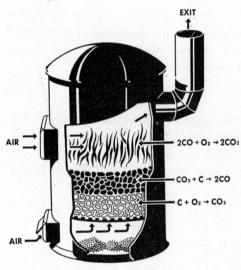

Fig. 26-5. Sequence of chemical reactions in a coal stove.

Gasoline consists of carbon and hydrogen. When this is burned in an automobile engine, the products are carbon dioxide, carbon monoxide, and water. As everyone knows, the carbon monoxide is a dangerous hazard in a closed garage with a car engine running.

Carbon monoxide is generally described as odorless. The boiling point of the gas is $-190°$ C., almost the same as liquid air. It is not very soluble in water, and, in contrast to carbon dioxide, carbon monoxide does not form an acid in water.

Carbon monoxide burns in air with a beautiful blue flame, the product being carbon dioxide. Also, it is a powerful reducing agent, as is shown by passing the gas over hot copper oxide.

$$CuO + CO \rightarrow Cu + CO_2$$

An important use of carbon monoxide is as an intermediate in the reduction of iron oxide to iron.

$$2C + O_2 \rightarrow 2CO$$

$$Fe_2O_3 + 3CO \rightarrow 2Fe + 3CO_2$$

A large number of deaths * occur every year from the accidental or suicidal breathing of carbon monoxide. Being colorless and odorless, the gas gives

* C. K. Drinker, *Carbon Monoxide Asphyxia* (New York: Oxford, 1938).

no warning of its presence until the victim through dizziness or collapse is unable to save himself. Domestic gas supplies are a frequent source of poison-. ing of persons with suicidal intent, or accidentally through improperly turned off valves or leaky pipes. The formation of carbon monoxide in coal fires has already been described. Escaping gas, through faulty flues or because of inadequate ventilation, is often the cause of death. Persons in burning buildings are often overcome and killed even though the fire never reaches them. This is because the deadly carbon monoxide is liberated during incomplete combustion of wood and other combustibles within the building.

The poisonous effects of carbon monoxide are governed by the concentration of the gas and the time of exposure. For example, if air contains 0.1 per cent (10 parts per 10,000) of carbon monoxide, breathing such air for one hour would produce unpleasant symptoms. Remaining in such an atmosphere for two hours would probably be fatal. Air containing 1 per cent of carbon monoxide causes death in a few minutes.

The poisonous action of carbon monoxide lies in its ability to combine with the red coloring matter, the hemoglobin, of the blood. The hemoglobin is then no longer able to perform its normal function of transporting oxygen to the tissues. The affinity carbon monoxide has for hemoglobin is 210 times that of oxygen. This accounts for the dangerous effect of breathing very small concentrations of carbon monoxide. Lack of oxygen in the tissues is, of course, always serious. Even if the victim recovers, there may be permanent injury to the brain, heart, and other organs.

The circumstances in which a victim of carbon monoxide poisoning is found generally leave little doubt as to the cause of his condition. The diagnosis is confirmed by the appearance of the patient. The compound, **carbonylhemoglobin,** formed by carbon monoxide and hemoglobin is bright clear red. Even in death, victims have a bright red color of fingernails and skin. Treatment of patients still living consists of removing them without delay to fresh air. If necessary, artificial respiration is given and pure oxygen is administered. Breathing is sometimes stimulated by adding a few per cent of carbon dioxide to the oxygen. In this way the carbonylhemoglobin is slowly decomposed and replaced by the normal oxyhemoglobin, the compound of hemoglobin and oxygen. The carbon monoxide can be expelled in about thirty minutes. It is, of course, necessary that the patient avoid exertion and so keep his oxygen needs at a minimum.

Small animals with high metabolic rates succumb to carbon monoxide more quickly than man. For this reason canaries are sometimes taken into suspected atmospheres in mines. The canaries show distress before the miners are affected. Various commercial devices serve the same purpose. Some of these operate on the principle that carbon monoxide may be oxidized over a catalyst to carbon dioxide. The heat liberated in this reaction is sufficient to operate an alarm. In military gas masks a catalyst called *hopcalite,* a mixture of oxides such as Ag_2O, Co_2O_3, MnO_2, and CuO, is used to oxidize carbon monoxide to the harmless carbon dioxide.

174. CARBON DIOXIDE, OCCURRENCE AND PRODUCTION *

The importance of carbon dioxide in nature and in industry is so great that we shall devote more space to it than to any other chemical compound, with the single exception of water. The concentration of carbon dioxide in the atmosphere is low. But it is a food for the vegetable kingdom. Its importance in the chemistry of living matter can scarcely be overemphasized. In regions remote from cities and other disturbing influences, the carbon dioxide in the air averages about 3 volumes of CO_2 per 10,000 volumes of air, or 0.03 per cent. Near the polar regions the concentration may be somewhat lower. In cities and especially in enclosed spaces such as subways, the carbon dioxide concentration may be two or three times

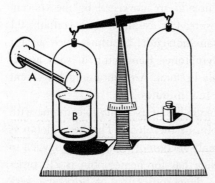

Fig. 26-6. Experiment for demonstrating that carbon dioxide has a higher density than air. Gas poured from cylinder A into beaker B tips the balance. (After W. Mcpherson and W. E. Henderson, *A Course in General Chemistry,* Ginn and Company, 1936. By permission)

higher. Although these amounts are never very large, yet the weight of carbon dioxide in the atmosphere has been estimated at the staggering total of 2×10^{12} tons.

The rather high density of carbon dioxide tends to make it lie near the ground and to flow, like water, to low places. Consequently, wherever large amounts of the gas issue from the ground, there is a displacement of air from the region, making it impossible for animals to breathe. This situation exists in the Valley of Death, in Java. This valley was visited in the year 1830 by A. Loudon from whose journal the following is quoted: †

Balor, 4th July, 1830. Early this morning we made an excursion to the extraordinary valley, called by the natives *Guwo Upas,* or *Poisoned Valley:* it is three miles from Balor, on the road to the Djiang. . . . We took with us two dogs and some fowls, to try experiments in this poisonous hollow. On arriving

---

* E. L. Quinn and C. L. Jones, *Carbon Dioxide* (New York: Reinhold, 1936).
† *The Edinburgh New Philosophical Journal* (Jameson's) 12:102 (1831).

at the foot of the mountain, we dismounted and scrambled up the side, about a quarter of a mile, holding on by the branches of trees, and we were a good deal fatigued before we got up the path, being very steep and slippery, from the fall of rain during the night. When within a few yards of the valley we experienced a strong nauseous suffocating smell, but, on coming close to the edge, this disagreeable smell left us. We were now all lost in astonishment at the awful scene before us. The valley appeared to be about half a mile in circumference, oval, and the depth from 30 to 35 feet, the bottom quite flat,—no vegetation,—some very large, in appearance, river stones, and the whole covered with the skeletons of human beings, tygers, pigs, deer, peacocks, and all sorts of birds. We could not perceive any vapour or any opening in the ground, which last appeared to be of a hard sandy substance. The sides of the valley from the top to the bottom are covered with trees, shrubs, etc. It was now proposed by one of the party to enter the valley; but at the spot where we were, this was difficult, at least for me, as one false step would have brought us to eternity, as no assistance could be given. We lighted our cigars, and, with the assistance of a bamboo, we went down within 18 feet of the bottom. Here we did not experience any difficulty in breathing, but an offensive nauseous smell annoyed us. We now fastened a dog to the end of a bamboo, 18 feet long, and sent him in, we had our watches in our hands, and in 14 seconds he fell on his back, did not move his limbs or look round but continued to breathe 18 minutes. We then sent in another, or rather he got loose from the bamboo, but walked in to where the other dog was lying: he then stood quite still, and in 10 seconds he fell on his face, and never moved his limbs afterwards: he continued to breathe for 7 minutes. We now tried a fowl, which died in $1\frac{1}{2}$ minutes. We threw in another, which died before touching the ground. During these experiments we experienced a heavy shower of rain; but we were so interested by the awful scene before us, that we did not care for getting wet. On the opposite side, near a large stone, was the skeleton of a human being, who must have perished on his back, with the right arm under the head; from being exposed to the weather, the bones were bleached as white as ivory. I was anxious to procure this skeleton, but any attempt to get at it would have been madness.

Carbon dioxide dissolves in water. The solubility depends upon the pressure, in accordance with Henry's Law. The oceans contain dissolved carbon dioxide and the total weight so dissolved is estimated at 20 to 30 times as much as is present in the atmosphere. The oceans act as vast reservoirs of carbon dioxide, dissolving more or liberating more as the partial pressure of the gas varies in the atmosphere. In this way the oceans help to maintain a steady concentration of carbon dioxide in the air. This, in turn, has a profound effect on the climate of the whole world and on the growth of all living matter.

The action of the oceans in maintaining an equilibrium concentration of carbon dioxide in the atmosphere is important because carbon dioxide is constantly being added to the air from various sources and is constantly being removed for other purposes. These opposing tendencies do not necessarily operate at the same rate. Carbon dioxide is being added to the air from natural sources as already described, from the burning of wood, coal, and petroleum, and from the respiration of animals. All these sources would probably increase the carbon dioxide content of the atmosphere a few tenths of a per cent per year and would in time lead to serious fouling of the atmosphere if reverse processes were not constantly in operation. Factors which tend to decrease the carbon dioxide in the air are the respiration of vegetation, which uses up CO_2 and gives off O_2; organisms, such as the coral polyp, which synthesize calcium carbonate; and the weathering of certain types of rocks such as *labradorite* to *kaolin*. The action of the oceans is to smooth out fluctuations in the supply and demand for atmospheric carbon dioxide.

Pure carbon dioxide is easily prepared by burning pure carbon or coke in an excess of oxygen,

$$C + O_2 \rightarrow CO_2 + 97 \text{ kcal.}$$

or if the gas is contaminated with carbon monoxide, this may readily be oxidized by passing the gas mixture over hot copper oxide.

$$CO + CuO \rightarrow Cu + CO_2$$

Other combustible substances containing carbon may serve as sources of carbon dioxide. For instance natural gas is largely methane which, on burning in air, gives a mixture of carbon dioxide, water, and, of course, nitrogen.

$$\underset{methane}{CH_4} + 2O_2 \rightarrow CO_2 + 2H_2O$$

Carbonates such as sodium carbonate or calcium carbonate, limestone, give off carbon dioxide when they are strongly heated.

$$CaCO_3 \rightarrow CaO + CO_2$$

This is the reaction used in the production of lime. Sometimes the carbon dioxide can be recovered as a by-product. Another method for obtaining carbon dioxide from carbonates is to treat them with an acid.

$$CaCO_3 + 2HCl \rightarrow CaCl_2 + H_2O + CO_2$$

This method is convenient for laboratory use but is not very practical industrially unless some marketable by-product is involved.

The fermentation of molasses to yield ethyl alcohol is accompanied by the evolution of carbon dioxide. This is a reaction of importance in the manufacture of industrial alcohol.

$$C_6H_{12}O_6 \rightarrow 2C_2H_5OH + 2CO_2$$

A somewhat similar reaction occurs when starch is fermented to butyl alcohol and acetone. These are very great producers of carbon dioxide as a by-product. A large fraction of all carbon dioxide made for sale is produced in this way. Elaborate purification is necessary before fermentation carbon dioxide can be sold. One method for doing this is to adsorb the impurities in activated charcoal.

Carbon dioxide is, of course, a gas, but it is sold as a liquid or as a solid. Below 31° C., under pressure, it may exist as a liquid and as such is sold in steel cylinders. The pressure necessary to liquefy carbon dioxide at ordinary temperatures is nearly 70 atmospheres. This pressure requires strong, heavy cylinders which add considerably to the cost of distribution.

Solid carbon dioxide, not long ago a laboratory curiosity, is now familiar to all as **"Dry-Ice."** Under normal atmospheric pressure carbon dioxide does not exist as a liquid but passes directly from gaseous to solid states at −78.5° C. Commercially, liquid carbon dioxide produced by compression is allowed to expand into a container. The latent heat of evaporation is sufficient to cool part of the carbon dioxide to a white "snow," which is pressed into blocks for sale.

175. CARBON DIOXIDE, PROPERTIES AND USES

At ordinary temperatures and pressures, carbon dioxide is a colorless gas. It may have a very slight odor but ordinarily this is not detectible. The molecular weight of 44 is considerably higher than that of nitrogen or of oxygen, consequently the density of the gas is higher than that of air, with the peculiar results already described. Below −78.5° C. carbon dioxide exists as a solid from which it sublimes directly to the gaseous state. The solid may be handled, with care, but if pressed on the skin, frozen patches resembling burns will develop. Under elevated pressure liquid carbon dioxide is formed. Above 31° C. it is impossible to liquefy carbon dioxide no matter what pressure is employed. This temperature is spoken of as the **critical temperature.** (See Fig. 26-7.) The critical temperature is defined as the highest temperature at which a substance may exist as a liquid. If the liquid is heated above the critical temperature, the surface of the liquid suddenly disappears, and the whole containing vessel becomes filled with the substance, now in the gaseous state. Each substance has its own critical temperature: for instance that of hydrogen is $-241°$ C., that of water $358°$ C.

When solid carbon dioxide is converted to a gas, the latent heat of sublimation is about 137 calories per gram. The thermochemical equation for this change is therefore

$$CO_2 \text{ (solid)} \rightleftarrows CO_2 \text{ (gas)} - 6.0 \text{ kcal.}$$

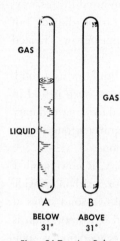

GAS

LIQUID

GAS

A
BELOW
31°

B
ABOVE
31°

Fig. 26-7. A. Below 31° C. carbon dioxide is easily liquefied by application of pressure. B. Above 31° C. carbon dioxide cannot be liquefied.

The absorption of this heat permits the use of solid carbon dioxide as a refrigerant for keeping, for instance, ice cream.

Carbon dioxide does not burn, nor does it ordinarily support combustion. On the contrary, it extinguishes the flames of burning wood, coal, oil, and so forth, and upon this property rests its use as a fire-extinguishing agent. As such it acts solely as a blanket excluding air from the flames. Carbon dioxide is able to do this because of its high density.

Solution of carbon dioxide in water gives rise to **carbonic acid.** The equation for this reaction is often written:

$$CO_2 + H_2O \rightleftarrows H_2CO_3$$

The acid is, however, exceedingly weak. In all probability carbonic acid consists mostly of carbon dioxide dissolved in water; this reacts with the water to form a very small quantity of **bicarbonate ion,**

$$CO_2 + H_2O \rightleftarrows H^+ + HCO_3^-$$

and an even smaller amount of carbonate ion owing to secondary dissociation of the bicarbonate.

$$HCO_3^- \rightleftarrows H^+ + CO_3^=$$

Although the hydrogen ion concentration so produced is very small, it is nevertheless large enough to affect certain acid-base indicators and to impart a very slight sour taste to the solution. Carbonic acid readily reacts with bases and is therefore a useful and cheap neutralizing agent.

$$2NaOH + H_2CO_3 \rightarrow Na_2CO_3 + 2H_2O$$

The carbonates of many metals are insoluble in water. If, therefore, carbon dioxide is bubbled into water containing, say, a salt of calcium, or calcium hydroxide, a white precipitate of calcium carbonate is formed.

$$Ca(OH)_2 + CO_2 \rightarrow CaCO_3 + H_2O$$

This is the familiar limewater test for carbon dioxide. With this test it is very easy to demonstrate the presence of carbon dioxide in the exhaled breath. Simply breathe out through a tube into a test tube full of **limewater,** $Ca(OH)_2$ solution, and a white precipitate will soon appear. If the exhaled breath is bubbled through the mixture for several minutes more, the precipitate will disappear owing to the formation of the soluble salt calcium bicarbonate.

$$CaCO_3 + CO_2 + H_2O \rightleftarrows Ca(HCO_3)_2$$

If now the solution is boiled, the white calcium carbonate precipitate will reappear by reversal of the above reaction. The carbon dioxide is made less soluble in water by the increased temperature and so is forced out of solution; this permits the equilibrium to flow to the left. If limewater is left exposed to the air for several days it will develop a scum of calcium carbonate on the surface, owing to the presence of carbon dioxide in the atmosphere.

The action of atmospheric carbon dioxide on certain types of rocks is illustrated by its conversion of insoluble calcium silicate to soluble calcium bicarbonate.

$$CaSiO_3 + 2H_2O + 2CO_2 \rightarrow Ca(HCO_3)_2 + H_2SiO_3$$

In this, and other ways, various silicate rocks are broken up, and, over great intervals of time, mountain ranges are leveled and dispersed.

Carbon dioxide is reduced by carbon, a reaction which takes place rapidly

$$CO_2 + C \rightarrow 2CO - 39 \text{ kcal.}$$

at elevated temperatures, and which has already been discussed in connection with the preparation of carbon monoxide.

The principal uses of carbon dioxide are in refrigeration, and in carbonating beverages. Large amounts are also used in coal mining and in fire extinguishers. These uses, it will be noted, depend more on the physical properties of the carbon dioxide than on its chemical properties. Great quantities of carbon dioxide are used in the growth of vegetation, but discussion of this natural use must be deferred to a later section.

176. CARBON DIOXIDE AND LIVING MATTER

Under the influence of light, growing vegetation takes carbon dioxide from the air and, with the addition of water, converts it to the carbohydrates of which plant tissues are largely made. For this reaction the energy derived from light is neecssary; hence the name **photosynthesis.** The reaction takes place in the presence of chlorophyll, the green coloring matter of plant life. Chlorophyll acts as a catalyst. The photosynthesis of carbohydrates produces oxygen as a waste product. Plants, therefore, under the action of light and in contrast to animals, take in carbon dioxide and give off oxygen. This reaction is of such importance that it will receive more extensive treatment in a later chapter.

Plants take in carbon dioxide through minute openings, or *stomata,* generally situated on the under side of the leaf. It will be recalled that the concentration of carbon dioxide in the atmosphere is small, about 0.03 per cent. A large tree must, during the course of its growth, have removed carbon dioxide from a good many millions of cubic yards of air.

The action of plant life in removing carbon dioxide from the air and restoring oxygen was first stated by Joseph Priestley, the distinguished discoverer of oxygen. In his own words: *

These proofs of a partial restoration of air by plants in a state of vegetation, though in a confined and unnatural situation, cannot but render it highly probable, that the injury which is continually done to the atmosphere by the respiration of such a number of animals, and the putrefaction of such masses of both vegetable and animal matter, is, in part at least, repaired by the vegetable creation, and notwithstanding the prodigious mass of air, that is corrupted daily by the above mentioned causes, yet, if we consider the immense profusion of vegetables upon the face of the earth, growing in places suited to their nature, and consequently, at full liberty to exert all their powers, both inhaling and exhaling, it can hardly be thought, but that it may be sufficient counterbalance to it, and, that the remedy is adequate to the evil.

The surprising thing about Priestley's words is not their accuracy but that they were written even before the discovery of oxygen.

Animal tissues consist in large part of carbon. This carbon must be oxidized to provide energy for the performance of work and for keeping the body warm. For this purpose oxygen is inhaled and transported by the arterial blood hemoglobin to the tissues throughout the body. Carbon dioxide is one of the products of tissue oxidation, and, as we have seen, it dissolves in the venous blood and is exhaled from the lungs. Carbon dioxide is therefore a normal waste-product of the animal body. In human beings the concentration of carbon dioxide in the exhaled breath is normally about

* *Philosophical Transactions of the Royal Society of London, 62:127* (1772).

5 per cent by volume. But carbon dioxide is not only a waste-product of animal metabolism; it is of the very greatest importance in control of the respiration and the circulation. The concentration of carbon dioxide in the blood is normally maintained within very narrow limits. If the concentration rises—owing, for instance, to muscular activity—breathing is stimulated and the excess carbon dioxide is permitted to escape through the lungs. The effect on the nerve centers controlling the breathing rate seems to be largely a matter of the acidity of the blood which, of course, is raised by increased carbon dioxide content.

A very small addition to the normal carbon dioxide in the air stimulates breathing to a remarkable degree. Air containing 5 per cent of carbon dioxide increases the volume of inhaled air from about 7.5 to over 25 liters per minute. There is also a marked increase of blood-flow through the brain. These facts make carbon dioxide of great value in medicine. It possesses actions which may be produced by no other drug. Generally carbon dioxide is administered in concentrations of 5 to 10 per cent in air. It is used to stimulate breathing in cases of asphyxia, in newborn babies, and during and after the use of anesthetics in major surgical operations.

177. CARBONATES, BICARBONATES

Calcium carbonate, or **limestone,** is one of the commonest of minerals. It extends in vast bands across the continent of North America, and in Europe and Asia over a thousand miles wide and tens of thousands of feet deep. Calcium carbonate is continually being formed throughout the world by the action of waters bearing calcium ions and dissolved carbon dioxide, and by the growth and decay of living organisms. *Sandstone* consists of sand grains cemented together with calcium carbonate; *dolomite,* of which whole mountains are often made, is a double carbonate of calcium and magnesium, $MgCO_3 \cdot CaCO_3$.

Limestone is one of the commonest of structural materials. Large quantities are also used in the production of lime, calcium oxide.

$$CaCO_3 \xrightarrow{\text{heat}} CaO + CO_2$$

It will be recalled that calcium carbonate dissolves in water containing excess carbon dioxide. This occurs through formation of the soluble compound, calcium bicarbonate.

$$CaCO_3 + CO_2 + H_2O \rightleftarrows Ca(HCO_3)_2$$

The reaction is reversible, and calcium carbonate will precipitate again if the excess carbon dioxide is allowed to escape through boiling or by release of pressure. Caves are often formed by the action on limestone of water containing dissolved carbon dioxide. Sometimes when water carrying dissolved calcium bicarbonate emerges through the roof of a cave, the carbon dioxide escapes and calcium carbonate is deposited. Such deposits slowly grow into the beautiful **stalactites** found in many caves. If the water drops to the floor of the cave before depositing calcium carbonate, the structure formed is called a **stalagmite.** Sometimes the stalactites and stalagmites meet to form a pillar. Limestone caves have, therefore, a tendency to refill themselves.

Water containing dissolved calcium bicarbonate is hard water. It is, however, of the type called "temporary hardness," which is improved by boiling. Calcium carbonate is deposited, and the pure water is poured off. This procedure makes the water less objectionable for drinking and washing, but further treatment is generally necessary for industrial use.

There are several other forms of calcium carbonate found in nature. **Marble** consists of calcium carbonate crystals compactly wedged together. A variety of impurities distributed uniformly or in pleasing haphazard fashion often give great beauty to the polished stone. The master sculptors have used marble for their greatest works, and of it is made the exquisite fabric of the Taj Mahal in India.

Chalk and **coral** are other forms of calcium carbonate deposited by marine organisms. The magnitude of these building operations is astonishing. The Great Barrier Reef of Australia extends for over a thousand miles. It was made by the coral polyp, a little piece of animated jelly, taking calcium ions and carbonate ions from sea water and slowly building them into islands and gigantic reefs.

Pearls are formed similarly by the oyster trying to protect itself from an intruding irritation. A pearl is, therefore, no more than some calcium carbonate cemented together with a little organic matter.*

Sodium carbonate, Na_2CO_3, is another carbonate of major importance. This substance is also known as **soda** or **soda ash.** It is found in Lake Magadi in British East Africa and in Owens Lake and Searles Lake in California. A small amount is manufactured electrolytically, but most soda is made by the **Solvay process.** In this process carbon dioxide is derived from limestone.

$$CaCO_3 \rightarrow CaO + CO_2 \qquad (1)$$

The carbon dioxide then reacts with a solution of ammonia and sodium chloride in water.

* But, there are, as Browning says:
> "Two points in the adventure of the diver—
> One, when a beggar he prepares to plunge;
> One, when a prince he rises with his pearl."

$$CO_2 + NH_3 + NaCl + H_2O \rightarrow NaHCO_3 + NH_4Cl \qquad (2)$$

This reaction will be clearer if written in ionic form. The carbon dioxide in water forms hydrogen ions and bicarbonate ions: $CO_2 + H_2O \rightleftharpoons H^+ + HCO_3^-$; the ammonia forms ammonium ions and hydroxide ions: $NH_3 +$

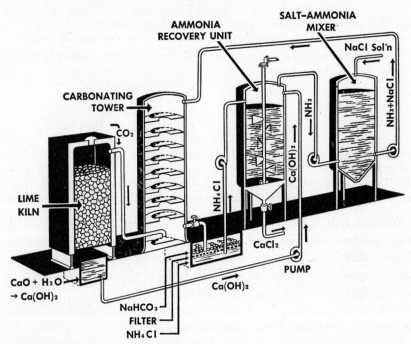

Fig. 26-8. Solvay-process flow-diagram. Carbon dioxide from the lime kiln is passed into the carbonating tower, where it meets ammonia, sodium chloride, and water. The products are sodium bicarbonate, which is removed for sale or for conversion to sodium carbonate, and ammonium chloride, which is treated with calcium hydroxide for recovery of the ammonia.

$H_2O \rightleftharpoons NH_4^+ + OH^-$; the sodium chloride is present as Na^+ and Cl^- ions. The hydrogen ions and hydroxide ions react to form water: $H^+ + OH^- \rightarrow H_2O$. Then, we have:

$$HCO_3^- + NH_4^+ + Na^+ + Cl^- \rightarrow \underline{NaHCO_3} + NH_4^+ + Cl^- \qquad (3)$$

Sodium bicarbonate is only moderately soluble. It precipitates and is filtered, purified, and dried. Some solid sodium bicarbonate, or **baking soda,** is sold as such, the remainder is heated to form sodium carbonate.

$$2NaHCO_3 \rightarrow Na_2CO_3 + H_2O + CO_2 \qquad (4)$$

The ammonia is recovered for use over again by using the calcium oxide of equation (1) on the ammonium chloride in equation (2).

$$2NH_4Cl + CaO \rightarrow 2NH_3 + CaCl_2 + H_2O \qquad (5)$$

The only by-product is calcium chloride, and nothing is wasted.

The late-eighteenth-century wars found France unable to secure an adequate supply of sodium carbonate. A prize of 100,000 francs was offered for the invention of a process for its manufacture. A successful process was developed by Nicolas Leblanc in 1787. The materials used were salt, coal, limestone, and sulfuric acid. The reactions were:

$$2NaCl + H_2SO_4 \rightarrow Na_2SO_4 + 2HCl$$

$$Na_2SO_4 + 2C \rightarrow Na_2S + 2CO_2$$

$$Na_2S + CaCO_3 \rightarrow Na_2CO_3 + CaS$$

Leblanc established this process in 1791 with the aid of a loan from the Duke of Orléans. Two years later the Duke was guillotined, Leblanc's patents were declared public property, and his plant was wrecked. He never received the prize-money, and in 1806 he died a poverty-stricken suicide. The process is now obsolete.

Washing soda is the decahydrate of sodium carbonate, $Na_2CO_3 \cdot 10H_2O$. This substance and soda ash rank among the most important of industrial "heavy" chemicals. They are used in the manufacture of glass, soap, and cleansers, and in the preparation of sodium hydroxide and other chemicals, paper pulp, textiles, and in petroleum refining.

Solutions of sodium carbonate are alkaline because the carbonate ion reacts as a base toward water. These solutions feel slimy.

$$CO_3^= + H_2O \rightleftarrows HCO_3^- + OH^-$$

Solutions of sodium bicarbonate, $NaHCO_3$, on the other hand are only very slightly alkaline.

$$HCO_3^- + H_2O \rightleftarrows H_2CO_3 + OH^-$$

Sodium bicarbonate is used in baking powders and in medicine. In medicine it is used to counteract excess stomach acidity and for certain other conditions. It is a very popular household remedy for stomach distress, but medical authorities are dubious about its therapeutic value.

Baking powders consist of sodium bicarbonate together with a substance which will produce an acid reaction to liberate carbon dioxide.

$$NaHCO_3 + H^+ \rightarrow Na^+ + H_2O + CO_2$$

The bubbles of carbon dioxide liberated in the cake dough make it rise and are trapped as the dough is cooked. Sour milk, which contains lactic acid, is sometimes used as the acid ingredient, but it is more convenient to use an acid-producing powder which will not liberate carbon dioxide until water is added. For this purpose **cream of tartar** is often used. Cream of tartar is potassium hydrogen tartrate, $KHC_4H_4O_6$. In the presence of water this reacts with sodium bicarbonate to yield carbon dioxide and sodium potassium tartrate, or Rochelle salt.

$$KHC_4H_4O_6 + NaHCO_3 \rightarrow CO_2 + H_2O + KNaC_4H_4O_6$$

The use of yeast to raise bread is a very different process, although, as before, carbon dioxide is the end product. The growing yeast cells liberate an enzyme which acts somewhat like a catalyst to hasten the decomposition of starch and sugar with the formation of carbon dioxide and water.

Potassium carbonate, K_2CO_3, is generally called **potash,** but the name potash is often used for other compounds of potassium. The principal use for this substance is as a fertilizer, potassium salts being indispensable for the growth of many crops. Large deposits of potassium salts are found in the Stassfurt beds in Germany. At one time this source formed a world monopoly. In the United States potash is obtained principally from Searles Lake in California where the brine contains nearly 5 per cent of potassium chloride, and from Carlsbad, New Mexico, where the potassium is present as silvinite, a mixture of KCl and NaCl, and as polyhalite, $K_2SO_4 \cdot MgSO_4 \cdot 2CaSO_4 \cdot 2H_2O$.

178. CARBIDES, CYANIDES

Most metals unite with carbon to form what are called carbides. Most, but not all of these, are formed by heating the metals with carbon. Several of the carbides have interesting and useful properties. Silicon carbide, SiC, or **Carborundum** is an abrasive, being almost as hard as diamond. It is used for making grindstones and cutting wheels. Carbides of tungsten and of tantalum are used for high-speed machine tools. Iron carbide, Fe_3C, or cementite, is formed during the manufacture of steel. It contributes to the special characteristics of this alloy. Calcium carbide, on treatment with water, yields acetylene which may be burned to give heat or light. At one time bicycle lamps employing this principle enjoyed considerable popularity.

$$CaC_2 + 2H_2O \rightarrow Ca(OH)_2 + \underset{(acetylene)}{C_2H_2}$$

Another important type of carbon compound is the cyanides. Sodium cyanide is made commercially in several ways, one of which is to heat soda with coke and nitrogen (from air). Iron is used as a catalyst.

$$Na_2CO_3 + 4C + N_2 \rightarrow 2NaCN + 3CO$$

Sodium cyanide is a white solid. Like all cyanides it is extremely poisonous. The lethal dose for a man is about 0.1 gram. The salt is used in the metallurgical extraction of gold, in various electroplating operations, and as a source of hydrogen cyanide, HCN.

$$NaCN + H_2SO_4 \rightarrow NaHSO_4 + HCN$$

Hydrogen cyanide, or prussic acid, is a colorless gas (boiling point 26° C.) with an odor of bitter almonds. It is an exceedingly dangerous poison. It is used as a disinfectant and to rid ships and buildings of vermin. Its use for this purpose is hazardous and should never be attempted by an inexperienced person.

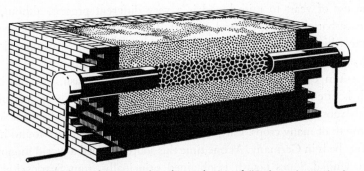

Fig. 26-9. Electric furnace used in the production of "Carborundum." The furnace is loaded with sand and coke plus a little ordinary salt and some sawdust. The electric current passed between graphite rods produces a temperature of about 3000° C. At this temperature silicon carbide (Carborundum) is produced, $SiO_2 + 3C \rightarrow SiC + 2CO$.

EXERCISES

A. *Define or explain the following:*

activated charcoal
adsorption
baking powder
baking soda
bicarbonate ion
biosphere
B.T.U. (compare with calorie)
carbon black
carbonic acid
carbonylhemoglobin
Carborundum
chalk, coral
charcoal
coal (anthracite, bituminous, etc.)
coal gas
coal tar
coke

cream of tartar
critical temperature
destructive distillation
diamond
"Dry-Ice"
graphite
limestone
limewater
marble
organic chemistry
photosynthesis
potash
soda ash
stalactite (stalagmite)
washing soda
water gas

B. *Indicate procedures and, where possible, all equations:*

 1. How is charcoal obtained?
 2. How do gas masks work?
 3. What is the difference in arrangement of atoms between diamond and graphite? How is charcoal related to these? Compare properties of all three forms.
 4. How is graphite manufactured?
 5. What is the chemical composition of coal? How is it found?
 6. C (hot) + H_2O (steam) →
 7. Describe reducing action of carbon; of carbon monoxide.
 8. Describe preparation of carbon monoxide.
 9. Describe the mechanism by which carbon monoxide acts as a poison.
10. Compare physical and chemical properties of carbon monoxide and carbon dioxide.
11. How is Dry-Ice made?
12. Give equations for several methods for obtaining carbon dioxide.
13. Describe ionization of carbonic acid.
14. Give equations for precipitation of calcium carbonate and re-solution in excess carbon dioxide.
15. Compare the relation of carbon dioxide to animal life and to plant life.
16. Describe the manufacture of washing soda and baking soda.

C. 1. Carbon dioxide is a product of the combustion of carbon, yet magnesium will burn in carbon dioxide. How is this possible?
 2. Assuming that a sample of coal is 90 per cent carbon and that this carbon is all converted to carbon dioxide during combustion: what weight of air is necessary to burn one ton (about 1000 kg.) of coal?
 3. What is the significance of the word "molecule" as applied to (a) diamond, (b) carbon dioxide, (c) calcium carbonate?
 4. What would be the effect of increasing pressure on the equilibrium re-action for the formation of methane (CH_4) from carbon monoxide and hydrogen ($CO + 3H_2 \rightleftarrows CH_4 + H_2O$)?
 5. Gasoline is a mixture, but is approximately represented by the formula C_7H_{16}. Indicate by a balanced equation how carbon monoxide, carbon dioxide, and water could be formed by combustion of gasoline in an automobile engine.
 6. In Chapter 24 the statement is made that the conversion of 1 g. of matter into energy would be equivalent to the burning of roughly 3000 tons of coal. Check this statement by appropriate calculations.
 7. Below there is an outline of a Periodic Table similar to those at the head of many chapters in this book. Without reference to the text, locate the following elements: aluminum, argon, beryllium, boron, bromine, calcium, carbon, chlorine, copper, fluorine, helium, hydrogen, iodine,

iron, lead, magnesium, mercury, neon, nitrogen, oxygen, phosphorus, potassium, silicon, silver, sodium, sulfur, tin, uranium, zinc.

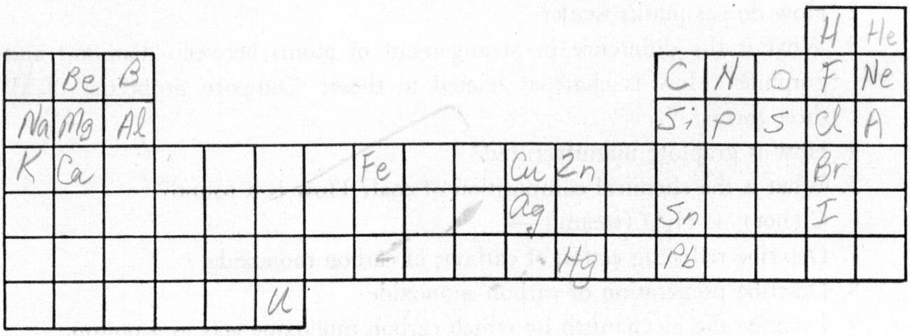

														H	He
	Be	B										C	N	O	F	Ne
Na	Mg	Al										Si	P	S	Cl	A
K	Ca					Fe			Cu	Zn					Br	
								Ag			Sn			I	
								Hg	Pb						
				U											

HYDROCARBONS

In the previous chapter we addressed ourselves to several different carbon compounds. But carbon also forms hydrides of a general type C_mH_n. These compounds are called hydrocarbons. The number of known hydrocarbons runs into the tens of thousands, and the number of those theoretically possible has the almost unique distinction of approaching infinity.

179. STRUCTURAL ISOMERISM

If a mixture of carbon monoxide and hydrogen at high pressure is passed over a copper catalyst, there is produced a colorless, poisonous liquid known as methanol. If now this methanol is treated with hot concentrated sulfuric acid, there is evolved a colorless gas having a pronounced characteristic odor. The gas is known as *dimethyl ether*. It contains carbon, hydrogen, and oxygen in the following percentages:

$$C = 52.2\%; \quad H = 13.0\%; \quad \text{and} \quad O = 34.8\%$$

We may, therefore, calculate the simplest, empirical formula by the usual method of dividing each percentage by the corresponding atomic weight. The empirical formula so obtained is C_2H_6O.

The molecular weight of this compound is easily found by the vapor-density method, by which we may ascertain that 22.4 liters of the vapor, corrected to standard conditions, weigh 46 grams. The formula C_2H_6O is, therefore, the true molecular formula for this gas, dimethyl ether.

Now, if we take some wine or other intoxicating beverage, and carefully distill it, we can isolate a colorless liquid having a slight odor. This liquid is called *ethanol*. The liquid also has the formula C_2H_6O and a molecular weight of 46. We are then faced with the peculiar situation that there are two compounds, one a gas and the other a liquid, and they both have the identical formula, C_2H_6O. This is a situation which we have not heretofore faced in the study of chemistry. These two compounds cannot be converted into each other by any simple operation. They cannot be considered to be allotropic modifications similar to those shown by sulfur and tin and other elements.

In almost all its compounds carbon has a valence of four. Almost the only notable exception is carbon monoxide. Similarly, hydrogen almost always has a valence of one, and oxygen of two. Let us see by what arrangements these elements could be linked together if we start with two carbons, six hydrogens, and one oxygen; and that the valences of these elements respectively are four, one, and two.

The possible arrangements of these atoms are quickly seen to be only two, namely:

only two possible arrangements

(a)

$$\begin{array}{ccc}
\text{H} & & \text{H} \\
| & & | \\
\text{H}-\text{C}-\text{O}-\text{C}-\text{H} \\
| & & | \\
\text{H} & & \text{H}
\end{array}$$

and

(b)

$$\begin{array}{cc}
\text{H} & \text{H} \\
| & | \\
\text{H}-\text{C}-\text{C}-\text{O}-\text{H} \\
| & | \\
\text{H} & \text{H}
\end{array}$$

The reader should satisfy himself that no other possible arrangement satisfies the conditions as to number and valence of the atoms.

It is clear, therefore, that one of these two molecules must be that of dimethyl ether and the other must be that of ethanol. Our next problem is to find which is which. First, we list some chemical properties of these two compounds.

One mole of ethanol reacts with one mole of hydrogen iodide to yield ethyl iodide, C_2H_5I, and water:

$$C_2H_6O + HI \rightarrow C_2H_5I + H_2O$$
ethanol

One mole of dimethyl ether reacts with two moles of hydrogen iodide to yield two moles of methyl iodide, CH_3I, and water:

$$C_2H_6O + 2HI \rightarrow 2CH_3I + H_2O$$
dimethyl ether

Turning back to the possible arrangements of atoms in these molecules, it is seen that formula (b) might be expected to yield C_2H_5I plus water, but that it is difficult to see how formula (a) could do so.

$$\begin{array}{cc}
\text{H} & \text{H} \\
| & | \\
\text{H}-\text{C}-\text{C}-\text{O}-\text{H} + \text{HI} \rightarrow \text{H}-\text{C}-\text{C}-\text{I} + \text{H}_2\text{O} \\
| & | \\
\text{H} & \text{H}
\end{array}$$

(There is obviously only one way to arrange the atoms in C_2H_5I, if iodine has a valence of one.)

On the other hand, it is seen that formula (a) might be expected to yield two molecules of CH_3I plus water, but that it is difficult to see how formula (b) could do this.

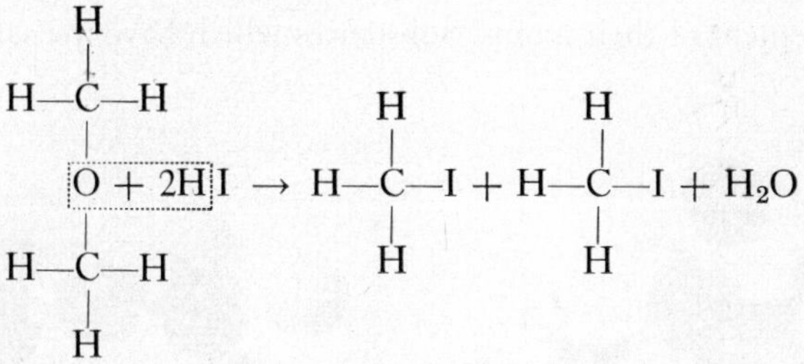

$$\begin{array}{c} H \\ | \\ H-C-H \\ | \\ O + 2H \; I \;\to\; H-C-I + H-C-I + H_2O \\ | \qquad\qquad\quad | \qquad\quad\; | \\ H-C-H \qquad\; H \qquad\quad H \\ | \\ H \end{array}$$

The evidence suggests that ethanol has the arrangement

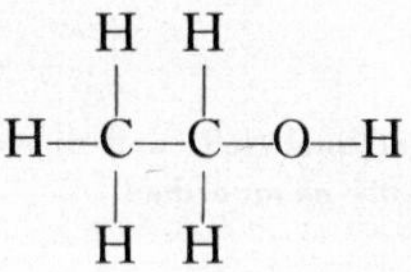

$$\begin{array}{c} H\;\;H \\ |\;\;\;\; | \\ H-C-C-O-H \\ |\;\;\;\; | \\ H\;\;H \end{array}$$

and that dimethyl ether is

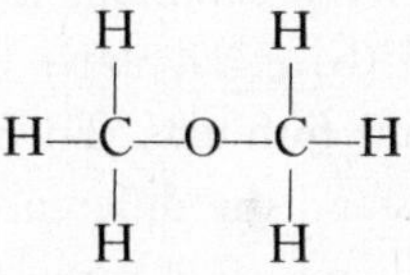

$$\begin{array}{c} H\qquad\; H \\ |\qquad\;\; | \\ H-C-O-C-H \\ |\qquad\;\; | \\ H\qquad\; H \end{array}$$

This view is confirmed by the fact that ethanol reacts with sodium much as water reacts with sodium, although less violently.

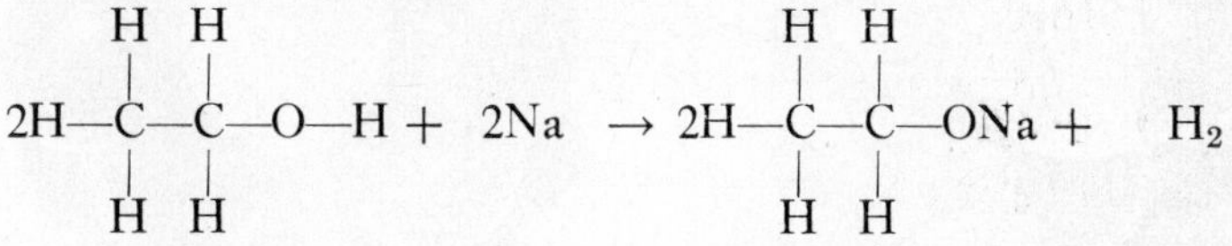

$$\begin{array}{c} H\;\;H \qquad\qquad\qquad\quad H\;\;H \\ |\;\;\;\; | \qquad\qquad\qquad\quad |\;\;\;\; | \\ 2H-C-C-O-H + 2Na \;\to\; 2H-C-C-ONa + \;\;H_2 \\ |\;\;\;\; | \qquad\qquad\qquad\quad |\;\;\;\; | \\ H\;\;H \qquad\qquad\qquad\quad H\;\;H \end{array}$$

ethanol   + sodium →   sodium ethoxide   + hydrogen

$$2H-O-H + 2Na \to 2H-O-Na + \;\;H_2$$

water   + sodium → sodium hydroxide + hydrogen

On the other hand, dimethyl ether is without action on sodium.

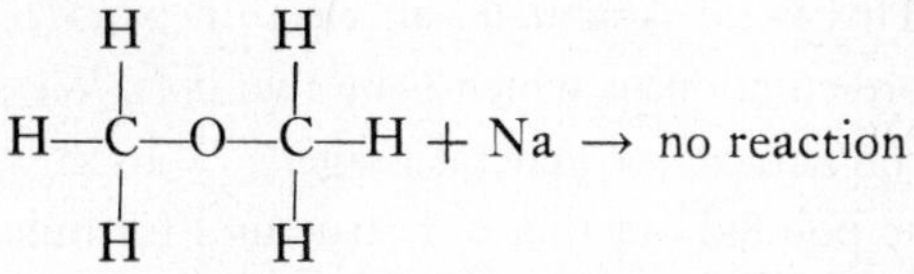

$$\begin{array}{c} H\qquad\; H \\ |\qquad\;\; | \\ H-C-O-C-H + Na \;\to\; \text{no reaction} \\ |\qquad\;\; | \\ H\qquad\; H \end{array}$$

Note that both water and ethanol must have an —OH group, but that dimethyl ether has none.

This, and similar lines of reasoning, completely establish the atomic arrangement in these two compounds. Ethanol and dimethyl ether differ only in the arrangement of their atoms. Substances which have the same empirical

Fig. 27-1. Molecular models of ethanol (*left*) and dimethyl ether (*right*). In these models the distance between atoms is greatly exaggerated.

formula and the same molecular weight are called **structural isomers.** The phenomenon, which is extremely common, is called **structural isomerism.** The formula such as (a) and (b) given above which illustrate the structural isomerism are called **structural formulas.** Their widespread use is essential in order that we may understand the differences between the myriad compounds which make up the chemistry of carbon.

Fig. 27-2. Models of ethanol and dimethyl ether in which an appropriate relation is maintained between sizes of the atoms and their distance apart.

In these structural formulas we have made use of a line (—) to represent a valence bond. This bond is actually an electron pair (or covalent) bond, the customary representation of which is by two dots. We shall find the line somewhat more convenient for general usage.

It should also be pointed out that our structural formulas are not pictures or accurate diagrams of the molecules; they are merely symbolic representations. For one thing, the molecules are actually three-dimensional, rather than two. Efforts have been made to construct scale models of these molecules, and some of these efforts have proved highly instructive (Figs. 27-1, 27-2).

180. SATURATED HYDROCARBONS

Methane is a colorless, odorless gas having the formula CH_4. The structural formula is

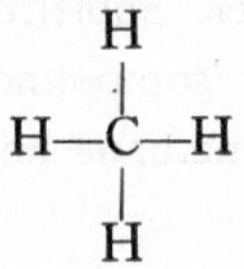

$$
\begin{array}{c}
\text{H} \\
| \\
\text{H--C--H} \\
| \\
\text{H}
\end{array}
$$

but a more accurate representation would show that the four hydrogen atoms are attached to the carbon as at the four corners of a tetrahedron. All the bonds are equivalent, and each bond is at as large an angle as possible from the other bonds. The actual **tetrahedral** angle, the angle between any two valence bonds in methane, is about $109°$.

Methane is the chief constituent in natural gas, and it is formed as a by-product in the petroleum industry. It is present in some coal mines and, when mixed with certain proportions of air, becomes a dangerous explosive known as "fire-damp."

Methane burns readily in air, with the formation of carbon dioxide and water.

$$CH_4 + 2O_2 \rightarrow CO_2 + 2H_2O + \text{heat}$$

The reaction is strongly exothermic. Methane also reacts with chlorine. This reaction proceeds when a mixture of methane and chlorine is heated, especially in the presence of light. The reaction involves the replacement, or substitution, of the hydrogen atoms in methane by chlorine atoms.

$$CH_4 + Cl_2 \rightarrow CH_3Cl + HCl$$

The reaction is known as a **substitution.** The product CH_3Cl is methyl chloride. Further treatment with chlorine yields CH_2Cl_2, $CHCl_3$, and CCl_4. These are, respectively: methylene chloride, chloroform, and carbon tetrachloride.

Methane is by no means the only important hydrocarbon. The compound ethane, C_2H_6, is also found abundantly as a constituent of petroleum gases, or as a by-product of the petroleum industry. It is also a colorless gas, the structural formula of which is:

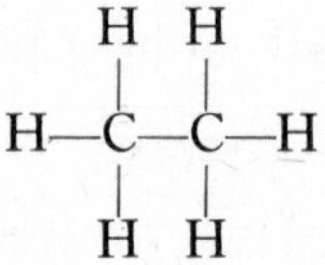

$$
\begin{array}{ccc}
\text{H} & \text{H} \\
| & | \\
\text{H---C---C---H} \\
| & | \\
\text{H} & \text{H}
\end{array}
$$

H
H : C : H
H

The reactions of ethane are much like those of methane. Burning in air yields carbon dioxide and water. Substitution with chlorine can yield a considerable variety of different compounds.

Other compounds related to methane and ethane include the following:

Name	Formula
Propane	C_3H_8
Butane	C_4H_{10}
Pentane	C_5H_{12}
Hexane	C_6H_{14}
Heptane	C_7H_{16}

The structural formula for propane offers no special difficulty. There is obviously only one possibility:

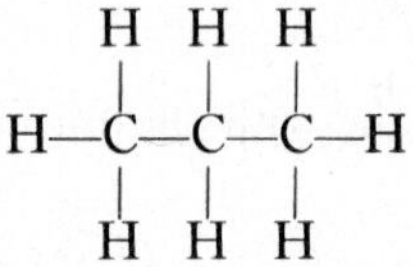

$$
\begin{array}{ccc}
\text{H} & \text{H} & \text{H} \\
| & | & | \\
\text{H---C---C---C---H} \\
| & | & | \\
\text{H} & \text{H} & \text{H}
\end{array}
$$

but when we come to butane there are clearly two possible structural isomers:

$$
\begin{array}{cccc}
\text{H} & \text{H} & \text{H} & \text{H} \\
| & | & | & | \\
\text{H---C---C---C---C---H} \\
| & | & | & | \\
\text{H} & \text{H} & \text{H} & \text{H}
\end{array}
\qquad
\begin{array}{ccc}
\text{H} & \text{H} & \text{H} \\
| & | & | \\
\text{H---C---C---C---H} \\
| & | & | \\
\text{H} & \text{H---C---H} & \text{H} \\
& | & \\
& \text{H} &
\end{array}
$$

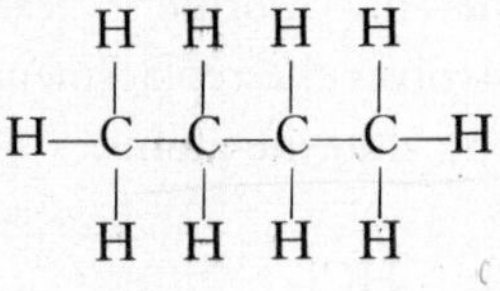

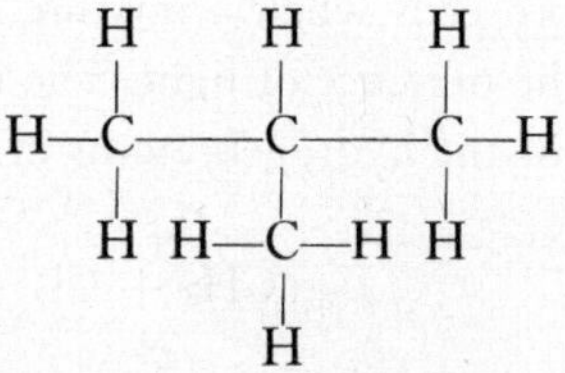

For pentane there are three possible structural isomers; for hexane there are five; and the number then increases very rapidly.

It will be noted that all these compounds may be represented by a general formula:

$$
C_nH_{2n+2}
$$

saturated hydrocarbon

Compounds for which such a general formula is possible constitute a **homologous series.** The particular homologous series representable by C_nH_{2n+2} is called the **paraffin** series. The term paraffin means "unreactive." This particular series of hydrocarbons is also said to be **saturated,** because of this relative lack of chemical activity.

A very large number of saturated hydrocarbons, or paraffins, is known. An even greater number is theoretically possible. The following table gives the name, boiling point, melting point, formula, and number of structural isomers for some members of the series up to C_{40}.

TABLE 19

SOME SATURATED HYDROCARBONS

Name	Boiling Point, °C.	Melting Point, °C.	Formula	Number of Structural Isomers
Methane...........	−161.5	−182.4	CH_4	1
Ethane.............	−88.6	−183.3	C_2H_6	1
Propane...........	−42.1	−187.7	C_3H_8	1
Butane.............	0.5	−138.4	C_4H_{10}	2
Pentane...........	36.1	−129.7	C_5H_{12}	3
Hexane............	68.7	−95.3	C_6H_{14}	5
Heptane...........	98.4	−90.6	C_7H_{16}	9
Octane.............	125.7	−56.8	C_8H_{18}	18
Nonane...........	150.8	−53.5	C_9H_{20}	35
Decane............	174.1	−29.7	$C_{10}H_{22}$	75
Undecane..........	195.9	−25.6	$C_{11}H_{24}$	159
Dodecane..........	216.3	−9.6	$C_{12}H_{26}$	355
Tridecane..........	234	−6.2	$C_{13}H_{28}$	802
Tetradecane........	251.6	5.5	$C_{14}H_{30}$	1855
Eicosanes..........	345	36	$C_{20}H_{42}$	366,319
Tetracontanes.......		81	$C_{40}H_{82}$	62,491,178,805,831

(both increase as mol. wt. increases)

It will be noted that the lower (fewer carbon atoms) paraffins are gases; those from C_5 to C_{20} are liquids at room temperature; the higher members are solids. These hydrocarbons constitute the mixtures known as "bottled gas," gasoline, kerosene, Diesel fuel, lubricating oils, and certain types of waxes.

There is one type of saturated hydrocarbon which does not fall into the C_nH_{2n+2} class. Examples of this other class include C_3H_6 and C_6H_{12}. It will be noted that these contain two less hydrogen atoms than the paraffins. These compounds are known to have closed ring structures, as follows:

$$
\begin{array}{cc}
\text{H} & \text{H} \\
& \diagdown \diagup \\
\text{H} \quad \text{H} & \text{H} \quad \text{C} \quad \text{H} \\
\diagdown \quad \diagup & \diagup \diagdown \diagup \diagdown \\
\text{H} \quad \text{C} \quad \text{H} & \text{H}-\text{C} \qquad \text{C}-\text{H} \\
\diagdown \quad \diagdown \quad \diagup & \\
\text{C} & \text{C} \\
\diagup \quad \diagdown & \text{H}-\text{C} \qquad \text{C}-\text{H} \\
\text{H} \qquad \text{H} & \diagdown \diagup \diagdown \diagup \\
& \text{H} \quad \text{C} \quad \text{H} \\
& \diagup \diagdown \\
& \text{H} \quad \text{H}
\end{array}
$$

These are known, respectively, as cyclopropane and cyclohexane. They are considered to be members of the series of **cycloparaffins.** Cyclopropane is used as an anesthetic, cyclohexane as an airplane fuel. These compounds are spoken of as *ring* compounds, as compared with the C_nH_{2n+2} type which are called *chain* compounds.

181. UNSATURATED HYDROCARBONS

If ethanol is passed over heated aluminum oxide, the ethanol decomposes yielding **ethylene,** C_2H_4, and water. In this reaction the alumina acts as a catalyst.

$$
C_2H_5OH \xrightarrow{\text{(catalyst)}} C_2H_4 + H_2O
$$
$$
\text{ethanol} \qquad\qquad \text{ethylene + water}
$$

Industrially, the reverse process is important, ethanol being made from ethylene and water. The availability of ethylene as a large-scale by-product of the petroleum industry has led to its use in manufacturing many substances, of which ethylene glycol (Prestone), mustard gas, and ethyl ether (for anesthetics) are a few.

Ethylene, C_2H_4, has fewer hydrogen atoms than does the corresponding saturated hydrocarbon ethane, C_2H_6. The structural formula which seems to be necessary for ethylene, and which is supported by the reactions of this compound, is one containing two valence bonds between the carbon atoms.

$$
\begin{array}{cc}
\text{H} & \text{H} \\
| & | \\
\text{C} & = \text{C} \\
| & | \\
\text{H} & \text{H}
\end{array}
$$

The molecule is said to contain a double bond, and to be **unsaturated.**

Ethylene is a colorless gas with a moderately sweet odor. When the gas is inhaled, unconsciousness results. It is widely used as an anesthetic in hospitals. Ethylene is also used because of its apparent ripening effect on citrus fruits.

Ethylene burns vigorously in air, yielding carbon dioxide and water. Some carbon is often deposited because of incomplete combustion. Mixed with suitable concentrations of air or oxygen, ethylene is a powerful explosive. A mixture of ethylene and air must be handled with extreme caution.

The most characteristic reactions of ethylene, and those which distinguish it sharply from the saturated hydrocarbons, are those in which the double bond is removed. For instance, ethylene reacts with hydrogen in the presence of platinum as a catalyst. The product is ethane.

$$
\begin{array}{c}
\text{H} \quad \text{H} \\
| \quad\ | \\
\text{C}=\text{C} + \text{H}_2 \xrightarrow{\text{(Pt)}} \\
| \quad\ | \\
\text{H} \quad \text{H}
\end{array}
\quad
\begin{array}{c}
\text{H} \quad \text{H} \\
| \quad\ | \\
\text{H}-\text{C}-\text{C}-\text{H} \\
| \quad\ | \\
\text{H} \quad \text{H}
\end{array}
$$

Even more characteristic is the speed with which chlorine or bromine react with ethylene.

$$
\begin{array}{c}
\text{H} \quad \text{H} \\
| \quad\ | \\
\text{C}=\text{C} + \text{Br}_2 \rightarrow \\
| \quad\ | \\
\text{H} \quad \text{H}
\end{array}
\quad
\begin{array}{c}
\text{H} \quad \text{H} \\
| \quad\ | \\
\text{H}-\text{C}-\text{C}-\text{H} \\
| \quad\ | \\
\text{Br} \quad \text{Br}
\end{array}
$$

A drop or two of bromine water shaken with a test tube full of ethylene is almost instantly decolorized owing to formation of ethylene dibromide. Rapid reactions such as these are used for the identification of unsaturated hydrocarbons.

Like methane, ethylene is the first member of a homologous series. There is no compound (e.g., CH_2) containing only one carbon atom in this series. The general formula of the series is C_nH_{2n}. Examples other than ethylene are:

$$
\begin{array}{c}
\text{H} \quad \text{H} \quad \text{H} \\
| \quad\ | \quad\ | \\
\text{H}-\text{C}-\text{C}=\text{C} \\
| \quad\quad\ | \\
\text{H} \quad\quad \text{H}
\end{array}
\qquad \textit{8 e around each C (sharing)}
$$

propylene

$$
\begin{array}{c}
\text{H} \quad \text{H} \quad \text{H} \quad \text{H} \\
| \quad\ | \quad\ | \quad\ | \\
\text{H}-\text{C}-\text{C}-\text{C}=\text{C} \\
| \quad\ | \quad\quad\ | \\
\text{H} \quad \text{H} \quad\quad \text{H}
\end{array}
$$

butylene

$$H-\underset{\underset{H}{|}}{\overset{\overset{H}{|}}{C}}-\underset{\underset{H}{|}}{\overset{\overset{H}{|}}{C}}-\underset{\underset{H}{|}}{\overset{\overset{H}{|}}{C}}-\overset{\overset{H}{|}}{C}=\overset{\overset{H}{|}}{C}$$

amylene

It will be noted that, starting with butylene, several structural isomers are possible. Those for butylene are:

$$H-\underset{\underset{H}{|}}{\overset{\overset{H}{|}}{C}}-\underset{\underset{H}{|}}{\overset{\overset{H}{|}}{C}}-\overset{\overset{H}{|}}{C}=\overset{\overset{H}{|}}{C}$$

1-butene

$$H-\underset{\underset{H}{|}}{\overset{\overset{H}{|}}{C}}-\overset{\overset{H}{|}}{C}=\overset{\overset{H}{|}}{C}-\underset{\underset{H}{|}}{\overset{\overset{H}{|}}{C}}-H$$

2-butene

2-methylpropene

Names used to distinguish these structural isomers are shown.* The reader should convince himself that no other structural isomers of butylene are possible.

These substances all show the characteristic reactions of unsaturation. The homologous series C_nH_{2n} is known as the **olefin series** (sometimes as the ethylenic series) of unsaturated hydrocarbons.

If calcium carbide, CaC_2, is treated with water, there is evolved a gas with the formula C_2H_2. This is **acetylene.**

$$CaC_2 + 2H_2O \rightarrow Ca(OH)_2 + C_2H_2$$

Acetylene is a colorless gas with a peculiar odor. It is highly combustible and, mixed with air, it is dangerously explosive. Liquid acetylene is explosive. In spite of these hazards the compound has many important uses such as in the oxyacetylene torch for welding and cutting metals, and in the manufacture of acetic acid and synthetic rubber.

Like ethylene, acetylene reacts vigorously with bromine, but two moles of halogen are required for every mole of acetylene, instead of one as for ethylene.

$$C_2H_2 + 2Br_2 \rightarrow C_2H_2Br_4$$

The structural formula assigned to acetylene involves a triple bond, as follows:

$$H-C\equiv C-H$$

---

* There are several systems for naming organic compounds. We shall generally use the common name, but occasionally, as above, will be forced to use a more formal naming system.

Acetylene is the first member of a homologous series of unsaturated hydrocarbons having the general formula C_nH_{2n-2}. The second member is methylacetylene.

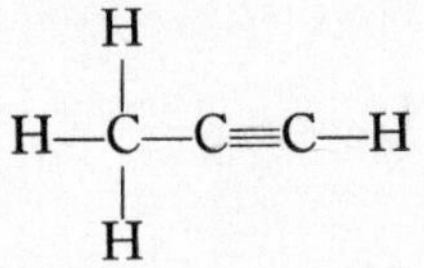

$$H-\underset{\underset{H}{|}}{\overset{\overset{H}{|}}{C}}-C\equiv C-H$$

These compounds are often called **acetylenic hydrocarbons.**

One final type of unsaturated hydrocarbons will be mentioned. These contain two double bonds in the same molecule. Two examples are:

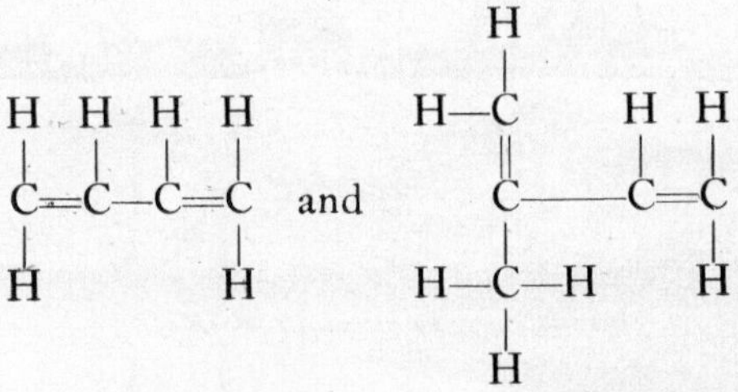

butadiene   isoprene

These and related compounds are of great importance in the chemistry of polymers such as plastics and rubbers. Compounds containing two double bonds are called **diolefins.**

We shall now review very briefly the several types of hydrocarbons discussed so far. The paraffins have the general formula C_nH_{2n+2}. They are saturated chain compounds. Saturated ring compounds are also known. The olefins and acetylenic hydrocarbons have the general formulas C_nH_{2n}, and C_nH_{2n-2}, respectively. They are unsaturated. Compounds with two double bonds are called diolefins.

aliphatic hydrocarbons

All the above types of compounds are known as *aliphatic* hydrocarbons. This is to distinguish them from another general class known as *aromatic* hydrocarbons. The aromatic hydrocarbons and their derivatives will be described in a later chapter.

182. PETROLEUM

The occurrence of the thick oily substance called petroleum is so familiar as to need no description. Petroleum occurs in large deposits in the United States, especially in Texas, California, Louisiana, Illinois, and Pennsylvania. It also occurs in major deposits in Canada, Venezuela, the Near East, the Caucasus, and in the South Pacific. Large parts of the world's economy and politics are related to the location and ownership of these petroleum resources.

The origin of petroleum is not known. Various theories include the idea of

Fig. 27-3. Typical location of oil. (*Chicago Natural History Museum*)

excretions from certain living organisms, and the action of radiations from the small amounts of radioactive elements present in the earth.

Petroleum consists of a complex mixture of hydrocarbons, together with varying amounts of compounds containing oxygen, sulfur, and nitrogen. The various hydrocarbons have widely different boiling points. Rough separations of the various hydrocarbons in petroleum may be made by *fractional distillation*. This is the basic operation in petroleum refining.

The fractional distillation of petroleum yields first the gaseous hydrocarbons, methane to butane. From 20° to 60° C. the fraction obtained consists largely of pentanes and hexanes. This fraction is called petroleum ether.

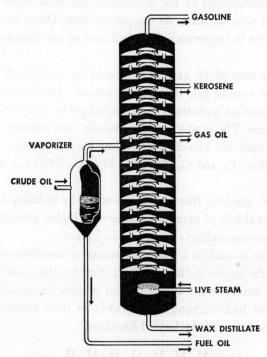

Fig. 27-4. Distillation tower for the separation of crude oil into its valuable components. The particular type of tower shown is known as a bubble-cap tower.

Gasoline is the fraction boiling between 40° and 205°. It consists of the mixed pentanes through the nonanes. At progressively higher temperatures the fractions are kerosene, gas oil, and lubricating oil. The residue from petroleum distillation is either asphalt or coke.

Petroleum has been shown to contain a large number of hydrocarbons, and a considerable number of these has been isolated by such operations as distillation, adsorption, extraction, etc. The number of isomers present for each of the higher hydrocarbons is very large, and the similarity in properties often shown by these isomers makes their separation difficult. It is, however, well established that petroleum contains hydrocarbons of the paraffin series running up to a hundred or more carbon atoms in the chain.

Petroleum also contains cycloparaffins such as cyclohexane, C_6H_{12}; and most petroleums contain a variety of aromatic hydrocarbons such as benzene, C_6H_6, and toluene, C_7H_8. The relative proportions of the different types of hydrocarbons in petroleum differ widely in oils from different localities, or even from wells in the same general area.

Before the development of the automobile the most important product from petroleum was kerosene. At the present time Diesel fuel is probably second to gasoline in importance. We shall confine our discussion chiefly to gasoline.

About 10 per cent of all gasoline produced in the United States is obtained from the natural gas. It is called "natural" gasoline, or casing-head gasoline. This gasoline is obtained from natural gas by compression, or by an adsorption process. The product is more volatile than refinery gasoline, and it is generally used for blending. A typical natural gasoline contains the following paraffins: C_3 and C_4, 20%; C_5, 30%; C_6, 24%; C_7, 20%; C_8, 4%; residue, 2%.

"Straight-run" gasoline, that is, gasoline made by ordinary fractional distillation, consists chiefly of paraffins of somewhat higher average carbon content, and of a correspondingly higher boiling point.

When gasoline is used in a high-compression automobile engine there is a tendency for the engine to "knock." This effect has the sound of a hammer rattling on the inside of the cylinders, and it leads to considerable loss of power. Different hydrocarbons differ widely in their tendency to knock Normal heptane is one of the loudest knockers,

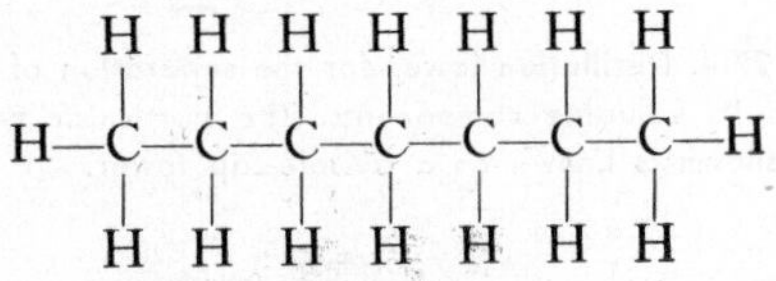

$$
\begin{array}{cccccccc}
& H & H & H & H & H & H & H \\
& | & | & | & | & | & | & | \\
H- & C- & C- & C- & C- & C- & C- & C-H \\
& | & | & | & | & | & | & | \\
& H & H & H & H & H & H & H
\end{array}
$$

n-heptane

octane number 0

while isooctane causes almost no knocking.

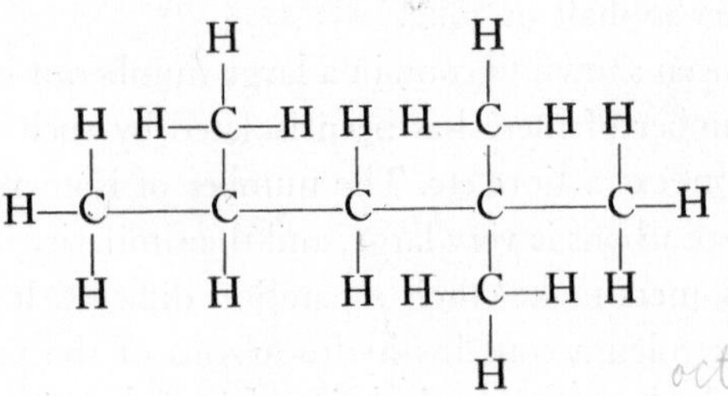

$$
\begin{array}{ccccc}
& H & & H & \\
& | & & | & \\
H & H-C-H & H & H & H-C-H & H \\
| & | & | & | & | \\
H-C & C & C & C & C-H \\
| & | & | & | & | \\
H & H & H & H-C-H & H \\
& & & | & \\
& & & H &
\end{array}
$$

isooctane

octane number 100

Automotive and petroleum engineers have an arbitrary system of comparing the knocking characteristics of a fuel. They refer to n-heptane as having an **octane number** of 0, and the octane number of isooctane as 100. Different gasolines differ widely in their octane number. In general, increasing branching of the hydrocarbon chain tends to increase the octane number. As is well known, the addition of certain compounds tends to increase the octane number. Of these antiknock compounds the most widely used is tetraethyllead, $Pb(C_2H_5)_4$.

The proportion of long-chain hydrocarbons in petroleum is much greater than can be used economically for lubricating oils and waxes. On the other hand, the proportion of hydrocarbons useful in the form of gasoline is actually rather small. It would be valuable to have some method for converting the longer chain hydrocarbons into C_6, C_7, C_8 hydrocarbons which could be sold as gasoline. Such a method is known as **cracking.** It consists of heating the higher boiling fractions under pressure until some of the longer molecules break down into mixtures of smaller molecules. The cracking processes have had the important effect of more than doubling the amount of gasoline obtainable from a given quantity of petroleum.

As an example of cracking we may take a hypothetical example. Suppose a petroleum fraction contains normal $C_{16}H_{34}$:

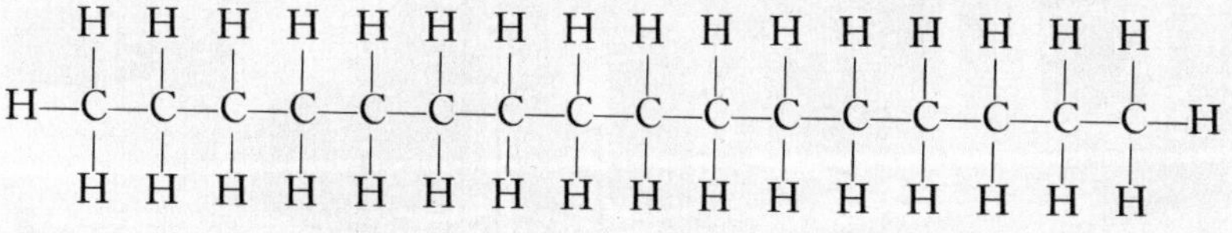

Under the influence of heat and pressure this molecule may break down to a mixture of C_8H_{18} and the olefin C_8H_{16}.

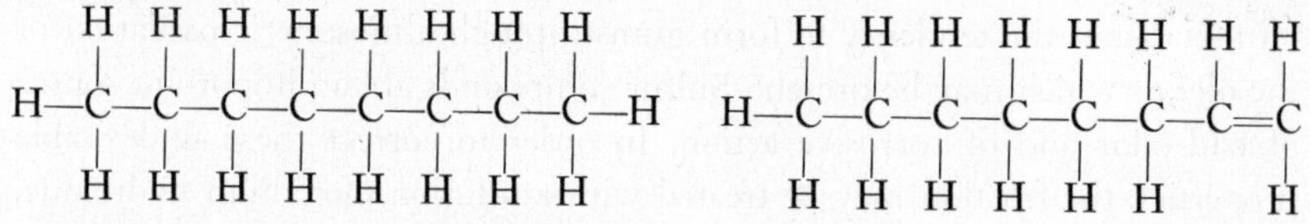

The presence of an unsaturated hydrocarbon in gasoline is not necessarily objectionable, and it may raise the octane number. Actually, such a simple cracking as that illustrated probably seldom if ever occurs in industrial operations. The reactions of cracking are complicated and not well understood. But the general principle is simply that of splitting large molecules into smaller molecules.

At the present time cracking is carried on by catalytic processes, as well as by the applications of heat and pressure. Modifications of these processes include molecular rearrangements (known as "reforming"), for the purpose of improving the octane numbers.

Petroleum fractions obtained by straight distillation or by cracking often require further treatment before they can be placed on the market. The chief objectionable properties requiring correction are the odor, the corrosive action

Fig. 27-5. An alkylation plant for the production of high-test gasoline. Large-scale chemical operations involve equally complex engineering operations.

on metal, and the tendency to form gums through atmospheric oxidation of the olefins which may be present. Sulfur compounds are an important source of bad odor and of corrosive action. In order to correct these undesirable properties, the fraction may be treated with a solution of sodium hydroxide, or by sulfuric acid. Various agents are used for special cases, one of the most commonly used being a solution of sodium plumbite, Na_2PbO_2. This is the so-called "doctor's solution" for "sweetening" gasolines containing sulfur compounds known as mercaptans. This whole sequence of operations leading to a marketable product is known as **refining.**

Petroleum refining includes several processes in addition to those mentioned. For instance, smaller molecules such as isobutene, C_4H_8, may be combined with each other and with hydrogen to form isooctane, to yield so-called polymer gasoline. *Alkylation* is a related process for making gasoline molecules out of smaller ones. Much aviation fuel is made by these processes.

So far we have made little reference to the higher molecular weight hydrocarbons which are used as lubricating oils. These certainly consist of a mixture of aliphatic and aromatic hydrocarbons but it is very difficult to isolate any one constituent. Animal and vegetable oils and fats are entirely different in chemical structure from petroleum products, although they have superficial resemblance. Vegetable oils are not infrequently added to petroleum oils to improve the lubricating properties. *Mineral oil* is simply another name for these particular fractions of refined petroleum. Greases, used for lubrication, are often complex mixtures of hydrocarbons and of certain types of soaps.

Gasoline and lubricants are not the only important products derived from petroleum. Among the chemical derivatives are large quantities of toluene for TNT production, and butadiene and isobutylene for synthetic rubber. Concerning these substances we shall have more to say later.

In this section we have touched upon the major products derived from petroleum. It is assumed that the reader is aware of the great part played by this natural resource in our civilization. From time to time it is prophesied that our world petroleum resources are approaching exhaustion. This is probably true. But that this is no cause for great alarm should be clear from our remarks in the following section.

183. SYNTHETIC GASOLINE

Coal probably consists of an extensive network of carbon atoms in rings of various sizes. The union of coal with hydrogen to form hydrocarbons is an attractive possibility because of the almost unlimited supplies of coal.

This problem, known as the **hydrogenation** of coal, received earliest attention in Germany because of that country's large coal reserves but almost negligible petroleum. The reasonably successful solution of the problem was in large part responsible for Germany's prolonged war effort.

Direct hydrogenation of powdered coal by hydrogen under high pressure and elevated temperature was operated in Germany under the name of the *Bergius process*. Various catalysts including compounds of iron, lead, and tin are used. The product resembles petroleum and may be separated by fractional distillation into gasoline and lubricating oils. One ton of gasoline is obtained from less than two tons of coal. The production of synthetic oil in Germany during 1940 by the Bergius process is said to have been 24 million barrels.

Another process, more interesting from a chemical point of view, is known as the *Fischer-Tropsch synthesis*. It will be recalled that water gas is a mixture of carbon monoxide and hydrogen which may be obtained by passing steam over hot coke. The coke is, of course, obtained from coal.

$$C + H_2O \rightarrow CO + H_2 \quad \text{water gas}$$

In the presence of iron or nickel catalysts water gas may be converted to methane and water, a process discovered by a celebrated French chemist, Paul Sabatier.

$$CO + 3H_2 \rightarrow CH_4 + H_2O \quad \text{presence of iron or nickel catalysts}$$

Fischer and Tropsch, two German chemists, showed in 1933 that the above reaction carried on in the presence of cobalt, and other catalysts, can yield a complex mixture of hydrocarbons. The product may be separated by fractional distillation into gasoline and Diesel fuel. A large part of Germany's fuel and oil needs in World War II were satisfied by this process.

An increasing amount of research is being done on the synthesis of gasoline, natural gas being an important raw material. If our petroleum resources were to be exhausted, there is no doubt that a reasonable satisfactory substitute derived from coal or natural gas would be on the market in a short time. The cost of such gasoline would not be much higher than present prices.

184. OTHER FUEL SOURCES

In addition to the hydrocarbon sources already described, namely petroleum and coal, there are two others which should be mentioned. These are **natural gas** and **oil shale**. The first is at present a very important source of energy and chemicals; the oil shales are in the development stage.

Natural gas has been referred to above. The term is generally applied to a mixture of lower paraffins containing mostly methane and ethane. For use in city and industrial gas systems the higher hydrocarbons are removed, leaving a gas consisting over 90 per cent of methane and ethane. There is an ample supply of natural gas in proved deposits to last for about half a century in the United States, and the probability is that much more gas will be discovered. The distribution of this gas in great pipelines spreading across the whole country is well known. The line known as the "Big Inch" carries gas from the Texas and Louisiana fields to the East Coast cities. Applications of natural gas to domestic and industrial heating are not the only uses of this substance. Large quantities of gas are used for the synthesis of higher hydrocarbons for use in aviation gasoline. Many varied chemical products are also made from the propane and butanes extracted from raw natural gas.

Oil shale as a possible fuel source is in a different category. In various parts of the world there are rock deposits which contain fairly large amounts of organic matter. If this rock is heated an oily substance may be removed. Deposits of such oil shales occur in Colorado, Utah, and Wyoming, and elsewhere. The oil obtainable from this source may be refined and various products such as gasoline and lubricating oils may be obtained. The total oil reserves available from this source appear to be quite large. The extraction of the oil is expensive and cannot compete with petroleum products, but in the event that the petroleum reserves are finally exhausted, the oil shales may become an important fuel source.

EXERCISES

A. *Define or explain the following (for particular compounds, include formula and properties):*

acetylene	octane number
acetylenic hydrocarbons	oil-shale
cracking of hydrocarbons	olefin
cycloparaffin (example) •	paraffin (in general sense)
diolefin	petroleum
ethane	petroleum refining
ethylene	saturated hydrocarbon
gasoline (composition)	structural formula
homologous series	structural isomerism
hydrocarbon	substitution reaction
hydrogenation of coal	tetrahedral angle
methane	unsaturated compound
natural gas	

B. *Indicate procedures and, where possible, all equations:*

1. Prove the structural formulas for ethanol and dimethyl ether.
2. $CH_4 + O_2 \rightarrow$
3. Describe the substitution of chlorine for hydrogen in methane (show all steps).
4. Write structural formulas for all paraffins up to C_6H_{14}. Include all isomers.
5. Write structural formulas for all cycloparaffins from C_3H_6 up to C_6H_{12}.
6. Describe the production of ethylene by catalytic dehydration of ethanol.
7. Describe the catalytic hydrogenation of ethylene; of propylene.
8. Describe the bromination (addition of bromine) to ethylene; to propylene.
9. Write structural formulas for all butenes.
10. Describe the production of acetylene from calcium carbide.
11. Describe the bromination of acetylene.
12. Give the structural formulas for two diolefins.
13. Construct a table showing general formula, name, and one definite example, for all series of hydrocarbons.
14. Describe the occurrence and composition of petroleum.

15. How is gasoline obtained?

16. Describe so-called "synthetic" gasoline production methods.

C. 1. A compound has the following composition: C = 52.2%, H = 13.0%, O = 34.8%. The density of the vapor (S.C.) is 2.06 g. per liter. Find the correct formula.

2. A compound has the formula $C_4H_{10}O$. It reacts with hydrogen iodide to yield ethyl iodide and ethanol.

$$C_4H_{10}O + HI \rightarrow C_2H_5I + C_2H_5OH$$

Criticize each of the following possible structural formulas:

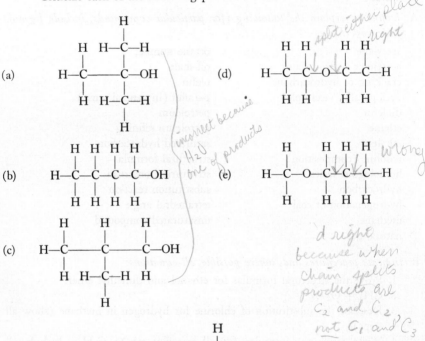

3. If methane has the structure

$$H-\overset{\displaystyle H}{\underset{\displaystyle H}{\overset{|}{\underset{|}{C}}}}-H$$

it would appear that the angle between each C—H bond would be 90°. How can the bond angle actually be 109°?

4. Write structural formulas for all possible isomers of heptane.

5. A sample of gasoline is believed to contain some unsaturated hydrocarbon. How could this be tested? Write structural formulas showing a possible reaction.

ALIPHATIC COMPOUNDS

185. ALKYL HALIDES

If methane is treated with chlorine, a reaction takes place yielding methyl chloride and hydrogen chloride.

$$CH_4 + Cl_2 \rightarrow \quad CH_3Cl \quad + HCl$$

methyl chloride

This reaction proceeds more vigorously in the presence of light. Methyl chloride is a colorless gas with a faint odor. The gas is toxic.

This reaction of methane with chlorine results in one hydrogen in the methane being replaced with a chlorine, while the other chlorine combines with the hydrogen to form hydrogen chloride. This is called a reaction of substitution. It is a reaction in which a halogen atom is substituted for a hydrogen atom. Reference was made to this reaction on page 513.

Methyl chloride is not the only chlorine compound which may be derived from methane. Further treatment with chlorine yields successively the following compounds:

Methylene chloride. . . . . CH_2Cl_2
Chloroform. . . . . $CHCl_3$
Carbon tetrachloride. . . . . CCl_4

Of these, chloroform and carbon tetrachloride are the most important. The former is a sweet-smelling liquid which was once the most important substance used for producing surgical anesthesia, and it is still widely used for this purpose. It is also widely used as a solvent. Carbon tetrachloride is a dense noninflammable liquid made chiefly by the action of chlorine on carbon disulfide. It is used in fire extinguishers and in dry cleaning.

The chlorine in the compounds discussed above may be replaced by other halogens. For instance, compounds analogous to those described are methyl bromide, CH_3Br; methyl iodide, CH_3I; bromoform, $CHBr_3$; and iodoform, CHI_3. In recent years certain fluorine derivatives of methane have become important in refrigeration; dichlorodifluoromethane, CCl_2F_2, is a colorless, nonpoisonous gas, widely used in domestic refrigerators and for air-conditioning units.

In all these halogen derivatives of methane it is believed that the molecules are not flat, as we write their structural formulas on paper or on a blackboard. Rather they are tetrahedral, as is the case for methane. In carbon tetrachloride the four chlorine atoms in each molecule are arranged as at the four corners of a regular tetrahedron. This arrangement of valence bonds is a fundamental property of the carbon atom, and is found in most carbon compounds.

The tendency to undergo substitution reactions is not limited to methane. Ethane, propane, butane, and in fact all the known paraffins undergo these reactions. For instance, ethane may react with chlorine to form ethyl chloride, C_2H_5Cl.

$$\begin{array}{cc} H & H \\ | & | \\ H-C-C-H \\ | & | \\ H & H \end{array} + Cl_2 \rightarrow \begin{array}{cc} H & H \\ | & | \\ H-C-C-Cl \\ | & | \\ H & H \end{array} + HCl$$

Similarly, propane, C_3H_8, forms propyl chloride, C_3H_7Cl, and butane, C_4H_{10}, forms butyl chloride, C_4H_9Cl. It will be noted that there is only one structural form of methyl chloride or of ethyl chloride, but that there are two isomers for propyl chloride, and an increasing number of isomers for the various halogen derivatives of butane and higher paraffins.

$$\begin{array}{ccc} H & H & H \\ | & | & | \\ H-C-C-C-Cl \\ | & | & | \\ H & H & H \end{array} \qquad \begin{array}{ccc} H & H & H \\ | & | & | \\ H-C-C-C-H \\ | & | & | \\ H & Cl & H \end{array}$$

The introduction of more than one halogen atom into paraffin molecules is also possible, and many such compounds are known. One of the most important is ethylene chloride, $C_2H_4Cl_2$. This compound is so named because it is easily made by the action of chlorine on ethylene.

$$\begin{array}{cc} H & H \\ | & | \\ C=C \\ | & | \\ H & H \end{array} + Cl_2 \rightarrow \begin{array}{cc} H & H \\ | & | \\ H-C-C-H \\ | & | \\ Cl & Cl \end{array}$$

ethylene + chlorine → ethylene chloride

Ethylene chloride is widely used as a solvent, and for other purposes.

It will be noted that the monohalogen derivatives (those with only one halogen atom per molecule) may be grouped to show their family relationships. Such a group constitutes a homologous series.

$$
\begin{array}{ll}
\text{Methyl chloride} \ldots \ldots \ldots & CH_3Cl \\
\text{Ethyl chloride} \ldots \ldots \ldots & C_2H_5Cl \\
\text{Propyl chloride} \ldots \ldots \ldots & C_3H_7Cl \\
\text{Butyl chloride} \ldots \ldots \ldots & C_4H_9Cl \\
\end{array}
$$

This particular series is known as the alkyl chloride series, but if *any* halogen is used, then we refer to it as the **alkyl halide** series.

It is clear that we could write R—Cl or R—X as a general formula for any alkyl chloride or alkyl halide respectively. In this case, the symbol R— would stand for any paraffin molecule from which one hydrogen atom had been removed. Such groups formed from paraffin molecules by the removal of one hydrogen atom are called **alkyl groups.** It should be emphasized that the alkyl groups are not compounds, but are rather groups of atoms from which compounds may be made by the addition of one or more atoms. In this respect the alkyl groups are analogous to ammonium, $NH_4{}^+$, and sulfate, $SO_4{}^{-2}$. But the alkyl groups are not ions, like $NH_4{}^+$ and $SO_4{}^{-2}$. A few important alkyl groups are as follows:

$$
\begin{array}{ll}
\text{Methyl} \ldots \ldots \ldots & CH_3\text{—} \\
\text{Ethyl} \ldots \ldots \ldots & C_2H_5\text{—} \\
\text{Propyl} \ldots \ldots \ldots & C_3H_7\text{—} \\
\text{Butyl} \ldots \ldots \ldots & C_4H_9\text{—} \\
\text{Amyl} \ldots \ldots \ldots & C_5H_{11}\text{—} \\
\text{Hexyl} \ldots \ldots \ldots & C_6H_{13}\text{—} \\
\end{array}
$$

186. ALCOHOLS

If an alkyl halide is treated with silver hydroxide the following reaction takes place: *

$$ R\text{—}X + AgOH \rightarrow R\text{—}OH + AgX $$

Taking a specific example, we see that methyl chloride could be converted to the corresponding hydroxy derivative as follows:

$$
\begin{array}{ccccc}
& H & & & H \\
& | & & & | \\
H\text{—}C\text{—}Cl & + & AgOH & \rightarrow & H\text{—}C\text{—}OH + AgCl \\
& | & & & | \\
& H & & & H \\
\end{array}
$$

* Silver hydroxide is unstable, but its action may be simulated by moist silver oxide.

The product CH_3OH is known as methyl alcohol, or methanol. It is the first member of a homologous series of compounds known as **alcohols,** which have the general formula R—OH where R— stands for any alkyl group.

The reaction of an alkyl halide with moist silver oxide is rarely used for the production of an alcohol, but the method is given here because it illustrates the relation between alcohols and alkyl halides. An alcohol may be considered as a hydrocarbon in which one hydrogen has been replaced by an —OH group; or, alternatively, as water in which one hydrogen has been replaced by an alkyl group.

R—H	R—OH	H—OH
hydrocarbon	alcohol	water

A few well-known alcohols and their formulas are given below:

Methyl alcohol (methanol)......... CH_3OH
Ethyl alcohol (ethanol)........... C_2H_5OH
Propyl alcohol.................... C_3H_7OH
Butyl alcohol.................... C_4H_9OH
Amyl alcohol.................... $C_5H_{11}OH$
Hexyl alcohol.................... $C_6H_{13}OH$
Decyl alcohol.................... $C_{10}H_{21}OH$
Cetyl alcohol.................... $C_{16}H_{33}OH$

It will be understood that the formula C_4H_9OH (butyl) actually may stand for:

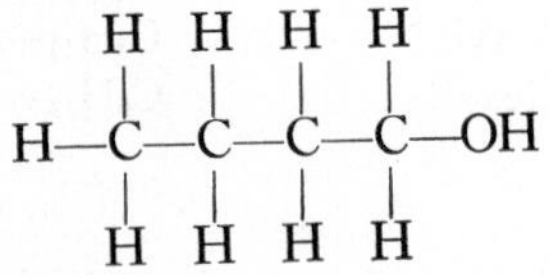

However, it will be clear that several structural isomers of this alcohol are possible. One of these isomers is:

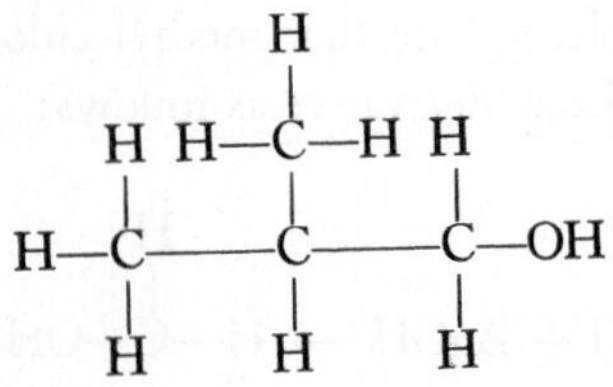

There are still other ways in which butyl alcohol may be written. The complete list is as follows:

$\left(C_4H_9OH \right)$

```
     H  H  H  H
     |  |  |  |
  H—C—C—C—C—OH
     |  |  |  |
     H  H  H  H
```

normal—(n-)butyl alcohol (a primary alcohol)

```
     H  H  H   H
     |  |  |   |
  H—C—C—C——C—H
     |  |  |   |
     H  H  OH  H
```

secondary—(sec-)butyl alcohol

```
           H
           |
      H  H—C—H
      |    |
   H—C————C————OH
      |    |
      H  H—C—H
           |
           H
```

tertiary—(tert-)butyl alcohol

```
         H
         |
    H  H—C—H  H
    |    |    |
 H—C————C————C—OH
    |    |    |
    H    H    H
```

isobutyl alcohol (a primary alcohol)

The designations *primary, secondary,* and *tertiary* refer to the presence of one, two, or three carbon atoms, respectively, attached to the *hydroxylated carbon atom* (the carbon with —OH attached to it).

The primary, secondary, and tertiary alcohols differ from each other in their chemical reactions, as will be described in the next section.

Methyl alcohol, or **methanol,** is an important article of commerce. It is made by the reaction of carbon monoxide with hydrogen under the influence of zinc and chromic oxides.

$$CO + 2H_2 \rightarrow CH_3OH$$

High pressures, and temperatures of the order of 350-400° C., are used in this important industrial reaction.

Before 1923 all methyl alcohol was prepared by the destructive distillation of wood. If wood is heated in the absence of air, it decomposes into charcoal and a mixture of vapors. The vapors contain methyl alcohol. This source of methyl alcohol is responsible for the common name "wood alcohol." Methyl alcohol production from wood was once a flourishing industry, but it was almost completely destroyed in a period of two or three years by the

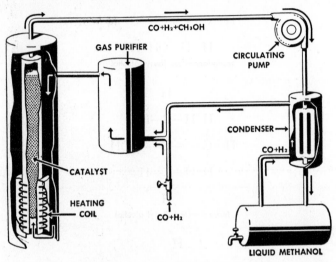

Fig. 28-1. Catalytic production of methyl alcohol. The mixture of carbon monoxide and hydrogen is passed over a catalyst at elevated temperature and pressure. The resulting mixture is pumped through a condenser which causes the alcohol to liquefy. The unreacted gases are then mixed with more carbon monoxide and hydrogen, purified, and returned to the catalyst chamber. (J. B. Conant, *Chemistry of Organic Compounds*, copyright 1939 by The Macmillan Company and used with their permission)

discovery of the synthetic process described above. This sequence of events is a good example of how scientific research may cause great and far-reaching economic changes. It is true that investments were lost and people thrown out of work by this change. It is also true that the change could not have occurred had not the synthetic alcohol been cheaper to produce than alcohol from wood. As a result of the new development, more alcohol is produced, more used, and a far wider employment and prosperity resulted. In the long run, the world benefits by such discoveries, but in the "short run," people may suffer. The importance of keeping abreast of scientific discoveries is clear. No manufacturer, no matter how apparently well entrenched, and no nation, no matter how rich and strong, can afford to neglect its scientific research activities. Neglect may mean loss of market or, indeed, of national existence.

Methyl alcohol is a colorless liquid with a slight characteristic odor. It boils at 66° C. The chief uses of this compound are as a *denaturant* for ethyl alcohol, as a solvent for shellac and varnish, as an antifreeze for automobile radiators, and for making formaldehyde. The use of methyl alcohol as a denaturant is for the purpose of preventing the use of ethyl alcohol for beverage purposes. Ethyl alcohol used for beverage purposes carries very high taxes, while that used for legitimate industrial purposes has no such tax. To prevent the illegal use of tax-free ethyl alcohol, it is treated with substances such as methyl alcohol which make it unfit to drink. During the prohibition period in the United States many tragedies resulted from people drinking ethyl alcohol containing methyl alcohol. Methyl alcohol is poisonous; sublethal doses lead to blindness.

Ethyl alcohol is also a substance of major importance. There are two principal methods for its manufacture. One of these is the fermentation of sugar or starch in the presence of yeast. This method has been used since earliest times for the preparation of intoxicating beverages. In the United States most ethyl alcohol is made by the fermentation of blackstrap molasses. Potatoes, and various grains, may also be used. The alcohol concentration reached by fermentation is not high, but the alcohol may be enriched by fractional distillation. We shall defer further consideration of the fermentation process until a later chapter, except to indicate that the net reaction of glucose being converted to alcohol may be represented as follows:

$$C_6H_{12}O_6 \rightarrow 2C_2H_5OH + 2CO_2$$

It will be noted that carbon dioxide is a by-product.

Ethyl alcohol may also be made synthetically through the action of ethylene on sulfuric acid, followed by hydrolysis.

The pure alcohol is a colorless liquid with a very faint odor. Most alcohol contains several per cent of water.

Nearly half of all industrial ethyl alcohol is used as antifreeze in automobile radiators. It is also widely used as a solvent in many chemical processes, and, outside the United States, it has had a considerable use mixed with gasoline as a motor fuel. In the pharmaceutical industry, solutions in ethyl alcohol are often prepared. They are known as **tinctures.** For instance, tincture of iodine is a solution of iodine and potassium iodide in alcohol and water.

The use of ethyl alcohol (grain alcohol) in intoxicating beverages is well known. It should be pointed out that such alcohol is small in amount compared with that used for nonbeverage purposes. Beers and wines contain up to about 10 per cent of alcohol. So-called "fortified wines" such as sherry, port, and champagne contain added alcohol up to about 20 per cent. Spirits such as whisky, bourbon, rum, and gin contain from 40 to 50 per cent alcohol.

The physiological action of alcohol is chiefly sedative. The dangers of its use to excess are so well known as to need no description here.

Several of the higher alcohols have important uses. Butyl alcohol is a valuable solvent. Some of the higher alcohols constitute the poisonous fusel oil often found in ethyl alcohol produced by fermentation.

It is quite possible for an organic molecule to contain more than one hydroxyl group, although these cannot both be on the same carbon atom. One such compound is **ethylene glycol,** which is marketed as an antifreeze under the name "Prestone." Like most alcohols it is poisonous if taken internally.

One example will be given of a trihydric alcohol, that is one which contains three —OH groups. This is **glycerol** (glycerine).

$$
\begin{array}{cc}
\begin{array}{c}
H \\
| \\
H-C-OH \\
| \\
H-C-OH \\
| \\
H
\end{array}
&
\begin{array}{c}
H \\
| \\
H-C-OH \\
| \\
H-C-OH \\
| \\
H-C-OH \\
| \\
H
\end{array}
\\
\text{ethylene glycol} & \text{glycerol}
\end{array}
$$

This compound is derived from fats as a by-product in the manufacture of soap. Glycerol is a viscous (syrupy) liquid, having a sweet taste. It is not toxic, and is often used in the preparation of drugs (elixirs), and of foods and cosmetics. An important application is in the manufacture of the powerful explosive glyceryl trinitrate, or nitroglycerin. Nitroglycerin mixed with wood pulp is **dynamite.**

$$
\begin{array}{c}
H \\
| \\
H-C-OH \\
| \\
H-C-OH \\
| \\
H-C-OH \\
| \\
H
\end{array}
+ 3HNO_3 \rightarrow
\begin{array}{c}
H \\
| \\
H-C-ONO_2 \\
| \\
H-C-ONO_2 \\
| \\
H-C-ONO_2 \\
| \\
H
\end{array}
+ 3H_2O
$$

glycerol　　+ nitric acid　→　glyceryl trinitrate　+　water

187. ETHERS, ALDEHYDES, KETONES

We turn now to three types of compounds which are structurally related to the alcohols. The first of these types is known as the ethers.

The general formula for an ether is $R—O—R$. The ether may be considered as derived from an alcohol, $R—OH$, by the replacement of a hydrogen atom by an alkyl group. The two alkyl groups in the ether may be the same or may be different. Thus, there are known dimethyl ether $CH_3—O—CH_3$, diethyl ether $C_2H_5—O—C_2H_5$, and methyl ethyl ether $CH_3—O—C_2H_5$. A very large number of different ethers is known, but by far the most important is diethyl ether, often known simply as "ether."

Diethyl ether is produced by removing one molecule of water from two molecules of ethyl alcohol. Concentrated sulfuric acid is used to remove the water. This reaction is carried out by heating alcohol and sulfuric acid, then continuously adding more alcohol as the ether distills out.

$$H-\underset{\underset{H}{|}}{\overset{\overset{H}{|}}{C}}-\underset{\underset{H}{|}}{\overset{\overset{H}{|}}{C}}-OH + HO-\underset{\underset{H}{|}}{\overset{\overset{H}{|}}{C}}-\underset{\underset{H}{|}}{\overset{\overset{H}{|}}{C}}-H \xrightarrow{(H_2SO_4)} H-\underset{\underset{H}{|}}{\overset{\overset{H}{|}}{C}}-\underset{\underset{H}{|}}{\overset{\overset{H}{|}}{C}}-O-\underset{\underset{H}{|}}{\overset{\overset{H}{|}}{C}}-\underset{\underset{H}{|}}{\overset{\overset{H}{|}}{C}}-H + H_2O$$

ethyl alcohol   →   diethyl ether   + water

The boiling point of diethyl ether is 34.6° C., only slightly above room temperature.

Diethyl ether is often used as a solvent in chemical processes. One of the most interesting of these uses is in the preparation of **Grignard reagents.** If an alkyl halide is placed together with metallic magnesium in ether a reaction occurs yielding a compound known as a Grignard reagent. An example is the reaction of ethyl bromide and magnesium:

$$C_2H_5Br + Mg \xrightarrow{(ether)} C_2H_5MgBr$$

ethyl bromide + magnesium → ethylmagnesium bromide
(a Grignard reagent)

Ether is almost the only solvent in which Grignards are formed. These substances are extremely useful in the synthesis of more complex organic compounds.

However, the most important use of ether is in surgical anesthesia. Breathing the vapor produces a state of unconsciousness from which the patient awakens without serious aftereffects. Ether was first used for this purpose by Dr. Crawford W. Long at Jefferson, Georgia, in 1842. The results did not have much influence on medical practice, and in 1846 the use of ether was rediscovered by a Boston dentist, W. T. G. Morton. The first successful demonstration at the Massachusetts General Hospital created a profound effect. People who have access to modern surgical practice have little conception of the horrors of surgery prior to the discovery of anesthesia. The patient was strapped down and held by groups of strong men while the doctor operated with utmost speed in an effort to complete the operation before the patient died or went mad through pain and terror. Numerous anesthetic agents are now available but ether remains the most widely used for major surgery. The discovery of anesthesia ranks among the very greatest of all scientific discoveries for the alleviation of suffering.

The second type of compounds to be discussed in this section is the **aldehydes.** It will be recalled that a primary alcohol has only one carbon atom attached to the hydroxylated carbon. If two hydrogen atoms are removed from such a molecule the product is called an aldehyde. Hence the formation of aldehydes proceeds by the oxidation of *primary* alcohols.

Taking the oxidation of methyl alcohol as our first example, we find that atmospheric oxygen in the presence of hot copper yields the aldehyde known as **formaldehyde.**

$$
\begin{array}{c}
\text{H} \\
| \\
\text{H}-\text{C}-\text{OH} + (\text{O}) \xrightarrow{(\text{Cu})} \ \text{H}-\overset{\overset{\displaystyle \text{O}}{\|}}{\text{C}}-\text{H} + \text{H}_2\text{O} \\
| \\
\text{H}
\end{array}
$$

methyl alcohol + oxygen → formaldehyde + water

Formaldehyde is a colorless gas with a disagreeable odor. It is poisonous and has some uses as an insecticide and fumigant, but its principal use is in the manufacture of synthetic plastics.

The oxidation of ethyl alcohol also produces an aldehyde. In this case the substance formed is called **acetaldehyde.**

$$
\begin{array}{c}
\text{H} \quad \text{H} \\
| \quad\ | \\
\text{H}-\text{C}-\text{C}-\text{OH} + (\text{O}) \ \rightarrow \ \text{H}-\overset{}{\underset{}{\text{C}}}-\overset{\overset{\displaystyle \text{O}}{\|}}{\text{C}}-\text{H} + \text{H}_2\text{O} \\
| \quad\ | \\
\text{H} \quad \text{H}
\end{array}
$$

ethyl alcohol + oxygen → acetaldehyde + water

A convenient oxidizing agent for this reaction is a mixture of sodium dichromate, $Na_2Cr_2O_7$, and concentrated sulfuric acid. The acetaldehyde is itself subject to oxidation, but because of its volatility it may generally be distilled from the reaction flask before it undergoes further oxidation.

Acetaldehyde is a volatile liquid with a sharp, disagreeable odor. Its principal use is as an intermediate in the manufacture of other compounds.

It will be noted that aldehydes have the general formula $R—\overset{\overset{\text{O}}{\|}}{C}—H$. In the case of formaldehyde $R—$ is simply a hydrogen atom. All aldehydes are very readily oxidized, and this is particularly true of formaldehyde. This property is the basis of several tests for aldehydes such as the silver-mirror test, the Benedict test, and others. If a slight excess of ammonium hydroxide is added to silver nitrate, the initial precipitate redissolves owing to formation of the complex ion, $Ag(NH_3)_2{}^+$. If now formaldehyde or almost any aldehyde is added, the silver is reduced to metallic silver. If the sides of the vessel are clean, the silver deposits as a mirror. The reaction is used not only as a test for formaldehyde, but in the silvering of mirrors. The reaction may be represented approximately as follows:

$$R—\overset{\overset{\text{O}}{\|}}{C}—H + 2Ag(NH_3)_2OH \rightarrow R—\overset{\overset{\text{O}}{\|}}{C}—ONH_4 + 2Ag + 3NH_3 + H_2O$$

| aldehyde | + | silver complex | → | ammonium salt | + silver + ammonia + water |

The oxidation of a *secondary* alcohol produces, not an aldehyde, but rather a compound known as a **ketone**. We shall take the oxidation of *iso*propyl alcohol as an example. The product in this case is the ketone called **acetone**.

$$\underset{\text{isopropyl alcohol}}{H—\overset{\overset{\text{H}}{|}}{\underset{\underset{\text{H}}{|}}{C}}—\overset{\overset{\text{OH}}{|}}{\underset{\underset{\text{H}}{|}}{C}}—\overset{\overset{\text{H}}{|}}{\underset{\underset{\text{H}}{|}}{C}}—H} + \underset{\text{+ oxygen} \rightarrow}{(O)} \rightarrow \underset{\text{acetone (a ketone)}}{H—\overset{\overset{\text{H}}{|}}{\underset{\underset{\text{H}}{|}}{C}}—\overset{\overset{\text{O}}{\|}}{C}—\overset{\overset{\text{H}}{|}}{\underset{\underset{\text{H}}{|}}{C}}—H} + \underset{\text{+ water}}{H_2O}$$

Acetone is an important industrial chemical. It is made not only by direct oxidation of isopropyl alcohol, but also by a variety of other processes of which fermentation of cornstarch is one.*

Acetone is a colorless liquid with a pronounced, not unpleasant odor. It is widely used as a solvent and in the manufacture of various chemicals and

* The fermentation process was devised by Dr. Chaim Weizmann early in World War I, and this development relieved a critical shortage in the British munitions industry. It is said that gratitude for Dr. Weizmann's discovery was of influence in connection with the celebrated Balfour Declaration relating to the establishment of a national homeland for the Jews in Palestine.

drugs. It is a common constituent in paint and varnish removers, but its use in nail-polish remover tends to crack the fingernails.

A general formula for ketones may be written $R-\overset{\overset{O}{\|}}{C}-R$, where the two alkyl groups may be the same, as in acetone, or different, as in methylethyl ketone, $CH_3-\overset{\overset{O}{\|}}{C}-C_2H_5$.

The reader may wonder what happens when a tertiary alcohol is oxidized. Such alcohols may be oxidized, but only by disruption of the carbon chain, so that the product molecules contain fewer carbon atoms than the original alcohol molecule.

188. ORGANIC ACIDS

In the previous section it was explained that aldehydes may be formed by the oxidation of alcohols. It was also stated that aldehydes readily undergo further oxidation. The products of this further oxidation are called **organic** (or **carboxylic**) **acids.** We shall take as an example the oxidation of ethyl alcohol through acetaldehyde to **acetic acid.**

$$ H-\overset{\overset{\displaystyle H}{|}}{\underset{\underset{\displaystyle H}{|}}{C}}-\overset{\overset{\displaystyle H}{|}}{\underset{\underset{\displaystyle H}{|}}{C}}-OH + (O) \rightarrow H-\overset{\overset{\displaystyle H}{|}}{\underset{\underset{\displaystyle H}{|}}{C}}-\overset{\overset{\displaystyle O}{\|}}{C}-H + (O) \rightarrow H-\overset{\overset{\displaystyle H}{|}}{\underset{\underset{\displaystyle H}{|}}{C}}-\overset{\overset{\displaystyle O}{\|}}{C}-OH $$

ethyl alcohol   + oxygen →   acetaldehyde   + more oxygen →   acetic acid

Acetic acid is a member of a homologous series for which the general formula may be written $R-\overset{\overset{O}{\|}}{C}-OH$. The characteristic, or functional, group of an organic acid is $-\overset{\overset{O}{\|}}{C}-OH$. It will be noted that although this group contains $-OH$ as an integral part, yet it is not an alcohol in any sense. The presence of the grouping $-\overset{\overset{O}{\|}}{C}-$ seems to confer acid properties on the $-OH$ group to which it is attached.

It may be wondered why such compounds are called acids. The reason is that they show typical reactions of common acids such as hydrochloric and sulfuric, although generally they are not such strong acids. For instance, acetic acid reacts with bases such as sodium hydroxide to form a salt, sodium acetate, plus water.

$$CH_3COOH + NaOH \rightarrow CH_3COONa + H_2O$$

The base is neutralized in such reactions just as it would be neutralized by any other acid. The organic acid gives up hydrogen ions, tastes sour in dilute

Fig. 28-2. Part of the analytic division of an industrial research laboratory. Every step in a complex industrial chemical operation must be subject to elaborate control by analytical procedures.

solution, and affects indicators. There is, however, one notable difference between most organic acids and many inorganic acids. In acetic acid there are altogether four hydrogen atoms, but only one of these ionizes and is replaceable by a metal.

$$\underset{\text{acetic acid}}{CH_3\overset{\overset{\displaystyle O}{\|}}{C}{-}OH} \rightleftarrows \underset{\text{acetate ion}}{\left[CH_3\overset{\overset{\displaystyle O}{\|}}{C}{-}O\right]^{-}} + \underset{\text{+ hydrogen ion}}{H^{+}}$$

The hydrogen atoms attached directly to carbon do not act like the hydrogen in the carboxyl group, $-\overset{\overset{\displaystyle O}{\|}}{C}{-}OH$. They are more like the hydrogen atoms in a paraffin.

The first acid in the homologous series to which acetic belongs is **formic**

acid, $H-\overset{\overset{O}{\|}}{C}-OH$. It will be noted that in this acid R— is simply a hydrogen atom. Formic acid is a colorless liquid with a strong pungent odor. It has a blistering action on the skin. The acid is present in nettles, bees, and ants (the Latin name for ant is *formica*). It has a number of uses in industry as an acid and as a reducing agent. The latter property depends upon its ready oxidation to carbon dioxide and water. Formic acid is often used in the laboratory to generate small amounts of carbon monoxide. A strong dehydrating agent such as *concentrated* sulfuric acid will bring about this change.

$$H-\overset{\overset{O}{\|}}{C}-OH \xrightarrow{(H_2SO_4)} CO + H_2O$$

Acetic acid is a substance of wide occurrence in nature and it is a substance of major importance in industry. The alcohol present in wine or hard cider is readily oxidized by air to acetic acid. This is the sour principle in vinegar, which consists essentially of a dilute solution of acetic acid in water. Pure acetic acid freezes at 16.6° C. and for this reason is often called "glacial acetic acid." The acid is a colorless liquid with a strong sharp odor of vinegar. It is a relatively weak acid. It is extensively used in the manufacture of textiles and of safety film. It is also used in preparing white lead and Paris green.

A few of the higher acids in the same homologous series will be mentioned. These are propionic, C_2H_5COOH; butyric, C_3H_7COOH; palmitic, $C_{15}H_{31}COOH$; and stearic, $C_{17}H_{35}COOH$. Reference to some of these will be made again later.

With the exception of formic acid, all carboxylic acids form compounds called **acid anhydrides.** For instance, two molecules of acetic acid may be thought of as losing one of water to form acetic anhydride, although the actual manufacture is more difficult.

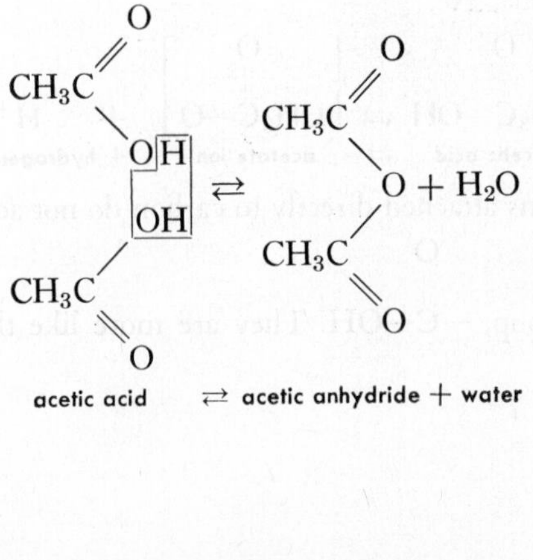

acetic acid $\rightleftarrows$ acetic anhydride + water

This substance is an important industrial chemical; it is used in the preparation of other organic compounds.

It is possible for organic acids to have more than one carboxyl group in the same molecule. An example of this is oxalic acid, which has the structure shown:

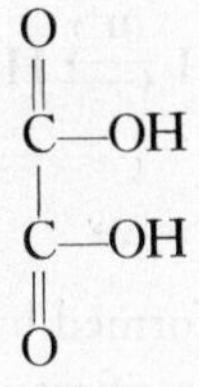

$$
\begin{array}{c}
\text{O} \\
\parallel \\
\text{C—OH} \\
| \\
\text{C—OH} \\
\parallel \\
\text{O}
\end{array}
$$

oxalic acid

In this case, both hydrogen atoms may be replaced, as in sodium oxalate.

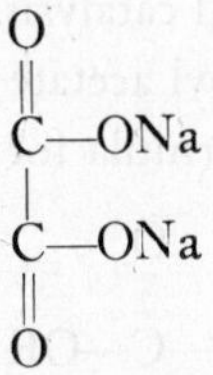

$$
\begin{array}{c}
\text{O} \\
\parallel \\
\text{C—ONa} \\
| \\
\text{C—ONa} \\
\parallel \\
\text{O}
\end{array}
$$

sodium oxalate

Still other acids of interest are lactic, found in sour milk, and citric, which is present in many fruits.

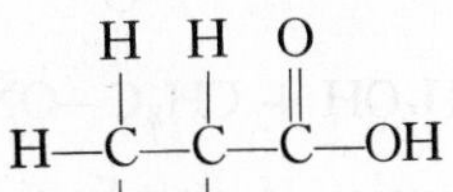

$$
\begin{array}{c}
\text{H H O} \\
| \ | \ \parallel \\
\text{H—C—C—C—OH} \\
| \ | \\
\text{H OH}
\end{array}
$$

lactic acid

$$
\begin{array}{c}
\text{H O} \\
| \ \parallel \\
\text{H—C—C—OH} \\
| \\
\text{O} \\
\parallel \\
\text{HO—C—C—OH} \\
| \\
\text{O} \\
\parallel \\
\text{H—C—C—OH} \\
| \\
\text{H}
\end{array}
$$

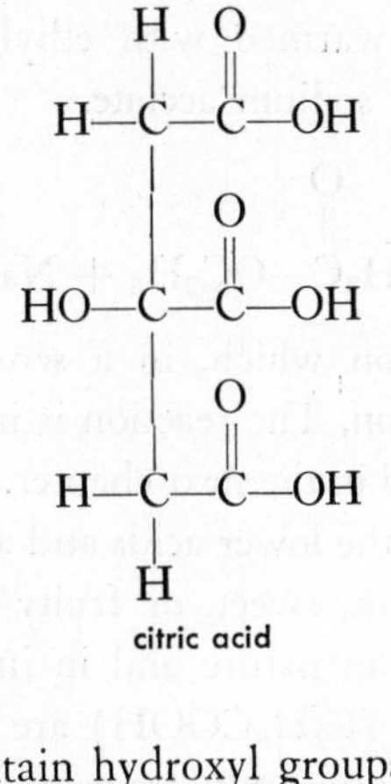

citric acid

It will be noted that these compounds contain hydroxyl groups as well as carboxyl groups. They possess in some degree the properties both of acids and of alcohols.

189. ESTERS

Alcohols are able to react with acids with formation of compounds called esters. If ethyl alcohol and acetic acid are taken as an example, the product formed is ethyl acetate, and water is simultaneously eliminated.

$$
\underset{\text{acetic acid}}{\text{H}-\overset{\overset{\displaystyle H}{|}}{\underset{\underset{\displaystyle H}{|}}{C}}-\overset{\overset{\displaystyle O}{\|}}{C}-\text{OH}} \; + \; \underset{\text{ethyl alcohol}}{\text{HO}-\overset{\overset{\displaystyle H}{|}}{\underset{\underset{\displaystyle H}{|}}{C}}-\overset{\overset{\displaystyle H}{|}}{\underset{\underset{\displaystyle H}{|}}{C}}-\text{H}} \; \overset{(\text{H}^+)}{\rightleftharpoons} \; \underset{\text{ethyl acetate (an ester)}}{\text{H}-\overset{\overset{\displaystyle H}{|}}{\underset{\underset{\displaystyle H}{|}}{C}}-\overset{\overset{\displaystyle O}{\|}}{C}-\text{O}-\overset{\overset{\displaystyle H}{|}}{\underset{\underset{\displaystyle H}{|}}{C}}-\overset{\overset{\displaystyle H}{|}}{\underset{\underset{\displaystyle H}{|}}{C}}-\text{H}} \; + \; \underset{+ \text{ water}}{\text{H}_2\text{O}}
$$

The reaction in which an ester is formed by the union of an alcohol and an acid is called **esterification.** The esterification reactions are catalyzed by the presence of hydrogen ions, so that a few drops of sulfuric acid added to the reaction mixture will greatly hasten formation of the ester. The reactions of esterification are reversible and have often been used in studies of reaction velocity, chemical equilibrium, and catalysis.

Esters similar in structure to ethyl acetate are formed generally by alcohols and organic acids. The general formula for an ester may be written

$$
\overset{\overset{\displaystyle O}{\|}}{\text{R}-\text{C}-\text{OR}'} \quad \textit{ester}
$$

where the two R— groups may be the same or different.

If a base is added to an ester the reverse of esterification tends to proceed. This is true because the base reacts with the acid as soon as the latter is formed, thus removing it from the equilibrium. For instance, if sodium hydroxide is warmed with ethyl acetate, the ester is decomposed to ethyl alcohol and sodium acetate.

$$
\overset{\overset{\displaystyle O}{\|}}{\text{CH}_3\text{C}-\text{OC}_2\text{H}_5} + \text{NaOH} \rightarrow \text{C}_2\text{H}_5\text{OH} + \overset{\overset{\displaystyle O}{\|}}{\text{CH}_3\text{C}-\text{ONa}}
$$

This reaction which, in a sense, is the reverse of esterification, is called **saponification.** The reaction is important in the manufacture of soap, as will be described in the next chapter.

Esters of the lower acids and alcohols are generally volatile colorless liquids with pleasant, sweet, or fruity odors. They are substances of considerable importance in nature and in industry. Many organic acids such as butyric and valeric (C_4H_9COOH) are especially foul-smelling. But their esters are frequently pleasantly fragrant. Esters or mixtures of esters are often the source of flavor and fragrance of fruits and flowers. Artificial flavorings and perfumes are compounded of esters mixed in proportions to simulate various natural products. Among the esters often employed are ethyl formate,

$HC-OC_2H_5$; and isoamylacetate, $CH_3\overset{\text{O}}{\overset{\|}{C}}-OC_5H_{11}$, which is the principal constituent of banana oil. Large amounts of simple esters such as butyl acetate, $CH_3\overset{\text{O}}{\overset{\|}{C}}-OC_4H_9$, are used as solvents for automobile lacquers.

190. AMINES AND AMIDES

Two other types of organic compounds to which brief reference will be made are amines and amides. The first may be considered to be a derivative of a hydrocarbon by replacement of a hydrogen by $-NH_2$, while the second may be considered to be a derivative of an organic acid by replacement of the $-OH$ in the carboxyl group by $-NH_2$. General formulas for these two types of compounds are, therefore, as follows:

$$R-NH_2 \qquad R-\overset{\text{O}}{\overset{\|}{C}}-NH_2$$
$$\text{amine} \qquad\qquad \text{amide}$$

It will be noted that both types of compounds may be regarded as derivatives of ammonia in which one hydrogen has been replaced respectively by an $R-$ group, and by an $R-\overset{\text{O}}{\overset{\|}{C}}-$ group.

We shall not concern ourselves with the preparation or properties of these compounds except to mention a few examples. Methylamine, $H-\overset{\overset{\text{H}}{|}}{\underset{\underset{\text{H}}{|}}{C}}-NH_2$

is a gas, as is ethylamine, $H-\overset{\overset{\text{H}}{|}}{\underset{\underset{\text{H}}{|}}{C}}-\overset{\overset{\text{H}}{|}}{\underset{\underset{\text{H}}{|}}{C}}-NH_2$. These substances have odors not unlike that of ammonia, but the tendency is for the amines to smell more fish-like. Certain amines occur in decaying fish. Amines are of great importance in connection with the chemistry of living matter. We shall make frequent reference to these compounds later.

Examples of amides are acetamide, $CH_3\overset{\text{O}}{\overset{\|}{C}}-NH_2$, and propionamide, $C_2H_5\overset{\text{O}}{\overset{\|}{C}}-NH_2$. Our principal interest in these substances will be in connection with nylon and related high polymers. However, a substance which may be regarded as the diamide of carbonic acid is a compound of great importance as a product of metabolism in the animal organism. It is called *urea.*

$$
\begin{array}{c}
\text{OH} \\
| \\
\text{C}=\text{O} \\
| \\
\text{OH}
\end{array}
\qquad\qquad
\begin{array}{c}
\text{NH}_2 \\
| \\
\text{C}=\text{O} \\
| \\
\text{NH}_2
\end{array}
$$

carbonic acid   urea

191. FUNCTIONAL GROUPS

We conclude this chapter with a review of the various types of compounds which have been presented. It will have been noted that each type of compound is characterized by a special grouping of atoms. The group which is characteristic of a particular type of compound is called a **functional group.**

$$
\begin{array}{c}
\text{O} \\
\parallel
\end{array}
$$

Thus $-\text{C}-\text{OH}$ is the functional group for an organic acid. We shall present a table which includes the type of compound, a general formula, the functional group, and a specific example, together with the name of the example.

TABLE 20

Type	General Formula	Functional Group	Example	Name
Paraffin........	R—H	—H	CH_4	Methane
Alkyl halide....	R—X	—X	C_2H_5Cl	Ethyl chloride
Alcohol........	R—OH	—OH	CH_3OH	Methyl alcohol
Ether..........	R'—O—R	—O—	CH_3—O—C_2H_5	Methylethyl ether
Aldehyde.......	R—$\overset{\text{O}}{\overset{\parallel}{\text{C}}}$—H	—$\overset{\text{O}}{\overset{\parallel}{\text{C}}}$—H	CH_3—$\overset{\text{O}}{\overset{\parallel}{\text{C}}}$—H	Acetaldehyde
Ketone.........	R'—$\overset{\text{O}}{\overset{\parallel}{\text{C}}}$—R	—$\overset{\text{O}}{\overset{\parallel}{\text{C}}}$—R	CH_3—$\overset{\text{O}}{\overset{\parallel}{\text{C}}}$—$CH_3$	Acetone
Organic acid....	R—$\overset{\text{O}}{\overset{\parallel}{\text{C}}}$—OH	—$\overset{\text{O}}{\overset{\parallel}{\text{C}}}$—OH	$CH_3\overset{\text{O}}{\overset{\parallel}{\text{C}}}$—OH	Acetic acid
Ester..........	R'—$\overset{\text{O}}{\overset{\parallel}{\text{C}}}$—OR	—$\overset{\text{O}}{\overset{\parallel}{\text{C}}}$—OR	$CH_3\overset{\text{O}}{\overset{\parallel}{\text{C}}}$—$OC_2H_5$	Ethyl acetate
Amine.........	R—NH_2	—NH_2	$C_2H_5NH_2$	Ethylamine
Amide.........	R—$\overset{\text{O}}{\overset{\parallel}{\text{C}}}$—$NH_2$	—$\overset{\text{O}}{\overset{\parallel}{\text{C}}}$—$NH_2$	$CH_3\overset{\text{O}}{\overset{\parallel}{\text{C}}}$—$NH_2$	Acetamide

There are other types of compounds known, but those described are among the types most frequently encountered, and these are the types to which we shall have reference in later chapters. The reader should memorize the functional groups for each kind of compound. Otherwise it will be impossible to follow the discussion in the following chapters.

EXERCISES

A. *Define or explain the following:*

alkyl group	functional group
acid anhydride	saponification
denaturant	substitution reaction
dynamite	tincture
esterification reaction	

B. 1. Use structural formulas to show functional groups for the following types of compound: hydrocarbon, alkyl halide, alcohol, ether, aldehyde, ketone, organic acid, ester, amine, amide.

2. Use structural formulas to show the following alkyl groups: methyl, ethyl, propyl (2 isomers), butyl (all possible isomers), amyl (1 example only).

3. Show general formulas for the following types of compounds: hydrocarbon, alkyl halide, alcohol, ether, aldehyde, ketone, organic acid, ester, amine, amide.

4. Write structural formulas for each of the following: methyl chloride, methylene chloride, chloroform, propane, propyl bromide (all possible isomers), ethanol, methylethyl ether, acetaldehyde, methylethyl ketone, formic acid, acetic acid, propionic acid (3 carbons), methyl acetate, ethyl formate, methylamine, acetamide, acetic anhydride.

5. Identify the following as to type of compound only:

$$\underset{C_3H_7CH}{\overset{\overset{\textstyle O}{\|}}{}} \qquad \underset{C_2H_5COCH_3}{\overset{\overset{\textstyle O}{\|}}{}} \qquad C_5H_{11}OC_2H_5$$

6. Name the following:

$$\underset{CH_3C-OH}{\overset{\overset{\textstyle O}{\|}}{}} \qquad \underset{CH_3C-CH_3}{\overset{\overset{\textstyle O}{\|}}{}} \qquad \underset{\underset{H\ H\ H}{|\ \ |\ \ |}}{\overset{H\ H\ H}{\overset{|\ \ |\ \ |}{H-C-C-C-OH}}} \qquad C_3H_7NH_2$$

7. Using structural formulas write complete equations for each of the following:

a. formation from methane of methyl chloride, methyl bromide

b. preparation of ethylene chloride

c. action of moist silver oxide on an alkyl halide

d. synthesis of methanol

e. formation of glyceryltrinitrate

       f. formation of diethyl ether
       g. stepwise oxidation of a primary alcohol (two steps)
       h. formation of a ketone
       i. formation of a silver mirror
       j. an esterification reaction
       k. a saponification reaction

C. 1. Write ionic equations showing how acetic acid could be neutralized by sodium hydroxide. Recall that sodium acetate in solution will conduct the electric current.

    2. In the formation of an ester, say ethyl acetate, from ethanol and acetic acid, it is not clear if the oxygen in the water molecule comes from the alcohol or from the acid. Design an experiment using a tracer element to obtain some evidence on this matter.

    3. Write all possible structural isomers of dichloropropane, $C_3H_6Cl_2$.

    4. A solution consisting of 0.0810 g. of acetic acid dissolved in 60.0 g. of benzene freezes at 5.34° C. The normal freezing point of pure benzene is 5.40°, and the molecular depression constant is 5.12°. Comment on this.

CARBOHYDRATES
29 AND FATS

192. SUGARS

The roots, leaves, bark, and stems of plants all contain large quantities of substances for which a general formula may be written $C_m H_{2n} O_n$. These substances are called **carbohydrates.** They contain carbon, hydrogen, and oxygen, and with few exceptions the proportion of hydrogen is twice that of oxygen. The formula might be written $C_m (H_2 O)_n$, in which it would appear that these compounds actually contain water, and are to be considered as hydrates of carbon. This is not the case. The name "carbohydrate" is misleading. Nevertheless, the name is retained. It should be understood that it is incidental in these compounds that there should be twice as many hydrogen atoms as oxygen.

There are known a very large number of different carbohydrates. In this section we shall refer to the simplest class, which includes the ordinary sugars. Out of the many kinds of sugars which are known we shall consider only three. These are *glucose* (dextrose or corn sugar), *fructose* (fruit sugar), and *sucrose* (ordinary cane sugar). The first to be considered is glucose.

Glucose is widely distributed in plants. It has, as is well known, a characteristic sweet taste. The formula is $C_6 H_{12} O_6$.

The structural formula for glucose was, for many years, thought to be as follows:

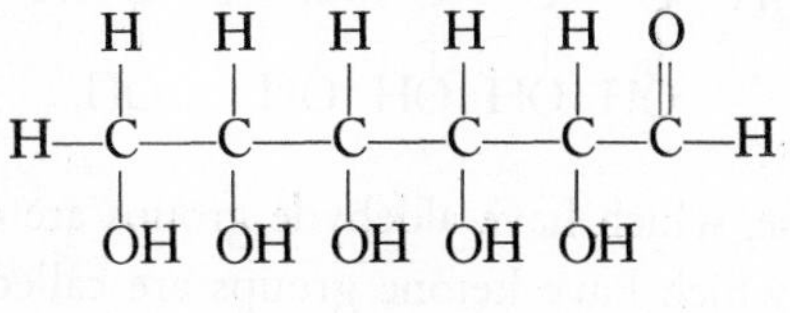

$$\begin{array}{cccccc} H & H & H & H & H & O \\ | & | & | & | & | & \| \\ H-C & -C & -C & -C & -C & -C-H \\ | & | & | & | & | & \\ OH & OH & OH & OH & OH & \end{array}$$

It will be noted that this formula consists of a straight chain of six carbon atoms, and includes five alcohol (—OH) functional groups and one alde-

hyde ($-\overset{\text{O}}{\overset{\|}{C}}-H$) functional group. It is now known that glucose has several possible configurations of which one is that given above, while another is a ring structure.

$$\underset{\substack{\text{aldehyde (chain) form of glucose}}}{\overset{\substack{H \quad\; H \quad\; H \quad\; H \quad\; H \quad\; O}}{H-\underset{OH}{C}-\underset{OH}{C}-\underset{OH}{C}-\underset{OH}{C}-\underset{OH}{C}-\overset{\|}{C}-H}} \rightleftarrows \underset{\substack{\text{hemiacetal (ring) form of glucose}}}{\begin{array}{c} \overset{OH\quad OH}{HC-\!-\!CH} \\ HC-OH \quad HC-OH \\ HC-\!-\!O \\ CH_2OH \end{array}}$$

In the previous chapter reference was made to the reaction of an aldehyde with **Benedict's solution** or Fehling's solution. The former consists of an alkaline solution of copper sulfate to which sodium citrate is added to prevent precipitation of copper hydroxide. Under the influence of a reducing agent, such as an aldehyde, the copper is reduced to cuprous oxide, Cu_2O, which appears as a precipitate varying in color from yellowish green to red.

Glucose reacts with Benedict's solution, giving the characteristic cuprous oxide precipitate. This test is used in the diagnosis of diabetes. In diabetic conditions sugar is found in the blood or urine in large amounts. A sample of urine is treated with Benedict's solution. Appearance of the cuprous oxide precipitate is generally proof that diabetes is present. The test is used not only for diagnostic purposes, but also to aid in controlling the disease under treatment with insulin.

Fruit sugar, or **fructose,** is also widely distributed in nature. Fructose also has the formula $C_6H_{12}O_6$, but in contrast to glucose it contains a ketone group rather than an aldehyde group. Several structural formulas are believed to exist for fructose, the chain formula being as follows:

$$\underset{\substack{OH\;\;\; OH\;\;\; OH\;\;\; OH \qquad OH}}{\overset{\substack{H \quad\;\; H \quad\;\; H \quad\;\; H \quad\;\; O \quad\;\; H}}{H-\underset{}{C}-\underset{}{C}-\underset{}{C}-\underset{}{C}-\overset{\|}{C}-\underset{}{C}-H}}$$

Sugars, like glucose, which have aldehyde groups are called *aldoses,* while those, like fructose, which have ketone groups are called *ketoses.* There are many aldoses and ketoses known of about the same complexity as glucose and fructose, but some of the most interesting sugars are more complicated. Sucrose or ordinary cane sugar is one of these.

Sucrose occurs in sugar cane, sugar beet, maple sugar, and honey. It is one of the most widely produced and utilized of all organic compounds. The average American manages to eat his own weight in sucrose every year.

The formula for sucrose is $C_{12}H_{22}O_{11}$; hence it would appear to contain two of the simpler sugar molecules less one molecule of water. This is confirmed by the reaction of sucrose with water in the presence of a trace of acid or other catalyst.

$$\text{sucrose} + H_2O \xrightarrow{(H^+)} \text{glucose} + \text{fructose}$$

This process of converting sucrose to a mixture of glucose and fructose occurs in the intestine, and in various industrial and domestic cooking processes. It is called inversion of sugar, and the mixture of glucose and fructose is referred to as **invert sugar.**

This relationship of sucrose to glucose and fructose, plus the fact that sucrose does not affect Benedict's solution, has led to the belief that sucrose contains two ring structures. These are formed from the glucose and fructose less one molecule of water, as follows:

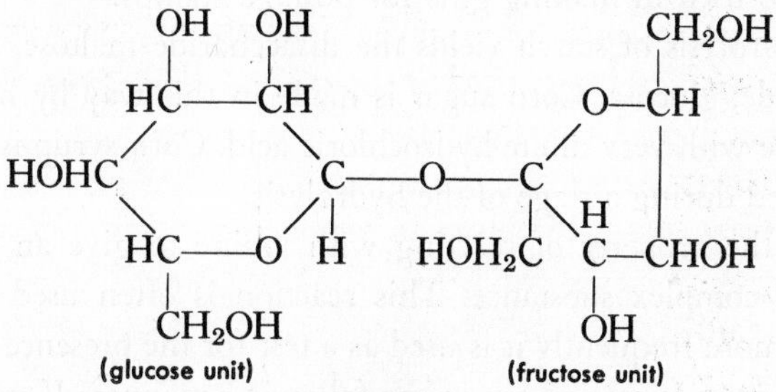

(glucose unit)   (fructose unit)

sucrose

Structures such as sucrose containing two simpler sugar units are called **disaccharides,** while those like glucose and fructose are called **monosaccharides.** Many examples of each are known. Compounds containing more than a few of these simpler sugar groups are called **polysaccharides,** and to these our attention will be now directed.

193. STARCH

Cereal grains such as wheat, oats, barley, and corn contain a polysaccharide called starch. This is also present in large proportion in potatoes and in certain fruits. The molecule of starch is large with a molecular weight of several thousand. What we know about the structural formula for starch is largely derived from the products obtained when starch is hydrolyzed or otherwise broken down chemically. The final product obtained by hydrolyzing starch is glucose; consequently it is believed that starch contains glucose rings connected together as they are in some of the disaccharides. A possible structural formula for starch is shown below:

```
        H H            ┌   H H           ┐   H H
        C—C        O   │   C—C        O  │   C—C        OH
       /O  O\    /   \ │  /O  O\    /   \│  /O  O\    /
  HOHC  H  H  C   │ C   H  H  C   │ C   H  H  C
      \ H  /    \ │ H\ H  /  H   │ H\ H  /  H
        C—O        H │   C—O          │   C—O
        │            │   │         ─┘x │   │
       CH₂OH        └   CH₂OH          CH₂OH
```

glucose unit

starch

The value of x, shown in the formula, may be several hundred or thousand; but the exact value is unknown. It will be noted that the formula for starch may be represented $(C_6H_{10}O_5)_n$.

The hydrolysis of starch is an important reaction. Partial hydrolysis yields **dextrin,** a substance of smaller molecular weight than starch, yet not so small as the disaccharides. Dextrin is formed when starched goods are ironed. Dextrin is also used in making glue for postage stamps.

Further hydrolysis of starch yields the disaccharide maltose, and then the monosaccharide, glucose. Corn sugar is made in this way by heating starch under pressure with very dilute hydrochloric acid. Corn syrup is a mixture of sugars obtained during a stage of the hydrolysis.

Starch has the property of reacting with iodine to give an intense blue-black colored complex substance. This reaction is often used as a test for starch. Even more frequently it is used as a test for the presence of an oxidizing agent. The test is carried out in the following manner: If starch is mixed with potassium iodide no reaction occurs because iodide ion, I^-, does not cause formation of the blue-black compound. If now a trace of oxidizing agent is added, such as chlorine, Cl_2, the iodide ion is oxidized to free iodine which instantly reacts with the starch, yielding the colored complex.

194. FERMENTATION

Production of alcohol by the fermentation of fruit juices is one of the oldest industries of which we have any knowledge. Carbohydrate raw materials which may be used for this purpose include molasses, sugar, starch, and wood.

The procedure is to prepare a solution or suspension of molasses or other raw material in water, at the proper temperature, and with a very slight acid concentration. To this solution special cultures of yeast are added. The particular yeast growth used is generally *Saccharomyces cerevisiae,* which does not grow wild but has been cultivated for centuries for brewing and baking.

The growing yeast secretes substances which act as catalysts for the decomposition of the sugar. These substances are called **enzymes.** Enzymes perform many important functions in the chemistry of living matter, and we shall have reference to them later in connection with the processes of digestion and metabolism. Enzymes are complex organic compounds of poorly understood structure. Many different enzymes are known and they catalyze many different types of reactions. For instance, an enzyme called *sucrase* which is secreted by yeast, is able to catalyze the decomposition of sucrose to a mixture of glucose and fructose. Another enzyme called *zymase,* also secreted by yeast, converts glucose and fructose to ethyl alcohol and carbon dioxide.

$$C_{12}H_{22}O_{11} + H_2O \xrightarrow{\text{(sucrase)}} C_6H_{12}O_6 + C_6H_{12}O_6$$

sucrose   glucose   fructose

$$C_6H_{12}O_6 \xrightarrow{\text{(zymase)}} 2C_2H_5OH + 2CO_2$$

glucose or fructose   ethyl alcohol   carbon dioxide

The enzymes from yeast will not break down starch molecules. If starch is used as the raw material for making alcohol it is necessary to use an enzyme which will convert the starch into a disaccharide. The enzyme used for this purpose is *diastase.* Diastase is obtained from sprouting barley which has been heated to stop growth of the barley, but not so hot as to destroy the enzyme. Barley treated in this way is known as **malt.**

The actual mechanism of alcoholic fermentation is very complex, and the equations above merely show the initial and final stages.

The induction of chemical reactions by microorganisms such as yeast and bacteria is known as **microbiological chemistry.** Many of these reactions are important in nature and in industry. In some cases, as for yeast, the micro-organism secretes a substance which catalyzes a reaction. In such cases the enzyme is in no sense alive; it differs from ordinary inorganic catalysts only in being more complex and in having been itself synthesized by a living organism. In other cases the living organism is able to bring about compli-cated chemical changes during its growth. Perhaps all such processes involve enzymes, but in the former case the pure crystalline enzymes have been iso-lated and studied, even though their chemical structures are not yet under-stood.

A few microbiological processes will be mentioned, in addition to the im-portant alcoholic fermentation.

Reference has already been made to the production of acetone by fermenta-tion of starch. This reaction is caused by a strain of bacteria known as *Clos-tridium acetobutylicum Weizmann,* discovered by Chaim Weizmann. This process contributed to the winning of World War I. The products are actually a mixture of butyl alcohol, acetone, and ethyl alcohol. In normal times the process is operated for the production of butyl alcohol which is used in the form of the ester butyl acetate as a solvent for lacquers.

Lactic acid is another substance made by microbiological action. This is the principal acid in sour milk. Lactic acid is made industrially by the fermentation of molasses, whey, or corn sugar. The bacteria used are *Lactobacillus delbruckii* and *Lactobacillus bulgaricus*. Similarly, bacteria of the family *Acetobacter* are able to oxidize ethyl alcohol to acetic acid. A reaction of this type accounts for the conversion of wine to vinegar.

Molds are able to cause certain chemical changes. Oxalic and citric acids may be made in this way, and the flavor of Roquefort cheese is caused by traces of higher fatty acids which are liberated from the fats of butter by the characteristic blue-green mold *Penicillium roquefortii*. The most spectacular case of synthesis by molds is that of penicillin, to which reference will be made in a later chapter.

One of the most astonishing cases of microbiological action is the synthesis of the extremely poisonous gas trimethylarsine, $(CH_3)_3As$. Certain strains of molds can synthesize and liberate this gas from arsenous oxide, As_2O_3, or from other arsenic compounds. A few deaths have occurred from breathing trimethylarsine liberated into rooms in this way from molds growing on wallpaper, the pigments of which have contained arsenic.

195. CELLULOSE

The third type of carbohydrate to which we shall refer is cellulose. This is the most widely distributed polysaccharide. It constitutes a large part of wood and of other matter of vegetable origin. Cotton is almost pure cellulose, as is linen.

The cellulose molecule is very large with a molecular weight running into hundreds of thousands. The fact that cellulose is a polysaccharide is demonstrated by the hydrolysis of sawdust to sugar by the action of dilute acids. The structure of the cellulose molecule is very like that of starch, except that it is larger, with minor differences in the arrangement of the units.

Good-quality filter paper is almost pure cellulose. Paper is made from material which is rich in cellulose. Such materials are wood, corn stalks, straw, and old rags. Noncellulose material must first be removed. In wood the chief substance to be removed is lignin. This is separated from the cellulose by treatment of the wood with sodium bisulfite and sulfurous acid (the "sulfite" process). The creamy fluid containing the cellulose is then slowly dried and pressed until a sheet of paper is formed.

Paper used for magazines or for writing purposes is coated or impregnated with "fillers," and "sizing" materials such as titanium dioxide, glue, starch, and silicates which make the paper less transparent and more suitable for taking ink.

Numerous products besides paper are derived from cellulose. One of these is **rayon.** Cellulose is insoluble in water, but it will dissolve in several reagents of which one is a mixture of alkali and carbon disulfide. The process in which this solvent is used is called the viscose process. Compounds containing alcohol groups dissolve in this reagent to form substances known as

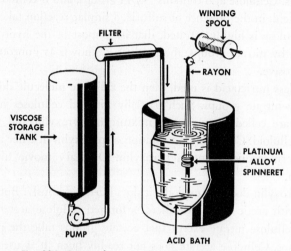

Fig. 29-1. Process for converting viscose into rayon thread. (After A. L. Elder, E. C. Scott, F. A. Kanda, *Textbook of Chemistry,* Harper and Brothers, 1948. By permission)

xanthates, and cellulose is no exception. The reaction may be represented in this way:

$$R\text{—}OH + \quad CS_2 \quad + NaOH \rightarrow RO\overset{\displaystyle S}{\overset{\|}{C}}\text{—}SNa$$

an alcohol + carbon disulfide + a base → a xanthate

The xanthates form a thick, viscous solution, from which the name viscose is derived. When the xanthates are treated with acids they decompose, yielding the original alcohol. Thus, cellulose xanthate treated with sulfuric acid gives the original cellulose.

In the manufacture of rayon, cellulose derived from cotton, or other source, is formed into *viscose.* (See Fig. 29-1.) The viscose solution is then forced through fine holes into an acid bath. The viscose is converted back into cellulose as it comes in contact with the acid. The chief difference between the rayon fiber so produced and the original cotton fiber is that the former is a long, uniform, tubular thread, while the cotton fiber is short and irregular. The rayon thread is then, of course, woven into cloth and made into wearing apparel. This industry is of tremendous size.

If the viscose is forced into the acid as a thin sheet, instead of a thread, then the familiar Cellophane is obtained.

In our discussion of glycerol we mentioned how glyceryl trinitrate, or nitroglycerin, could be made by treating glycerol with a mixture of nitric and sulfuric acids. Cellulose also contains —OH groups, and if cellulose is treated with nitric acid, in the presence of sulfuric, a similar reaction takes place.

If the cellulose is highly nitrated, that is, if most of the hydroxyl groups are replaced by nitrate groups, the product is known as guncotton, an important explosive.

If rather less nitric acid is used, then the cellulose molecule does not take up so many nitrate groups. Such partially nitrated celluloses have several uses. They are called **pyroxylin.** A mixture of pyroxylin and camphor is known as celluloid. Collodion is a solution of pyroxylin in ether and alcohol. Many modern lacquers contain pyroxylin. Ordinary movie film is made of pyroxylin.

While pyroxylin does not explode, it does burn vigorously. But if cellulose is treated with acetic anhydride there is formed cellulose acetate, which is similar to cellulose nitrate except that acetate groups take the place of the nitrate groups. Cellulose acetate does not readily burn. It is used for movie safety film, and for making textiles.

196. OPTICAL ISOMERISM

In previous chapters reference has been made to structural isomers, such as the two forms of propyl alcohol. In this section there is presented a different kind of isomerism. This is known as optical isomerism, and it forms an important branch of organic chemistry.

Ordinary light consists of transverse electromagnetic vibrations or waves. In this respect light is similar to radio waves, infrared, ultraviolet, and X rays. Light waves may be regarded as similar to waves on water, with an important difference. The waves on water, as in oceans and lakes, merely vibrate vertically—that is, the water merely moves up and down as the wave goes forward. Light waves act as though the motion is in every possible plane, as if the water were to move sideways and at every possible angle, as well as up and down.

While light waves normally vibrate in every possible plane, it is comparatively easy to restrict the vibrations to one plane only. In these circumstances the light waves would more closely resemble waves on water. This restriction of the vibrations to one plane is accomplished by placing in the path of the light a piece of Iceland spar, which is a transparent form of the mineral calcite, $CaCO_3$. A similar result is obtained by passing light through a sheet of the synthetic material known as Polaroid.

The light which emerges from the Iceland spar crystal looks the same as ordinary light, but it is easy to prove that it vibrates in one plane only. Such light is said to be **polarized**. Specially prepared crystals for obtaining polarized light are

Fig. 29-2. The diagram at the *left* represents approaching electromagnetic vibrations (of light); only two of all possible vibration planes are shown. The diagram at *right* represents the same beam of light after it has been polarized by passage through a Nicol prism.

called *Nicol prisms*. If the beam of polarized light is now made to pass through a second Nicol prism no light will emerge, *provided* that the second Nicol prism is turned at right angles to the first. If both prisms are turned at the same angle the light will go through both, but if they are turned at different angles the plane of vibration which is permitted to pass the first prism cannot pass through the second.

Fig. 29-3. Action of parallel, and of crossed, Nicol prisms to the passage of light.

An apparatus consisting of two Nicol prisms so that light is passed first through one and then through the other is called a **polarimeter**. Light of a single wave-length as from a sodium lamp is often used for the polarimeter. If the two prisms are set at the same angle, the light passes right through the apparatus and may be observed at an eyepiece.

In 1815 the French scientist Biot made the remarkable discovery that certain

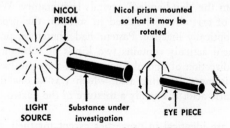

Fig. 29-4. Principle of the polarimeter.

organic compounds possess the power of rotating the plane of polarized light. Suppose the two prisms in the polarimeter are set at the same angle. Light, of course, passes through. Now suppose a solution of sugar is placed in a glass vessel between the two prisms. The light will be found to have been cut off. But if the second prism is slowly rotated, a position will be found at which the light again passes through the apparatus.

This effect, known as **optical rotation,** is as if the sugar twisted the plane of vibration of the light. Sometimes the twisting is to the right and sometimes to the left. The effect occurs with substances dissolved or melted, as well as for crystalline substances. Substances which show this effect are said to be optically active. Those which twist the plane to the right are said to be **dextrorotatory;** those which twist the plane to the left are **levorotatory.** Many naturally occurring organic compounds show this effect.

An understanding of optical activity was obtained from the beautiful experiments performed by the great French chemist Louis Pasteur about the middle of the nineteenth century. When crystals of quartz are examined, it is sometimes found that the various crystal faces in two specimens are identical except that one crystal is related to the other as the right hand is to the left. These are referred to as hemihedral forms of quartz. The phenomenon of **hemihedry** occurs in numerous substances, but ordinarily it is not well developed.

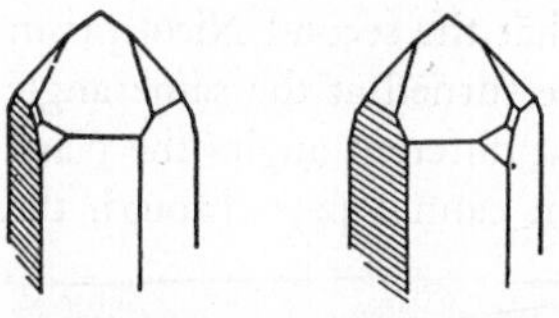

LEFT-HANDED   RIGHT-HANDED
QUARTZ   QUARTZ

Fig. 29-5. Hemihedral forms of quartz.

Pasteur undertook the investigation of tartaric acid and of certain tartrates. These are found in grapes and as a by-product in the manufacture of wine. These substances are all dextrorotatory, and Pasteur first found that crystals of tartaric acid and tartrates show evidence of hemihedry, but that the crystals are all hemihedral in the same sense; that is, only one of the two possible forms is present. This observation suggested to Pasteur that there might be a relationship between hemihedry and optical activity.

Pasteur next investigated certain salts of racemic acid which is identical in chemical composition with tartaric acid, and which is also a by-product of wine manufacture, but which shows no optical activity. When these salts were allowed to crystallize they formed *both* types of hemihedral crystals. Pasteur painstakingly picked out the "right-" and "left-handed" crystals, and made solutions of each. The solution prepared from the "right-handed" crystals proved to be dextrorotatory and those from the "left-handed" crystals levorotatory. When equal weights of the two kinds of crystals were mixed in solution the product was, like the starting material, optically inactive. Pasteur had, therefore, proved that optically inactive racemic acid actually contains two kinds of substances, and that these differ only in the direction of optical rotation that they produce. Such substances are called **optical isomers.** Racemic acid, which was at one time thought to be different from tartaric acid, is actually a mixture of the dextro- and levo- forms of tartaric acid.

Optical isomers are identical in properties except for their action on polarized light. They have the same melting and boiling points, and they react in the same way towards most reagents. The separation of a mixture of optical isomers is, therefore, a matter of considerable difficulty. Pasteur achieved a separation by painstakingly picking out the hemihedral forms of the crystals, but this method is not generally available. Optically inactive mixtures of optical isomers are referred to as **racemic mixtures**—the name racemic being no longer restricted to the mixture of tartaric acid isomers.

Fig. 29-6. Louis Pasteur

Louis Pasteur was born in France in 1822. His educational career was distinguished more by sincerity and persistence than by brilliance.

On December 27, 1892, the greatest gathering of medicine and science ever seen took place in Paris to honor Pasteur on his seventieth birthday.

In addition to his classic experiments in optical isomerism Pasteur established the nature of fermentation, investigated anaerobic life, overthrew the doctrine of spontaneous generation of life, contributed to the germ theory of disease, invented "pasteurization" of milk, saved the wine and silk-worm industries of France, conquered anthax and hydrophobia, and laid the groundwork for aseptic surgery.

Pasteur died in 1895. Few men of science have so earned the gratitude of mankind, or been so richly rewarded in life. (*Bettmann Archive*)

At the time when Pasteur made his brilliant experiments it was by no means understood why optical isomers should exist. He suggested what later proved to be the correct explanation, namely, that the molecules of tartaric acid possess a lack of symmetry of such nature that a dextro-molecule could not be superimposed upon a levo-molecule, but that the mirror-image (the image viewed in a mirror) of the dextro-molecule could be superimposed directly on the levo-molecule. The two forms of molecules are then related as the hemihedral faces of certain crystals, that is, as the right hand is to the left. However, the true understanding of this effect was first announced by van't Hoff in Holland, and by Le Bel in France, in 1874. Their theory, announced independently, is substantially as follows:

I

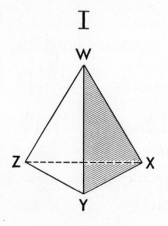

II

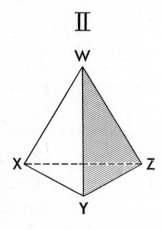

Van't Hoff – Le Bel Theory

Each carbon atom possesses four valences, and these valences are directed as toward the four corners of a tetrahedron, the carbon atom being at the center of the tetrahedron. If the valences of the carbon atom are attached to *four different* atoms or groups of atoms, then two distinct arrangements are possible.

These different arrangements are a little difficult to visualize unless one has a three-dimensional model. But it should be clear from the diagrams that tetrahedron I is structurally the same as tetrahedron II except for the fact that they could not be superimposed on each other. But tetrahedron I could be superposed on the *mirror-image* of tetrahedron II. A carbon atom which is thus attached to four different atoms or groups of atoms is called an **asymmetric carbon atom.** Optical isomerism is found in substances containing asymmetric carbon atoms. The two forms are referred to as the *d-* and *l-* forms (short for dextro- and levo-).

Let us now see how tartaric acid and other optically active compounds contain asymmetric carbon. The structural formula for tartaric acid is as follows:

$$\begin{array}{c} \text{H} \quad\quad \text{O} \\ | \quad\quad\ \ || \\ \text{HO-C*-C-OH} \\ | \\ \text{HO-C*-C-OH} \\ | \quad\quad\ \ || \\ \text{H} \quad\quad \text{O} \end{array}$$

asymmetric carbon atom

It will be noted that this compound actually contains two asymmetric carbon atoms (C*), that is, carbon atoms connected to four different groups. The four

different groups in the case of tartaric acid are HO—, H—, $-\overset{\overset{\displaystyle O}{\displaystyle ||}}{\text{C}}-\text{OH}$, and

$\text{HO}-\overset{\overset{\displaystyle |}{\displaystyle }}{\underset{\underset{\displaystyle H \ \ O}{\displaystyle | \ \ ||}}{\text{C}}}-\text{C}-\text{OH}$. Another example is lactic acid:

$$\begin{array}{c} \text{H} \quad\quad \text{O} \\ | \quad\quad\ \ || \\ \text{HO-C*-C-OH} \\ | \\ \text{CH}_3 \end{array}$$

Optical isomerism may be shown by any compound in which the general grouping

$$\begin{array}{c} \text{W} \\ | \\ \text{Z-C-X} \\ | \\ \text{Y} \end{array}$$

occurs, in which W, X, Y, and Z are different atoms or groups of atoms.

Thus, the sugars show excellent examples of optical isomerism.

$$\begin{array}{c} \text{H} \quad \text{H} \quad\ \text{H} \quad\ \text{H} \quad\ \text{H} \quad\ \text{O} \\ | \quad\ | \quad\ | \quad\ | \quad\ | \quad\ || \\ \text{H-C---C*---C*---C*---C*---C-H} \\ | \quad\ | \quad\ | \quad\ | \quad\ | \\ \text{OH} \ \text{OH} \ \text{OH} \ \text{OH} \ \text{OH} \end{array}$$

In glucose there are actually four asymmetric carbon atoms. It will be understood that while substances such as these can show optical activity, yet many samples are racemic mixtures containing the two forms in equal proportions. Many natural substances show activity, but most laboratory-prepared samples are racemic mixtures.

The natural occurrence, or synthesis, of optically active compounds is apparently an inheritable characteristic which is passed on through successive generations of plants and animals. It so happens that the great majority of optically active natural substances are dextrorotatory.

The direct synthesis of separate *d*- and *l*- forms of compounds in the laboratory is a problem that has been much studied. It is referred to as asymmetric synthesis. The problem has in part been solved through the use of reagents which are themselves optically active, but no general solution to the problem has as yet been found.

197. PHOTOSYNTHESIS

One of the most important reactions in all chemistry is the photochemical synthesis of carbohydrates by living plants. This is the process whereby plants take carbon dioxide from the air and convert it into carbohydrates, with the aid of water and inorganic material from the soil, and of energy from sunlight. Animals are quite unable to perform this synthesis. For this reason animals obtain carbohydrate in their diets from plants.

This reaction, which is called photosynthesis, may be represented very simply by the equation:

$$n\mathrm{CO_2} + n\mathrm{H_2O} \xrightarrow{\text{(light)}} (\mathrm{CH_2O})_n + n\mathrm{O_2}$$

It will be noted that oxygen is liberated, and, as is well known, oxygen actually is given off by growing plants. However, the equation given above is grossly oversimplified. The photosynthetic reaction is highly complicated, and is by no means thoroughly understood.

Energy necessary for the reaction is absorbed from sunlight by the green coloring matter of the leaves. This substance is **chlorophyll.** One form of chlorophyll probably has the formula given at top of next page.

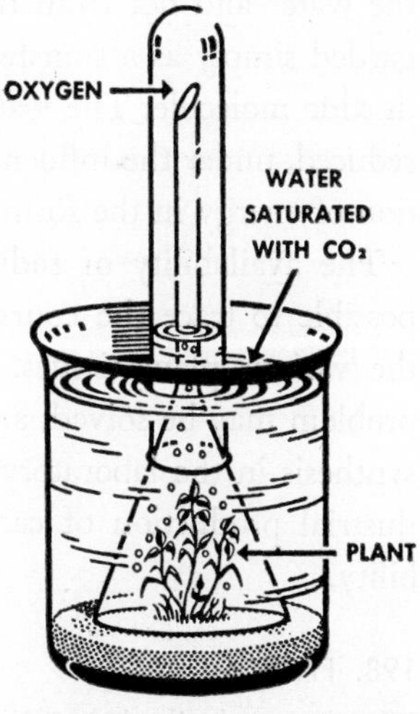

Fig. 29-7. Demonstration that green leaves placed in water saturated with carbon dioxide and exposed to sunlight liberate oxygen. (After A. L. Elder, *Textbook of Chemistry*, Harper and Brothers, 1941. By permission)

Notice that the chlorophyll molecule has a magnesium atom at its center. It is a remarkable fact that chlorophyll is closely related chemically to hemin,

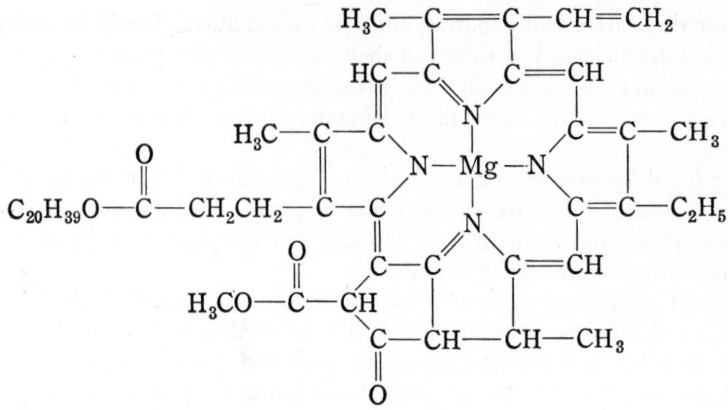

$$H_3C-C=\!\!=C-CH=CH_2$$
$$HC-C \qquad C=\!\!=CH$$
$$H_3C-C-C \qquad N \qquad C=\!\!=C-CH_3$$
$$\qquad\qquad N-Mg-N$$
$$C_{20}H_{39}O-\overset{O}{\overset{\|}{C}}-CH_2CH_2-C-C \qquad N \qquad C=\!\!=C-C_2H_5$$
$$\overset{O}{\overset{\|}{\qquad}} \qquad C-C \qquad C=\!\!=CH$$
$$H_3CO-\overset{O}{\overset{\|}{C}}-CH \qquad\qquad$$
$$\qquad C-CH-CH-CH_3$$
$$\qquad \overset{\|}{O}$$

the red coloring matter in the blood, except that hemin contains an iron atom rather than magnesium.

The use of oxygen-18 as a tracer has definitely established one fact in connection with photosynthesis—namely, that the liberated oxygen comes from the water and not from the carbon dioxide. The chief reaction may be regarded simply as a transfer of hydrogen from a water molecule to a carbon dioxide molecule. The water may be said to be oxidized, the carbon dioxide reduced, under the influence of the catalyst chlorophyll and with the absorption of energy in the form of light.

The availability of radioactive carbon from the uranium pile makes it possible to trace the course of carbon atoms from carbon dioxide through the various plant tissues. It seems probable that within a few years this problem may be solved, and that the production of carbohydrates by photosynthesis in the laboratory may become possible. Perhaps the large-scale industrial production of carbohydrates from coal and water is also a possibility.

198. FATS

The fats and oils that occur widely in matter of animal and vegetable origin are shown by their properties to be esters. Thus lard, butter, tallow, olive oil, cottonseed oil, castor oil, linseed oil, and cod liver oil are all esters of the alcohol glycerol. This is easily proved by treatment of the fat or oil with sodium hydroxide. The products are glycerol plus the sodium salt of an organic acid.

The acids which combine with glycerol to form fats and oils are long chain **fatty acids** of which stearic ($C_{17}H_{35}COOH$) is an example. It is curious that the straight-chain acids having an even number of carbon atoms greatly predominate in nature. Fats have been identified in which the number of carbon atoms in the acid chain may be as few as four or as many as twenty-six.

All fats are actually mixtures of esters, but sometimes one ester is present in large amount. Lard contains a fairly large percentage of the glycerol ester of stearic acid. The name of this compound is *glyceryl tristearate*. It is a *tri-stearate* because the glycerol molecule has three functional groups. The formula for glyceryl tristearate is as follows:

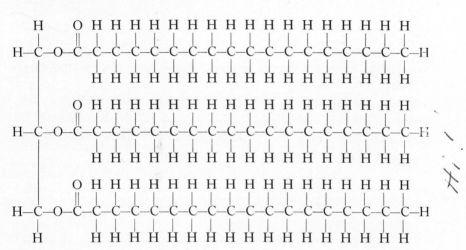

For convenience we shall write the formulas of other fats in the following pattern:

$$
\begin{array}{c}
\text{H} \quad\quad \text{O} \\
| \quad\quad\quad || \\
\text{H}-\text{C}-\text{O}-\text{C}-\text{C}_{17}\text{H}_{35} \\
| \\
\quad\quad\quad \text{O} \\
\quad\quad\quad || \\
\text{H}-\text{C}-\text{O}-\text{C}-\text{C}_{17}\text{H}_{35} \\
| \\
\quad\quad\quad \text{O} \\
\quad\quad\quad || \\
\text{H}-\text{C}-\text{O}-\text{C}-\text{C}_{17}\text{H}_{35} \\
| \\
\text{H}
\end{array}
$$

Another fat, which occurs in olive oil, coconut oil, and also in lard, is glyceryl tripalmitate. Palmitic acid is $C_{15}H_{31}COOH$. Glyceryl tripalmitate is therefore,

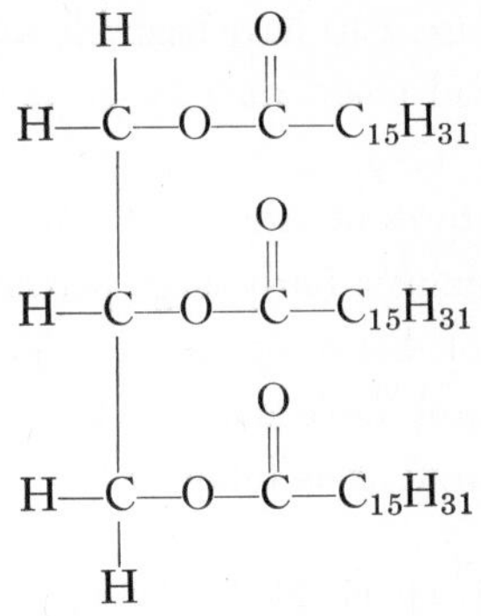

$$H\text{---}\overset{\overset{\displaystyle H}{|}}{C}\text{---}O\text{---}\overset{\overset{\displaystyle O}{\|}}{C}\text{---}C_{15}H_{31}$$

$$H\text{---}\overset{|}{C}\text{---}O\text{---}\overset{\overset{\displaystyle O}{\|}}{C}\text{---}C_{15}H_{31}$$

$$H\text{---}\overset{|}{\underset{\underset{\displaystyle H}{|}}{C}}\text{---}O\text{---}\overset{\overset{\displaystyle O}{\|}}{C}\text{---}C_{15}H_{31}$$

For convenience, fats are generally named by changing the ending of the acid to -*in*. Thus, glyceryl tristearate becomes "stearin," and glyceryl tripalmitate is "palmitin."

Stearin and palmitin are both solid fats. A liquid ester, known as *olein*, differs from stearin and palmitin in being derived from an unsaturated organic acid. This is oleic acid, $C_{17}H_{33}COOH$, which has a double bond at the middle of the carbon chain. The formula for olein is

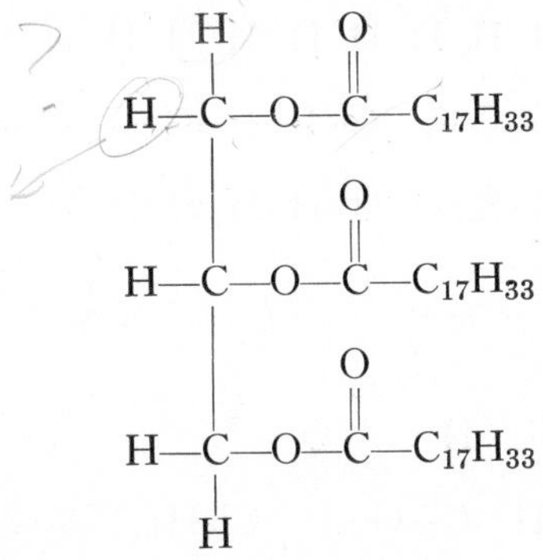

$$H\text{---}\overset{\overset{\displaystyle H}{|}}{C}\text{---}O\text{---}\overset{\overset{\displaystyle O}{\|}}{C}\text{---}C_{17}H_{33}$$

$$H\text{---}\overset{|}{C}\text{---}O\text{---}\overset{\overset{\displaystyle O}{\|}}{C}\text{---}C_{17}H_{33}$$

$$H\text{---}\overset{|}{\underset{\underset{\displaystyle H}{|}}{C}}\text{---}O\text{---}\overset{\overset{\displaystyle O}{\|}}{C}\text{---}C_{17}H_{33}$$

Many vegetable oils, such as cottonseed oil and cod liver oil contain olein. In general the glyceryl esters derived from saturated long-chain acids are solids at room temperature, and those derived from unsaturated acids are liquids.

The reader should clearly distinguish between oils derived from animal and vegetable matter as contrasted with mineral oil derived from petroleum. Vegetable and animal oils are glyceryl esters, mineral oils are hydrocarbons. In spite of the similarity in superficial appearance these two classes of compounds are entirely different in structure and in chemical properties.

Butter is somewhat different from other fats because it contains several per cent of glyceryl esters containing much shorter acid chains. One of these is butyric acid, which occurs as butyrin in butter to the extent of about 3 per cent. Rancid butter owes its odor in part to the butyric acid which is liberated.

One of the characteristic reactions of fats is that with strong bases. This has already been referred to as saponification. The reaction yields glycerol plus a soap. The saponification of stearin may be represented as follows:

$$
\begin{array}{c}
\text{H}\quad\text{O}\\
|\qquad\parallel\\
\text{H—C—O—C—C}_{17}\text{H}_{35}\\
|\\
\quad\quad\text{O}\\
\quad\quad\parallel\\
\text{H—C—O—C—C}_{17}\text{H}_{35} + 3\text{NaOH} \rightarrow\\
|\\
\quad\quad\text{O}\\
\quad\quad\parallel\\
\text{H—C—O—C—C}_{17}\text{H}_{35}\\
|\\
\text{H}
\end{array}
\qquad
\begin{array}{c}
\text{H}\\
|\\
\text{H—C—OH}\\
|\\
\text{H—C—OH} +\\
|\\
\text{H—C—OH}\\
|\\
\text{H}
\end{array}
\qquad
3\text{C}_{17}\text{H}_{35}\text{C}
\begin{array}{c}
\quad\text{O}\\
\diagup\!\!\diagup\\
\diagdown\\
\quad\text{ONa}
\end{array}
$$

stearin	+	sodium hydroxide	$\rightarrow$	glycerol	+	sodium stearate (a soap)

Fatty acid salts are known as **soaps.** Thus, the salt sodium stearate

$$\text{C}_{17}\text{H}_{35}\overset{\displaystyle\text{O}}{\overset{\parallel}{\text{C}}}\text{—ONa}$$

is a typical soap. The manufacture of soap is a large-scale industry. The fat is mixed with a slight excess of sodium hydroxide and the mixture is heated by steam. When the reaction is complete, common salt (NaCl) is added. This precipitates the soap as a thick curd. The soap curds are washed, then formed into bars, cakes, or flakes, as required for the market. The by-product in soap manufacture is, of course, the glycerol which remains in solution and which may be recovered as desired.

It will be recalled that glycerol esters of saturated long-chain fatty acids are solids at room temperature, but that those esters derived from unsaturated acids are liquids. Cottonseed oil is an example of a vegetable glyceryl ester derived from appreciable amounts of the unsaturated acids oleic and linoleic. Cottonseed oil has a somewhat unpleasant taste and a tendency to turn rancid.

The only difference between a vegetable oil and a solid fat is the unsaturated bond, or bonds, which may exist in the former. It is possible to change a vegetable oil into a solid fat by a process known as **hydrogenation.** If the oil is treated with hydrogen in the presence of finely divided nickel, as a catalyst, the hydrogen adds to the double bond as shown:

$$
\begin{array}{c}
\text{H}\;\text{H}\;\text{H}\;\text{H}\\
|\;\;|\;\;|\;\;|\\
\text{—C—C}\!\!=\!\!\text{C—C—} + \text{H}_2 \rightarrow\\
|\;\;\quad\quad|\\
\text{H}\quad\quad\text{H}
\end{array}
\qquad
\begin{array}{c}
\text{H}\;\text{H}\;\text{H}\;\text{H}\\
|\;\;|\;\;|\;\;|\\
\text{—C—C—C—C—}\\
|\;\;|\;\;|\;\;|\\
\text{H}\;\text{H}\;\text{H}\;\text{H}
\end{array}
$$

forming a saturated chain. The hydrogenation of olein to stearin may be represented as follows:

$$
\begin{array}{ccc}
& \text{H} \quad\; \text{O} & \text{H} \quad\; \text{O} \\[4pt]
& \text{H}-\overset{|}{\underset{|}{\text{C}}}-\text{O}-\overset{\|}{\text{C}}-\text{C}_{17}\text{H}_{33} & \text{H}-\overset{|}{\underset{|}{\text{C}}}-\text{O}-\overset{\|}{\text{C}}-\text{C}_{17}\text{H}_{35} \\[6pt]
& \qquad\quad \text{O} & \qquad\quad \text{O} \\[4pt]
& \text{H}-\overset{|}{\underset{|}{\text{C}}}-\text{O}-\overset{\|}{\text{C}}-\text{C}_{17}\text{H}_{33} + 3\text{H}_2 \xrightarrow{\text{(Ni)}} & \text{H}-\overset{|}{\underset{|}{\text{C}}}-\text{O}-\overset{\|}{\text{C}}-\text{C}_{17}\text{H}_{35} \\[6pt]
& \qquad\quad \text{O} & \qquad\quad \text{O} \\[4pt]
& \text{H}-\overset{|}{\underset{|}{\text{C}}}-\text{O}-\overset{\|}{\text{C}}-\text{C}_{17}\text{H}_{33} & \text{H}-\overset{|}{\underset{|}{\text{C}}}-\text{O}-\overset{\|}{\text{C}}-\text{C}_{17}\text{H}_{35} \\[4pt]
& \text{H} & \text{H}
\end{array}
$$

This process is often called hardening, because the ester tends to become a solid as the hydrogenation proceeds. Olein is a liquid, but stearin is a solid melting at 71° C.

Hydrogenation, as described above, was originally developed by a French chemist, Paul Sabatier. The process is very widely used industrially for the production of such substances as "Crisco" and of margarine. Soybean oil and peanut oil are also subjected to hydrogenation, and such oils, together with cottonseed oil, are often thus treated prior to their use in the manufacture of soap.

Fats and vegetable oils belong to a group of compounds of natural origin called **lipoids.** These substances are all characterized by being soluble in oil but insoluble in water. They are nearly all esters of long-chain fatty acids. Lipoids are of great importance in the study of living matter. Phospholipoids occur in all plant and animal cells. They are fats in which one of the fatty acid groups is replaced by a complex phosphoric acid group. The most commonly occurring phospholipoids are the lecithins from which may be obtained a nitrogen compound known as choline. A form of lecithin may be represented as follows:

$$
\begin{array}{l}
\text{H} \quad\; \text{O} \\[4pt]
\text{H}-\overset{|}{\underset{|}{\text{C}}}-\text{O}-\overset{\|}{\text{C}}-\text{R} \\[6pt]
\qquad\quad \text{O} \\[4pt]
\text{H}-\overset{|}{\underset{|}{\text{C}}}-\text{O}-\overset{\|}{\text{C}}-\text{R}' \\[6pt]
\qquad\quad \text{O}^{-} \\[4pt]
\text{H}-\overset{|}{\underset{|}{\text{C}}}-\text{O}-\overset{}{\underset{\underset{\text{O}}{\|}}{\text{P}}}-\text{OCH}_2\text{CH}_2\text{N}^{+}(\text{CH}_3)_3
\end{array}
$$

These substances are abundant in such tissues as brain, liver, kidney, heart, egg yolk, etc. They are probably of importance in the mechanism by which the body derives energy through the oxidation of fats and carbohydrates.

199. METABOLISM OF CARBOHYDRATES AND FATS

The substances necessary to sustain life include proteins, fats, carbohydrates, vitamins, minerals, water, and oxygen. In the present section we shall describe how carbohydrates and fats are used by the animal organism. The process by which digested nutrients are converted to other substances in the body is known as **metabolism.**

The primary function of carbohydrates and fats in diet is to serve as sources of energy. If the diet is rich, some of the energy is stored in the form of fat. If the diet is too lean, this stored fat is used up and the individual becomes emaciated. The function of carbohydrates and fats is in sharp contrast to those of proteins and the other nutrients. Proteins, for instance, serve in the diet for building and rebuilding tissue.

The energy available from foods is stated in calories. It will be recalled that a thermochemical equation gives not only the products formed but also the amount of heat liberated or used up. Thus the burning of carbon may be shown as follows:

$$C + O_2 \rightarrow CO_2 + 94,380 \text{ calories}$$

This shows that one mole (12 g.) of carbon unites with oxygen to form one mole (44 g.) of carbon dioxide, and that during this process 94,380 calories of heat are liberated. In a similar way a weighed quantity of sugar could be burned and the calories liberated determined. Tables are available showing the calorie value of different foods. A few examples are shown in Table 21. Notice that the energies are given in kilocalories (1 kilocalorie = 1000 calories) per 100 g. of food.

TABLE 21

Calorie Value of Various Nutrients per 100 G. of Food

Bacon	517 kcal.
Bread	261
Lettuce	18
Sugar	400
Mayonnaise	719

It will be clear that foods undergo oxidation in the body, and that the ultimate products include carbon dioxide and water. The energy liberated during this process keeps the body warm and supplies the ability to do work. A man doing normal work requires about 3000 kilocalories per day.

For carbohydrates to be utilized by animals they must be in the form of monosaccharides. The saliva and gastric juices contain enzymes which rapidly convert sugars and starches to the simpler molecules. Enzymes able to do this include amylase, maltase, sucrase, and lactase. In many cases the enzyme is given a name resembling that of the substrate upon which it is effective.

Utilization of monosaccharides in the animal is exceedingly complicated, and it must suffice here to say that much carbohydrate is normally stored in the liver in the form of glycogen, and that, as required, this is liberated into the blood in the form of glucose. The ultimate products of oxidation are, of course, carbon dioxide and water which are eliminated.

A somewhat similar course is followed by fats in the diet. The fats pass unchanged through the stomach but are hydrolyzed to glycerol and fatty acids in the intestine through the action of enzymes called *lipases*. The hydrolized fats are absorbed into the intestimal mucosa where the original fats appear to be resynthesized. The blood carries tiny droplets of fat to various tissues where it may be deposited as fatty tissue. When the fat is oxidized to provide energy, the final products are, again, carbon dioxide and water.

It may be mentioned that animals are able to convert carbohydrate into fat, because animals can gain in weight, with accumulation of fat, even though fat is rigidly excluded from the diet. Adequate carbohydrate must be provided. This process is known as *biosynthesis*.

EXERCISES

A. *Define or explain the following:*

asymmetric carbon atom	lipoid (no formula)
carbohydrate	malt
cellulose	metabolism
chlorophyll (no formula)	microbiological chemistry
dextrin	mono-, di-, and polysaccharide
dextro-, levo-rotatory	optical isomerism
enzyme	optical rotation
(a) fat	polarimeter
fatty acid	polarized light
hemihedry	pyroxylin
invert sugar	racemic mixtures

B. 1. What is the chemistry involved in the diagnosis of diabetes?

2. Compare the structures of glucose, fructose, sucrose, starch, and cellulose, so far as possible.

3. Show how the starch-iodide test may be used to detect a strong oxidizing agent such as chlorine or ozone.

4. Describe microbiological processes, with particular reference to the production of ethanol.

5. How is rayon made?

6. How is guncotton made?

7. How did Pasteur show that "racemic" acid is a mixture of optical isomers?

8. What is the van't Hoff-Le Bel theory to explain optical isomerism?

9. Photosynthesis is certainly one of the most important of all chemical processes. Outline the chemical changes involved.

10. Illustrate the formation of an edible fat from an unsaturated vegetable oil.

11. How is soap made?

12. When a nutrition expert says that a certain food has a certain calorie value, just exactly what does he mean?

13. Describe the metabolism (chemical changes in the body) undergone by carbohydrates and fats.

C. 1. Two compounds (A and B) have the same formula, namely, C_3H_7Br. Compound A on treatment with moist silver oxide yields C_3H_8O which, on oxidation, yields only C_3H_6O. Compound B, on the other hand, on treatment with moist silver oxide yields C_3H_8O, but oxidation of this yields in turn C_3H_6O and then $C_3H_6O_2$. The last turns litmus red, and, when warmed with ethanol in the presence of a drop of sulfuric acid, yields an unusually sweet-smelling substance with the formula $C_5H_{10}O_2$. Trace all steps, using structural formulas, name all compounds, and identify A and B with structural formulas.

2. Indicate which of the following compounds might form optical isomers and which not.

3. Give the structural formula for a hydrocarbon which is optically active.
4. Design an experiment to prove that the oxygen evolved during photosynthesis comes from the water. Note that there are no useful radioactive isotopes of oxygen, but that O^{18} is available.
5. It would seem that the photosynthesis reaction, under the influence of chlorophyll as a catalyst, is the reverse of the metabolism reaction under the influence of enzyme catalysts whereby carbohydrate is converted to carbon dioxide and water. But catalysts are not supposed to be able to shift chemical equilibria. Explain this.
6. Write an ionic equation representing the action of hard water on soap.

AROMATICS AND
30 HETEROCYCLICS

Let us learn to dream, gentlemen, then perhaps we shall find the truth—F. A. Kekulé

200. BENZENE

When soft coal is heated in the absence of air, a variety of valuable substances is obtained. These products include coal gas, ammonia, coal tar, and coke. Among these products there may be isolated appreciable quantities of a colorless liquid having a characteristic, not unpleasant, odor. The melting point is 5.4° C. and the boiling point 80.1° at 760 mm. pressure. The vapors are inflammable and somewhat toxic. This substance is known as **benzene,** although the technological literature often uses the German name *benzol*.

Benzene is a substance of great scientific and practical interest. It is the first member of a series of hydrocarbons which is entirely different in structure and properties from the aliphatic hydrocarbons described in an earlier chapter.

The molecular formula for benzene is C_6H_6. That is to say, there are equal numbers of carbon atoms and hydrogen atoms in the molecule; and the molecular weight is 78 as found by vapor density measurements.

Such a formula suggests the highly unsaturated compound acetylene, C_2H_2. But benzene shows no indication of being unsaturated in the sense that ethylene and acetylene are unsaturated. The latter compounds vigorously react with bromine and other agents. Benzene is almost inert to bromine except under special conditions of heating or the presence of catalysts. While the formula of benzene suggests a high degree of unsaturation, the chemical properties establish that it is a relatively inert compound.

The structural formula for such a compound as benzene poses a very difficult problem. This problem was solved to a reasonably satisfactory degree in 1865 by a German chemist, August Kekulé. This was forty years after the discovery of benzene by Michael Faraday.

In Kekulé's time, the available experimental evidence was fragmentary, but the reasoning he used in reaching the accepted structural formula for benzene is substantially as follows:

By sufficiently vigorous means, each of the six hydrogen atoms in the benzene molecule may be replaced, or substituted, by other atoms, for which we shall use the symbol X. The several products are then C_6H_5X, $C_6H_4X_2$, $C_6H_3X_3$, $C_6H_2X_4$, C_6HX_5, and C_6X_6. Considering the first product only, Kekulé found that there is only one structural isomer for C_6H_5X. Hence the six hydrogen atoms in benzene must all be equivalent, that is, in a similar geometrical configuration. Normal hexane, by contrast, gives three different monosubstituted derivatives.

Fig. 30-1. Friedrich August Kekulé

Kekulé was born in Germany in 1829. Unlike several distinguished chemists, he showed unusual ability as a student. He entered university with the intention of becoming an architect, but it was in the field of molecular architecture that he became famous.

Kekulé's structural formula for benzene and his contributions to molecular structure had somewhat the same effect on organic chemistry as Mendeleev had on inorganic chemistry. They unified a great field of learning and permitted spectacular advances in many directions.

Kekulé was a professor of chemistry at Ghent and at Bonn. Many famous men were educated under him. He died in 1896. (Culver Service)

Kekulé also noted that $C_6H_4X_2$ occurs in three different structural isomers. The same is true of the trisubstituted derivative $C_6H_3X_3$. On the basis of these facts Kekulé concluded that the only acceptable structural formula for benzene is one in which all six carbons are arranged in a ring.

$$
\begin{array}{c}
\text{H} \\
| \\
\text{C} \\
\diagup \quad \diagdown \\
\text{H—C} \qquad \text{C—H} \\
| \qquad\qquad | \\
\text{H—C} \qquad \text{C—H} \\
\diagdown \quad \diagup \\
\text{C} \\
| \\
\text{H}
\end{array}
$$

It will be seen that this formula accounts for the existence of only one isomer for C_6H_5X, namely

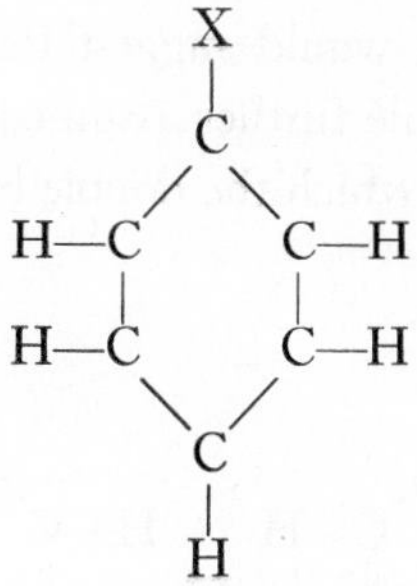

$$
\begin{array}{c}
X \\
| \\
C \\
\diagup \quad \diagdown \\
H-C \qquad C-H \\
| \qquad\qquad | \\
H-C \qquad C-H \\
\diagdown \quad \diagup \\
C \\
| \\
H
\end{array}
$$

and of three isomers for each of $C_6H_4X_2$ and $C_6H_3X_3$.

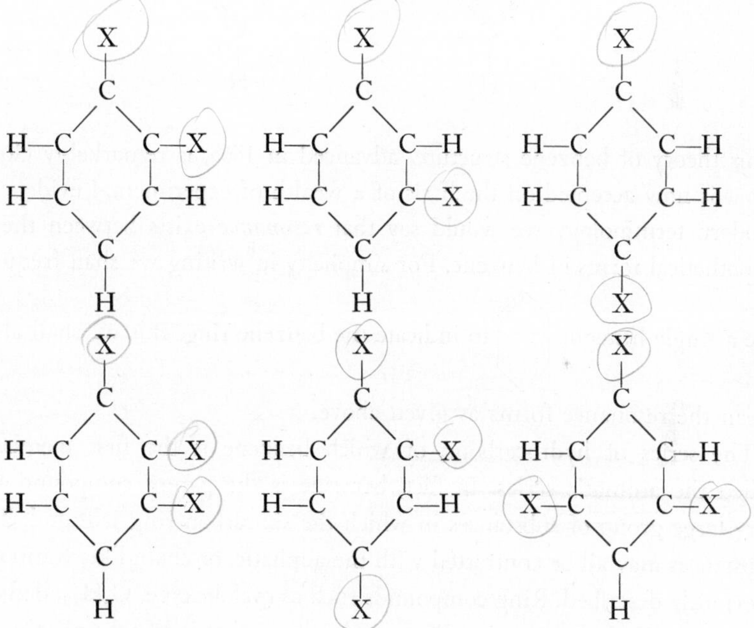

$$
\begin{array}{ccc}
X & X & X \\
| & | & | \\
C & C & C \\
H-C \quad C-X & H-C \quad C-H & H-C \quad C-H \\
H-C \quad C-H & H-C \quad C-X & H-C \quad C-H \\
C & C & C \\
| & | & | \\
H & H & X
\end{array}
$$

$$
\begin{array}{ccc}
X & X & X \\
| & | & | \\
C & C & C \\
H-C \quad C-X & H-C \quad C-X & H-C \quad C-H \\
H-C \quad C-X & H-C \quad C-H & X-C \quad C-X \\
C & C & C \\
| & | & | \\
H & X & H
\end{array}
$$

The reader should satisfy himself that no other isomers are possible.

Of course, this structural formula for benzene has been reached only by ignoring the supposed valence of four for carbon. This difficulty was, in turn, explained by assuming that the alternate bonds were double.

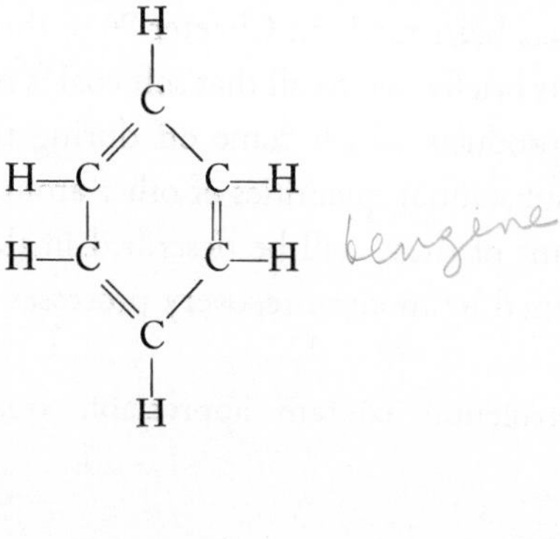

$$
\begin{array}{c}
H \\
| \\
C \\
\diagup\!\!\!\diagup \quad \diagdown \\
H-C \qquad C-H \\
| \qquad\qquad \| \\
H-C \qquad C-H \quad \textit{benzene} \\
\diagdown \quad \diagup\!\!\!\diagup \\
C \\
| \\
H
\end{array}
$$

However, this assumption would suggest that benzene ought to be unsaturated like ethylene. Kekulé further assumed that benzene actually exists in two inseparable forms, in which the double bonds change positions.

$$
\begin{array}{ccc}
\text{H} & & \text{H} \\
| & & | \\
\text{C} & & \text{C} \\
\text{H--C} \quad \text{C--H} & \rightleftarrows & \text{H--C} \quad \text{C--H} \\
\text{H--C} \quad \text{C--H} & & \text{H--C} \quad \text{C--H} \\
\text{C} & & \text{C} \\
| & & | \\
\text{H} & & \text{H}
\end{array}
$$

exemplify resonance

This theory of benzene structure, advanced in 1865, is remarkably close to what is now accepted on the basis of a wealth of experimental evidence. In modern terminology we would say that *resonance* exists between the two hypothetical forms of benzene. For simplicity in writing we shall frequently

use a single hexagon to indicate the benzene ring. But we shall always

mean the resonance forms as given above.

The series of hydrocarbons, of which benzene is the first member, is called the **aromatic series.** In fact, benzene is the parent compound for a very large group of substances in which the six-carbon ring is found. These substances may all be contrasted with the aliphatic, or chain-like, compounds previously described. Ring compounds such as cyclohexane, C_6H_{12}, definitely belong to the aliphatic series. We see, therefore, that it is not only the ring, but the ring together with the resonance, that gives the aromatic series its characteristic properties. The name aromatic is derived from the fact that many fragrant substances such as oil of bitter almonds, oil of wintergreen, and many other oils and balsams belong to this class of compounds.

Reference has been made in Chapter 26 to the important coal-tar industry. Reviewing this briefly, we recall that soft coal is heated out of contact with air. The volatile products which come off during this process contain not only benzene but substantial quantities of other aromatic compounds. Some of the more important of these will be described in the next section. The yield of benzene obtained by modern recovery processes is about 2 gallons per ton of coal.

Certain petroleums contain appreciable quantities of aromatic hydrocarbons. The Borneo oils are said to contain as much as 39 per cent of such substances.

The principal uses of benzene are as a motor fuel and in making plastics.

201. BENZENE DERIVATIVES

It will be recalled that removal of a hydrogen atom from the molecule of a saturated hydrocarbon yields an alkyl group. Thus, the ethyl group, C_2H_5, may be regarded as derived from ethane, C_2H_6. Similarly, the removal of a hydrogen from benzene yields C_6H_5 which is known as the **phenyl group.**

Combination of the phenyl group with various functional groups yields a great variety of compounds, of which some of the important types will be mentioned.

The union of a phenyl group with chlorine yields the compound phenyl chloride or chlorobenzene, analogous to ethyl chloride.

phenyl chloride or chlorobenzene   ethyl chloride or chloroethane

Chlorobenzene is readily made by treating benzene with chlorine in the presence of ferric chloride as a catalyst.

Compounds such as chlorobenzene are called **aryl halides,** just as ethyl chloride is an alkyl halide.

Replacement of the chlorine in chlorobenzene by a hydroxyl, —OH, group might be expected to yield an alcohol because —OH is the functional group for an alcohol. The substance so formed is thus called **phenol,** with the characteristic -ol ending (as in methanol and ethanol).

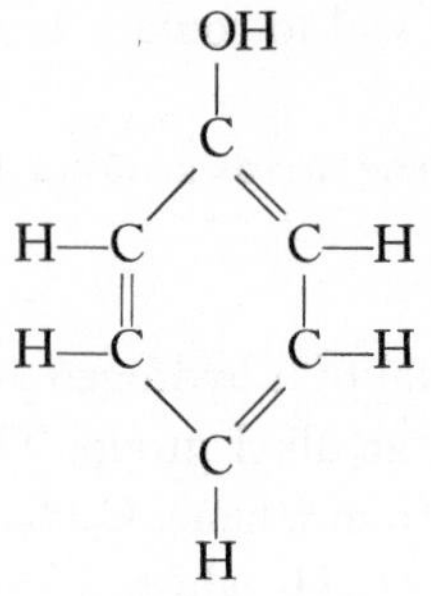

$$
\begin{array}{c}
\text{OH} \\
|\\
\text{C}\\
\end{array}
$$

phenol

However, phenol is actually an acid although an exceedingly weak one. This substance is a white solid, obtained from coal tar. It is often known as car-bolic acid, and is a powerful and widely used germicide. Large amounts of phenol are made from benzene for the production of certain kinds of plastics.

The more conventional type of aromatic acid is illustrated by **benzoic acid,** which is simply a combination of a phenyl group and the functional group of an acid.

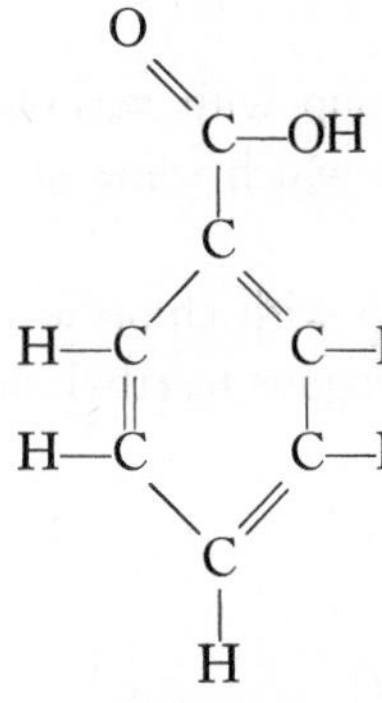

benzoic acid

Aromatic aldehydes, esters, ketones, ethers, and amines are illustrated by the compounds below:

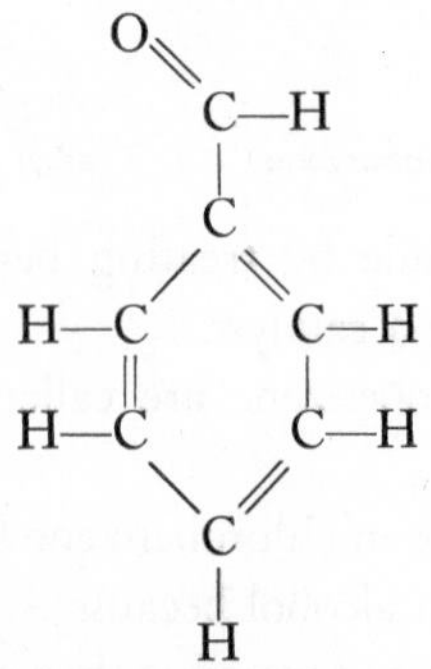

benzaldehyde (oil of bitter almonds)

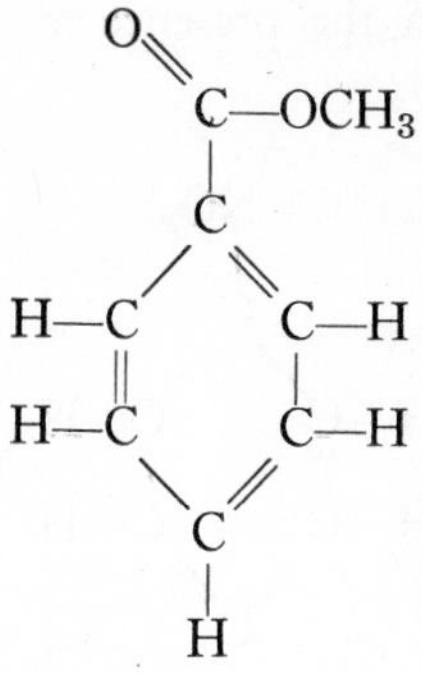

methyl benzoate (an ester)

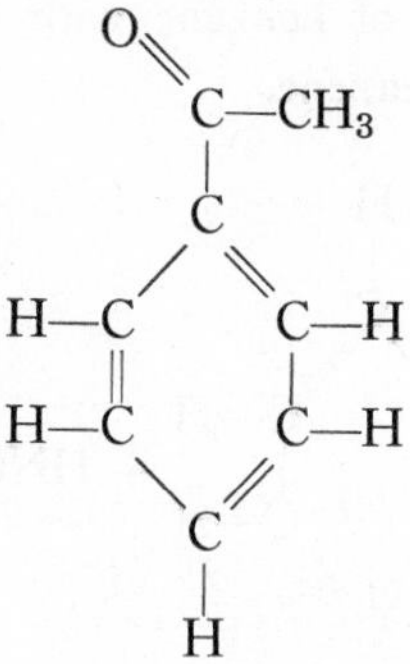

acetophenone (a ketone)

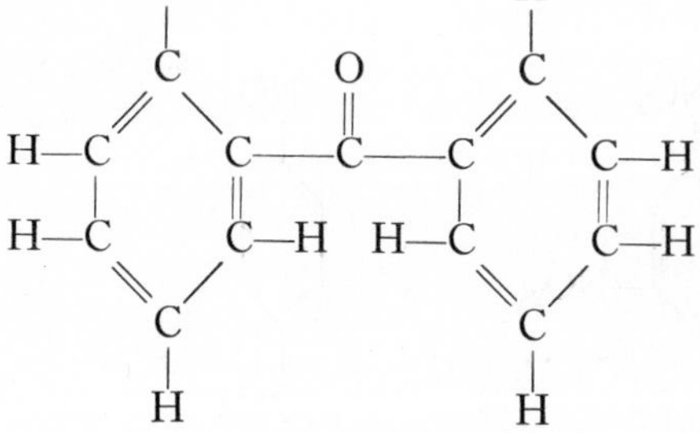

benzophenone (a ketone)

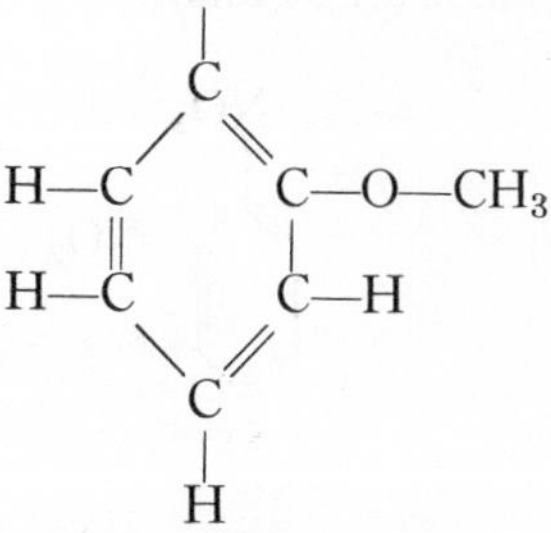

anisole (methylphenyl ether)

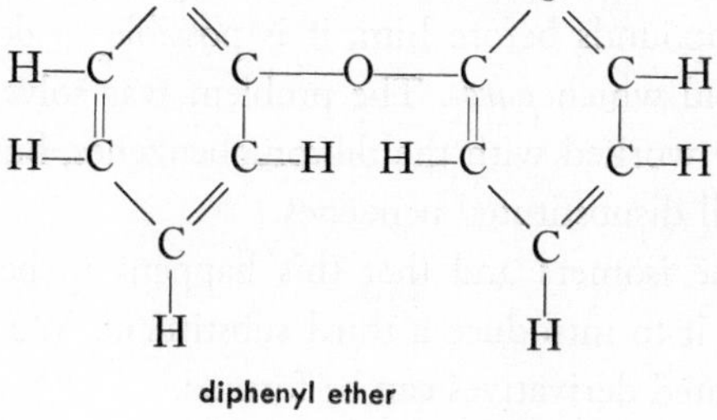

diphenyl ether

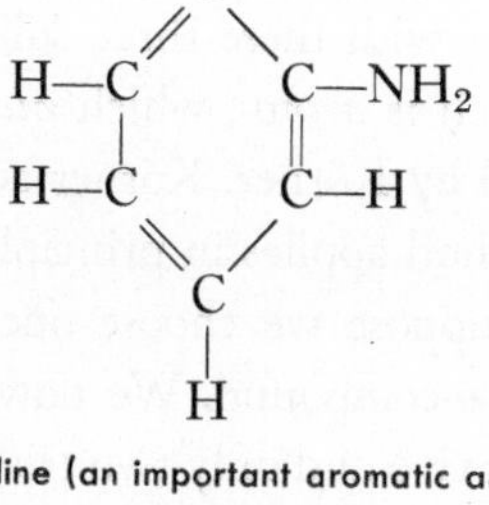

aniline (an important aromatic amine)

Treatment of benzene with nitric acid in the presence of sulfuric acid yields **nitrobenzene.**

$$
\begin{array}{ccc}
\underset{\substack{\text{H}\\|\\\text{C}\\ \diagup\!\!\diagdown}}{} & & \\
\text{H---C} \quad \text{C---H} & & \\
\text{H---C} \quad \text{C---H} & + \text{HNO}_3 & \xrightarrow{[\text{H}_2\text{SO}_4]} \\
\text{C} & & \\
\text{H} & &
\end{array}
\quad
\begin{array}{c}
\text{NO}_2 \\ | \\ \text{C} \\ \diagup\!\!\diagdown \\
\text{H---C} \quad \text{C---H} \\
\text{H---C} \quad \text{C---H} \\
\text{C} \\ | \\ \text{H}
\end{array}
\; + \text{H}_2\text{O}
$$

The use of excess nitric acid leads to the introduction of more nitro, $-\text{NO}_2$, groups into the benzene ring with the formation of dinitrobenzene, and still higher substitution products. If we attempt to write the structural formula for dinitrobenzene we observe that there are three and only three possibilities. These are as follows:

ortho-   meta-   para-

(Note that for convenience we write the benzene ring as a simple hexagon.) The above formulas correspond to three known structural isomers of dinitrobenzene. They are named respectively *ortho-, meta-,* and *para*dinitrobenzene. This nomenclature is applied to all disubstituted benzene derivatives such as the dichlorobenzenes, the dibromobenzenes, and so forth.

The three dinitrobenzenes are all solids, but they differ in properties sufficiently so that they may all be easily separated. The reader may wonder how, with these three solid compounds before him, it is possible to decide which is *ortho-,* which *meta-,* and which *para-.* The problem was solved in 1874 by Körner. Körner actually worked with the dibromobenzenes, but his method applies in principle to all disubstituted benzenes.

Suppose we choose one of the isomers and that this happens to be the *ortho*-compound. We now treat it to introduce a third substituent. We find that two and only two trisubstituted derivatives can be formed.

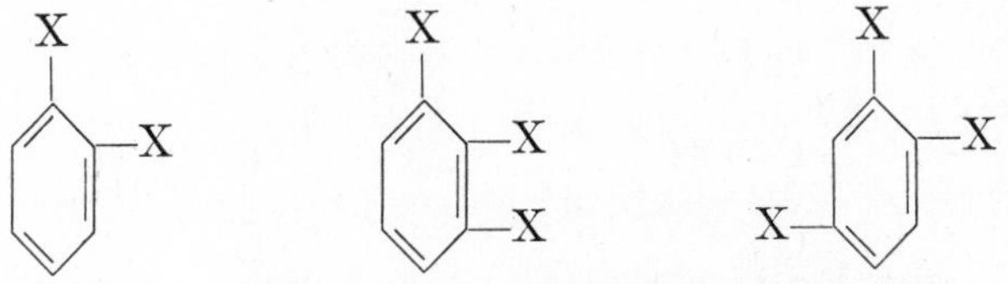

ortho-   yields   2 possible trisubstituted derivatives

If we had taken the *meta*-isomer to start with, we should have found three possible trisubstituted derivatives, as shown below:

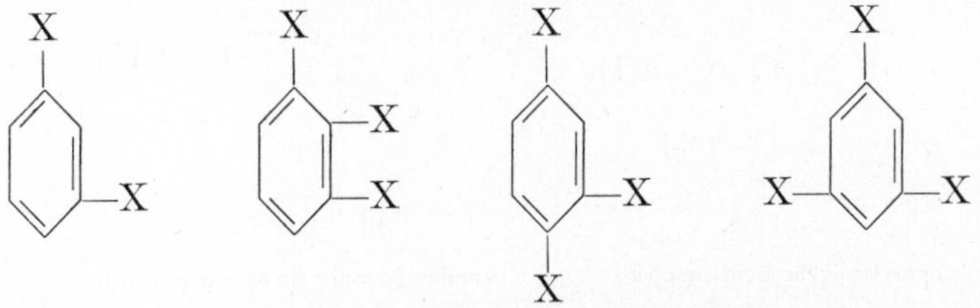

meta-   yields   3 possible trisubstituted derivatives

On the other hand, the *para*-compound could yield only one trisubstituted derivative.

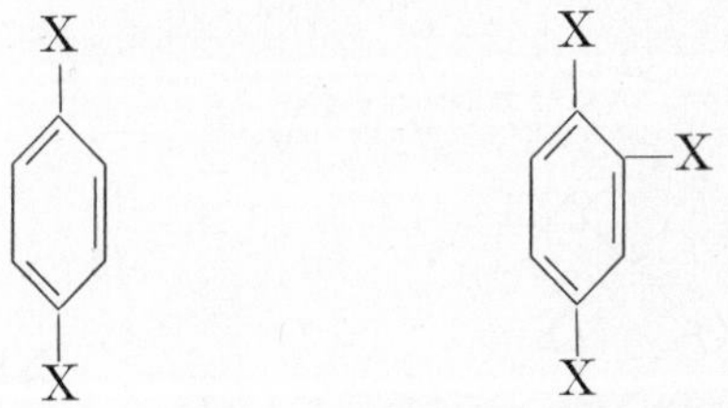

para- yields only 1 possible trisubstituted derivative

The reader should carefully convince himself regarding the total possible trisubstituted derivatives in each case.

By this tedious but elegant method it is possible to assign structural formulas to the various disubstituted structural isomers.

It will be recalled that more than one functional group may be present in a single molecule. This occurs in such substances as glycerol, glucose, and aminoacetic acid. We shall conclude this section with a few interesting compounds from the aromatic series:

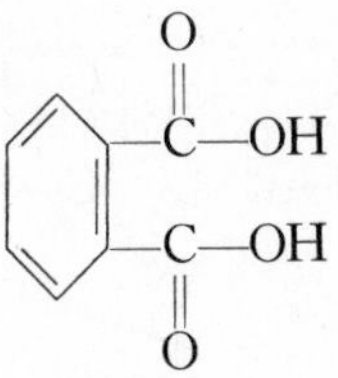

phthalic acid

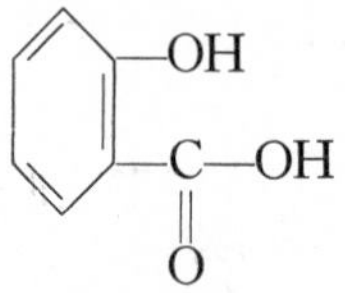

salicylic acid

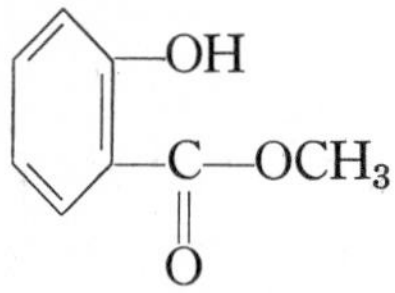

methyl salicylate (oil of wintergreen)

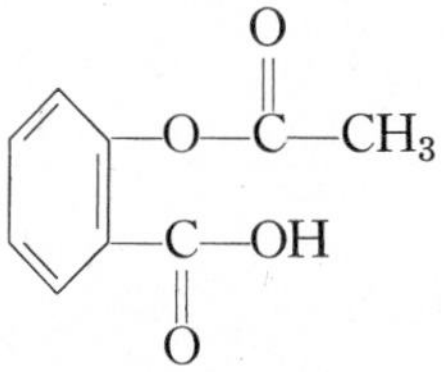

acetylsalicylic acid (aspirin)

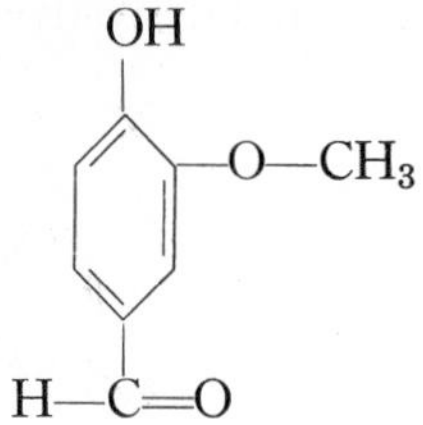

vanillin (vanilla flavoring and odor)

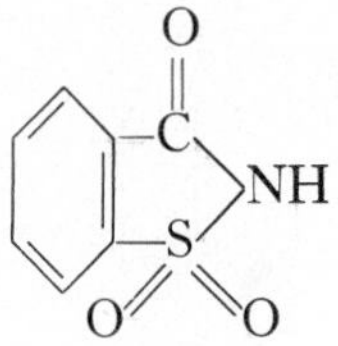

saccharin

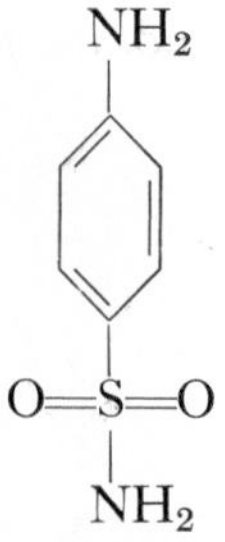

sulfanilamide

202. TOLUENE AND RELATED COMPOUNDS

Another aromatic hydrocarbon of importance is toluene. This compound has the structural formula shown:

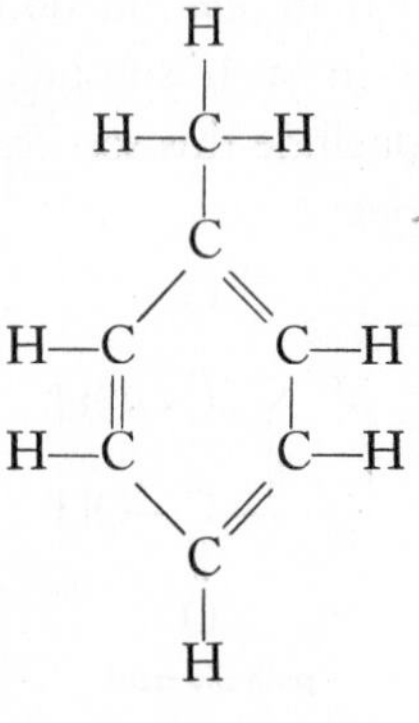

toluene

in which one hydrogen in benzene is replaced by a methyl group. Toluene may be regarded as a hydrocarbon formed from an aromatic (phenyl) group, and an aliphatic (methyl) group. Many such compounds are known.

Toluene is a colorless liquid with a boiling point of 110.6° C., somewhat higher than that of benzene. It is recovered from the distillation of coal, as is benzene, the yield amounting to about half a gallon of toluene per ton of coal. The toluene obtained from coal is, however, in no way sufficient for the great demands caused by World War II in the production of explosives. It was fortunate, therefore, that in 1940 there was developed a process known as *cyclization,* or *aromatization,* for producing toluene from one of the aliphatic hydrocarbons in petroleum.

It was found that *n*-heptane, a constituent of petroleum, could be converted to toluene in the presence of appropriate catalysts. The reaction may be represented as follows:

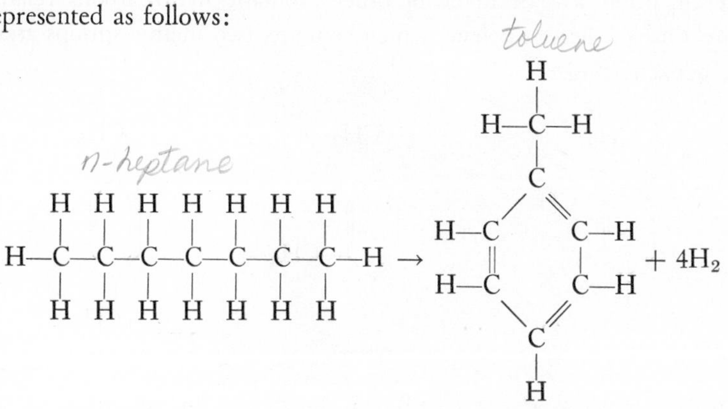

This important reaction proceeds with excellent yield of toluene, in the presence of oxides of chromium or molybdenum supported on aluminum oxide.

Toluene is used in the manufacture of one of the most important high explosives, **trinitrotoluene (TNT).** This compound is obtained by treating toluene with a mixture of nitric and sulfuric acids.

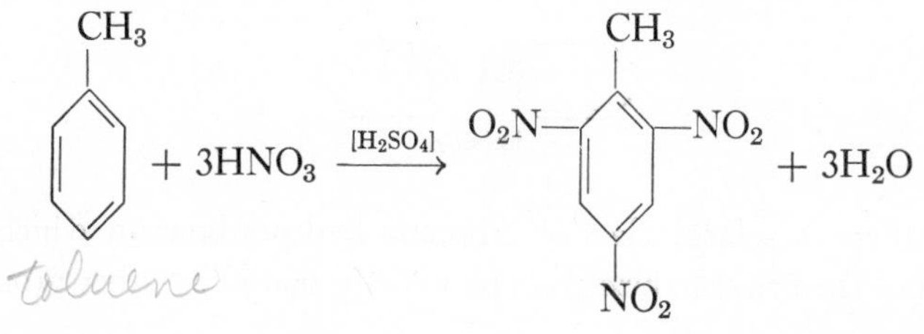

It will be noted that several isomers are possible, in addition to the desired product shown above. The other isomers are undesirable and, although not formed in large amount, must be removed from the product.

The importance of TNT as an explosive is determined not only by its fairly simple production process at a reasonable cost, but also because of its resistance to shock and its low melting point. Many substances which explode violently cannot be used for commercial or military purposes because they are too sensitive to shock and likely to explode prematurely. TNT can withstand a very heavy blow without exploding, yet when it is detonated the explosion is violent. Furthermore, the low melting point makes it possible to liquefy the TNT with steam. As a liquid it may be poured into shells and bombs. The actual detonation of the TNT is caused by a small charge of lead azide or other sensitive detonator.

Brief mention will be made of other aromatic hydrocarbons related to toluene. One of these is **xylene,** which contains two methyl groups attached to the benzene ring.

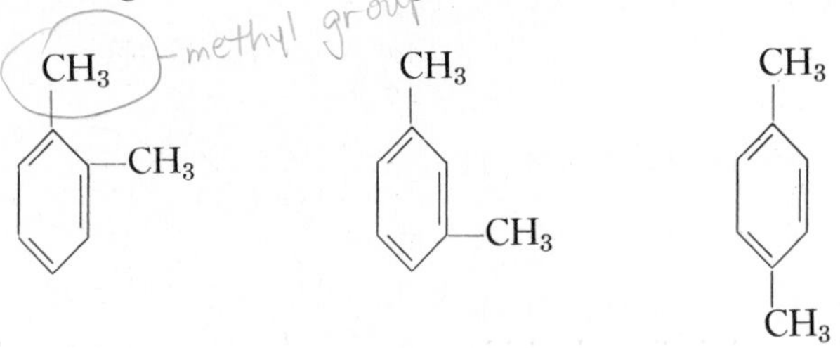

xylenes

It will be noted that three isomeric xylenes are possible. Similarly, it is possible to have 4, 5, or 6 methyl groups attached to the ring, or to have various numbers of other alkyl or aryl groups attached. The number of aromatic hydrocarbons possible is thus seen to be very large indeed.

203. POLYNUCLEAR HYDROCARBONS

In the above section it was implied that two or more aryl groups could combine to form a hydrocarbon. Two phenyl groups may unite as shown to form a substance known as diphenyl.

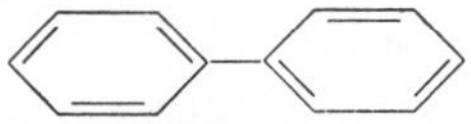

diphenyl

However, there is a large class of aromatic hydrocarbons in which one or more sides of the benzene hexagon are actually shared by other groups. The

most abundant of these "fused ring" hydrocarbons is **naphthalene,** the structural formula for which is as follows:

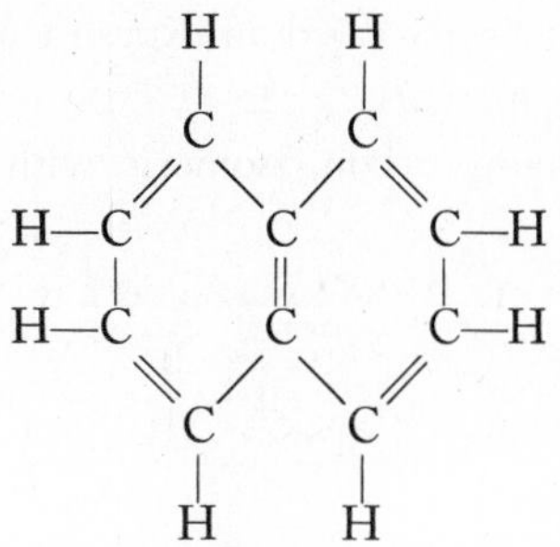

naphthalene

Compounds containing two or more fused benzene rings, as in naphthalene,
are called **polynuclear hydrocarbons.**

Naphthalene is the principal single compound present in coal tar. It is an
abundant and inexpensive raw material for making intermediates for plastics
and dyes. Naphthalene is a solid with the familiar odor of mothballs. At one
time it was widely used as a moth repellent but for this purpose it has been
to a considerable degree replaced by newer substances, such as *para*-dichloro-
benzene. Very large amounts of naphthalene are used for the manufacture of
phthalic acid by oxidation over a catalyst containing vanadium oxide. The
phthalic acid or phthalic anhydride is in turn used for making plastics and
dyes.

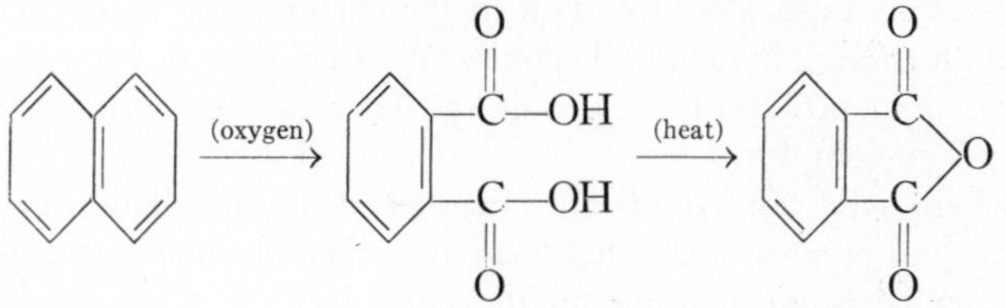

naphthalene   phthalic acid   phthalic anhydride

Many other polynuclear hydrocarbons are known. Of these only two will
be mentioned, **anthracene** and **phenanthrene.**

Anthracene has three rings.

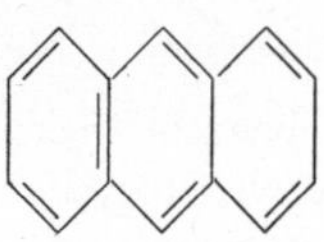

anthracene

This compound is a solid obtained from coal tar. It is used as an intermediate in making dyes. Anthracene shows an unusual bluish green fluorescence when it is exposed to ultraviolet light. Reference was made to this property in an earlier chapter in which was described an experiment for making visible the fumes from evaporating mercury.

Another polynuclear hydrocarbon, isomeric with anthracene, is phenanthrene.

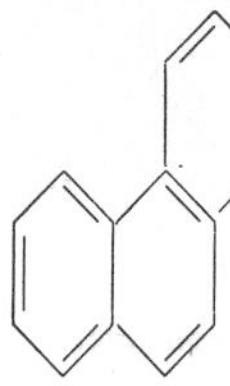

phenanthrene

This compound is also found in coal tar. It is closely related structurally to certain hormones and other substances of interest in the chemistry of living matter.

204. HETEROCYCLICS

Several important classes of organic compounds contain atoms other than carbon as part of a ring structure. It will be recalled that glucose and other saccharides may occur in a ring structure containing an oxygen atom in addition to several carbons. Cyclic, or ring, compounds in which the rings contain unlike atoms are called **heterocyclic compounds.** Phthalic anhydride, to which reference has already been made, is another example of a heterocyclic compound.

Heterocyclics are especially important in the chemistry of living matter and in substances with strong physiological activity. We shall refer to a few of the simpler heterocyclic compounds and then, in this and later chapters, present several compounds of greater complexity.

Several heterocyclic compounds are obtained by the distillation of coal, along with benzene and other aromatic hydrocarbons. One of these is thiophene, which is a five-membered ring containing an atom of sulfur.

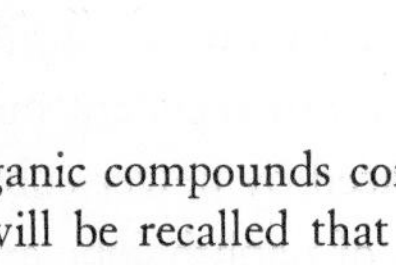

thiophene

This compound closely resembles benzene in its properties, and is often found as an impurity in benzene. Another heterocyclic is pyridine, which contains five carbons plus one nitrogen in the ring.

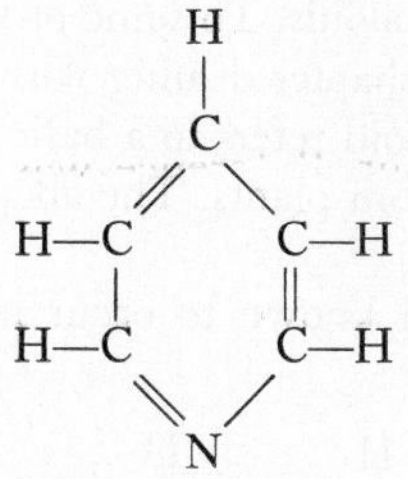

$$
\begin{array}{c}
\text{H} \\
| \\
\text{C} \\
\diagup\diagdown \\
\text{H—C} \qquad \text{C—H} \\
| \qquad\qquad || \\
\text{H—C} \qquad \text{C—H} \\
\diagdown\diagup \\
\text{N}
\end{array}
$$

pyridine

The heterocyclic quinoline may be regarded as resulting from the fusion of a benzene ring and a pyridine ring. These compounds are also derived from coal.

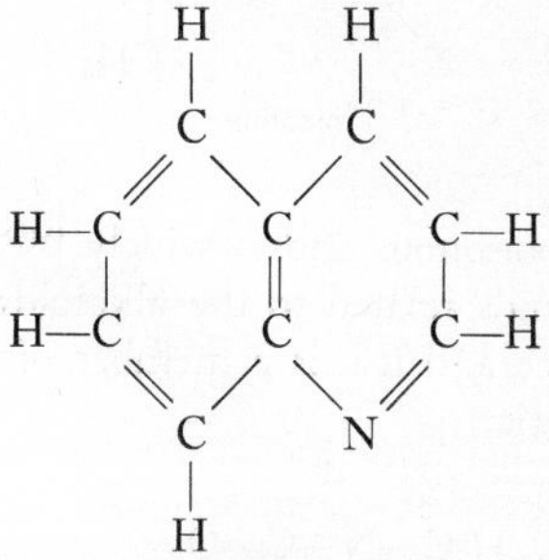

quinoline

The heterocyclic containing four carbons and one oxygen is known as furan.

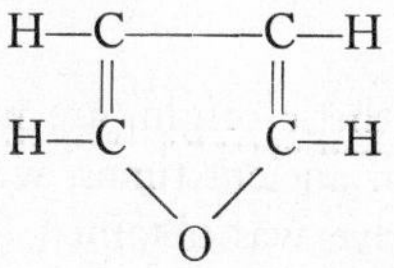

$$
\begin{array}{c}
\text{H—C} \text{———} \text{C—H} \\
|| \qquad\qquad || \\
\text{H—C} \qquad \text{C—H} \\
\diagdown\diagup \\
\text{O}
\end{array}
$$

furan

An important derivative of furan is furfural, which is made from corncobs or oat hulls.

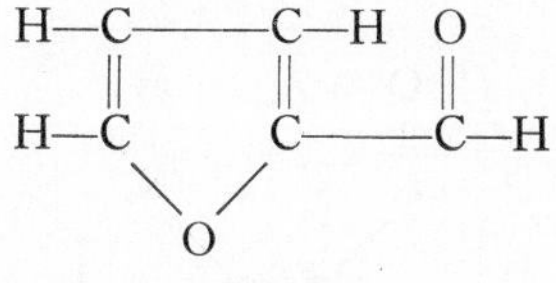

furfural

It is one of the cheapest aldehydes available and is made commercially on a large scale for use as a solvent, in paint removers, and in the manufacture of plastics.

One of the most interesting classes of heterocyclics is the group of naturally occurring compounds called **alkaloids.** To some of the most important of these we shall make reference in a later chapter dealing with compounds of general physiological interest. The name alkaloid refers to a basic substance containing nitrogen, and generally to one derived from plants. The alkaloids have strong physiological activity.

The alkaloid nicotine is well known to occur in tobacco. It may be regarded as a pyridine derivative.

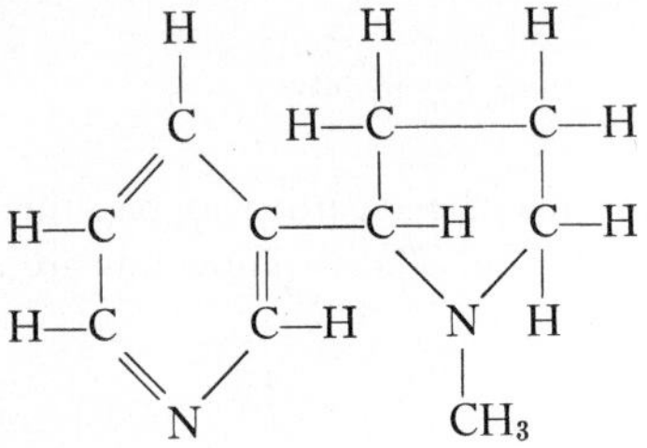

nicotine

This compound is highly poisonous and is widely used as an insecticide.

Other groups of compounds related to the alkaloids include the purines. Caffeine, which occurs in coffee and tea, is a member of this group. It has applications in medicine as a diuretic.

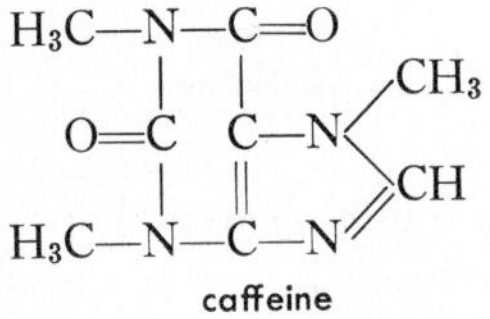

caffeine

Many dyes, of natural or synthetic origin, are heterocyclic compounds. One of these is Tyrian purple which, in ancient times, was so highly prized that its use was restricted to royalty. The dye was obtained from a snail. The art of using this substance was lost during the Dark Ages, but the type of snail which secretes the dye was rediscovered in Ireland in 1684. Actually the snail secretes a colorless compound which is oxidized by air to the purple dye. The structural formula of Tyrian purple is shown below. The dye is of no practical importance at the present time.

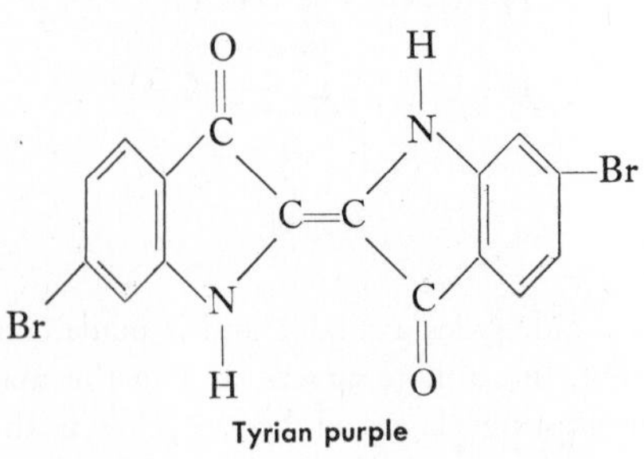

Tyrian purple

Another class of dyes is derived from phthalic acid. These are known as phthaleins. One of these is the familiar indicator phenolphthalein. This compound may be made by reacting phthalic anhydride with phenol. This yields the colorless compound shown.

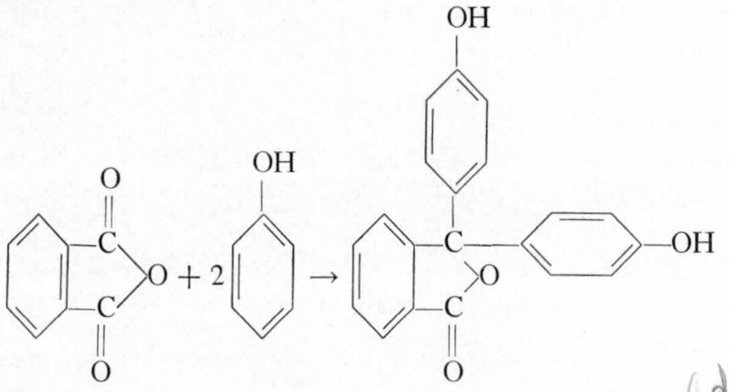

phenolphthalein (colorless) (dye)

If phenolphthalein is added to a basic solution, there is formed the red sodium salt, as shown.

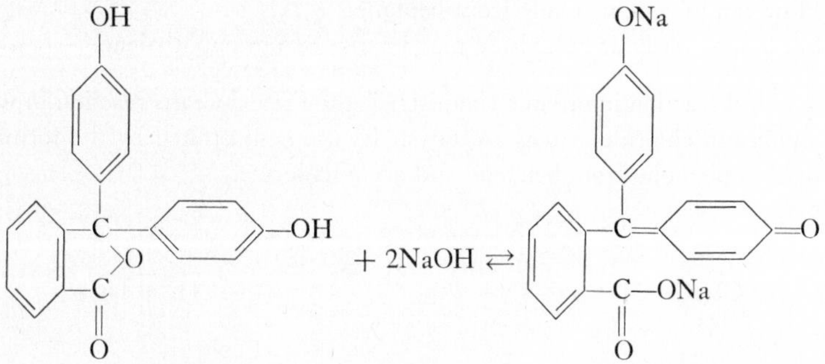

colorless   red

This is the basis of the indicator action of this compound.

EXERCISES

A. *Define or explain the following:*

alkaloid	dye
aromatic hydrocarbon	heterocyclic
aryl group	polynuclear hydrocarbon

B. 1. *Write structural formulas for the following:*

    a. benzene

    b. *ortho-, meta-,* and *para*-dichlorobenzene

    c. phenol.

    d. the phenyl group

e. benzaldehyde
f. benzoic acid
g. an ester of benzoic acid (name it)
h. an aromatic ketone (name it)
i. an aromatic ether (name it)
j. aniline
k. nitrobenzene
l. phthalic acid
m. salicylic acid
n. acetylsalicylic acid (aspirin)
o. toluene
p. TNT
q. naphthalene, anthracene, phenanthrene
r. xylene

2. Describe the reasoning used to establish the Kekulé formula for benzene.
3. Give the preparation of chlorobenzene; of nitrobenzene.
4. Suppose you had, for the first time, prepared dinitrobenzene. What method could you use to tell whether your compound was the *ortho-, meta-,* or *para-* derivative?
5. How can toluene be made from heptane?
6. Show how phthalic anhydride may be made from naphthalene.

C. 1. A useful reaction in organic chemistry is the Friedel-Crafts reaction in which aluminum chloride acts as a catalyst. Its use is illustrated by the formation of acetophenone from benzene and acetyl chloride.

acetyl chloride

Show how the Friedel-Crafts reaction could be used for the preparation of benzophenone.

2. A modification of the Friedel-Crafts reaction to form acetophenone is to use as starting materials benzene and acetic anhydride. Acetic acid is formed as a by-product. Write an equation for this reaction.

3. The Friedel-Crafts reaction may likewise be used to cause the formation of ethylbenzene from benzene and ethylene. Show how this might be accomplished.

4. The text states that there are three different monosubstituted derivatives of normal (straight-chain) hexane. Prove that this is so.

5. Many indicators, like phenolphthalein, are actually weak acids and hence may be considered in accordance with the theory presented in Chapter 23. Let an indicator be represented as HPn, and the color change as a neutralization:

$$HPn + OH^- \rightleftarrows Pn^- + H_2O$$

(one color   (another color
in acid)   in base)

The ionization constant for phenolphthalein is 2.0×10^{-10}. Obviously, the color will be half changed when $[HPn] = [Pn^-]$.

a. Calculate the pH at which phenolphthalein will be half changed (from colorless to red).
b. Will the color change sharply at a definite pH or will it change over a considerable range of pH?
c. The ionization constant for methyl red is 5×10^{-6}. At what pH will this indicator be half changed?
d. Do all indicators change color at the same pH? Does the color change occur at the neutral point, namely pH 7?

CHAPTER

31

CHEMOTHERAPEUTIC AGENTS AND PHYSIO-LOGICALLY ACTIVE COMPOUNDS *

I was sufficiently interested to pursue the subject—Alexander Fleming

Throughout this book, reference has often been made to the **physiological activity,** that is, the action on living organisms, shown by many elements and compounds. Reference has also been made to the use of certain substances for their action as drugs, or **chemotherapeutic agents.** In the present chapter we shall present several additional physiologically active substances. Out of the many hundreds of compounds showing such activity our choice will include compounds of very great importance and interest. Some attention will also be devoted to substances of historical interest in the drug industry.

205. LOCAL ANESTHETICS

Reference has been made in earlier chapters to substances such as ether, chloroform, and ethylene which produce unconsciousness, or general anesthesia. In this section attention will be directed to two substances which produce insensibility to pain in the particular area of the body to which they are applied. The removal of a tooth, for instance, is made comparatively painless by the injection of a substance which renders the tissue in the neighborhood insensitive for a period of minutes or hours. Such a substance is called a **local anesthetic,** in contrast to those such as ether which are general anesthetics. The coca plant, *Erythroxylon* coca, is native to Bolivia and Peru. For centuries the Indians in those countries have chewed the leaves of the plant to lessen hunger and increase endurance. The active substance obtained from coca leaves is cocaine, the structural formula of which is as follows:

---

* See Goodman and Gilman, *The Pharmacological Basis of Therapeutics* (New York: Macmillan, 1941).

$$H_2C-CH \underline{\hspace{3cm}} CH-\overset{\displaystyle \overset{O}{\parallel}}{C}-OCH_3$$

$$N-CH_3 \quad H-\overset{\displaystyle O}{\underset{\displaystyle |}{C}}-O-\overset{\displaystyle \overset{O}{\parallel}}{C}-\langle \hspace{-0.3cm}\bigcirc\hspace{-0.3cm}\rangle$$

$$H_2C-CH \underline{\hspace{3cm}} CH_2$$

cocaine

This was the first local anesthetic to be discovered. In the middle of the nineteenth century it was observed that cocaine applied to the tongue, to the eye, or under the skin rendered the area insensitive to pain. The drug is, therefore, invaluable in minor though painful surgical procedures. No permanent injury results to the part of the body to which the cocaine is applied, and recovery is generally complete in a few hours. The first application to dentistry appears to have been made in 1884.

Cocaine is not without dangerous effects. It is a powerful poison; it sometimes produces eye injuries. Furthermore, it may produce excitement and pleasant hallucinations, including a feeling of great muscular and mental strength. Cocaine is often self-injected, or snuffed into the nose in the form of a powder, "snow," in order to produce these sensations. Such use leads to drug addiction with consequent mental and physical degeneration. These and other dangerous effects led as early as 1892 to a search for less hazardous compounds having comparable anesthetic action. The search was successful and in 1905 Einhorn prepared **procaine** (novocaine) which is now the most widely used of all local anesthetics.

One of the greatest advances which it would be possible to make in the field of chemotherapy is a clear understanding of the relation between chemical structure and physiological activity. No such understanding is at present available, but at least it is possible to relate physiological activity to certain structural groups in the molecule. When chemists attempt a problem such as the synthesis of a nondangerous substitute for cocaine, they try to find what part of the cocaine molecule is effective and which dangerous. This is done by making many different compounds structurally similar to cocaine but different in some respect. These compounds are then tested for anesthetic potency, for toxicity, for habit formation, and so forth. The compound procaine bears some resemblance structurally to cocaine, but the most undesirable parts of the molecule have apparently been eliminated. The resemblance to cocaine will be clear if the formula for procaine is twisted around so that the two formulas may be compared.

$$C_2H_5 \quad H_2C-O-\overset{\overset{\displaystyle O}{\|}}{C}-\langle\!\!\!\bigcirc\!\!\!\rangle-NH_2$$

$$C_2H_5-N———CH_2$$

procaine

It will be noted that the chief differences in procaine are that the ring structure to the left has been eliminated, as has the ester group at the upper
right-hand corner. A *para*-amino group has been added to the benzene ring.

Procaine has excellent local anesthetic action, it is not habit-forming, and
its toxicity is much less than that of cocaine. Similar advances make a stimulating and fascinating field of research for the chemist.

206. ANTISYPHILITICS

A major branch of chemotherapy is the selective destruction or inactivation
of pathogenic (disease-producing) organisms within the body of the host.
The great problem of chemotherapy is to produce chemical compounds which
will achieve this end without harming the patient. At the beginning of the
twentieth century there were only three specific remedies known for infectious diseases. These were mercury for syphilis, cinchona bark for malaria,
and ipecacuanha for dysentery. All three had been known for centuries.

Towards the end of the nineteenth century the full implications of two
great scientific advances began to be clear. These were the fact that infectious
diseases are due to microorganisms, as established by Robert Koch (1876),
and the theory of structural organic chemistry advanced by Kekulé (1865)
and elaborated by many others. These advances have led, in due course, to
some of the greatest blessings ever gained by mankind. In this and the following three sections we shall develop in some detail the steps which led to
the discovery of arsphenamine, of the newer antimalarials, of the sulfa drugs,
and of penicillin.

In recent years arsphenamine has been displaced by penicillin for the
treatment of syphilis. Nevertheless we shall devote attention to it, because
it represents the first very great triumph in the field of planned research for
the cure of a terrible disease.

A German scientist, Paul Ehrlich (1854-1915), devoted most of his life to
showing that molecules can be constructed showing selective action against
disease-producing organisms without harming the patient. As a medical student he had observed that certain dyes are able to stain tissue selectively,
that is, to stain some kinds of tissue but not others. Ehrlich thought that if a
dye could be obtained which would stain disease-producing organisms but

not normal tissue, then it might be possible to introduce some poisonous chemical group to the dye. The microorganism would absorb the dye and thereby come in contact with the poisonous group. A step in the right direction was taken when it was found that Methylene Blue, a well-known dye, selectively stains certain parasites.

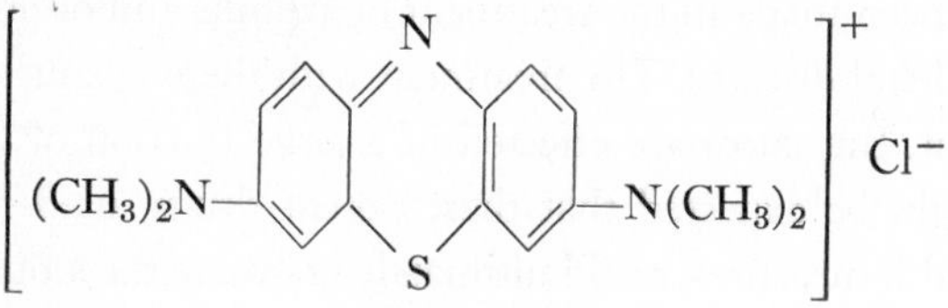

$$\left[(CH_3)_2N - \overset{\displaystyle N}{\underset{\displaystyle S}{\bigcirc\bigcirc}} - N(CH_3)_2 \right]^+ \quad Cl^-$$

Methylene Blue

It was later found that another dye, Trypan Red, not only selectively stained trypanosomes in infected mice but showed a little destructive action against these microorganisms.

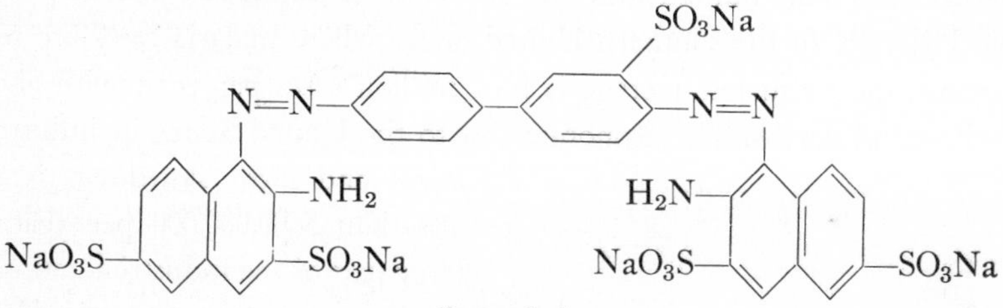

$$NaO_3S - \overset{-NH_2}{\underset{-SO_3Na}{\bigcirc}} - N=N - \bigcirc - \bigcirc - \overset{SO_3Na}{N=N} - \overset{H_2N-}{\underset{NaO_3S-}{\bigcirc}} - SO_3Na$$

Trypan Red

Ehrlich thought that the mild poisonous action of Trypan Red toward trypanosomes might be due to the *azo* groups ($-N=N-$) which the molecule contains.

It then occurred to Ehrlich that arsenic, a neighbor of nitrogen in the Periodic Table, would be more poisonous. He set out to make dyes comparable to Trypan Red but containing arsenic instead of nitrogen. It was already known that an arsenic compound, Atoxyl, had some activity against trypanosomes.

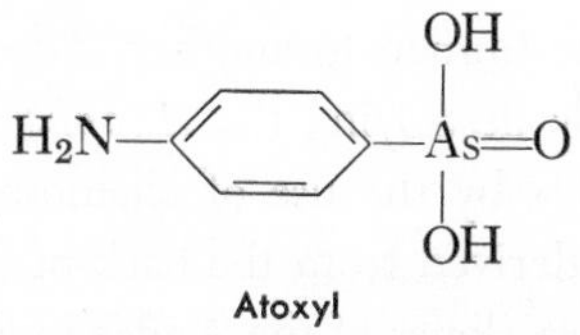

$$H_2N - \bigcirc - \overset{OH}{\underset{OH}{As=O}}$$

Atoxyl

In 1907 Ehrlich and his coworkers made arsphenamine. It was the 606th compound made in this study; hence the drug is popularly called "606." The German trade name is Salvarsan.

$$H_2N \qquad\qquad\qquad NH_2$$

$$HO-\langle\!\!\!\bigcirc\!\!\!\rangle-As{=}As-\langle\!\!\!\bigcirc\!\!\!\rangle-OH$$

arsphenamine

Since that time many new arsenicals have been synthesized and many advances have been made in the treatment of syphilis and of other trypanosomal and spirochetal diseases. The treatment with these agents is not easy and not too pleasant. But cures are effected in a large fraction of fairly early infections. It might be expected that these potent drugs, used in conjunction with public health measures, could ultimately eradicate the scourge of syphilis. The careful, brilliant, and systematic work of Ehrlich early in the twentieth century gave chemotherapy its greatest stimulus.

207. ANTIMALARIALS

Malaria causes more human suffering and more economic loss than any other tropical disease. In the southern United States where malaria rates are relatively low, the estimated average is four million cases per year, with about four thousand deaths. The economic cost to the United States in industrial losses and farm slowdown is not less than $500,000,000 per year. A large part of the industrialization of the South in recent years is due to steady progress in combating this disease. In India until recently there were one million deaths per year from malaria.

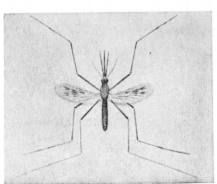

Fig. 31-1. Anopheles mosquito, carrier of malaria. (*United States Public Health Service*)

Malaria in human beings is caused by species of the protozoan *Plasmodia*. The disease is transmitted by females of the *Anopheles* mosquito, which by biting infected persons, carry the disease from one human to another. Adequate control of malaria would best be achieved by destroying the *Anopheles* mosquito, but control and cure are often possible by the use of chemotherapeutic agents.

Quinine is an alkaloid derived from the bark of the cinchona tree, which is native to the high eastern slopes of the Andes in South America. The first account of its value in the treatment of malaria occurs about the year 1633 in the writings of an Augustinian monk, named Calancha. The pure alkaloid was first isolated from cinchona bark in 1820.

The artificial cultivation of cinchona is difficult, and during the middle of the nineteenth century the Dutch government devoted much effort to growth of the tree in Java. This effort was successful, and the Dutch East Indies have for many years been the chief source of quinine.

The structure of the quinine molecule is known:

$$H_2C-CH$$
$$OH \quad CH_2 \quad CHCH=CH_2$$
$$HC-HC \quad CH_2$$
$$CH_3O \quad N-CH_2$$
$$N$$

quinine

But it is unusually complicated, and attempts to synthesize the compound were not successful until 1944. The method of synthesis is complicated and expensive. It is doubtful if synthetic quinine could ever compete with natural cinchona in normal times.

Quinine has been an indispensable drug. Without its aid the white man could scarcely have explored the tropics, much less have developed those regions economically. The native populations have, to be sure, a certain immunity to some of the strains of malaria, but this immunity is by no means complete. Quinine generally keeps the malaria victim free from the attacks of chills which are a chief symptom of the disease. Quinine may also prevent development of the symptoms if taken in adequate prophylactic doses. But quinine does not prevent the spread of the disease and does nothing to stamp it out. Consequently, much research has been done to discover new compounds which would take the place of quinine.

This chemical research for quinine substitutes received an extraordinary impetus during World War II. The Japanese invasion of the South Pacific cut off from the United States all important sources of quinine, rubber, and tin. We shall describe briefly some of the complicated chemistry involved in relieving the quinine shortage. The United States was faced with the problem of sending large armies into areas in which malaria was endemic. The men in our armies had little or no natural immunity to the disease, and it was well understood that in particularly dangerous areas every man in a contingent could be a victim. Malaria was obviously at least as dangerous an enemy as the Japanese. It must be understood that even if the South Pacific cinchona trees had remained in Allied hands, the supply of quinine would have been only a fraction of that actually required.

Two powerful synthetic antimalarial drugs were developed in Germany some years before World War II. The first was given the trade name of Plasmochin. It is derived from the heterocyclic compound quinoline.

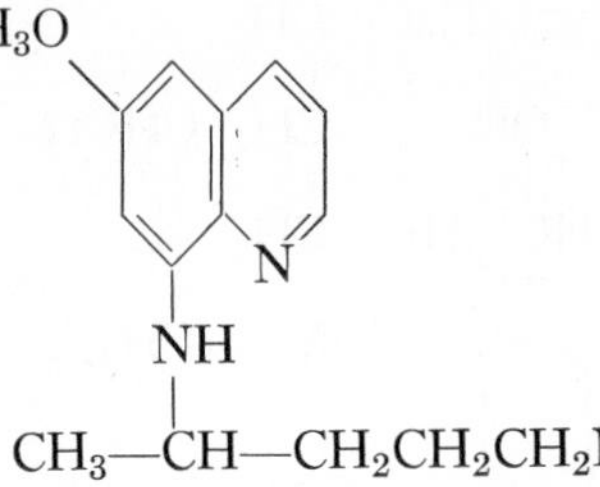

$$CH_3O$$

$$CH_3-CH-CH_2CH_2CH_2N(C_2H_5)_2$$

NH

Plasmochin

The second drug was given the trade name Atebrin. This compound contains a three-ring nitrogen group known as acridine.

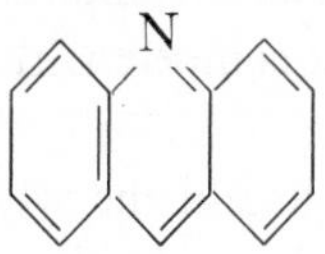

Cl

N

—OCH₃

NH

$$CH_3CHCH_2CH_2CH_2N(C_2H_5)_2$$

acridine 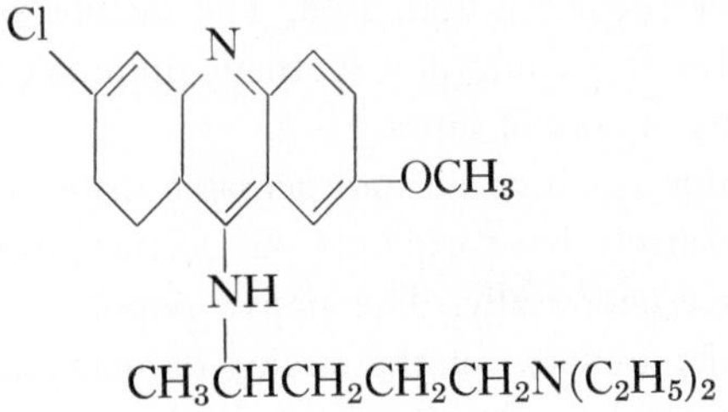   Atebrin

The malaria parasite has a complicated life-cycle, and some drugs are effective against one stage but not another. For general prophylactic use Atebrin proved to be a fairly effective substitute for quinine. Production of this drug, sometimes called quinacrine hydrochloride, skyrocketed from practically nothing to about seven million tablets per day during 1943.

Atebrin, although a reasonably acceptable substitute for quinine, does not prevent infection, and sometimes produces unwanted effects. Its use gives a yellow color to the skin. Throughout World War II some very intensive research was conducted on the synthesis of more satisfactory antimalarials. This search was successful to the degree that compounds are now available which are many times as effective as quinine. Most of these newer drugs are, like Plasmochin, derived from quinoline, or related compounds. One of the most effective new antimalarials (Pentaquine) is shown below, together with its chemical name.

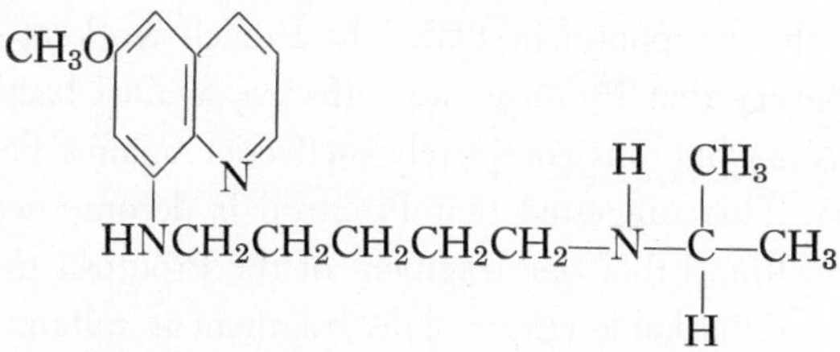

$$CH_3O$$

8-(5-isopropylaminopentylamino)-6-methoxyquinoline

$$HNCH_2CH_2CH_2CH_2CH_2-\overset{H}{\underset{}{N}}-\overset{CH_3}{\underset{H}{C}}-CH_3$$

This compound, taken together with quinine, effects a *cure* of vivax malaria.

208. SULFA DRUGS

When Ehrlich made his celebrated discovery of arsphenamine it was thought that many other advances in chemotherapy would soon be made. Actually no very spectacular discoveries were made until about 1935. But since that time we have entered into a veritable golden age of chemotherapy with one dreadful disease after another yielding to the combined forces of chemistry and medicine.

It will be recalled that the dye Trypan Red was shown by Ehrlich to have some bactericidal action. Search for more effective agents of this general type was continued in the laboratories of the German dye trust, I.G. Farbenindustrie, under the direction of Horlein, and later of Domagk. After the synthesis of five or six thousand compounds one was found in 1932 that showed startling promise. This compound was named Prontosil.

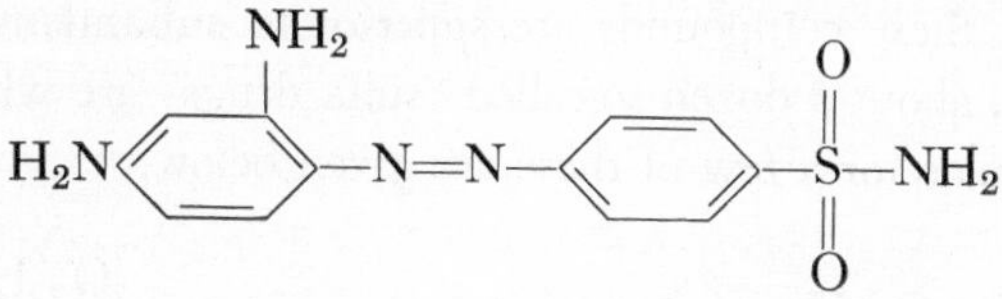

$$H_2N-\underset{NH_2}{\bigcirc}-N=N-\bigcirc-\overset{O}{\underset{O}{S}}-NH_2$$

Prontosil

Domagk found that mice when forced to swallow substantial amounts of Prontosil were completely protected against hemolytic streptococci, which are normally always fatal. In the same year a German doctor cured a child of staphylococcal septicemia with the same compound. However, the German results were kept as secrets, and no general medical use of Prontosil resulted. The compound and its structure were indicated in a German patent merely as a dye.

In the meantime a group of investigators at the Pasteur Institute in Paris suspected that the dye might have bactericidal action. After unsuccessful efforts to obtain some Prontosil from Germany, Tréfouëls and Fourneau made some of the compound in 1935. The French workers soon made the surprising discovery that Prontosil was effective against bacteria in the living body (*in vivo*) but was completely ineffective against bacteria in a test tube (*in vitro*). This suggested that Prontosil is decomposed in the body, and it was soon found that one fragment of the Prontosil molecule was responsible for its remarkable effects. This fragment is sulfanilamide.

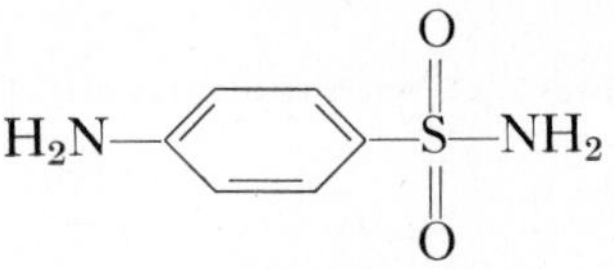

$$H_2N-\langle\rangle-\overset{\overset{O}{\|}}{\underset{\underset{O}{\|}}{S}}-NH_2$$

sulfanilamide

Various diseases against which sulfanilamide and related compounds are effective were soon reported in the medical literature, and in a very short time the treatment and prognosis for several dreadful diseases had been completely altered. The death rate from meningitis was cut from 40 per cent to 3.5 per cent. Bacillary dysentery was effectively controlled. The mortality rate for pneumonia was cut to a tenth. Erysipelas and gonococcal infections have been brought under control. Sulfanilamide was first synthesized in 1908 as a step in making dyes, but its potent medicinal properties lay unrecognized for more than a quarter of a century.

During the years immediately following 1935 several thousand compounds related to sulfanilamide were synthesized and tested for activity against bacteria. A few of these compounds are superior to sulfanilamide for certain purposes. In all, about a dozen so-called "sulfa drugs" are widely used. The structural formulas for a few of these are given below.

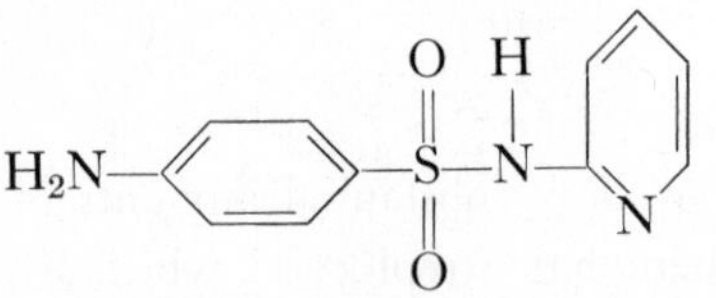

sulfapyridine

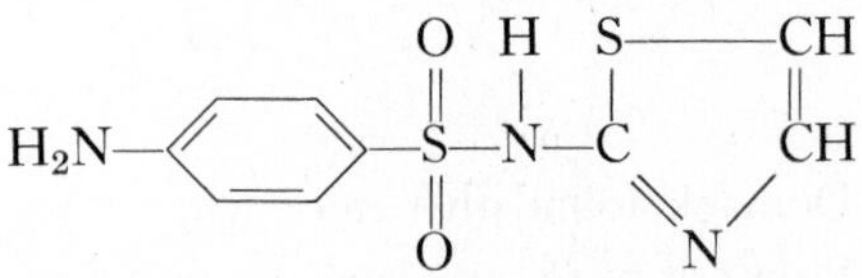

sulfathiazole

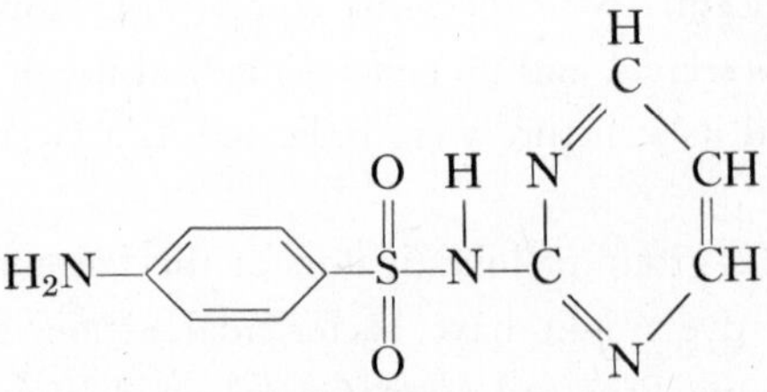

sulfadiazine

Early in the history of sulfa drugs it was found that these compounds do not kill bacteria but merely stop their multiplication. They are said to be *bacteriostatic* rather than *bactericidal*. The disease is brought under control because once the bacteria stop multiplying, the body's natural defenses can soon overcome those bacteria present.

This peculiar action of the sulfa drugs has led to considerable research, partly of a theoretical nature, on the mechanism by which the drugs exert their effects. The results of this work may, in the long run, prove to be even more important than the drugs themselves.

It has been found that small amounts of the compound *para*-aminobenzoic acid completely counteract the bacteriostatic action of the sulfa drugs. That is, if a little *p*-aminobenzoic acid is added to bacteria along with some sulfa drug, the bacteria multiply and flourish just as if no drug were present. *P*-Aminobenzoic acid is a vitamin necessary for the growth of microorganisms. Examination of the structure of the molecule shows that it bears a fairly close resemblance to sulfanilamide.

$$H_2N-\langle \ \rangle-\overset{\displaystyle O}{\overset{\displaystyle \|}{C}}-OH$$

p-aminobenzoic acid

A current theory for the bacteriostatic action of the sulfa drugs is that the bacteria are "tricked" into accepting the sulfa because of its structural similarity to the vitamin. But the sulfa drug lacks the potency of the vitamin in stimulating some essential step in the life process of the bacteria. Consequently, the bacteria fail to multiply.

It will be clear that this conception of sulfa-drug activity opens a new approach to chemotherapy. Perhaps the time will come when we know enough about life processes to devise molecules which will interfere with the development of all harmful growths, including malignant tumors, as well as microorganisms. If such a time ever arrives, then Ehrlich's fondest hopes may be surpassed.

209. PENICILLIN

Living organisms protect themselves from enemies in many ways. One of the most subtle protective mechanisms is the secretion of substances which interfere with the metabolic processes of other organisms. This is known as *antibiotic* activity, and the chemical substances thus secreted are known as **antibiotics.**

Antibiotic activity is not particularly new. Pasteur and others reported that contaminants from air and soil had some inhibiting effect on the growth of disease-producing bacteria. But no important development came from these early observations.

In 1929, Alexander Fleming was working in London at St. Mary's Hospital. He had set aside some laboratory cultures of the disease-producing *staphylococcus aureus*. Some time later he noticed that the culture had become contaminated with a green mold, and that the bacteria were being killed in the vicinity of the mold. Fleming grew more of the mold and discovered that the mold, or a secretion from it, was remarkably effective against gonococci, pneumococci, staphylococci, and streptococci. The mold which had accidentally found its way into the original culture was a species of *Penicillium,* not dissimilar to the mold which sometimes grows on bread in the summer. Fleming named the antibacterial substance **penicillin.**

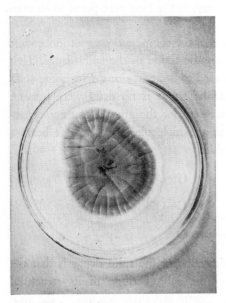

Fig. 31-2. *Penicillium notatum,* from which penicillin is obtained.

The discovery of penicillin, which has saved countless thousands of lives, is thus seen to be a lucky accident. But it is a typical example of what is sometimes called "deserved good fortune." Fleming was working in the general research field of antibacterials; he was alert to notice what had happened. A great discovery exists first as an attitude of the mind. As Fleming later wrote: "I was sufficiently interested to pursue the subject. The appearance of the culture plate was such that I thought it should not be neglected." Few men have more richly deserved the Nobel Prize which he was awarded.

Attempts by Fleming and others to isolate and purify penicillin were unsuccessful. In 1937, however, a group of bacteriologists and chemists headed by Howard Florey and Ernest B. Chain, at Oxford University, began to re-examine the possibilities of penicillin. By 1940 they had enough of the reasonably pure compound to show that penicillin surpassed the famed sulfa drugs in antibacterial action, and that it had an astonishing lack of toxicity for the patient.

Under the lash of wartime necessity the pharmaceutical industry undertook the most vigorous research and far-reaching expansion of production facilities in its history. Late in 1945 production became adequate for combined military and civilian requirements.

The production of penicillin is a difficult process. Study of various molds as sources of the drug resulted in higher yields being obtained, and the addition of the proper chemicals to the growing mold also increased the yield. The mold is allowed to grow in a nutrient solution, from which the penicillin is recovered by extraction in an organic solvent, or sometimes by adsorption on charcoal. A rather tedious series of purification steps finally yields the pure penicillin. The penicillin is a rather unstable compound, and this adds to the difficulty of purification.

Parallel with studies on production methods for penicillin, there were carried on fundamental studies on the molecular structure of the compound. The structure proved to be particularly difficult, less because of its complexity than because of the peculiar arrangement of atoms, and the instability of the compound.

Fig. 31-3. Photomicrograph of characteristic spore-head in *Penicillium notatum*.

Furthermore, it developed that there are several kinds of penicillin. One variety is now known to have the structure given below.

$$\text{HO—C—CH—N—C}$$

one form of penicillin (benzylpencillin G)

Other forms differ by having different acid groups in the lower right-hand corner of the structure as written.

Penicillin has had a remarkable effect on the prognosis for several dangerous infections. It is particularly effective against gas gangrene, mastoid infections, meningitis, brain abscesses, osteomyelitis, and a variety of "blood poisoning" infections. The drug supplements, rather than replaces, the sulfa drugs. It is much less toxic than the sulfa drugs.

Since the discovery of penicillin, many research studies have been directed to finding new antibiotics. These studies have been brilliantly successful, some of the most valuable new antibiotics being streptomycin, aureomycin, and chloromycetin.

One curious deficiency of penicillin will be mentioned. Bacteria tend to become resistant to it. After long use the drug may become quite without effect. The same is true to a degree with other drugs, including the sulfa drugs. Sometimes, however, an infection which has become resistant to one drug may be combated by switching to another, as for instance, changing from penicillin to a sulfa drug.

210. VITAMINS *

Anyone who has read the early history of North America or of early voyages of discovery will recall the disease called *scurvy* which plagued explorers and settlers. As early as 1720 it was known that green vegetables or citrus fruits would prevent the onset of the disease. In 1804 it became compulsory for all British sailors to have a daily ration of lemon or lime juice. This simple measure almost completely eradicated scurvy from the British navy.†

Recognition that certain factors in diet could prevent various diseases was slow. In 1885 a Japanese physician found that whole wheat or barley could reduce the incidence of the Asiatic disease *beriberi*. But it was scarcely until 1920 that general acceptance was won for the view that many serious conditions may be prevented by very small amounts of certain substances. These substances are generally present in a varied wholesome diet. The substances were first called "accessory diet factors." As more was learned about them it was thought that they were all amines, and they were named vitamines. Realization that many of the factors were not amines led to dropping of the *e* in the name. At the present time, thanks to the efficiency of advertising, the public is almost too conscious of vitamins.

In this section we shall make no effort to cover all known vitamins, but will describe a few representative examples, and then refer briefly to several others. Before the chemical constitution of the vitamins was understood, it was the custom to refer to them by letters, such as vitamin A, B, etc. As the structures became known, the tendency is towards using chemical names such as thiamine, niacin, and so forth, rather than letters.

The chemical structure of vitamin A was established by Karrer and his associates in 1931.

* Sherman and Lanford, *Essentials of Nutrition* (New York: Macmillan, 1940).
† The nickname "limeys" is still applied to British sailors.

$$CH_3 \quad CH_3$$

$$H_2C \quad \begin{matrix} C \\ \end{matrix} \quad C-CH=CH-\underset{\underset{CH_3}{|}}{C}=CH-CH=CH-\underset{\underset{CH_3}{|}}{C}=CHCH_2OH$$

$$H_2C \quad C-CH_3$$

$$CH_2$$

vitamin A

This substance does not occur in plants, but is formed in the liver from a plant pigment, carotene. The vitamin occurs abundantly in fish livers, from which it is extracted commercially. Carotene occurs in green leafy vegetables, and in carrots. The richness of color in the vegetable is a very rough index of the carotene content.

Deficiency of vitamin A (or of carotene) in the diet leads first to the condition known as night-blindness. The vitamin is apparently necessary for the complicated series of photochemical reactions that go on in the eye. Persons suffering from this condition may have to wait fifteen minutes or more before being able to see to a seat in the darkened theater. Prolonged deficiency of vitamin A in the diet leads to atrophy of the epithelial cells, and to a serious eye-condition known as *xerophthalmia*. Severe symptoms are rarely seen except in, for instance, depressed areas during and following wars, but mild "subclinical" symptoms may be of fairly widespread occurrence.

It may be added that the amount of vitamin required is very small, perhaps only a small fraction of a milligram per day, and that this amount is present in well-balanced diets.

One of the first so-called accessory diet factors to be recognized included that responsible for the cure of beriberi. This was called vitamin B. It is now recognized that the old vitamin B actually consists of a considerable number of different compounds, including the vitamins now known as thiamine (B_1), riboflavin, and nicotinic acid.

The structure of **thiamine** was established in 1936 by R. R. Williams as the result of many years of intensive research.

$$CH_3$$

$$N=C-NH_2\cdot HCl \qquad C=C-CH_2CH_2OH$$

$$CH_3-C \quad C-CH_2-N$$

$$N-CH \qquad Cl \quad CH-S$$

thiamine hydrochloride

The method originally used for obtaining this substance was from rice polishings. A few grams of thiamine are obtainable from a ton of polishings. The cost of obtaining the pure vitamin in this way is obviously high. The importance of obtaining the molecular structure of a substance such as thiamine is made clear when we consider that thiamine is now manufactured synthetically on a large scale for a few cents a gram.

Severe deficiency of thiamine in the diet leads to beriberi. The disease is still a major cause of death in certain countries, although the cure is now well understood. The symptoms of beriberi include a feeling of heaviness in the limbs, aching, and paralysis. There are also severe heart symptoms.

Beriberi is scarcely ever seen in the United States, but mild thiamine deficiency may be fairly widespread. In recent years physicians have become alert to this possibility. The condition is, of course, very easily treated. Wheat contains considerable thiamine, but much of this is lost in milling the wheat. Consequently white bread may lack this important diet requirement. At the present time most of the bread sold in the United States is artificially enriched with thiamine. In some states the enrichment is required by law.

Another vitamin present in the complex originally called B is **nicotinic acid.** The deficiency disease is *pellagra*. The acid was recognized by Elvehjem in 1937 as being effective in preventing the disease blacktongue in dogs. It was soon after shown to prevent pellagra in man.

nicotinic acid

The structure is seen to be very simple. Actually, nicotinic acid was first made in 1867 by the oxidation of nicotine, but its physiological function was not recognized. To avoid possible confusion with the very poisonous nicotine, nicotinic acid has been renamed **niacin.** The vitamin is abundant in liver, yeast, red meats, and kidney. The synthesis and manufacture of the vitamin on a large scale give no difficulty.

Pellagra is all too common, especially among poorer classes in the South. The chief symptoms are widespread eruptions on the skin, together with diarrhea, and mental depression. The symptoms may be controlled by appropriate doses of nicotinic acid.

Reference to scurvy, the vitamin-C deficiency disease, has been made above. Vitamin C is now called **ascorbic acid.**

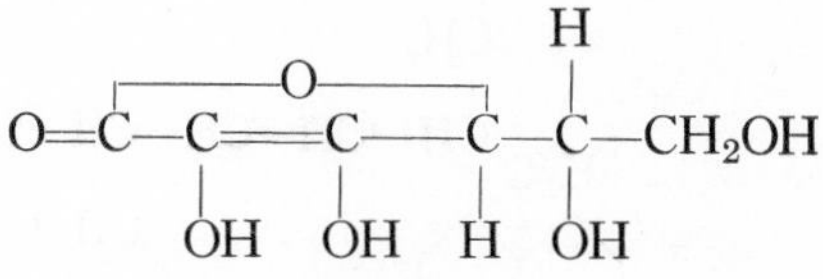

ascorbic acid

(handwritten left margin near ascorbic acid)

$$\overset{O}{\overset{\|}{-C}}-OH$$

(It may be wondered why this is called an acid when it does not appear to have any acid functional group. The acid properties are due to the

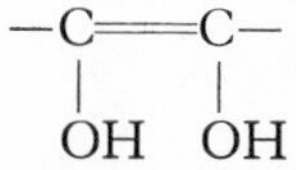

$$-\underset{\underset{OH}{|}}{C}=\underset{\underset{OH}{|}}{C}-$$

group which this molecule contains.) Isolation and recognition of the pure vitamin from lemon juice was made in 1932 by King. The compound is optically active and only the levo-form possesses antiscorbutic (antiscurvy) properties. The vitamin is abundant in citrus fruits.

The symptoms of scurvy include multiple hemorrhages, loss of teeth, and weakness in bone structure. These symptoms are rapidly alleviated by administration of the vitamin.

One of the most elusive of vitamin problems has proved to be D, the compound or compounds which prevent *rickets*. A major difficulty in understanding this problem was the fact that cod liver oil prevents rickets, but that mere exposure of the patient to sunshine seems also to prevent the disease.

Thanks to the work of Steenbock and many others, it is now realized that certain substances normally present in animals and in certain foods may be converted into antirachitic (antirickets) vitamins by exposure to sunshine or to ultraviolet light. One of these vitamin precursors, or provitamins, is ergosterol.

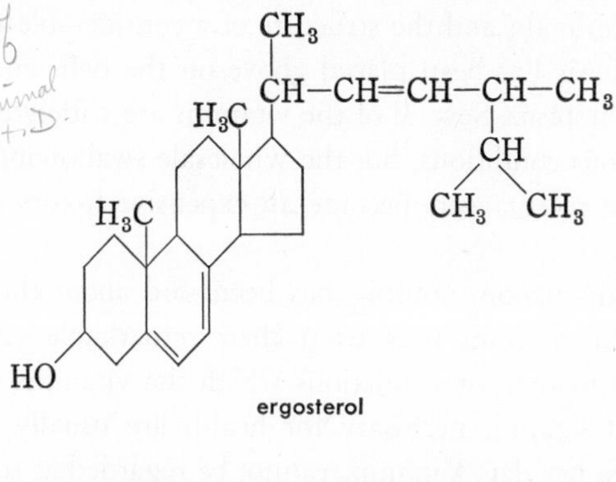

(handwritten notes) veg. source of Vit. D

calciferol = animal source of Vit. D.

ergosterol

If this substance is irradiated with ultraviolet light, it is converted into a series of products, one of which, known as vitamin D_2 or calciferol, has strong antirachitic activity.

vitamin D$_2$

The compounds most effective against rickets in human beings are not necessarily those most effective in animals. This is particularly true for chicks. The poultry industry uses large quantities of a related vitamin known as D$_3$, which occurs in fish-liver oils and which has a minor difference in structure from D$_2$.

The vitamins D are obtained from fish-liver oils, along with vitamin A. Furthermore, the quantity of vitamin present in various foods may be increased by irradiation with ultraviolet light. This is the reason many foods are sold as being "irradiated."

Interest in vitamin D is always exceptionally high. This is not only because of the antirachitic activity, but because the structure of these compounds shows a close resemblance to the sex hormones and to other compounds of great biochemical interest.

Rickets is another disease which is all too common. It is characterized by faulty bone development.

Several other vitamins are important in preventing specific conditions in humans and in animals, and the structure of a considerable number of these is known. Emphasis has been placed above on the deficiency diseases associated with the vitamins. Several of the vitamins are widely used in medicine for treating various conditions, but the wholesale swallowing of vitamins by the public has in recent years become an expensive luxury of very dubious value.

In the above discussion, nothing has been said about the possible mechanisms by which vitamins may exert their remarkable effects on animal health. It is easy to state two functions which the vitamins do not perform. The amounts of vitamin necessary for health are usually of the order of milligrams or less per day. Vitamins cannot be regarded as sources of energy, or as structural material for the building of tissue. The amount of vitamin required for health is far too small for either of these functions.

The small amounts of vitamin required suggests a catalytic, or enzymatic, function in the body. A hint in this direction has been found in the occurrence of substances closely related to several vitamins in certain prosthetic (i.e., functional) groups of enzymes. The vitamin riboflavin has been recognized as a component of several enzymes. Thiamine has been found to be present in carboxylase, an enzyme involved in the metabolism of carbohydrate. Similarly, nicotinic acid and ascorbic acid are related to enzyme systems, and vitamin A is definitely related to the protein, "visual purple," that occurs in the retina of the eye. The proteins which make up enzymes are themselves exceedingly complicated. For that matter, we know little about the actual mechanism of the simplest enzymatic or catalytic action. But it is definitely beginning to appear that the vitamins are essential groups in enzymes which are, in turn, essential for various life processes.

211. INSECTICIDES AND PLANT GROWTH FACTORS

Not infrequently in preceding chapters we have referred to substances such as Paris green, lead arsenate, and nicotine, which are used as insecticides. During the years of World War II some remarkably effective new insecticides and insect repellents became available. Of these, none has received so much publicity as DDT. This substance is almost miraculous in controlling such disease-carrying insects as the body-louse, the fly, and the mosquito. It is also effective against a wide variety of agricultural pests, but there is evidence that some insects develop a tolerance for it.

The popular name DDT is an abbreviation for dichlor-diphenyl-trichloroethane. Of the several isomers of this compound the one most effective, and manufactured in largest amount, is 1-trichloro-2,2-bis(p-chlorophenyl)ethane. This compound is easily made by the reaction of chloral hydrate and chlorobenzene in the presence of sulfuric acid.

chloral hydrate   chlorobenzene   DDT

It is now manufactured by the thousands of tons.

The history of DDT is not unlike that of some other recent discoveries of great value. The compound was first prepared in 1874. No consideration seems to have been given to its practical use until the J. R. Geigy Company in Basle, Switzerland, undertook a research program on new mothproofing agents. As a result of fifteen years' work Paul Müller reached the conclusion in 1936-37 that a compound having the structure of DDT would be an effective insecticide. This proved to be the case. The use of DDT in the United States is covered by patents held by the Geigy Company.

In the summer of 1942 a small quantity of DDT was exported by the Geigy Company to its New York office, and made available for testing. At a time when great efforts were being expended on insecticide research, the remarkable properties of DDT soon became widely known, and production on a large scale was initiated.

The great utility of DDT lies in several factors. It is made easily and cheaply; it is effective against an unusually large variety of insects; it is very much less toxic to animals and humans than most other insecticides, and the effects of spraying last as a rule for weeks or months. Perhaps the most spectacular example of its effectiveness was control of a threatened typhus epidemic in Naples just after the invasion of Italy. This terrible disease is carried by the body louse. A liberal dusting of the body and clothes with DDT powder was all that was necessary. However, it marked the first time in history that a typhus epidemic had been brought under control in such circumstances.

Since the introduction of DDT, much effort has gone into seeking other related types of compounds, with similar properties. An unusually effective compound is hexachlorocyclohexane.

hexachlorocyclohexane

It is a curious fact that of several structural isomers known for this compound only one is very useful as an insecticide.

We conclude this chapter with a brief account of some substances which show unusual effects toward plant life. The action of such substances may be not unlike that shown by some compounds described above.

It has been known for some time that certain alkaloids have the property of causing multiplication of the chromosomes of cells. Colchicine, an alkaloid obtained from the autumn crocus, has been used to develop interesting mutations in plants. Other substances regulate plant growth. Vitamin B (thiamine) is a powerful root growth stimulant, as is α-naphthylacetic acid. However, most interest has been aroused by the substance known as 2,4-D, or 2,4-dichlorophenoxyacetic acid.

This substance acts as a plant "hormone," stimulating root growth. In very low concentrations it has been used in the propagation of plants to induce rooting. But in larger concentrations 2,4-D so stimulates the growth process that the plant uses up all its reserves and dies out completely, even down to the deepest root. The action of 2,4-D is selective, in that it kills broad-leaved plants, but not grasses. When used at proper concentrations it is astonishingly effective against dandelions, poison ivy, water hyacinth, and many other noxious weeds. Great care must be taken to see that it does not reach valuable shrubbery, vegetables, or flowers, but at proper concentrations and times it is safe to use on grass and on most grainfields.

During the war many possible growth-regulating compounds were tested. It is probable that other weed killers of even greater selectivity will become available.

EXERCISES

A. *Define or explain the following:*

anesthesia (general and local)	pellagra
antibiotic	physiological activity (or action)
antimalarial	prophylactic
antisyphilitic	rickets
bactericidal	scurvy
bacteriostatic	sulfa drug
beriberi	vitamin
chemotherapy	xerophthalmia
in vivo, in vitro	

B. 1. In considerable detail give the history, chemistry, and results associated with (a) local anesthesia, (b) antisyphilitics, (c) malaria, (d) sulfa drugs, and (e) penicillin.

2. List various vitamins, showing name of vitamin, deficiency disease and symptoms, and common source of vitamin.

3. What methods are used by chemists in trying to synthesize improved chemotherapeutic agents?

4. What is the significance of p-aminobenzoic acid in chemotherapy?

5. With what discoveries in chemotherapy are the following names associated: Einhorn, Ehrlich, Fleming?

6. Write structural formulas for: quinoline, sulfanilamide, p-aminobenzoic acid, niacin (nicotinic acid), and DDT.

C. 1. Identify the functional groups: primary alcohol, secondary alcohol, aldehyde, ketone, ether, organic acid, ester, and amine, so far as they are to be found in the following molecules: procaine, quinine, p-aminobenzoic acid, benzylpenicillin, vitamin A, 2,4-D.

2. In earlier chapters we have referred to several types of reactions shown by organic compounds. These reactions include oxidation, reduction, hydrogenation, substitution, dehydration, esterification, and saponification. Illustrate each with a definite example.

3. Write structural formulas for each of the following: optically active butyl alcohol, benzoic anhydride, tribromoethanol, fluoroform, *ortho*-chlorobenzoic acid, *para*-chlorotoluene, cycloheptane, thiourea ("thio" means "sulfur"), methoxyacetic acid, methyloctyl ketone, phenyl benzoate, propylene glycol, salicylaldehyde, paradiphenylbenzene, hexaphenylethane.

4. A method available for synthesizing hydrocarbons is to treat an alkyl (or aryl) halide with metallic sodium. This is known as the Wurtz reaction. It is illustrated as follows:

$$2CH_3I + 2Na \rightarrow C_2H_6 + 2NaI$$

a. Show how the Wurtz reaction might be used to prepare hexane, eicosane ($C_{20}H_{22}$), and diphenyl.

b. What would be the probable result of trying to make heptane by reacting equal quantities of butyl iodide and propyl iodide with sodium?

HIGH POLYMERS

Few modern developments have intruded so closely into our private lives as has the class of substances known popularly as "plastics." Our fountain pens, cars, toothbrushes, shoes, raincoats, and radios all contain plastics.

The term "plastic" is used by chemists in a somewhat restricted sense, and in this chapter we shall refer to such substances as **high polymers.** The significance of this name should become clear as we describe the molecular structure of these substances. Several times in the past pages, reference has been made to substances such as cellulose which have extremely large molecules, but the molecules of which are made up of recurring units. For instance, it may be recalled that the formula for cellulose may be written $(C_6H_{10}O_5)_n$. There is a unit, $C_6H_{10}O_5$, which is repeated a large number of times in the molecule.

Cellulose is an example of a naturally occurring high polymer. It will be recalled that cellulose is in some contrast to a substance such a glucose which has a rather modest molecular weight. Similarly cellulose nitrate and cellulose acetate may be regarded as plastics, or high polymers. These are examples of synthetic high polymers, at least to the extent that the original molecule has been considerably modified.

The formation of a polymer may be regarded in the following way. Suppose we have a molecule X, and that this molecule is able to unite with itself to form X_2. (Such a case actually occurs in the equilibrium $2NO_2 \rightleftarrows N_2O_4$.) But suppose that the molecule X is able to continue uniting with itself to form very long chains which might be indicated thus.

$$X-X-X-X-X-X-X-X$$

The resulting large molecule is called a polymer of X. The word "polymer" is derived from the Greek meaning "many times." In speaking of polymers it is the custom to refer to the single unit (X in the above case) as a **monomer.** If the molecular weight of the polymer is very large, the substance is said to be a high polymer.

With this brief introduction it is hoped that the reader will understand in a general way the significance of the term polymer. But a thorough under-standing is scarcely possible without extensive reference to specific examples.

212. POLYETHYLENE   *high polymer of ethylene*

If ethylene is subjected to high pressure in the presence of an appropriate catalyst, the following reaction takes place:

$$
n\underset{\underset{\text{H}}{|}}{\overset{\overset{\text{H}}{|}}{\text{C}}}{=}\underset{\underset{\text{H}}{|}}{\overset{\overset{\text{H}}{|}}{\text{C}}} \rightarrow -\underset{\underset{\text{H}}{|}}{\overset{\overset{\text{H}}{|}}{\text{C}}}-\underset{\underset{\text{H}}{|}}{\overset{\overset{\text{H}}{|}}{\text{C}}}-\underset{\underset{\text{H}}{|}}{\overset{\overset{\text{H}}{|}}{\text{C}}}-\underset{\underset{\text{H}}{|}}{\overset{\overset{\text{H}}{|}}{\text{C}}}-\underset{\underset{\text{H}}{|}}{\overset{\overset{\text{H}}{|}}{\text{C}}}-
$$

the reaction continuing until all the monomer indicated is used up. This may be represented more simply as:

$$ n\text{C}_2\text{H}_4 \rightarrow [-\text{CH}_2-]_{2n} $$
ethylene   polyethylene

the square brackets being used here to represent the molecular unit, $-\text{CH}_2-$, which is repeated over and over again in the high polymer molecule. Ethylene combines with itself in this way to form long hydrocarbon chains, the molecular weights of which may be in the tens of thousands.

This high polymer is generally called polyethylene, although it is also known by the trade name "polythene." The high polymer molecules must, of course, possess a double bond, but one double bond in a molecule con-taining hundreds of atoms is quite negligible. The total length to which each polymer molecule grows is determined in part by impurities, accidentally or intentionally added, which are able to terminate the growing chain. Poly-ethylene is a translucent, tough material, insoluble in all solvents at ordinary temperatures, and resistant to chemical action. It may be molded into sheets, tubes, or objects of almost any special design. Its special electrical prop-erties make it valuable in the design of radio equipment, and its cheapness and serviceability find it a host of uses. A valuable related high polymer is sold under the name **Teflon**. In this substance the hydrogen atoms in ethyl-ene have been replaced by fluorines.

$$ n\text{F}_2\text{C}{=}\text{CF}_2 \rightarrow \left[-\underset{\underset{\text{F}}{|}}{\overset{\overset{\text{F}}{|}}{\text{C}}}- \right]_{2n} $$
tetrafluoroethylene   Teflon

Teflon is quite extraordinarily tough and resistant to solvent or chemical action.

The study of high polymers such as polyethylene poses some special problems in determination of the molecular weight. Depression of the freezing point is seldom sufficiently sensitive for molecular weights above a few thousand. The vapor density method is inapplicable because high polymers cannot be vaporized without decomposition. Several methods have been successfully applied to molecular weight determination in the range of tens to hundreds of thousands of molecular weight units. One of these is the osmotic pressure method. Osmotic pressure depends on the concentration and molecular weight of the solute and hence, if an appropriate solvent can be found, serves to estimate molecular weights up to about half a million. Another method is based on the ultracentrifuge. A substance of large molecular weight tends to settle out of solution, and the rate of sedimentation is proportional to the molecular weight. Gravity is insufficient to bring about sedimentation in high polymer molecules because normal diffusion opposes sedimentation. But the ultracentrifuge multiplies the gravitational force many times and brings about appreciable sedimentation which may be observed and used to calculate the molecular weight. A third method for molecular weight determination depends on the scattering of light by polymer molecules. The intensity and nature of light scattered, as in the Tyndall effect, depend on the molecular dimensions.

213. RUBBER

Early explorers in North America found the Mexican natives playing with balls made of an elastic substance derived from certain trees. This substance was introduced into Europe about 1772 and small pieces of the gum were sold as erasers. The name "rubber" is derived from this use. It is a curious commentary on our language that the word rubber should now also refer to a waterproof covering for shoes.

The chief source of rubber is the sap of *Hevea brasiliensis* which is extensively cultivated in the Dutch and British East Indies. The sap is obtained as a milky fluid when the tree is cut through the outer bark. This fluid is a colloidal suspension of rubber in water. If the fluid is acidified, the colloidal rubber coagulates and may be pressed into sheets or balls. The rubber is often called *caoutchouc,* from South American Indian words meaning "tears of the wood." Crude rubber is sticky and sensitive to changes of temperature, but if it is heated with sulfur it undergoes a process known as *vulcanization* and becomes an extremely useful substance, as we all know.

If rubber is strongly heated there may be distilled out a liquid called **iso-prene.** This is an unsaturated hydrocarbon having the following formula:

$$H_2C=\underset{\underset{\text{isoprene}}{|}}{\overset{\overset{\displaystyle CH_3}{|}}{C}}-CH=CH_2$$

Fig. 32-1. Tapping a rubber tree.

Rubber is a polymer of isoprene. Rubber is, therefore, a hydrocarbon, although natural rubber contains small amounts of fatty acids, proteins, and other substances.

The molecular weight of rubber is very high and rather difficult to measure. Various lines of evidence point to average molecular weights of from 200,000 to 400,000. All the rubber molecules are probably not of the same molecular weight, but they are all very large.

A study of how the isoprene units are combined to form giant molecules is a matter of some difficulty. Fortunately, rubber reacts with a variety of reagents such as ozone, chlorine, and (under proper conditions) with hydrogen. It has been concluded that rubber consists of long chains, as shown:

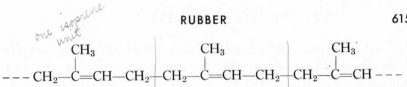

one isoprene unit

$$--- CH_2 - \overset{\overset{\textstyle CH_3}{|}}{C} = CH - CH_2 - CH_2 - \overset{\overset{\textstyle CH_3}{|}}{C} = CH - CH_2 - CH_2 - \overset{\overset{\textstyle CH_3}{|}}{C} = CH ---$$

The above formula shows only three isoprene units in combination. It must be understood that the molecule actually extends for thousands of such units. It will be noted also that there is some rearrangement of the double bonds in formation of the polymer from isoprene.

Fig. 32-2. A reactor used in making synthetic rubber. This is a sharp contrast to the scene in Fig. 32-1.

It might be thought that the manufacture of synthetic rubber would be simple. All we have to do is cause isoprene to polymerize. If isoprene is shaken with hydrochloric acid a rubber-like substance is actually obtained. But this has not proved to be a practical method for making synthetic rubber.

The general structure of rubber as outlined above is verified by X-ray studies. The remarkable elasticity of rubber seems to be related to the long molecules, which are normally coiled and twisted. But if the rubber is stretched, these molecules easily elongate to many times their coiled-up length.

The **vulcanization** of rubber was discovered by Charles Goodyear in 1838. The mechanical changes involved in this very important process are believed to be related to cross-links formed by sulfur atoms between adjacent rubber molecules. For instance, two adjacent rubber molecules may be united through a sulfur atom as shown

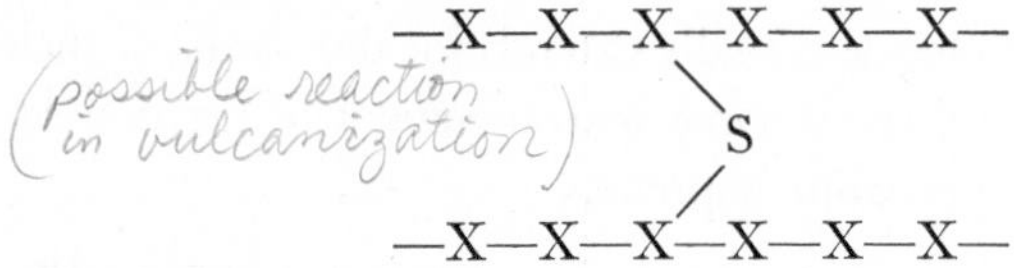

$$-X-X-X-X-X-X-$$

(possible reaction in vulcanization)

$$\begin{array}{c} \backslash \\ S \\ / \end{array}$$

$$-X-X-X-X-X-X-$$

where X stands for an isoprene unit. This cross-linking might be expected to give mechanical strength to the rubber, especially if the cross-linking is fairly extensive. Other changes probably occur during vulcanization.

When, early in 1942, the United States was cut off from all but a trickle of natural rubber, the situation called for drastic measures. The celebrated Baruch Committee report pointed out that we are a "nation on wheels" and that our industrial economy would collapse unless rubber were made available. Fortunately, the basic chemistry of synthetic rubber production was fairly well understood, and it was also realized that the various synthetics had special properties. The rubber chosen for the mass production necessary to avoid losing the war was that known as GR-S. The production method of this polymer will be described in some detail.

Butadiene undergoes polymerization under the influence of various reagents, but the product is not very satisfactory as a rubber substitute.

$$H_2C{=}CH{-}CH{=}CH_2$$
butadiene

Another substance which readily undergoes polymerization is the aromatic compound, **styrene.**

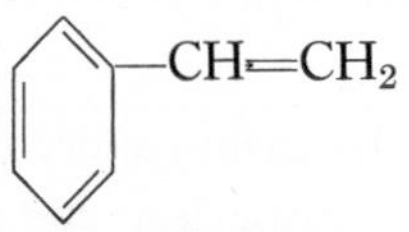

$$\bigcirc{-}CH{=}CH_2$$
styrene

But this also gives a polymer of no use as a rubber. The secret of successful rubber synthesis lies in what is called **copolymerization,** or the simultaneous polymerization of two monomers. Copolymerization does not mean that the two monomers polymerize independently and form merely a mechanical mixture of polymers. The two substances are actually incorporated into the polymer chains. In GR-S the styrene content is about 25 per cent. It is difficult to write a structural formula which properly represents GR-S, but the method of incorporation of the styrene groups may be indicated as follows:

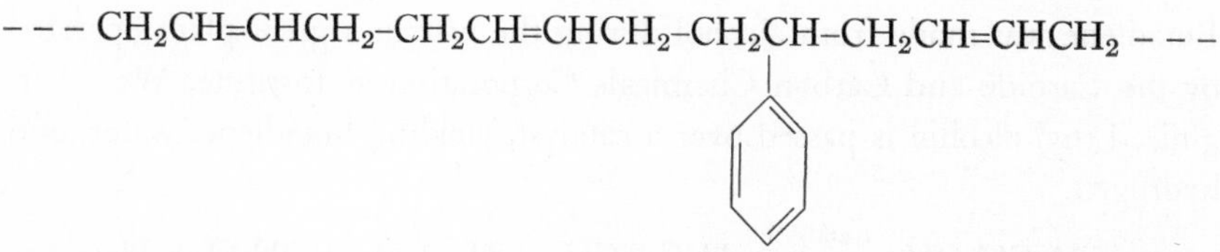

$$- - - CH_2CH{=}CHCH_2{-}CH_2CH{=}CHCH_2{-}CH_2CH{-}CH_2CH{=}CHCH_2 - - -$$

The final product is a long-chain butadiene polymer in which are attached aromatic groups at various intervals. Furthermore, the chains appear to be cross-linked at various places. The amount of cross-linking modifies the properties of the rubber, and may be controlled by the addition of agents called "chain-modifiers."

Much high-polymer production is now done by a process known as **emulsion polymerization.** The monomeric reagents are mixed and then emulsified (to form colloidal droplets) in water, with the addition of various emulsifying agents. The polymerization then proceeds within each tiny droplet. Emulsion polymerization gives a rapid reaction with excellent control of temperature and of product uniformity.

The two substances butadiene and styrene are prepared by several processes.

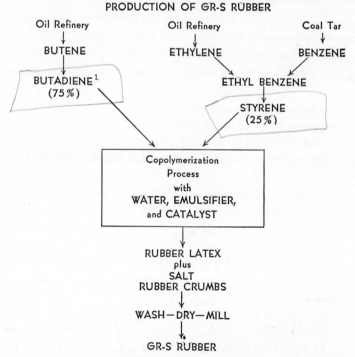

PRODUCTION OF GR-S RUBBER

Oil Refinery → BUTENE → BUTADIENE[1] (75%)

Oil Refinery → ETHYLENE → ETHYL BENZENE → STYRENE (25%)

Coal Tar → BENZENE → ETHYL BENZENE

Copolymerization Process with WATER, EMULSIFIER, and CATALYST

↓

RUBBER LATEX plus SALT RUBBER CRUMBS

↓

WASH—DRY—MILL

↓

GR-S RUBBER

[1] Also can be produced from acetylene, natural gas, or alcohol made from grain or potato, or almost any starchy vegetable material or refinery gas. (Rubber Manufacturer's Association)

Butadiene was made from alcohol during the war in a great plant operated by the Carbide and Carbon Chemicals Corporation at Institute, West Virginia. Ethyl alcohol is passed over a catalyst, yielding butadiene, water, and hydrogen.

$$2CH_3CH_2OH \xrightarrow{\text{(catalyst)}} H_2C{=}CH{-}CH{=}CH_2 + 2H_2O + H_2$$

Styrene is produced from benzene and ethylene by the following steps, the first of which involves the Friedel-Crafts reaction with aluminum chloride as a catalyst:

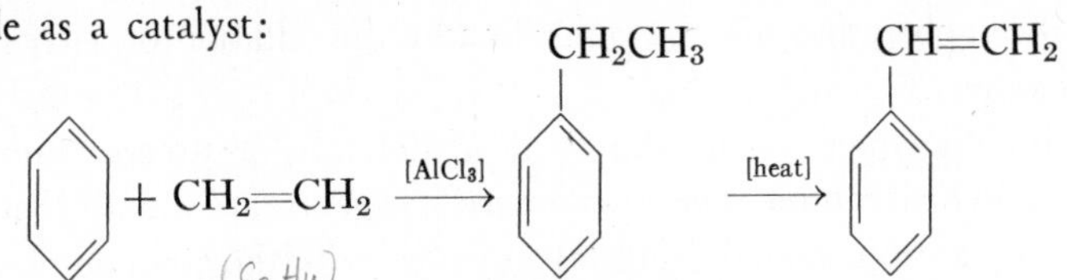

benzene +   ethylene   → ethyl benzene   →   styrene

Synthetic rubber was in production to the extent of over a million tons per year during the war. (See chart on page 617.)

214. METHYL METHACRYLATE, AND RELATED POLYMERS

The dream of a flexible glass is one which has stimulated the imaginations of chemists for generations. Ordinary glass is an extremely useful product, but it has the weakness of being brittle. The development of clear transparent high polymers is certainly one of the major achievements in polymer chemistry.

A considerable variety of compounds undergo polymerization to form partially transparent solids. Among these are vinyl chloride, $CH_2{=}CHCl$, and styrene. But the most interesting products from the standpoint of transparency are polymers produced from **methyl methacrylate,** and related compounds.

The structure of the ester monomer methyl methacrylate will be clear from a consideration of the following formulas:

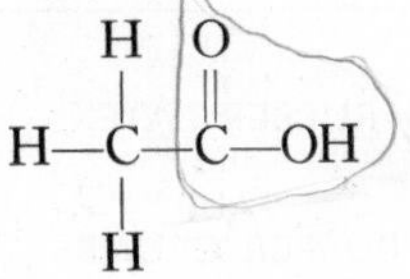

acetic acid

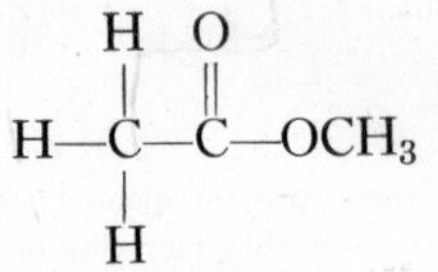

methyl acetate 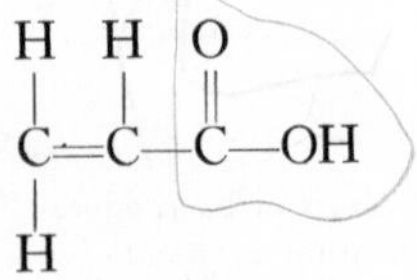   acrylic acid

$$
\begin{matrix}
\text{H} & \text{H} & \text{O} \\
| & | & \| \\
\text{C}=\text{C}-\text{C}-\text{OCH}_3 \\
| \\
\text{H}
\end{matrix}
\qquad\qquad
\begin{matrix}
\text{H} & \text{CH}_3 & \text{O} \\
| & | & \| \\
\text{C}=\text{C}\text{---}\text{C}-\text{OCH}_3 \\
| \\
\text{H}
\end{matrix}
$$

methyl acrylate   methyl methacrylate

Methyl methacrylate readily polymerizes yielding a clear transparent "glass." The polymerization may be represented as follows:

$$
n\begin{matrix}
\text{H} & \text{CH}_3 & \text{O} \\
| & | & \| \\
\text{C}=\text{C}\text{---}\text{C}-\text{OCH}_3 \\
| \\
\text{H}
\end{matrix}
\rightarrow
\left[
\begin{matrix}
\text{H} & \text{CH}_3 \\
| & | \\
-\text{C}-\text{C}- \\
| & | \\
\text{H} & \text{C}=\text{O} \\
& | \\
& \text{OCH}_3
\end{matrix}
\right]_n
$$

methyl methacrylate monomer   polymer

This polymer, which is sold under trade names such as Plexiglas and Lucite, may be made into sheets or various articles as desired. The injection molding process, by which the polymer is forced under pressure into a mold, is widely used with this polymer. Methyl methacrylate is widely used for transparent parts of airplanes, such as noses, blisters, etc. Its uses include furniture parts, and "contact" eyeglasses. Its use has become so widespread as to need no further description. The polymer is highly transparent, is

Fig. 32-3. Cast sheets of methyl methacrylate polymer. This material is sold under trade names such as "Lucite" and "Plexiglas."

strong though flexible, and is considerably lighter than glass. It is, however, much softer, and therefore more readily scratched, than glass. There is no question that this polymer fills a long-felt need and that its production and applications will continue to grow rapidly.

215. DACRON AND NYLON

Few accomplishments in the realm of synthetic organic chemistry have contributed so much to feminine happiness as Nylon. The research studies which led to Dacron, to Nylon, and to many other polymeric materials were initiated in 1930 by W. H. Carothers, working in the Laboratories of E. I. du Pont de Nemours and Company.

Those high polymers described in the preceding sections have all been formed through direct addition of one monomer molecule to another. This has been possible because all the monomer molecules described contained at least one double bond. Polymerization of this type is called **vinyl**, or addition, polymerization. That to be described in this section involves the splitting out of a molecule of water. It is called **condensation** polymerization.

It will be recalled that phthalic acid has the structural formula given below. This compound may exist in several isomeric forms, of which another is terephthalic acid, also shown below.

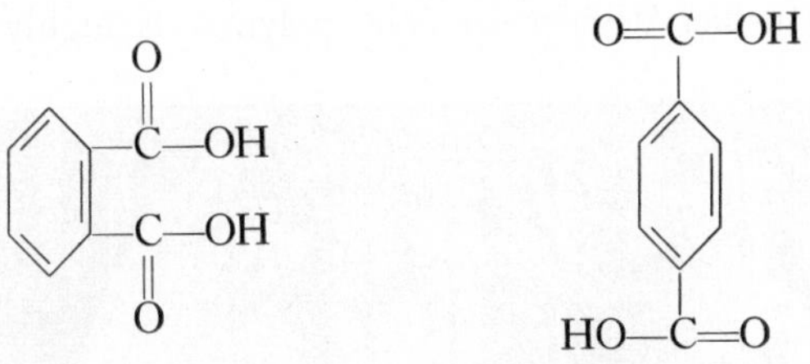

phthalic acid   terephthalic acid

Terephthalic acid may form an ester, as may any other organic acid. If the acid should unite with the dihydric alcohol, ethylene glycol, then the product would be as shown.

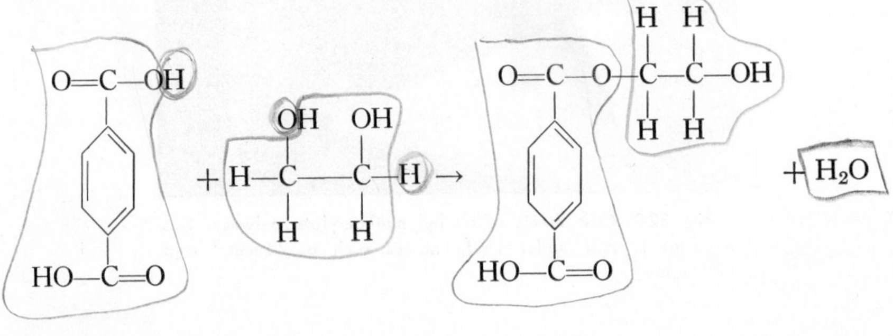

Now, because of the fact that both the acid and the alcohol, in this case, are bifunctional it is possible for a further condensation to take place, yielding a polymer molecule of the following structure:

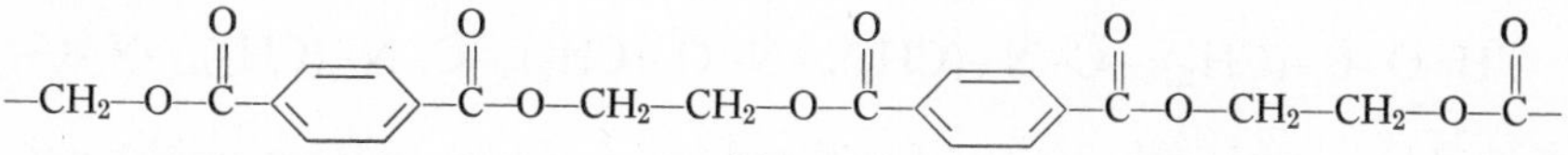

$$-CH_2-O-\overset{\overset{\displaystyle O}{\|}}{C}-\langle\ \rangle-\overset{\overset{\displaystyle O}{\|}}{C}-O-CH_2-CH_2-O-\overset{\overset{\displaystyle O}{\|}}{C}-\langle\ \rangle-\overset{\overset{\displaystyle O}{\|}}{C}-O-CH_2-CH_2-O-\overset{\overset{\displaystyle O}{\|}}{C}-$$

Dacron

This polymer is called polyethylene terephthalate. It is sold in the United States under the trade name Dacron, in Britain as Terylene.

While Nylon is also manufactured by condensation, the structure differs considerably from that of Dacron. The chemical changes which occur in the production of Nylon will be illustrated first by reference to some simpler compounds and reactions. It will be recalled that an amine has the general

formula $R-NH_2$, and that an amide is $R-\overset{\overset{\displaystyle O}{\|}}{C}-NH_2$. It is possible to have an amine react with an acid to form a substituted amide. For instance, acetic acid may react with methyl amine as follows:

$$CH_3\overset{\overset{\displaystyle O}{\|}}{C}-OH + CH_3NH_2 \rightarrow CH_3\overset{\overset{\displaystyle O}{\|}}{C}-\underset{\underset{\displaystyle H}{|}}{N}CH_3 + H_2O$$

acid   amine   amide

Suppose now that instead of using acetic acid, we used an acid with two functional groups. With sufficient amine, it would be possible to form a **diamide**:

$$HO-\overset{\overset{\displaystyle O}{\|}}{C}-CH_2-CH_2-\overset{\overset{\displaystyle O}{\|}}{C}-OH + 2RNH_2 \rightarrow$$

dibasic acid   amine

$$R-\underset{\underset{\displaystyle H}{|}}{N}-\overset{\overset{\displaystyle O}{\|}}{C}-CH_2-CH_2-\overset{\overset{\displaystyle O}{\|}}{C}-\underset{\underset{\displaystyle H}{|}}{N}-R + 2H_2O$$

diamide

One further complication will now be introduced. We continue to use an acid with two functional groups, and we also use an amine with two functional groups; in other words, a **diamine**.

$$\text{HO}-\overset{\overset{\displaystyle O}{\|}}{\text{C}}-(\text{CH}_2)_n-\overset{\overset{\displaystyle O}{\|}}{\text{C}}-\text{OH} + \text{H}_2\text{N}-(\text{CH}_2)_n-\text{NH}_2 \rightarrow$$

$$\text{H}-\text{O}-\overset{\overset{\displaystyle O}{\|}}{\text{C}}-(\text{CH}_2)_n-\overset{\overset{\displaystyle O}{\|}}{\text{C}}-\overset{\overset{\displaystyle H}{|}}{\text{N}}-(\text{CH}_2)_n-\overset{\overset{\displaystyle H}{|}}{\text{N}}-\overset{\overset{\displaystyle O}{\|}}{\text{C}}-(\text{CH}_2)_n-\overset{\overset{\displaystyle O}{\|}}{\text{C}}-\overset{\overset{\displaystyle H}{|}}{\text{N}}-(\text{CH}_2)_n-\overset{\overset{\displaystyle H}{|}}{\text{N}}-\overset{\overset{\displaystyle O}{\|}}{\text{C}}-$$

It will be seen that the union of acid and amine groups to form amides may now proceed indefinitely, and that this is possible because of the *bifunctional* character of both the acid and the amine. As water is eliminated, we should call the process "condensation polymerization." This kind of polymer is referred to as a **polyamide.** It is readily drawn into long fibers suitable for making textile fabrics. The product is not a synthetic silk, but it is chemically related to silk which is a protein and doubtless also contains amide linkages.

The exact polymer commonly used in Nylon is that in which the diamine has six carbon atoms.

$$\text{H}_2\text{N}-\text{CH}_2-\text{CH}_2-\text{CH}_2-\text{CH}_2-\text{CH}_2-\text{CH}_2-\text{NH}_2$$
hexamethylene diamine

This is hexamethylene diamine, and the dibasic acid used is adipic acid, which happens also to have six carbons.

$$\text{HO}-\overset{\overset{\displaystyle O}{\|}}{\text{C}}-\text{CH}_2-\text{CH}_2-\text{CH}_2-\text{CH}_2-\overset{\overset{\displaystyle O}{\|}}{\text{C}}-\text{OH}$$
adipic acid

Because both components have six carbons, the polymer is sometimes called "6-6." A complete formula for Nylon may, therefore, be indicated as follows:

$$---\overset{\overset{\displaystyle O}{\|}}{\text{C}}-(\text{CH}_2)_4-\overset{\overset{\displaystyle O}{\|}}{\text{C}}-\underset{\underset{\displaystyle H}{|}}{\text{N}}-(\text{CH}_2)_6-\underset{\underset{\displaystyle H}{|}}{\text{N}}-\overset{\overset{\displaystyle O}{\|}}{\text{C}}-(\text{CH}_2)_4-\overset{\overset{\displaystyle O}{\|}}{\text{C}}-\underset{\underset{\displaystyle H}{|}}{\text{N}}-(\text{CH}_2)_6-\underset{\underset{\displaystyle H}{|}}{\text{N}}-\overset{\overset{\displaystyle O}{\|}}{\text{C}}-(\text{CH}_2)_4-\overset{\overset{\displaystyle O}{\|}}{\text{C}}---$$
Nylon

The molecular weight of the polymer is from 10,000 to 25,000. The properties and uses of both Nylon and Dacron are so familiar as to require no description here.

216. ORGANOSILICON POLYMERS

Silicon is directly below carbon in the Periodic Table, but the chief interest in silicon has been with respect to natural silicates, to silica, and to glasses. The fact that silicon forms hydrides of the type Si_nH_{2n+2} has been known for a long time, as has the fact that certain silicon compounds polymerize to form substances of very high molecular weight. But the spectacular advances in silicon polymer chemistry were the result in part of the stimulus provided by World War II.

An outstanding characteristic of carbon is its ability to form very long chains of atoms in which one carbon is linked directly to the next. Similar chains of silicon atoms are not very stable, and have not been prepared with over about six silicon atoms. On the other hand, it will be recalled that silica consists of very large groups of silicon atoms joined together through an oxygen atom. The linkage —Si—Si—Si— is not very stable, but the linkage —Si—O—Si—O—Si— seems to be very stable.

Compounds in which the silicon-oxygen bond occurs, and in which the remaining valences are filled by hydrogen, are called **siloxanes**.

$$
\begin{array}{ccccccc}
 & H & & H & & H & \\
 & | & & | & & | & \\
H- & Si & -O- & Si & -O- & Si & -H \\
 & | & & | & & | & \\
 & H & & H & & H &
\end{array}
$$

trisiloxane

Such molecules may be quite large, with many silicon atoms. In such cases the compounds are called **polysiloxanes**.

$$
\begin{array}{ccccccc}
 & H & & \left[\; H \;\right. & & H & \\
 & | & & | & & | & \\
H- & Si & -O & \left| -Si- \right. O & \left. \right|- & Si & -H \\
 & | & & | & & | & \\
 & H & & \left. H \;\right]_n & & H &
\end{array}
$$

polysiloxane

It will be noted that the recurring unit in polysiloxane is $\left[\begin{array}{c} H \\ | \\ -Si-O- \\ | \\ H \end{array}\right]$.

Now if the hydrogen atoms are replaced by alkyl groups we obtain a typical **organosilicon polymer**. If the alkyl groups are methyl, then the recurring group is

$$
\left[\begin{array}{c} CH_3 \\ | \\ -Si-O- \\ | \\ CH_3 \end{array}\right]
$$

The initial work on these substances indicated that they might be considered as ketones of silicon. It is now understood that they are not ketones, but the name **silicone** has been retained.

It will be clear that many different organosilicon polymers are possible, depending on the choice of alkyl (or aryl) groups, and on the extent of cross-linking between chains, and on other factors. We shall not go into detail concerning these many modifications, but will indicate in a general way two methods for preparing silicones. In outline, the first large-scale method was to substitute alkyl groups for some of the chlorine in silicon tetrachloride, then to hydrolyze and condense to silicones.

Silicon tetrachloride may be made from sand, coke, and chlorine.

$$SiO_2 + 2C + 2Cl_2 \rightarrow SiCl_4 + 2CO$$

The alkyl groups may be introduced through the agency of a Grignard reagent.

$$Mg \quad + \quad RCl \quad \rightarrow \quad RMgCl$$

magnesium + alkyl chloride → Grignard reagent

The reaction of silicon tetrachloride with the Grignard yields a mixture of chlorosilanes, which are indicated as follows:

$$SiCl_4 \quad + RMgCl \rightarrow \begin{cases} RSiCl_3 \\ R_2SiCl_2 \\ R_3SiCl \end{cases}$$

silicon tetrachloride + Grignard → a mixture of chlorosilanes

The mixture of chlorosilanes is separated by distillation, then hydrolyzed and condensed to the polymer. Taking R_2SiCl_2 as an example, we have:

$$R_2SiCl_2 + 2H_2O \rightarrow R_2Si(OH)_2 + 2HCl$$

$$nR_2Si(OH)_2 \rightarrow \left[\begin{array}{c} R \\ | \\ -Si-O- \\ | \\ R \end{array} \right]_n + nH_2O$$

A simpler method for making chlorosilanes has been developed in the laboratories of the General Electric Company. Silicon, in the presence of copper catalyst, may be made to react directly with alkyl halide to form a mixture of chlorosilanes. These are separated by distillation, and hydrolyzed as indicated above.

$$Si + RCl \xrightarrow{[Cu]} \begin{cases} RSiCl_3 \\ R_2SiCl_2 \\ R_3SiCl \end{cases}$$

The various organosilicon polymers have interesting properties. Some of them are oils which remain liquid at very low temperatures and which show an astonishingly small change of viscosity as the temperature is changed. Their application as lubricants is obvious.

The rigidity of the silicones depends largely on the amount of cross-linking. Those with extensive cross-linking are solids. One of the most important applications is an electrical insulating paste for use at sparkplug terminals for aircraft. The silicones do not burn and they withstand unusually high temperatures. They find application as electrical insulation for operation at high temperatures. Certain organosilicon compounds also find application in making surfaces water-repellent. A much-publicized silicone is called "bouncing putty" because it may be squeezed into any desired shape, like putty, but if thrown on the floor it will bounce like a rubber ball.

The organosilicon polymers are not direct competitors of the polymers described in preceding sections. They are unique substances with special applications. Their most outstanding characteristic is great stability. Perhaps they should be regarded as intermediate in properties and uses between organic plastics on the one hand and glass and ceramic materials on the other.

Fig. 32-4. Victor Grignard

Grignard was born in France in 1871. He was educated at the University of Lyons and later became professor of chemistry there.

Grignard developed the interesting compounds which bear his name. These are of the general formula R—MgX, where R is an alkyl or aryl group, and X is a halogen. These compounds exist in ether solution. They were partly discovered by Grignard's teacher, P. A. Barbier.

The Grignard reagents have proved to be of extraordinary usefulness in synthetic organic chemistry. It might be said that Grignard placed in his fellow chemists' hands one of their most powerful tools. For his work in this field he was awarded the Nobel Prize in 1912. He died in 1935. (*French Embassy, Information Division*)

EXERCISES

A. *Define or explain the following:*

butadiene (structure)
caoutchouc
condensation polymerization
copolymerization
diamide
diamine
emulsion polymerization
high polymer
isoprene (structure)

monomer
organosilicon polymer
polyamide
polymer, polymerization
rubber (approximate structure)
siloxane
styrene (structure)
vinyl (or addition) polymerization

B. *Use structural formulas and equations wherever possible.*

1. Indicate the preparation and structure of the following high polymers: (a) polyethylene, (b) synthetic rubber, (c) polymethyl methacrylate, (d) polyethylene terephthalate, (e) a polyamide, and (f) an organosilicon polymer.

2. Describe methods available for finding the molecular weight of a high polymer.

3. Describe the chemistry of vulcanization.

4. What points of resemblance, and what differences, are there between the structure and properties of polymers such as polyethylene and polymethylmethacrylate, on the one hand, and organosilicon polymers on the other?

5. What is Teflon?

C. 1. Trace the manufacture of an organosilicon polymer back to the raw materials: sand, salt, natural gas, water, etc.

2. Assuming that the yield of product is only 65 per cent of theoretical, what weight of silicon must be taken to obtain one ton (1000 kg.) of organosilicon polymer in which the recurring unit is

$$\begin{bmatrix} & CH_3 & \\ & | & \\ -Si&-O- \\ & | & \\ & CH_3 & \end{bmatrix}$$

3. Write possible structural formulas for the high polymers formed from (a) vinyl chloride, $H_2C{=}CHCl$; and (b) styrene.

4. Write a possible structural formula for the high polymer formed from a mixture of phthalic anhydride and glycerol. (Phthalic anhydride reacts with an alcohol to form an ester, just as phthalic acid, but less water is split off.)

5. A certain high polymer has a molecular weight of 500,000. How much does this molecule weigh, in grams?

6. From the standpoint of chemical structure and valence forces, compare any high polymer with sodium chloride, with silicon dioxide, and with carbon dioxide.

7. Several times we have referred to the Grignard reagent. Such organic compounds have a great variety of uses in the synthesis of organic compounds. One example of its use is the following synthesis of tertiary butyl alcohol from acetone plus a suitable Grignard:

$$CH_3Br + Mg \xrightarrow{\text{(ether solution)}} \begin{array}{c} H \\ | \\ H-C-Mg-Br \\ | \\ H \end{array}$$

methyl bromide   methyl magnesium bromide
                                  (a Grignard)

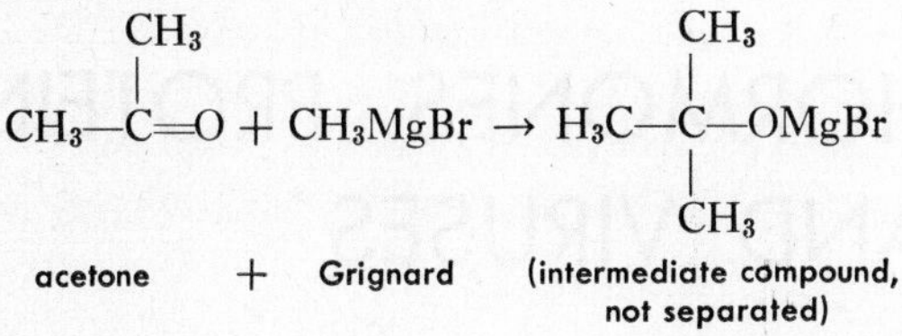

$$\underset{\substack{acetone}}{\overset{\displaystyle CH_3}{\underset{\displaystyle |}{CH_3-C=O}}} + \underset{\substack{Grignard}}{CH_3MgBr} \rightarrow \underset{\substack{\text{(intermediate compound,}\\ \text{not separated)}}}{\overset{\displaystyle CH_3}{\underset{\displaystyle |}{\underset{\displaystyle |}{\overset{\displaystyle |}{H_3C-C-OMgBr}}}}}$$

$$\underset{\substack{intermediate}}{\overset{\displaystyle CH_3}{\underset{\displaystyle |}{\underset{\displaystyle |}{\overset{\displaystyle |}{H_3C-C-OMgBr}}}}} + \underset{\substack{water}}{H_2O} \rightarrow \underset{\substack{\text{tertiary butyl}\\ \text{alcohol}}}{\overset{\displaystyle CH_3}{\underset{\displaystyle |}{\underset{\displaystyle |}{\overset{\displaystyle |}{CH_3-C-OH}}}}} + \underset{\substack{\text{magnesium}\\ \text{hydroxybromide}}}{MgOHBr}$$

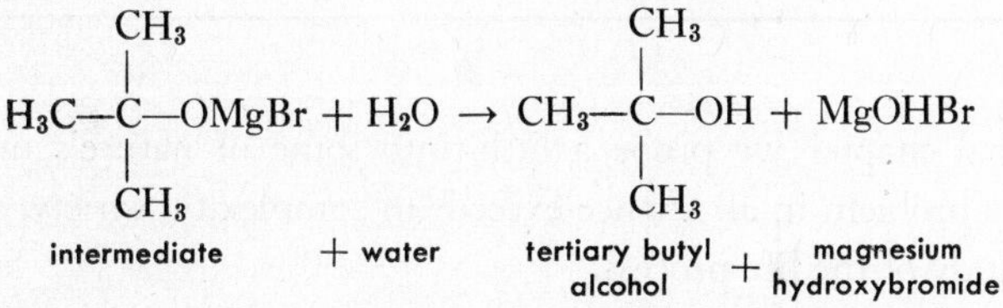

Using the above as an example, show how to obtain the following tertiary alcohol:

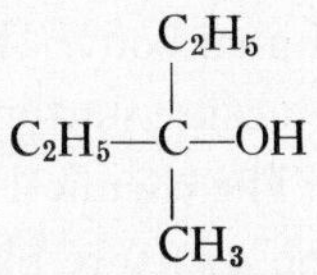

$$\overset{\displaystyle C_2H_5}{\underset{\displaystyle CH_3}{\underset{\displaystyle |}{\overset{\displaystyle |}{C_2H_5-C-OH}}}}$$

8. Grignards will react with aldehydes in a manner almost exactly analogous to the above. Show how to prepare isopropyl (secondary propyl) alcohol from acetaldehyde.

HORMONES, PROTEINS,

33 AND VIRUSES *

In this final chapter we probe a little into some of nature's most obscure secrets. No problem in all science exceeds in complexity, variety, and elusiveness the study of the life process.

217. HORMONES

Hormones are compounds which are synthesized and secreted by ductless, or endocrine, glands within the animal body. They exert a regulatory influence upon body functions. They often cause startling symptoms if present in either too small or too large amounts. The chemical composition of some hormones is well understood; of others the structure remains unsolved. In this section we shall describe a few representative hormones, with remarks about their structures and functions.

The thyroid gland is situated at the front of the neck. It contains a colloidal material of protein character, and from this material it is possible to isolate an amino acid having the structure shown below.

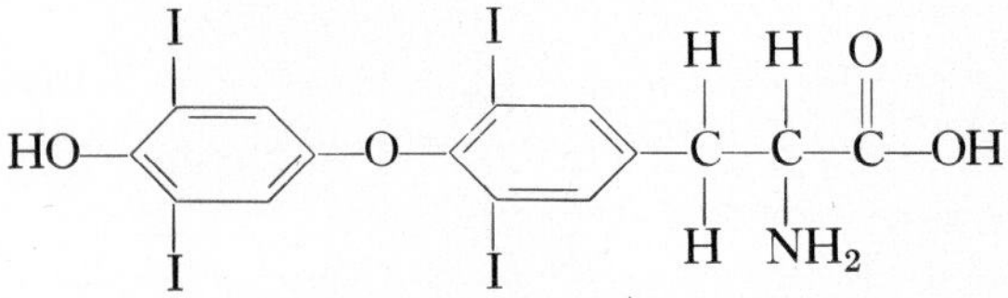

thyroxin

This substance is **thyroxin.** Some authorities consider thyroxin itself to be the hormone, others regard the colloidal protein as the hormone. In any event, thyroxin is responsible for the remarkable effect of the thyroid secretion on body functions.

Effects of insufficient thyroxin are seen when the thyroid gland is diseased or lacking in activity (*hypothyroidism*). Symptoms depend upon whether the

* See Harrow, *Textbook of Biochemistry* (Philadelphia: Saunders, 1944).

deficiency occurs in adults or in young children. For adults the condition is known as *myxedema,* which is characterized by a sharp decrease of metabolic rate. The face is expressionless and puffy; the skin appears to be thickened; weakness and anemia are often present.

Administration of proper amounts of thyroxin usually brings about a dramatic relief of symptoms, and with continuous treatment the symptoms do not return.

In early childhood thyroid deficiency leads to the distressing condition known as *cretinism.* The child is dwarfed, the expression is stupid, and mental development is greatly retarded. The cretin may develop into a normal individual only if the hormone treatment is started early in life, but in favorable cases improvement is spectacular.

If the thyroid gland is overactive (*hyperthyroidism*) the symptoms are much the reverse. The metabolic rate is high, the patient is nervous, the eyes often protrude. This condition is often treated by surgery, but it may be recalled that radioactive iodine is also used. The iodine is, of course, used by the gland to synthesize thyroxin, but the radioactive atoms partly destroy the gland and so reduce its capacity to generate more thyroxin.

Thyroxin is readily made synthetically. Its chemical structure has been known since 1926.

An interesting example of thyroid research is found in experiments on the radioactive element number 85, now called astatine. This element is directly below iodine in the Periodic Table. If astatine is given to animals it collects in the thyroid gland, much the same as does iodine. It appears, therefore, that the animal organism is unable to distinguish between these two elements. The astatine is detectable in the gland by virtue of its radioactivity.

Another hormone is **adrenaline,** or epinephrine. This substance is secreted by the adrenal glands which are situated just above the kidneys. The structure of the adrenaline molecule is much simpler than that of most hormones.

adrenaline

Adrenaline has a complex effect on the cardiovascular system. The intravenous injection of extremely small amounts of this hormone causes an amazing increase of blood pressure. Some authorities think that adrenaline is secreted by the adrenal glands during emotional excitement or in emergency situations where the body needs extra energy. Whatever may be its exact natural function, adrenaline has proved to be a very useful drug. It is used to control hemorrhage because of the constricting action it has on blood vessels. The drug is, for instance, often employed in tonsillectomy. Occasionally adrenaline has been successfully used for direct injection into the heart in patients apparently dead of shock, or in those undergoing surgery.

We turn now to a remarkable group of compounds known as **steroids.** It may be recalled that in an earlier chapter reference was made to phenanthrene, an isomer of anthracene.

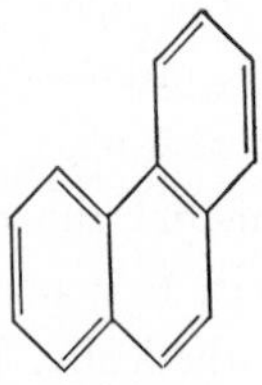

phenanthrene

The phenanthrene ring system constitutes the basic structural unit in steroids. Among the important compounds containing this ring system we may mention morphine, cholesterol, ergosterol, cortisone, and the sex hormones.

Morphine is an indispensable drug. It has a powerful analgesic action, and is very widely used by medical men in relieving unbearable pain. The compound is an alkaloid which occurs naturally in opium.

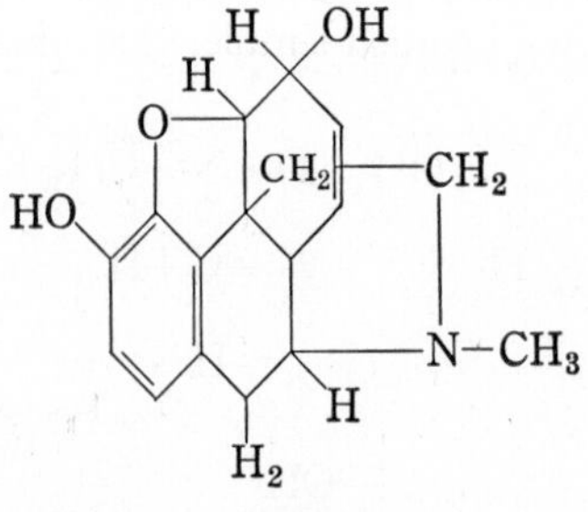

morphine

Cholesterol occurs in all animal tissue, especially in the spinal cord and brain.

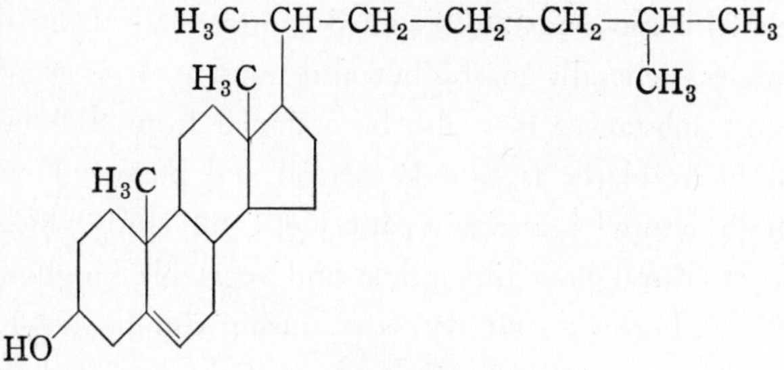

$$H_3C-CH-CH_2-CH_2-CH_2-CH-CH_3$$

cholesterol

Ergosterol has already been described as a precursor of vitamin D, while cortisone is a new drug of inestimable value in the treatment of arthritis and perhaps many other ills.

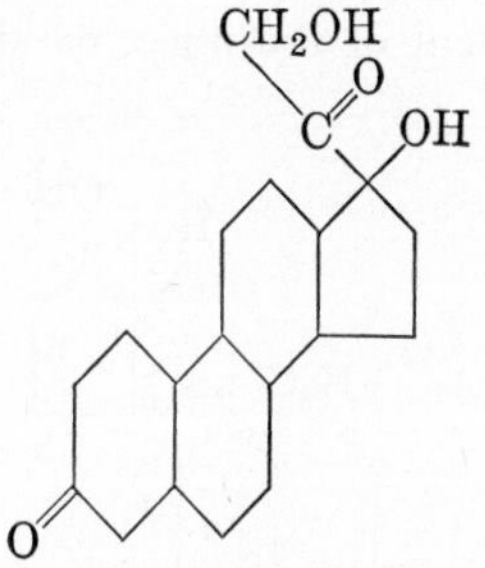

cortisone

The sex hormones are substances secreted by the testes and ovaries. They control sexual processes and secondary sexual characteristics, but they are also important in the general maintenance of health. Many sex hormones are now known, and synthetic compounds have been developed showing sex hormone activity. We shall confine our discussion to two natural hormones, one showing *estrogenic* and the other *androgenic* activity. The significance of these terms is that the first controls natural processes in the female, the other in the male.

The hormone estradiol is a typical estrogenic steroid hormone.

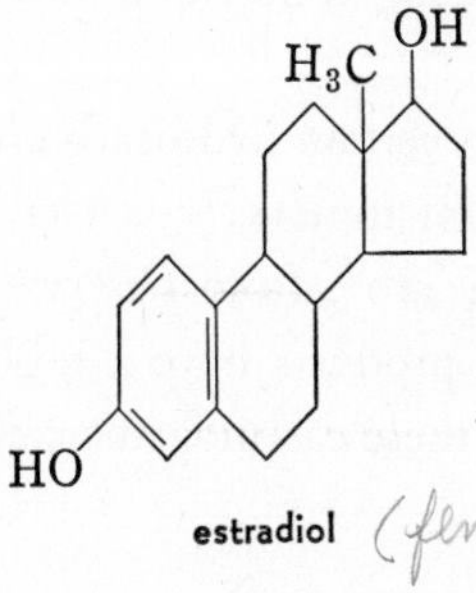

estradiol (female)

This and related compounds are obtained commercially from the urine of pregnant females, generally mares, but also humans. It is paradoxical that these estrogenic substances may also be obtained from stallion urine, and from such unlikely places as palm-kernel oil and pussy-willow flowers. It seems as though nature has a certain pattern of compounds which is repeated in various forms throughout the animal and vegetable kingdoms.

The female sex hormones are necessary during childhood for normal development of the sex organs, for the texture of the hair and skin, the distribution of fat, and the characteristic voice. Artificial injection of hormone cannot compensate entirely for natural failure, but the sex hormones have applications in medicine for relieving symptoms of the menopause, and other conditions.

One of the most prominent of the male, or androgenic, sex hormones is testosterone.

testosterone (male)

This substance was originally extracted from male sex glands, but it may be made from cholesterol. Lack of the hormone in youth precludes the possibility of normal growth and sexual development; removal after adult growth is complete leads to a gradual regression of secondary sexual characteristics.

The androgenic hormones have not been used in medicine for very long. There is evidence that to some degree nature's failure may be overcome by use of the pure hormones as drugs. There has been, however, considerable nonsense in popular advertising concerning supposed rejuvenation of aged males.

It is a remarkable fact that certain hydrocarbons, structurally related to the steroids, can induce malignant tumors, or cancer. Such substances are called *carcinogenic*. This discovery arose from observations that workers exposed repeatedly to coal tar or its products have a high incidence of skin cancer. Dibenzanthracene is one of these carcinogenic compounds.

dibenzanthracene

If this substance is repeatedly rubbed on the skin, or inserted under the skin, a skin cancer may result. Certain of the carcinogenic hydrocarbons are quite closely related to steroids occurring naturally in the body. It has been thought that one cause of cancer might be related to faulty degradation of the natural steroids. This view is by no means established, but it has led to some valuable work on possible causes of cancer.

A discussion of one other hormone, insulin, will be deferred until a later section.

218. CHROMATOGRAPHY

In the study of steroids, and of many other substances, much use is made of a method called "chromatography." This will be illustrated first with reference to the ordinary, or conventional, kind of chromatography.

A vertical glass tube is filled with some strongly adsorbing substance, of which finely powdered aluminum oxide is one example. Into the top of the tube there is poured a solution containing two or more dissolved steroids, or other substances, which it is desired to separate. The steroids will be adsorbed on the alumina, but the tenacity with which they are held to the alumina will, in general, be different for different steroids. The more weakly held steroid will therefore tend to flow down the tube and will be concentrated in a different region from the more strongly adsorbed steroid. The separation of the several steroids may be increased by allowing pure solvent to flow down over the alumina. If the adsorbed substances happen to be colored they will become visible as distinct colored bands in the tube, hence the name *chroma*tography. But colorless substances may also be separated. If it is so desired the contents may be removed from the tube and the several bands separated by hand and washed free from the alumina.

A valuable variant of this method is known as paper chromatography. Here the adsorbent is a sheet of paper, such as filter paper. One edge of the sheet is dipped into a solvent. The solvent then creeps up the paper just as blotting paper will soak up water. The steroids, or other substances, to be separated are placed as a spot just above the liquid solvent. The whole apparatus is protected from evaporation by a cover. Now, through preferential adsorption on the paper, the solvent will carry the various steroids present up the paper at different rates until they are clearly separated as different spots, where they may be identified. It is obvious that the amounts of material which may be separated by this method are not large, but paper chromatography has proved to be of extraordinary value in the study of complex mixtures such as those described above and in the next section.*

219. PROTEINS

It will be recalled that matter of vegetable origin consists in large part of cellulose. Similarly, animal matter consists in large part of substances called *proteins*. Proteins are characterized by extremely high molecular weights, by always containing nitrogen, and by a marked instability to heat and to chemical treatment. They have no definite melting point, they only occasionally can be crystallized, and, in general, their study is tedious and complex. But it must be realized that these substances make up a large part of animal tissue. If we thoroughly understood proteins we would have taken a long step toward understanding the life process.

Examples of various proteins are egg albumin, myosinogen (from muscle), glutenin (from wheat), zein (from corn), elastin (from ligament), and globin (from hemoglobin). Proteins often are found combined with other compounds. Examples of such "conjugated" proteins are found in glandular tissue, bone, milk, and egg yolk. The chemical elements always present in proteins are carbon, hydrogen, oxygen, and nitrogen. Many proteins also contain sulfur. Phosphorus and other elements are not infrequently present in small amounts. The molecular weights of proteins run from around 20,000 to 20,000,000.

Proteins have a number of characteristic chemical reactions, one of the most familiar of which is called *denaturation*. Heat, the action of acids or alkalis, and a considerable variety of chemical agents have the ability to bring about this change. The coagulation of an egg during cooking is an illustration of denaturation. Denatured proteins are less soluble than "native" proteins, and they always lose such physiological activity as they may have possessed. By the physiological activity of proteins we mean such as the hormone action of insulin, the oxygen-carrying capacity of hemoglobin, or the enzyme activity of pepsin, trypsin, and so forth.

Another of the outstanding chemical properties of proteins is the reaction shown on hydrolysis. If simple proteins are treated with dilute acid or alkali, or by certain enzymes, they undergo a reaction of hydrolysis. The product of hydrolysis is a mixture of **amino acids.** This reaction has led, more than

* H. G. Cassidy, *Adsorption and Chromatography* (New York: Interscience, 1951).

any other, to what understanding we possess of the chemical structure of proteins.

In a previous chapter brief reference was made to amino acids. They are compounds which contain the functional groups of an organic acid and of an amine. The simplest amino acid is aminoacetic. This substance is often called **glycine.**

Glycine, in common with other amino acids, has a tendency to react with itself to form a so-called *zwitterion,* or double-ion, as indicated below.

$$
\underset{\substack{\displaystyle | \\ \displaystyle NH_2}}{H-\overset{\overset{\displaystyle H}{|}}{C}-\overset{\overset{\displaystyle O}{\|}}{C}-OH} \quad \rightleftarrows \quad \underset{\substack{\displaystyle | \\ \displaystyle NH_3{}^+}}{H-\overset{\overset{\displaystyle H}{|}}{C}-\overset{\overset{\displaystyle O}{\|}}{C}-O^-}
$$

aminoacetic acid (glycine)   zwitterion form of glycine

The most surprising chemical fact about proteins is that in spite of their great complexity, only about 25 different amino acids have been derived from them. All proteins yield a mixture of amino acids, but the distribution in different proteins varies widely. For instance, gelatin is rich in glycine, and contains minor amounts of other amino acids. Keratin (from wool) yields very little glycine, but is rich in other amino acids. Some of the 25-odd amino acids are apparently absent from certain proteins: thus, egg albumin contains no glycine.

We shall not take space to describe all the amino acid groups that occur in proteins, but will mention a few in addition to glycine. Those selected for mention are as follows:

$$
\underset{\substack{\displaystyle | \quad | \\ \displaystyle H \ \ NH_2}}{H-\overset{\overset{\displaystyle H}{|}}{C}-\overset{\overset{\displaystyle H}{|}}{C}-\overset{\overset{\displaystyle O}{\|}}{C}-OH}
$$

alanine

$$
\bigcirc\!\!-\underset{\substack{\displaystyle | \quad | \\ \displaystyle H \ \ NH_2}}{\overset{\overset{\displaystyle H}{|}}{C}-\overset{\overset{\displaystyle H}{|}}{C}-\overset{\overset{\displaystyle O}{\|}}{C}-OH}
$$

phenylalanine

$$
\underset{\substack{\displaystyle | \quad | \\ \displaystyle H \ \ H}}{S-\overset{\overset{\displaystyle H}{|}}{C}-\overset{\overset{\displaystyle NH_2}{|}}{C}-\overset{\overset{\displaystyle O}{\|}}{C}-OH}
$$
$$
\underset{\substack{\displaystyle | \quad | \\ \displaystyle H \ \ NH_2}}{S-\overset{\overset{\displaystyle H}{|}}{C}-\overset{\overset{\displaystyle H}{|}}{C}-\overset{\overset{\displaystyle O}{\|}}{C}-OH}
$$

cystine

tryptophan

$$\begin{array}{c}
\quad\quad\quad\quad\quad \text{H}\ \ \text{H}\ \ \text{O} \\
\quad\quad\quad\quad\quad |\ \ \ |\ \ \ \| \\
\text{N}\text{---}\text{---}\text{C}\text{---}\text{---}\text{C}\text{--}\text{C}\text{--}\text{C}\text{--OH} \\
\|\quad\quad\quad \|\quad\quad |\ \ \ | \\
\text{H--C}\quad\quad \text{C--H}\ \ \text{H}\ \ \text{NH}_2 \\
\quad \diagdown\quad\diagup \\
\quad\quad \text{N} \\
\quad\quad | \\
\quad\quad \text{H}
\end{array}$$

histidine

The remaining 20 or so amino acids derived from proteins are of comparable complexity with those given above.

The fact that these amino-acid groups are found in proteins gives us a clue as to the structure of the proteins. We know that amino acids are capable of combining with each other. This mechanism was used in the formation of the polyamide, Nylon, described in the last chapter. The union of two glycine units is indicated below:

$$\begin{array}{c}
\ \ \ \text{O}\quad\quad\quad\quad\quad \text{O}\quad\quad\quad\quad\quad \text{O}\ \ \ \text{H}\ \ \text{O} \\
\ \ \ \|\quad\quad\quad\quad\quad \|\quad\quad\quad\quad\quad \|\ \ \ |\ \ \ \| \\
\text{H}_2\text{C--C--}\boxed{\text{OH}} + \text{H}_2\text{C--C--OH} \rightarrow \text{H}_2\text{C--C--N--C--C--OH} \\
|\quad\quad\quad\quad\quad\quad |\quad\quad\quad\quad\quad\quad |\ \ \ |\ \ \ | \\
\text{NH}_2\quad\quad\quad \boxed{\text{H}}\text{--N--H}\quad\quad\quad \text{NH}_2\ \ \text{H}\ \ \text{H}
\end{array}$$

glycylglycine (a dipeptide)

The substance formed by the union of two amino acids is called a **dipeptide;** that formed from many amino acid units is called a **polypeptide.** It will be clear that the amino-acid groups need not be the same.

According to a theory of protein structure many amino acid molecules, of

$$\text{O}$$
$$\|$$
various kinds, aggregate through peptide (--C--N--) linkages to form tre-
$$|$$
$$\text{H}$$

mendous molecules of proteins. The formation of proteins, in this view, is a branch of polymer chemistry.

In view of recent successes in making high polymers it might be thought that the synthesis of proteins would not be too difficult. It is true that polypeptides may be synthesized fairly readily, and that some quite high molecular weight substances have recently been made in this way. But the exact configurations that seem to determine the varied properties of the proteins continue to elude us, and may do so for some time to come.

It is well known that protein is an important food. The animal organism does not use protein directly, but first breaks the protein down by enzyme action to the various amino acids. Some of the amino acids are then utilized to build and repair tissue by a process which appears to be just the reverse of the initial hydrolysis. Other fractions of amino acids are used for the formation of particular compounds needed by the body, while still other fractions are deaminated, that is, changed so that the amino-acid group is lost. Such deaminated compounds may be oxidized finally to carbon dioxide and water, or converted to glucose and fatty acids. The amino groups contribute to the formation of urea, which is excreted in the urine.

The metabolism of protein is obviously very complicated. The end products are often different in different species of animals, and in various pathological conditions.

Insulin is one of several known protein hormones. The disease diabetes is caused by lack of an internal secretion of the pancreas. This secretion is the substance now called **insulin.** Insulin is actually secreted by tiny glands called *islands of Langerhans.* Failure of the body to obtain adequate insulin results in incomplete carbohydrate metabolism with the piling up of sugar in the blood, and to a degree in the urine. Symptoms of the disease include rapid loss of weight, extreme weakness, and coma. The disease can sometimes be treated by rigid control of the diet. More often the disease was fatal until insulin was discovered and made available for treating diabetics.

The discovery of insulin is a classic in medical history. It had been known since 1890 that a secretion from the pancreas was related to diabetes. But all efforts to obtain the secretion failed. We understand now that the pancreas also secretes an enzyme *trypsin* which destroys the protein insulin during attempts to obtain the hormone from the animal glands. This explanation was correctly surmised by a group at the University of Toronto headed by H. Banting. In 1921 they succeeded in isolating insulin, and in a short time it became available for the treatment of diabetics.

The effect of insulin therapy on diabetes is dramatic. It will be recalled that Benedict's solution or Fehling's solution may be used to estimate the sugar in the urine. With this control method it is possible to regulate injections of insulin to the body needs so that the symptoms of diabetes do not occur. There is some danger in the use of too much insulin because then the sugar in the blood drops to too low a level and the patient shows symptoms of shock. There is also the difficulty that the drug cannot be taken by mouth, but must be injected, and that injections have to be repeated quite frequently, ranging from once a day to several times a day. Much effort has been spent on trying to correct these difficulties. But in spite of such drawbacks insulin remains a marvelous advance in medicine.

Until quite recently it has been impossible to write a structural formula for any protein. But insulin is a protein—perhaps a little less complex than most —and the structure of insulin has been deduced by F. Sanger and his associates at Cambridge University (1952). The molecule, like other proteins, is made up of amino acids linked together as shown above. The order in which these amino acids are present in the molecule has been found by hydrolyzing the insulin into di- and tripeptides, then applying paper chromatography and other procedures to find the acids which are joined together. This procedure is not unlike the solution of a jigsaw puzzle. The insulin molecule is by far the most complex for which the structure is known.

We conclude this section with some remarks about three other proteins of interest, namely, **hemoglobin, blood plasma,** and **enzymes.**

Careful treatment of red blood cells yields a crystallizable red compound with the apparent formula $(C_{738}H_{1166}O_{208}N_{203}S_2Fe)_n$. Estimates of molecular weight indicate that n has a value of four. This compound has an unusual ability to give up or take in a certain amount of oxygen. The formula above is for the oxygenated form which is called *oxy*hemoglobin. The protein without this extra oxygen is called hemoglobin.

Hydrolysis of hemoglobin yields 94 per cent of a protein called *globin,* and 6 per cent of a compound called *hemin.* In contrast to globin, the structural formula for hemin is known, but this knowledge was obtained only after exhaustive research for forty years. The formula for hemin resembles that for chlorophyll, except that the molecule of the latter contains magnesium instead of iron.

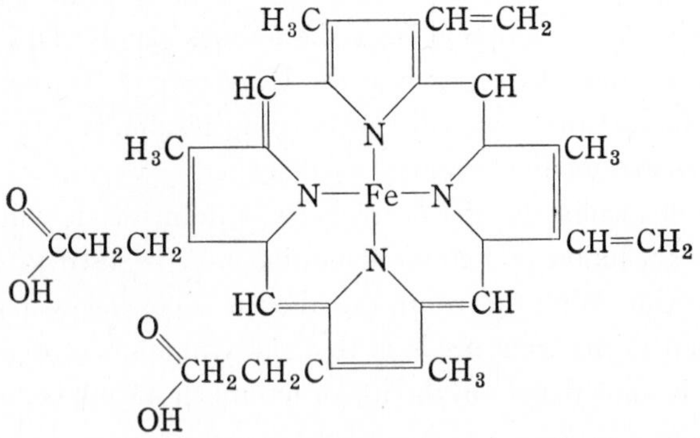

hemin

Hemoglobin is an example of a conjugated protein. The hemin part of hemoglobin is the part responsible for the sensitivity of the molecule to oxygen. Such a group, which imparts special properties to a protein molecule, is often referred to as a "prosthetic" group.

The peculiar effectiveness of hemoglobin in the blood resides in the ability of oxygen to combine rather loosely with the iron atoms. Apparently one molecule of oxygen may unite with one iron atom, or a total of four oxygen molecules to one hemoglobin molecule. This union with oxygen occurs in the lungs where venous blood, partially freed from oxygen, picks up a fresh supply. As is well known, the oxygenated blood, containing oxyhemoglobin, is pumped around to the various tissues where the oxygen is given up. The peculiar property of hemoglobin is the relative ease with which oxygen may be taken up or given off by the iron atom as it occurs in the prosthetic group. In recent years other compounds have been found which have this property of readily taking up or giving off oxygen. Most of these "imitation" hemoglobins contain cobalt rather than iron.

Blood contains, in addition to red and white cells, a yellow fluid which may be separated by centrifugation. This yellow fluid is called *plasma*. It contains about 7 per cent protein.

Several different proteins may be separated from plasma. The processes used for separation include migration in an electrical field, sedimentation, and fractional precipitation. The principal proteins obtained are albumins, globulins, and fibrinogen. The last named is the substance which is transformed into insoluble threads during the complex blood-clotting process.

The use of plasma to combat shock and loss of blood during the war will be recalled. The study of the individual proteins present in plasma may be expected to yield information on the strange process of antibody formation whereby an animal gains immunity against certain diseases.

It has already been pointed out that enzymes are proteins. Some of these compounds have been isolated and crystallized. Pepsin is an enzyme present in gastric juice. It has been crystallized as an apparently pure compound which contains all the enzymatic activity of the natural gastric juice. The molecular weight of crystalline pepsin is about 40,000. Pepsin is able to hydrolyze proteins into comparatively simple substances, and performs this important function in the animal organism.

220. VIRUSES

Pasteur and Koch showed in the latter part of the nineteenth century that many diseases are caused by microorganisms. It was soon realized that no microrganisms could be found associated with several of the most dangerous diseases. Bacteria were found, for instance, for diphtheria and syphilis, but not for smallpox and rabies.

The first demonstration that certain communicable diseases were caused by a "contagious living fluid" was made by a Russian scientist, Beijerinck, in

1892. He worked, not with a disease found in animals, but with a disease known as *tobacco mosaic,* which attacks tobacco plants. Beijerinck demonstrated that this disease was caused by a substance which could not be observed under the microscope, and which passed through a filter which was fine enough to stop all known microorganisms. Beijerinck referred to this material as a "contagious living fluid." We now call such material a **virus.**

Since 1892 many diseases have been shown to be caused by viruses. Among these, in addition to those mentioned above, are influenza, yellow fever, and poliomyelitis. The influenza pandemic of 1918 was one of the three greatest outbreaks of disease in history, and the only one caused by a virus. About 15 million people died within a four-month period, a death rate unsurpassed in all recorded knowledge.

The nature of viruses remained completely obscure until 1935. Some, if not most, authorities maintained that the viruses were merely extremely small microorganisms, too small to be seen under the microscope.

The study of viruses was undertaken about 1932 by Wendell Stanley at the Rockefeller Institute near Princeton, New Jersey. Stanley undertook to work with the virus which causes tobacco mosaic, and he hoped to isolate and observe the disease-producing substance. He was encouraged by progress which had been made in the same Institute in purifying and crystallizing certain enzymes. By a tedious process of precipitation with ammonium sulfate, and related methods, Stanley was able to isolate a crystallizable protein which appeared to be the actual disease-producing virus. The preparation of this material was doubly difficult because of the readiness with which it could be destroyed by almost all common laboratory procedures.

Stanley's discovery was greeted with considerable incredulity. The idea of a microorganism existing as a crystallizable chemical compound seemed incompatible with all preconceived notions regarding such material. It was obviously a question whether the virus was an organism or a molecule. Some persons suggested, in fun, that Stanley's material should be called an *organule,* or a *molecism.*

In spite of these doubts, it was soon shown that the crystallized material possessed the disease-producing ability of the virus, and that it was a protein, containing the usual assortment of amino acids. Since 1935 many different viruses have been purified and crystallized, and it is now well established that viruses are proteins and that they can be isolated and studied like other chemical compounds. In 1946 Stanley was awarded part of the Nobel prize in chemistry for his discovery.

The chemical composition of tobacco mosaic virus is approximately as follows: carbon, 50%; hydrogen, 7%; nitrogen, 16%; phosphorus, 0.6%; and sulfur, 0.2%. Other viruses have comparable compositions. The size of the tobacco mosaic virus molecule has been estimated as about 4000 Ångström units long and 120 units in diameter.* The molecular weight of the virus molecule has been estimated by the same means that are available for other proteins. The molecular weight is about 20,000,000.

Fig. 33-1. Electron microscope picture of a crystal of bean mosaic virus. The magnification is about 80,000. The small dots are believed to be actual individual molecules, and the picture shows how these molecules are arranged in orderly rows to form the crystal. The crystal shown has cracked into two pieces. (*Courtesy Dr. R. W. Wyckoff, National Institute of Health*)

The virus has the property of reproducing itself when it is placed in the proper environment, that is, in plant cells. It also has the property, often associated with living material, of being able to mutate. **Mutation** is a sudden change of characteristics shown from one generation to another in a family of living organisms. For instance, the virus may suddenly become much more, or much less, virulent. Vaccination for smallpox involves inoculation with a mild, *mutated,* form of the smallpox virus.

Viruses also have the property of inducing the formation of **antibodies** in the host. A person who has, for instance, lived through an attack of small-

* 1 centimeter = 100 million Ångström units.

pox is generally immune to a second attack. This is because antibodies have been generated in his system, and these antibodies can successfully cope with any second exposure to the disease.

Some of the most interesting work on viruses, conducted mostly by Stanley and his associates, is the reversible inactivation of the virus. It has been found that treatment of the virus by very mild chemical agents, such as acids or bases, or oxidizing agents, may result in the virus losing its ability to cause the disease. It is intensely interesting to know precisely what chemical change can be brought about without permanent loss of the biological activity of the virus.

In a few cases it has been possible to inactivate the virus so far as disease production is concerned, but not to destroy or alter the virus molecule otherwise. In such cases injection of the inactivated virus may still lead in the plant or animal to production of antibodies, but the patient is spared an actual attack of the disease. Sometimes this process is simply a case of inactivation of the virus. In other cases it has been possible to cause the virus to mutate with the production of a less virulent strain.

Work of this kind is of the utmost importance in medical research. Perhaps within a few years it may be possible to modify the viruses of some of the most terrible of diseases such as poliomyelitis, so that inoculation against them will be no more difficult than against smallpox or yellow fever. During World War II intensive research was carried on by Stanley and his associates in an effort to develop an agent for the control of influenza. This was done because of fear of another pandemic such as that of 1918. This work was successful, and there is now available a modified virus such that inoculation with it leads to the formation of suitable antibodies. Inactivation of the virus in this case was done by treatment of active influenza virus with formaldehyde. In this way the possibility of another disastrous influenza epidemic has been rendered much less probable.

Scarcely any problems in chemistry or medical science can exceed in interest those associated with disease-producing viruses. But there is another aspect to viruses. The materials first isolated by Stanley possess sets of properties which are difficult to reconcile. The first set is the usual number of properties possessed by pure chemical substances. These include crystalline form, molecular weight, and characteristic chemical properties. The second set of properties include those usually associated with living matter. These properties are the ability to reproduce and to undergo mutation.

Study of these properties of viruses suggests at once an obvious question. "Are the viruses alive?" To this question we can give no very satisfactory answer. The viruses seem to be at the borderline between living organisms and inanimate matter. In trying to answer the question we shall have to ask another: "What do we mean by *life?*" Perhaps when protein molecules become exceedingly complex, manifestations of life may arise as a molecular force. In preceding chapters we have described various physical forces such as electricity and light which arise under certain conditions of chemical and physical environment. Perhaps life is a force which arises when the proper molecular complexity has been achieved. Perhaps the virus molecules are those in which the first stirrings of this life-force are intruding upon our consciousness. Whatever may be the ultimate solution to this problem it seems not improbable that the twentieth, or at latest the twenty-first, century will have another achievement to its credit. This will not be like the liberation of atomic energy. Some day a scientist will synthesize a conjugated protein in his laboratory. Some day he will see that his protein is peacefully and quietly *alive*.

EXERCISES

A. *Define or explain the following:*

adrenaline	hypothyroidism, hyperthyroidism
antibody	insulin
blood plasma	mutation
carcinogenic hydrocarbon	myxedema
chromatography	pepsin
cretinism	thyroxin
diabetes	tobacco mosaic
enzymes	virus
hemoglobin	zwitterion
hormone	

B. 1. Describe in detail the function and chemistry of one important hormone, other than the sex hormones.
 2. Indicate, in general terms, the relation between various steroids and their physiological activity.
 3. Describe the discovery of insulin.
 4. What are the principal characteristics and reactions of proteins?
 5. How can amino acids combine to form polypeptides (structural formulas)?
 6. Why is so much significance attached to the isolation of tobacco mosaic virus?

C. 1. The compound oxyhemoglobin has been found to contain 0.335 per cent of iron. With this information find the minimum possible molecular weight for oxyhemoglobin.
 2. Compare the metabolism of carbohydrate, fat, and protein.
 3. The scientific concept of a molecule dates from about 1811. Trace the development of this idea in connection with substances such as carbon dioxide,

argon, sodium chloride, silica, carbon, high polymers, and viruses. Refer to the influence of such men as Avogadro, Gay-Lussac, Cannizzaro, Arrhenius, Lewis, and Stanley.

4. In a few sentences describe the life and chief accomplishments of the following: Arrhenius, Avogadro, Bohr, Boyle, Cavendish, M. Curie, Dalton, Davy, Faraday, Grignard, Kekulé, Lavoisier, Le Chatelier, Lewis, Mendeleev, Ramsay, Rutherford, Pasteur, Priestley, and Scheele.

5. In a word or two indicate the chief contribution to chemistry of each of the following: Aston, Becquerel, R. Brown, Carothers, Chadwick, Charles, Debye, Ehrlich, Einstein, Fermi, Fleming, Frasch, Graham, Haber, Hahn, Hall, Joliot, E. O. Lawrence, Leucippus, Moissan, Moseley, Sanger, J. J. Thompson, Torricelli, Urey, and Wöhler.

APPENDIX

Vapor Pressure of Water

Temperature °C.	Pressure mm.	Temperature °C.	Pressure mm.
0	4.6	50	92.0
5	6.5	60	148.9
10	9.1	70	233.3
15	12.7	80	354.9
16	13.5	90	525.5
17	14.4	95	633.7
18	15.3	96	657.4
19	16.3	97	681.9
20	17.4	98	707.1
21	18.5	99	733.1
22	19.6	99.2	738.5
23	20.9	99.4	743.8
24	22.1	99.6	749.2
25	23.5	99.8	754.6
26	25.0	100	760.0
27	26.5	100.2	765.5
28	28.1	100.4	771.0
29	29.7	100.6	776.5
30	31.5	101	787.6
35	41.8	105	906.4
40	54.9	110	1075.4

Weights and Measures

Length: 10 millimeters (mm.) = 1 centimeter (cm.) = 0.3937 inches (in.)
100 cm. = 1 meter (m.) = 39.37 in.
1000 m. = 1 kilometer (km.) = 0.6214 mile

Volume: 1000 cubic centimeters (cc.) = 1 liter (l.) or, more precisely, 1 l. = 1000.027 cc.
1 l. = 1.057 quarts (U. S.)

Weight: 1000 grams (g.) = 1 kilogram (kg.) = 2.205 pounds (lb.) avoirdupois
1000 kg. = 1 metric ton = 2205 lb. av.
1 lb. = 453.6 g.

DENSITIES OF THE ELEMENTS

Element	Density		Element	Density	
Aluminum	2.70	g/cc.	Molybdenum	10.2	
Antimony	6.68		Neodymium	6.9	
Argon	1.65	(solid)	Neon	1.0	(solid)
Arsenic	5.7	(gray)	Nickel	8.9	
Barium	3.5		Nitrogen	1.03	(solid)
Beryllium	1.80		Osmium	22.48	
Bismuth	9.80		Oxygen	1.42	(solid)
Boron	2.5		Palladium	12.0	
Bromine	3.4	(solid)	Phosphorus	1.82	(yellow)
Cadmium	8.6		Platinum	21.45	
Calcium	1.55		Potassium	0.86	
Carbon	3.51	(diamond)	Praseodymium	6.5	
Cerium	6.9		Protactinium	....	
Cesium	1.87		Radium	5	
Chlorine	1.9	(solid)	Radon	4	(solid)
Chromium	7.1		Rhenium	21.4	
Cobalt	8.9		Rhodium	12.5	
Columbium	8.4		Rubidium	1.53	(solid)
Copper	8.92		Ruthenium	12.2	
Dysprosium	....		Samarium	7.7	
Erbium	....		Scandium	2.5	
Europium	....		Selenium	4.5	(red)
Fluorine	1.3	(solid)	Silicon	2.4	
Gadolinium	....		Silver	10.5	
Gallium	5.91	(solid)	Sodium	0.97	
Germanium	5.36		Strontium	2.6	
Gold	19.3		Sulfur	2.0	
Hafnium	....		Tantalum	16.6	
Helium	0.126	(liquid)	Tellurium	6.24	(alpha)
Holmium	....		Terbium	....	
Hydrogen	0.08	(solid)	Thallium	11.85	
Indium	7.28		Thorium	11.2	
Iodine	4.93	(solid)	Thulium	....	
Iridium	22.4		Tin	7.31	(white)
Iron	7.86		Titanium	4.5	
Krypton	2.0	(solid)	Tungsten	19.3	
Lanthanum	6.15		Uranium	18.7	
Lead	11.34		Vanadium	5.96	
Lithium	0.53		Xenon	2.7	(solid)
Lutetium	....		Ytterbium	....	
Magnesium	1.74		Yttrium	5.51	
Manganese	7.2		Zinc	7.14	
Mercury	14.19	(solid)	Zirconium	6.4	

INDEX